Plant Growth and Development

McGRAW-HILL PUBLICATIONS
IN THE BIOLOGICAL SCIENCES

Consulting Editors
Robert L. Sinsheimer, Colin S. Pittindrigh,
Theodore H. Bullock, Sydney Brenner

Series in Cell Biology
Gray, Handbook of Basic Microtechnique

Series in Developmental Biology
Patten, Foundations of Embryology
Weichert, Anatomy of the Chordates

Series in Organism Biology
Mazia and Tyler, General Physiology of Cell
Specialization

Series in Physiology
Leopold, Plant Growth and Development

Series in Population Biology
Ehrlich and Holm, The Process of Evolution

Series in Systematic Biology
Hyman, The Invertebrates: Protozoa through
Ctenophora (vol. I)
————, The Invertebrates: Platyhelminthes
and Rhynchocoela (vol. II)
————, The Invertebrates: Acanthocephala,
Aschelminthes, and Entoprocta (vol. III)
————, The Invertebrates: Echinodermata
(vol. IV)
————, The Invertebrates: Smaller Coelomate
Groups (vol. V)
Mayr, Linsley, and Usinger, Methods and Prin-
ciples of Systematic Zoology

This symbol of the cephalopod *Nautilus*
appears on all McGraw-Hill Publications in the
Biological Sciences. It was chosen to represent
the just proportion of living structures and
to suggest the harmonious workings and
balanced arrangement of the parts and elements
of living things. The color of the binding
represents the Biological Series in which this
book is published.

Plant Growth and Development

A. CARL LEOPOLD

Professor of Horticulture
Purdue University

McGRAW-HILL BOOK COMPANY

New York
San Francisco
Toronto
London

37215

In its early, naïve stage, science . . . imagined that we could observe things in themselves, as they would behave in our absence. Naturalists . . . are now beginning to realize that even the most objective of their observations are steeped in the conventions they adopted at the outset . . . so that, when they reach the end of their analyses they cannot tell with any certainty whether the structure they have made is the essence of the matter they are studying, or the reflection of their own thought.

Pierre Teilhard de Chardin,
The Phenomenon of Man

Preface

As a treatise on plant physiology, this book has three directions of special emphasis: first, to develop the student's reliance on experiments in forming generalizations about his science; second, to depict science as a complex of imperfect approximations derived by the scientific method; and third, to reorganize the subject to make it more nearly representative of modern plant physiology in the laboratory and in the field.

I should like to explain the reasons for this approach. As a teacher, I am disturbed to find young professional plant physiologists who have so completely embraced the generalizations which have been tutored into them and which they have cherished and repeated for their examinations in the best tradition of scholasticism, that they do not really have a working knowledge of the science that they must revise and help to improve. Comprehension of the scientific generalization without knowledge of underlying specific experimental facts seems to me to be a poor tool for hewing out new science. Therefore, in this book I have drawn on experimental evidence insofar as possible to illustrate the concepts being discussed.

I am also disturbed to find that a large proportion of research workers do not realize when they enter this profession that the scientific method is an imperfect game—one that involves imperfect deductions from imperfect experiments; and that the nature of the game must lead to disagreement—sometimes quiet and rational, sometimes not. In using a case-history approach, I hope that the student will recognize the inconsistencies among the "facts" accumulated so far, and that this will make him a little more sanguine about the sharp disagreements between equally dependable scientists and will teach him to relish the exchange of criticism that sharpens good science and shrinks poor science.

The book is centered about the workings of the growing plant, without organized coverage of biochemistry and nutrition. This assumes a logical pedagogical division of the subject of plant physiology into a section on growth and development and another section on nutrition and metabolism. This is also done with the hope of maintaining an appropriate level of interest in the functions of the living plant, in the face of a current tendency toward preoccupation with grindates, supernates, and simulated life activities in test tubes without sufficiently clear relationship to the growth of the whole plant.

In short, it is hoped that the presentation here will paint an approximate picture of the status of this science today and at the same time will make the student think in terms of experimental units of information. The best experimental units incorporate the weaknesses of the human minds that conceived them and carried them out, and no generalization from these units is more dependable than the underlying experiments.

The biological puzzle is a dynamic and exciting one, including some pieces which are changing shape even as we try to fit them together, some that need to be polished and changed before they will be able to fit into their places, and some which have no apparent relevance to the rest of the pieces at hand. The challenge for the scientist is to fit together an improved picture, using his ingenuity to devise more precise reconstructions of the working mechanisms inside the living organism.

I wish to express special thanks to Profs. K. V. Thimann and W. K. Purves for reading the entire manuscript after the first draft, and for their many helpful suggestions. Thanks are also due to A. S. Crafts, R. H. Hageman, C. E. Hess, D. J. Morré, E. B. Oyer, G. F. Warren, and M. H. Zimmerman for help with specific chapters. For supplying photographs which had not been previously published, thanks are extended to Drs. A. S. Crafts, T. M. Das, G. Setterfield, T. E. Weier, and W. G. Whaley and the Electron Microscope Laboratory of the University of Texas.

I would also like to express appreciation to Dr. E. C. Stevenson for the numerous ways in which the department provided help, to the University of Hawaii for a Carnegie Visiting Professorship during which much of the writing was completed, and to friends and family whose assistance made the final processing stages endurable. Special thanks are due to John Leopold for help with the proofs and to Barbara Webster for helping in many ways.

A. Carl Leopold

Contents

ix

List of
Abbreviations

ATP	adenosine triphosphate
2,4-D	2,4-dichlorophenoxyacetic acid
DNA	deoxyribonucleic acid
GA	gibberellic acid
IAA	indole-3-acetic acid
LDP	long-day plant
NAA	α-naphthaleneacetic acid
Q_{10}	temperature coefficient
RNA	ribonucleic acid
SDP	short-day plant

Plant Growth and Development

1 | The cell and its habitat: an introduction

The fact that all complete living organisms are cellular and that all the larger organisms are multicellular suggests that there must be great advantages for living material to be enclosed within limiting walls or membranes; in fact, the cellular composition of organisms seems almost to be essential.

In view of current concepts of the origin of life on earth, there appear to be rational reasons for this cellular requirement. Oparin (1938) has developed a convincing suggestion that life evolved within a warm aqueous solution of a nutritive medium comprised of many organic and inorganic substances. The chemically catalyzed breakdown of these substances led to the localized production of energy, and gradually these energy sources became dominated by the products which were synthesized: more complex molecules such as proteins in gel-like droplets. As these arrays became self-replicating (probably as nucleoproteins), they had the capacity both for metabolic production of energy and for self-reproduction and so were living things. Inherent in this conceptual sequence is the inclusion of such living units into coacervate droplets or gels, which then would be structurally distinct. Not only would a droplet or gel hold the components, but it would also provide a molecular matrix more substantial than the surrounding aqueous medium. The development of an envelope enclosing this primitive ooze would have obvious mechanical advantages and would permit some regulation of the movement of metabolites. It could constrain metabolic substrates inside the cell as well as regulate the dissipation of metabolic products.

The nucleus is considered by Blum (1955) to be the basic unit of living material, and the multinucleate conditions of some plant tissues may represent reversions to this primitive form. It is logical to assume that as the primitive life forms proceeded to deplete the surrounding substrates, the development of a further en-

Fig. 1-1 | Photomicrograph of a single cell from tobacco callus growing in tissue culture. Note the cell wall, enclosing the cytoplasm which is drawn into strands by the development of vacuoles, and the nucleus near the center with its enclosed nucleolus (magnification about 1,000×). (*Photograph courtesy of* **T. M. Das,** *A. C. Hildebrandt, and A. J. Riker.*)

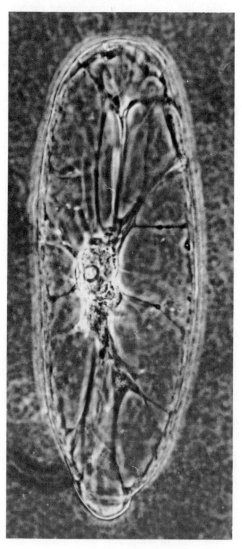

velope around a limited amount of plasmic material was advantageous in regulating the immediate environment around the nuclear unit. One is tempted to think of the cytoplasm as being a reconstruction of the nutritive medium in which life originated, but actually it has taken over essentially all the functions of respiration, leaving the nucleus with only the responsibility for replication of genetic information. In this sense the cell represents the ultimate unit of life in higher plants, with the requirements for self-replication being fulfilled by the nucleus and the requirements for metabolic production of energy being fulfilled by the surrounding cytoplasm.

As this hypothetical evolution of cellular organisms progressed, there would have been a gradual dwindling of the supply of organic substrates in the primitive medium and an increasing need for autotrophy. Of course, the photosynthetic apparatus did not then spring into being as a complete system, but it probably evolved as an elaboration of cellular systems which could convert light energy into chemical energy. Oparin (1938) suggested that photosynthesis evolved from systems in which light activation of metabolism had been achieved. Such primitive systems might have been pigment associations which brought about photoreduction reactions and thus benefited hydrolytic or reductive aspects of metabolism. The evolutionary development of the photosynthetic system which can reduce carbon dioxide made possible the continued progress of life on earth. With the development of this biosynthetic apparatus in its more complicated forms, it became essential that the system be enclosed in a locus with limited access between the reactive photosynthetic intermediates and the respiratory activities of the cytoplasm. The development of another envelope around the photosynthetic apparatus, the chloroplast, provided real advantages to the autotrophic cell in facilitating this separation.

The envelope system has been repeated

Fig. 1-2 | Electron micrograph of a cell in a corn root tip. Note the dark cell wall enclosing the cytoplasm with its various organelles (mitochondria, proplastids, Golgi bodies, and endoplasmic reticulum). In the center lies the large nucleus showing darker staining chromatin and enclosed in a membrane (magnification about 5,000×). (*Photograph courtesy of W. G. Whaley and the University of Texas Electron Microscope Laboratory.*)

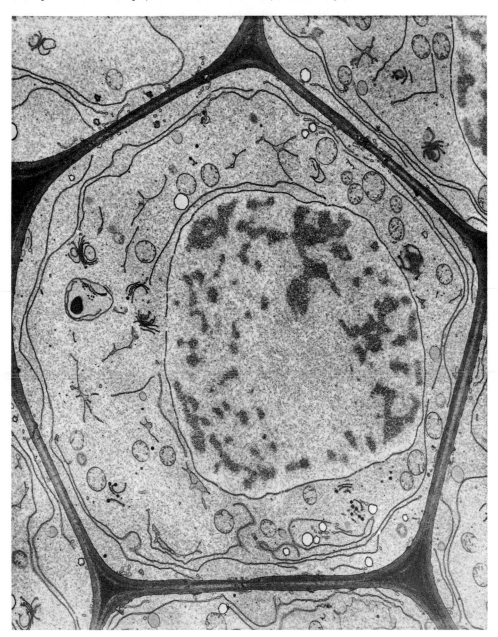

in mitochondria as an enclosure of metabolic systems for the production of energy through electron-transfer systems. It has been developed again around leucoplasts, which enclose some distinctive materials the role of which is not well understood. Finally, the envelope system has been applied to the vacuoles of plant cells, often large enclosures within the cell into which are secreted ions, salts, pigments, and often respiratory products which are not immediately useful to the cell.

The same types of membranes enclosing the principal cell organelles occur again as the endoplasmic reticulum—a network of membrane partitions through the cytoplasm —and the Golgi bodies—lenslike layers of membranes from which there appear to emerge vesicles enclosed again in the same type of membrane. The functions of the reticulum and Golgi bodies are not known. The reticulum appears to be a common site for the attachment of ribosomes and hence perhaps a site of protein synthesis.

These envelope systems appear to be repetitions of a single pattern of membrane structure. Each of the membranes is a double layer of protein substance with lipoidal material sandwiched between. The membranes are all of similar dimensions, ranging from 70 to 100 A in thickness. Interconnections of the reticulum with the nuclear membrane may provide access of materials from the nucleus to the cytoplasmic regions of the cell through the continuity of the inner lipoidal canal.

The membrane system is not just a protective sheath, however, for the double layer of protein incorporates many of the enzyme systems involved in plant metabolism. For example, many enzymes involved in electron-transfer systems are apparently integral parts of the structure of the mitochondrial membranes, their structural arrangement on the membrane being essential to the sequences of metabolic steps. The enzymes involved in the photosynthetic reduction of nucleotides and photophosphorylation are structurally incorporated into the lamellar membranes of the chloroplast along with chlorophyll.

The lipoidal material in the center of the membrane structure is probably the principal barrier to the passage of solutes into the cell and into the organelles and vacuole as well.

Subcellular structures

The nucleus includes the chromosomes, which are multiple strands of deoxyribonucleic acid (DNA) associated with protein and a little ribonucleic acid (RNA); these chromosomes are suspended in a matrix of proteinaceous material. The entirety is enclosed in a layer of the double membrane already described.

If the chromosome material is to direct the metabolism and growth of the whole cell, there should be some access of materials from the nucleus to the cytoplasm. Electron micrographs of nuclear membranes frequently show the presence of pores 400 to 500 A in diameter (faintly visible in Fig. 1-2), through which particles of RNA may move into the cytoplasm. Since the nucleus is a principal site of RNA synthesis and a large proportion appears in the cytoplasm as a constituent of ribosomes, it is thought that the RNA is synthesized in the nucleus as ribosomes which may then move into the cytoplasm via the pores and there direct protein synthesis.

The chloroplasts are smaller substructures in the cytoplasm, being mobile little spherules enclosed in the double membrane. They are ramified internally by repeated layers of the membrane (Fig. 1-3a). Cells which develop in darkness form smaller bodies, leucoplasts, with less definitive internal membrane patterns. Exposure to light causes drastic changes in the chloroplasts, including a sharp drop in RNA content and an abrupt multiplication and orientation of the interior membranes to form lamellae on which the chlorophyll is held. The structure of the chloroplasts is discussed in the section on photosynthesis (Chap. 2).

The mitochondria are still smaller spherules which are also mobile in the cytoplasm (Fig. 1-3*b*). They, too, are enclosed in the usual double-membrane envelope, the inner layer of which is invaginated to form christae. On these double-walled invaginations are arrayed the enzyme sequences for oxidative phosphorylation. Enclosed in the mitochondria are many of the principal metabolic systems, including those for organic acid and for fatty-acid metabolism. The mitochondria are most evident in young, growing cells, in which they are present in the greatest density. Their metabolic activities decline with cell age. They contain mostly lipoprotein and possibly some RNA, and their structural arrangement of enzymes provides a closed and protected system for many of the steps of oxidative metabolism.

Even smaller than the mitochondria are the ribosomes (Fig. 1-3*d*)—little particles of RNA and protein, 100 to 300 A in diameter, which float freely in the cytoplasm or are bound to the membranes of the endoplasmic reticulum. More than half of the cellular RNA is in the ribosomes, which are the principal sites of protein synthesis in the cell. They are considered to be formed in the nucleus, providing therefore a continuity between the genetic information of the chromosomes and the actual production of the individual enzymes in the cytoplasm for the completion of the heritable architecture of the genetic design.

In many plant cells, numerous small vacuoles in the cytoplasm may coalesce into a large single vacuole occupying the center of the mature cell. Enclosed by a double membrane too, this large watery sac does not have any recognizable internal structure but appears to be a sump into which ions and metabolic products are pumped by metabolic forces. In addition to providing the cell with a dump or storage area, the vacuole may provide a further benefit to large cells through the restriction of the metabolically active cytoplasm to the periphery of the cell in a position of optimal gas exchange with the outside.

Surrounding and supporting the cell contents is the cell wall—a laminated structure with a pectinaceous middle lamella common to pairs of adjoining cells and a thicker rigid wall mainly composed of cellulose fibrils in a matrix comprised of pectins, arabans, galactans, xylans, and other polysaccharides. During growth the wall undergoes extensive expansion by some combination of plastic enlargement and intussusception of new wall materials. The dynamic processes of growth occur principally in the cell structures associated with the wall itself, presumably in the form of enzymes attached to, or closely associated with, the inside surface of the cell wall. As the cell matures, the wall may become lignified and rigid.

Control systems

Knowledge of the organelles and their components within cells permits us to see structured levels of regulating systems. The basic regulating unit of the cell is the self-replicating DNA, located principally in the nucleus and containing in coded form instructions for the synthesis and assembly of all the component cell parts. Translating the DNA instructions is the apparent role of the RNA, which is mainly in the ribosomes. The RNA is formed on the DNA template and is organized into units which then apparently move out of the nucleus into the cytoplasm, where they direct the synthesis of protein. This step, controlled by the RNA template, yields the enzyme systems which determine the metabolic and morphologic features of the cell and thus of the organism.

One of the most exciting problems of molecular biology is the question of how

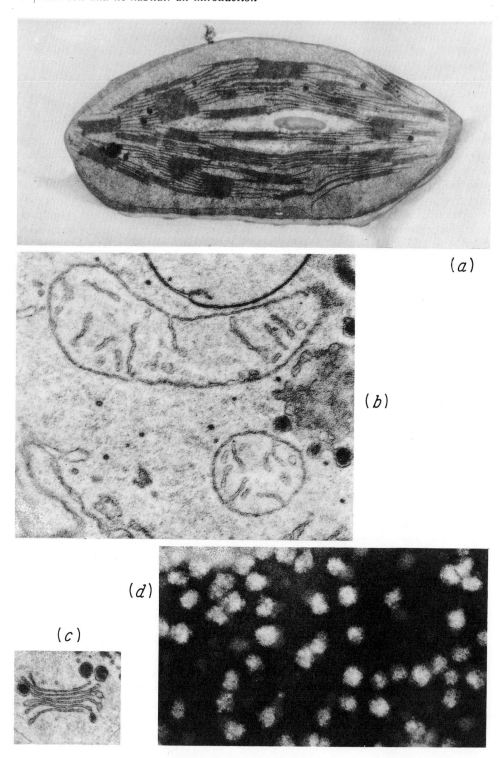

(a)

(b)

(d)

(c)

instructions to the cell or the organism can be changed with age, with the progress of reproduction, or by other developmental events. Since the basic instructions are written in DNA and the translation of instructions is carried out by RNA, changes in the instructions for development could occur in either of these structural components.

The facts of developmental plant physiology tell us clearly that the course of development can be altered by a brief environmental experience; that is, a short exposure to low temperatures or to long photoperiods can alter the course of development of the plant for an extended time. The means by which such a memory effect can occur should reside in an alteration of the nucleic acid instructions—not permanent in the heritable manner, but metastable or temporarily fixed. A similar alteration in instructions should occur with changes in developmental sequences, such as the changes from juvenility to maturity, from vegetative to reproductive states, and from maturity to senescence. The manner in which such alterations in the controls of growth and development might occur is not clear, but metastable changes are supremely characteristic of biological organisms. Brink (1962) has published an interesting description of some of these metastable states in plant development.

Three exciting possibilities have been proposed by which metastable changes in the direction of cell activities could be effected. Stedman and Stedman (1950) suggested that the action of some genes could be suppressed by histones which might become attached to the chromosomal DNA, and that other genes could be released by histone removal. This possibility has been given some experimental support in plant material by Gifford (1964) who has detected changes in the apparent amounts of histones in the nuclei of *Xanthium* meristems just after photoperiodic induction of flowering. Jacob and Monod (1961) have suggested another system which could regulate gene action, involving the metabolic production of inducers which can lead to the formation of some enzymes, and of suppressors which could block the formation of other enzymes. With gene systems (termed *operons*), which could interact through the production of mutually regulating materials, a given set of genetic templates could shift from one type of developmental directions to another. Lwoff and Lwoff (1962) have provided the basis for a third possible regulatory mechanism. From their studies of metastable changes in viruses induced by temperature experiences, they have proposed that environmental influences may alter the secondary structures of nucleic acids and of protein materials, thus altering their template or metabolic activities respectively. Each of these three suggestions holds promise as a possible mechanism for the metastable changes in plants with developmental shifts and environmental experiences. This is one of the most fundamental problems of all plant growth and development.

Fig. 1-3 | Electron micrographs of some plant-cell organelles. (*a*) A chloroplast from a bean leaf, showing the internal lamellae and a large central starch grain (magnification about 10,000×). (*b*) Mitochondria from a corn root tip, one longitudinal and one cross section, showing the internal christae (20,000×). (*c*) A Golgi body from a corn root tip, showing the lenslike layers of membrane and the dark vesicles emerging (20,000×). (*d*) Ribosomes of oat coleoptiles against a dark-stained background (80,000×). (*Photographs courtesy of E. Weier (a), W. G. Whaley and the University of Texas Electron Microscope Laboratory (b and c), and G. Setterfield (d).*)

Cell growth

If in evolutionary development each cell

were to remain as a discrete unit of life, one might imagine colonies of such cells growing in simple swarms. They would alter one another's form only in the manner that soap bubbles cause one another to be polyhedral instead of round. But unlike bubbles, a colony of closely adjoining cells will necessarily experience a competition for substrates and gas exchange and, in the case of the photosynthetic cells, a competition for sunlight as well. It is reasonable to assume that such competitive interactions provide strong evolutionary forces for more complex patterns of growth and differentiation. Groups of cells which could project themselves above their competitiors would achieve marked advantages. The multicellular plant with its specialization into structural organs adapted specifically for light utilization and gas exchange is the product of these evolutionary forces.

Differential growth permits the formation of organized tissues and organs. The evolution of multicellular plants has involved the development of biochemical and biophysical systems which can regulate differential growth.

The chemical means by which growth and development are controlled in the plant have become increasingly evident from research since 1930. Chemical species produced in one cell can affect the growth not only of that cell but also of others. A striking illustration of the mutual effects of cells on differentiation can be seen in the development of a simple meristem. In a tissue culture, after a colony of cells has reached a certain size there appear localized organized meristems, as shown in Fig. 1-4 (Steward et al., 1958). The first step in the emergence of the meristem seems to be the stimulation of one cell in the colony to commence divisions, and this apparently occurs immediately adjacent to a lignified cell—a simple vascular element—suggesting that the latter is providing some stimulus to cell division. More lignified cells are then laid down near the dividing cell, suggesting

that the dividing cells somehow encourage the formation of the lignified or vascular elements. This process is multiplied until there emerges finally a dome of meristem, with radial files of cells leading inward from it where growth by elongation and differentiation of the plant axis begins to take place. In this tissue-culture situation, we seem to be observing a recapitulation of the basic steps in the emergence of a tissue, with conspicuous implications of chemical messengers passing between the cells and regulating the sequence.

Meristems are known to be sources of hormonal influences which can stimulate cell enlargement and differentiation; in fact, the isolation of the plant hormone auxin revealed the major hormonal product of the terminal meristem. In addition to the ability of auxin to regulate growth of the files of cells below the meristem, it has become evident that it can also regulate differentiation. For example, Thimann and Went (1934) found that auxin could induce the differentiation of roots in cuttings, and Wetmore and Sorokin (1955) found that auxin could cause the differentiation of xylem cells in undifferentiated tissue cultures. Other growth substances participating in the control of tissue and organ differentiation will be discussed in later sections of this book, but the main issue here is that once cells of higher plants are growing together in a close community, the production of chemical materials in some of these controls both growth and differentiation of the cells of the community.

The chemical materials which participate in these controls create an orderly orientation of cell and tissue arrangements. This implies that there must be some polarity of movement of at least some of the controlling materials. With the discovery of auxin (Went, 1928), it was found that this hormone travels through some tissues with a strict and orderly polarity. This stimulator of cell and tissue differentiation is therefore capable of contributing to an orientation of growth processes through the polar distribution of its hormonal influences.

The biophysical influences on growth and differentiation of cells in the organism are much less clearly appreciated than the biochemical ones. Relatively few experimental approaches have been made to illuminate them, though there are clear indications that they are very important. The physical force of enclosure which the outer layers of a stem provide is involved in the differentiation of phloem and xylem. Brown and Sax (1962) found that relieving cells from that force by lifting them out on a flap cut from the stem led to a cessation of differentiation, only callus being formed from the cambium on the flap. Binding the flap back into the stem permitted restoration of differentiation. It is also commonly observed in tissue cultures that there is no apparent orientation of xylem until a cylinder of stem or root tissue has been developed and presumably there are pressures of enclosure by the outer layers of cells. The differentiation of endodermis tissues in roots has been demonstrated to be due in part to the gradient of oxidizing potential across the root as well as to the chemical substrates needed for construction of the tissues (van Fleet, 1954). There are evidences, therefore, that physical or biophysical forces do have a part to play in the control of growth and development.

The science of plant physiology, then, is developing a picture of the growth of cells together in multicellular organisms with orderly distributions of growth and morphogenesis being apparently brought about through systems of molecular ecology—the regulation of the cell by biochemical and biophysical forces.

Fig. 1-4 | The emergence of a meristem in a tissue culture of carrot phloem cells. At the top, cell division has occurred in a single cell adjacent to a lignified element. In the middle is a small cluster of lignified elements with a ring of dividing cells around it. At the bottom is the emerging young meristem, with radially arranged cell files and an orderly ring of dividing cells (Steward et al., 1958).

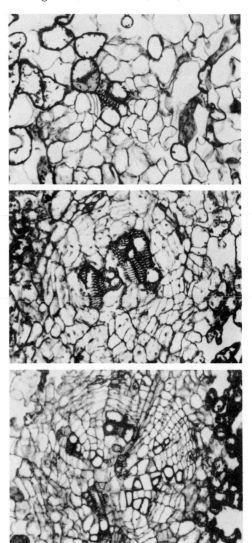

REFERENCES CITED

Blum, H. F. 1955. *Time's Arrow and Evolution.* Princeton University Press, Princeton, N.J. 219 pp.

Brink, R. A. 1962. Phase change in higher plants and somatic cell heredity. *Quart. Rev. Biol.*, 37:1–22.

Brown, C. L., and K. Sax. 1962. The influence of pressure on differentiation of tissues. *Am. J. Botany*, 49:683–691.

Galston, A. W. 1961. *The Life of the Green Plant.* Prentice-Hall, Inc., Englewood Cliffs, N.J. 116 pp.

Gifford, E. M. 1964. Developmental studies of vegetative and floral meristems. *Brookhaven Symp. Biol.*, 16:126–137.

Jacob, F., and J. Monod. 1961. Genetic regulatory mechanisms in the synthesis of proteins. *J. Mol. Biol.*, 3:318–356.

Lwoff, A., and M. Lwoff. 1962. Evenements cyclique et molecules metastables. *J. Theoret. Biol.*, 2:48–62.

Oparin, A. I. 1938. *The Origin of Life* (Tr. by S. Morgulis). The Macmillan Company, New York. 270 pp.

Stedman, E., and E. Stedman. 1950. Cell specificity of histones. *Nature*, 166:780–781.

Steward, F. C., M. O. Mapes, and K. Mears. 1958. Growth and organized development of cultured cells. II. Organization in cultures grown from freely suspended cells. *Am. J. Botany*, 45:705–708.

Thimann, K. V., and F. W. Went. 1934. On the chemical nature of the root forming hormone. *Proc. Koninkl. Ned. Akad. Wetenschap.*, 37:456–459.

van Fleet, D. S. 1954. Cell and tissue differentiation in relation to growth, pp. 111–129. E. J. Boell (ed.), *Dynamics of Growth Processes.* Princeton University Press, Princeton, N.J.

Went, F. W. 1928. Wuchsstoff und Wachstum. *Rec. Trav. Bot. Neerl.*, 25:1–116.

Wetmore, R. H., and S. Sorokin. 1955. On the differentiation of xylem. *J. Arnold Arboretum*, 36:305–317.

Part I | ASSIMILATION

2 | Photosynthesis

The ability of plants to produce organic materials from carbon dioxide has had a tremendous influence on the biosphere. Before the advent of photosynthetic plants, there was little or no oxygen in the earth's atmosphere. We must assume that the primitive metabolism by the earliest life forms was anaerobic and that ultraviolet radiation on the surface of the earth was much more intense than it is today, for ozone formed from atmospheric oxygen is a major filter of ultraviolet from sunlight. With the spread of photosynthetic plants over the surface of the land and the seas, an accumulation of oxygen resulted that provided a protective umbrella against ultraviolet radiation and an opportunity for the utilization of the more efficient aerobic types of metabolism. The organic products of photosynthesis provided the substrates on which biological organisms might live.

Photosynthetic fixation of carbon dioxide into organic materials is so extensive that the equivalent of the entire supply of carbon dioxide in the earth's atmosphere is recycled through plants every 250 years. This massive synthetic activity and its converse of respiration form an enormous buffering system which holds the carbon dioxide content of the atmosphere approximately constant.

The substances produced by photosynthesis and metabolism serve as buffers of the oxygen content of the world's atmosphere; in fact, photosynthesis is the principal source of oxygen in the atmosphere. However, because there is much more atmospheric oxygen than carbon dioxide, photosynthetic plants produce the equivalent of the world's supply of oxygen in a considerably longer time—an estimated 3,000 years. It seems likely, therefore, that photosynthetic activity and respiration provide a much weaker buffering system for the atmospheric oxygen.

The extent of photosynthesis can be expressed as the tons of carbon dioxide fixed per year. An estimated 15×10^{10} tons—

150 billion tons!—is fixed each year, the embodiment of biological foodstuffs. In the process, an estimated 120 billion tons of oxygen is set free. By far the greatest amount of photosynthesis occurs in the oceans, and only about 10 per cent in land plants. This is true in spite of the fact that on a unit-area basis, aerial plants have photosynthetic rates that are about ten times higher, principally because of their better gas-exchange relations.

Of the radiant energy reaching the earth from the sun, only about one-thousandth is captured in photosynthetic work. The efficiency of the photosynthetic process in green leaves is fairly great, however, as synthetic processes go. Net efficiencies as high as 25 per cent of the absorbed light have been reported under experimental conditions, but in the field they are ordinarily one-tenth of that.

Fig. 2-1 | Electron micrograph of a small section of a chloroplast, showing the membranous lamellae arranged in stacks on which the chlorophyll is borne. The loose granular material is the stroma in which the enzymes for the carbon transformations are located. (*Photograph by E. Weir.*)

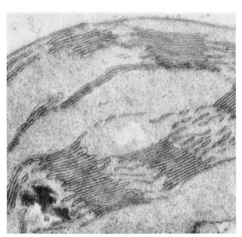

Structural requirements

In the utilization of light energy for organic syntheses, some reactive intermediate products are formed. If the photosynthetic pigments were free-floating in the cytoplasm, it would be physically impossible to bring about the production of carbohydrates because as the first labile intermediate was formed, it would be snatched up and reacted with other systems in the cytoplasm or in the surrounding environment. The completion of photosynthesis to form a carbohydrate can occur only under closed structural conditions such that as the energy is taken in, the synthesis of a complete and stable product can be completed before it is shunted out. The closed structure in which photosynthesis takes place in all higher plants is the chloroplast.

For a number of years it was felt that chloroplasts alone were inadequate for the complete reduction of CO_2 into carbohydrates, that is, that something else in addition to the chloroplast was necessary for the completion of photosynthesis. More recently it has become evident that the lack of photosynthetic activity of chloroplast preparations is a consequence of the loss of some of their enzymes during the separation from the cells (San Pietro, 1958). The chloroplast itself is, then, the complete structural and biochemical unit of photosynthesis in higher plants.

The structure of the chloroplast is shown in Fig. 1-3a. This little organelle, floating in the cytoplasm of the green cells of higher plants, consists of a double-layered membrane enclosing a liquid ground substance or stroma and interlaced by double-membraned lamellae, presumed to originate as invaginations of the interior layer of the outer membrane. At first, these lamellar structures are random in their arrangement within the developing chloroplast in, for example, an etiolated seedling. But with the exposure to light, the lamellae become oriented into flat layers as shown in Figs. 1-3 and 2-1, and chlorophyll molecules are probably localized on these layers. The flat lamellae develop in vertical piles, like stacks of coins, called *grana*. The light-driven reactions of photosynthesis take place on the grana, and subsequent reduction of carbon dioxide and the carbon interchanges which result finally in carbohydrate formation are carried out in the stroma. Thus starch grains develop appressed to the lamellae in the green grana. Electron photographs of the growing starch grains indicate that they cause a physical disruption of the lamellae. There probably is a rapid turnover of lamellae, with continued formation of new grana layers and chlorophyll under conditions where green leaf color is maintained.

Light is necessary not only for the development of orderly lamellar layers but also for the maintenance of lamellar structure. If a green leaf is placed in darkness, the development of etiolation is associated with a loss in the flat lamellar structures in the grana (von Wettstein, 1958).

The chloroplast is motile in the cytoplasm, but no evidence of a structural basis for its motility has been discovered. Chloroplasts lack respiratory enzymes and hence carry out only the biochemical steps associated with light and with several types of synthetic reactions. The origin of chloroplasts is obscure; it has been suggested that they may arise from other plastids by a process of budding.

The chlorophyll molecules are arranged in groups of four, with one carotenoid molecule associated with each group. Such an arrangement apparently contributes to the ready transmission of the excitation energy from one molecule of pigment to another, a feature of considerable importance in the utilization of weak light in photosynthesis. Since perhaps 10 quanta of light energy are required for each molecular synthesis, and since excited energy states from each absorbed quantum are extremely short-lived (in the order of thousandths of a second), the photoconductor qualities of the lamellae are clearly of extreme importance for photosynthesis, especially under weak light.

The algae have no grana in the chloroplasts, but the chlorophyll molecules are presumed to be arranged in monomolecular layers on more diffuse platelets.

The energy obtained from light drives four types of reactions in the chloroplast: (1) the photolysis of water (the Hill reaction), (2) photosynthetic phosphorylations, (3) the fixation of carbon dioxide, and (4) the synthesis of starch. The photolysis of water is apparently carried on in the lamellae within the grana, as is probably the photosynthetic phosphorylation. The subsequent steps of carbon dioxide fixation and starch synthesis are reactions of the soluble enzyme systems in the stroma of the chloroplasts.

The photosynthetic steps

The development of an understanding of biological phenomena usually takes place when a complex event is defined as a series of separate components or steps. The first to recognize that there were two main steps in photosynthesis was Blackman (1905), who noted that increases in light intensity would produce increases in photosynthesis only within a limited range, above which light increases were ineffective. He suggested that only a part of photosynthesis was driven by light and that when that part was saturated, further increases in light did not increase the rate. His suggestion implies that the response curves to light should rise in approximately a linear fashion and that they should then plateau abruptly, a situation which does not often occur (cf. Fig. 2-2).

The concept of light controlling only one part of a set of reactions was further developed by Brown and Escombe (1905). By revolving a disk in front of the light above a culture of *Chlorella* and using various sizes of apertures in the disk, they could

Fig. 2-2 | Saturation curves for photosynthesis of wheat seedlings with light intensities. The saturation level is much lower at low concentrations of CO_2, and the completeness of the saturation effect is likewise most pronounced there (Hoover et al., 1933).

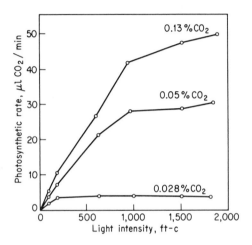

Fig. 2-3 | Photosynthesis of *Chlorella* under flashing light and varying dark periods between flashes. These data demonstrate a strong temperature sensitivity when the dark periods are short, indicating that a temperature-sensitive dark reaction is involved in photosynthesis (Emerson and Arnold, 1932).

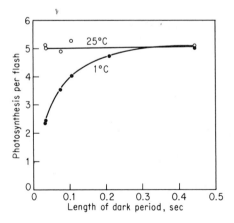

cut out fractions of the light without changing the intensity. Surprisingly, they found that the rate of photosynthesis was indifferent to the removal of as much as three-quarters of the light. This is explainable on the basis of two reactions, one that is driven by light and another that is independent of light, the latter limiting the rate of photosynthesis, especially at high light intensities. Emerson and Arnold (1932) used flashing neon bulbs with high intensities to develop this distinction further. They plotted photosynthetic rate against the length of the dark interval between uniform light flashes and compared such progress curves at different temperatures (Fig. 2-3). At 25°C the dark period was saturated at short intervals, and at 1°C it was saturated only at much longer intervals. From this they calculated that the Q_{10} for the dark reaction was 2.9, which is similar to that of an enzymatic reaction and too high for a photoreaction. By this neat experimental device, the existence of an enzymatic part in photosynthesis was positively established.

The first progress in the physical separation of the two steps of photosynthesis came with the experiments of Hill (1937), who separated chloroplasts from leaves and found that they could utilize light to produce oxygen, though they could not fix CO_2 into carbohydrates. This technique has provided an elegant means of studying the light reactions of photosynthesis. The separation of the second, or dark, reactions of photosynthesis was deferred for many years, until finally in 1958 Trebst et al. demonstrated the fixation of carbon dioxide by chloroplast fragments, separating the two steps in time by first applying light in the absence of CO_2 and then subsequently presenting the chloroplast pieces with CO_2 in the absence of light. The CO_2 was fixed into normal products of photosynthesis. They then separated the two steps morphologically and showed that the light reactions occurred in the green grana and the dark reactions in the surrounding stroma.

Arnon (1958) has suggested that the light step of photosynthesis provides high-energy bonds as reduced pyridine nucleotides and as adenosine triphosphate (ATP) and that the dark step is the utilization of this energy by the reduction of CO_2 into sugars and intermediates. By this concept, he would expect the light reaction to produce such materials as reduced triphosphopyridine nucleotide ($TPNH_2$) and ATP, and these would drive the dark reactions. He found that the addition of $TPNH_2$ and ATP to darkened chloroplast pieces did in fact permit the fixation of radioactive CO_2 without any light. Sample data from such an experiment are shown in Table 1.

Recognition of the two main steps in photosynthesis and the distinctive characteristics of each can explain many characteristics of photosynthetic rate curves, the Blackman type of saturation curve (Fig. 2-2) being due to limitations by the dark reactions at high light intensities, and the shift of the saturation curves at different temperatures being due to the greater temperature sensitivity of the dark reactions.

Much progress has been made in unraveling the complex pathways through which the fixed carbon can travel in the synthetic phases of photosynthesis, but for the present purposes it is sufficient to say that carbon dioxide is reduced with the fixation of the carbon probably onto ribulose diphosphate. The first product of the fixation is considered to be two molecules of phosphoglyceric acid, which then enter a maze of combining and counter-combining reactions leading finally to the formation of hexose and then of starch grains in the chloroplast.

The step of carbon dioxide incorporation is especially interesting since CO_2 levels are almost always suboptional in the field. The actual fixation reaction is irreversible and exergonic, properties which make possible the fixation of carbon dioxide photosynthetically at low partial pressures of CO_2 (Gaffron, 1960).

Table 1 | *Substitution for the light step in photosynthesis by preilluminated grana or by chemical energy sources (Arnon, 1958). Grana and stroma were separated by centrifugation of broken chloroplasts. The ATP and $TPNH_2$ were added at $2\mu M$.*

Treatment	$C^{14}O_2$ fixed, cpm
Stroma, preilluminated grana	96,000
Stroma, nonilluminated grana	4,000
Stroma, ATP	43,000
Stroma, ATP, $TPNH_2$	140,000

The commencement of photosynthesis with the advent of light shows an "induction period" during which full photosynthetic rates are not achieved. This period of more or less gradual acceleration of photosynthesis is believed to be due to the accrual of the intermediates in the carbon pathway before fixation can proceed at full speed. Figure 2-4 shows a typical curve for the induction period, which in many species lasts from 1 to 5 min (Aufdemgarten, 1939).

Fig. 2-4 | The induction period for the commencement of photosynthesis when light is applied to *Stichococcus*. Photosynthesis rises irregularly when 500 ft-c of light is applied after a 16-hr dark period; several minutes are required before photosynthesis proceeds at full rates (Aufdemgarten, 1939).

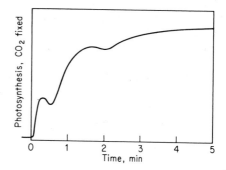

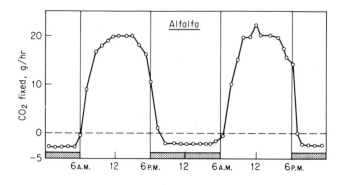

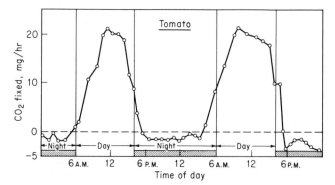

Fig. 2-5 | The diurnal CO₂ exchange curves for alfalfa plots (Thomas and Hill, 1949) and for tomato plants (Went, 1957).

The photosynthetic apparatus, thus, is a mechanism beautifully adapted for the efficient utilization of light energy. The chloroplast unit contains separate structural entities, the grana and stroma, to accomplish each of the two main photosynthetic steps or partial processes. Associated with these structures are the accessory enzyme systems needed for the conversion of light energy into chemical energy and for the synthesis of the final carbohydrate product, respectively. The photoreduction apparatus can be used for at least three other reductive steps: the phosphorylation of adenylates (photosynthetic phosphorylation), the reduction of TPN or DPN, and in special cases the reduction of inorganic nitrogen—each of which may greatly benefit the plant metabolism.

Photosynthetic rates

From a more ecological point of view, we have already seen that environmental factors such as temperature and carbon dioxide levels can impose heavy limits on the maximal photosynthetic responses to light. A list of environmental factors could be expanded to include water, nutrition of the plant, and inherent factors in the leaf such as adaptation and age.

Rates of photosynthesis for the entire plant can be readily followed by measurement of the depression of CO_2 in the ambient air; some sample results of diurnal rates are shown in Fig. 2-5. This type of curve, which is typical of many species, shows a peak near midday and a subsequent decline in the afternoon hours. The production of CO_2 by respiration in the dark is also evident in Fig. 2-5.

In many instances the diurnal pattern of photosynthesis shows a midday slump. This was described by Kursanov (1933) and by Harder (1933) in similar papers in the same issue of the same journal. To illustrate this type of diurnal photosynthetic pattern, data for apple leaves and potato leaves are plotted in Fig. 2-6 (Kursanov, 1933; Chapman, 1951). A depression of photosynthesis is often observed at about midday or shortly thereafter; then another peak occurs in the afternoon. Such a pattern has been described for many different species.

The explanation of the midday slump is complex and uncertain. Kursanov (1933) suggested that the accumulation of photosynthates could account for it since prevention of translocation out of the leaves by ringing accentuated the midday decline. A closure of stomata during the middle of the day is surely involved, associated with the higher transpiration rates at that time (Stålfelt, 1935). Deleterious effects from the high light intensity experienced at midday have also been considered, though Bohning (1949) found that even with uniform daylight intensities a midday slump occurred. The decline in CO_2 concentrations in the air would certainly contribute to the depressed photosynthetic rates, the content near the ground dropping as much as 25 per cent by midday (Huber, 1958*a*). The fact that some plants do not show a rise in photosynthesis again in the afternoon would match the CO_2 change very well (Uhl, 1937). Some authors have stated that the midday slump may result from different factors under different plant conditions, from carbohydrate accumulation in young leaves in the spring, or from stomatal closure in mature leaves in midsummer (von Guttenberg and Buhr, 1935; Kramer and Kozlowski, 1960).

The diurnal patterns of photosynthesis are superimposed on another periodicity—that of the seasonal variation of photosynthetic rates. As an illustration, the seasonal changes in accumulation of dry matter in *Sinapis alba* plants in the field are shown in Fig. 2-7. There is a rise in accumulation of dry matter into June, followed by a receding tendency for the rest of the growing season. The seasonal changes in photosynthetic potential can be observed when leaves are moved into standardized temperature and light conditions for each measurement, as illustrated by the comparisons of an evergreen and a deciduous species shown in Fig. 2-8 (Saeki and Nomoto, 1958). The evergreen *Shiia* has a low potential for photosynthesis through the winter months, which then rises to a broad peak during the growing season. In deciduous *Zelkowa* the potential peaks more markedly in the spring and then declines from July until November.

A comparison of the photosynthetic activities of leaves in various positions on the

Fig. 2-6 | Changes in photosynthesis during the day for apple (Kursanov, 1933) and for potato (Chapman, 1951), showing the midday slump of photosynthesis occurring in the late morning and early afternoon.

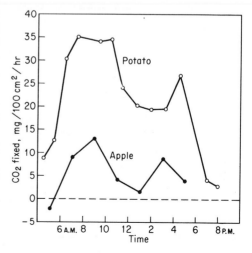

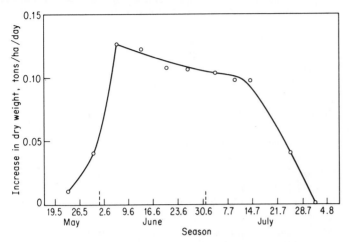

Fig. 2-7 | Seasonal changes in photosynthesis as indicated by changes in the daily production of dry matter by *Sinapis alba* plants (Boysen-Jensen, 1932).

plant indicates that the leaves which have almost reached full size are the most active. For example, Shiroya et al. (1961) exposed various leaves of tobacco to $C^{14}O_2$ and found the largest amounts of radioactive carbon accumulated in the newly expanded leaves. Progressively older leaves exhibited a distinct decline in photosynthetic activity (Fig. 2-9). Coincident with the optimal age for photosynthesis at the young expanded stage is the optimal light exposure of the young expanded leaves at the tips of the stems.

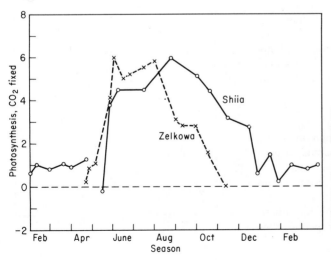

Fig. 2-8 | Seasonal changes in photosynthesis as indicated by CO_2 fixation by an evergreen (*Shiia*) and a deciduous plant (*Zelkowa*). For each reading the plants were moved into the greenhouse (20 to 25°C) and CO_2 fixation recorded as mg/50 cm²/hr. (Saeki and Nomoto, 1958).

Light as a factor

A principal variable in the environment affecting photosynthesis is light intensity. Several characteristics of the light-response curve can be useful in understanding the relations of light to photosynthesis. A schematic light curve for photosynthesis is shown in Fig. 2-10 with some of the main features indicated according to the scheme of Rabinowitch (1951). The steepness of the curve (A) is related to the quantum efficiency of the leaf and should be characteristic for a given leaf. The linear range of photosynthesis (B) will proceed as long as variables other than light are not critical. It will be foreshortened therefore by environmental conditions such as low CO_2 levels, temperatures, and air movement. The compensation point (C) will be altered by any factor influencing CO_2 exchange, such as, for example, the respiration rate or the CO_2 concentration. It rises with leaf age or with a depletion of CO_2 levels around the leaf. The saturation intensity (D) is strongly influenced by the adaptation of the leaf, being lower for shade leaves than for sun leaves of the same species. The saturation intensity changes with environmental variables which alter the length of the linear range of photosynthesis. The maximum photosynthetic rate (E), when all environmental variables are provided at optimal levels, will range between about 8 and 80 mg CO_2 per hr per 100 cm² of leaf (Rabinowitch, 1951). These five features of the light-response curves are useful criteria for comparisons of photosynthetic responses of plants to external and internal variables.

In an early work on photosynthesis, Boysen-Jensen (1932) demonstrated many of the principal facts about light effects. First, he showed that a single oat leaf held perpendicular to the light source may be saturated at much lower light intensities than the intact plant (Fig. 2-11). One should logically expect this, as the intact plant will have much of its leaf area partly shaded or in various angular positions, and hence the incident light will be less than the ambient light. This difference between individual leaves and intact plants underlies an argument about the light intensities needed for plant growth. Some investigators assert that intensities above about 1,000 ft-c are of no increased value to the plant since photo-

Fig. 2-9 | The decline of photosynthetic activity in tobacco leaves with age. Each leaf was exposed to $C^{14}O_2$ for 50 min under 2,000 ft-c of light (Shiroya et al., 1961).

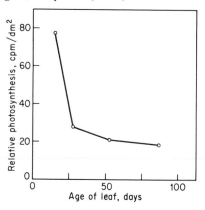

Fig. 2-10 | A model light-intensity curve for photosynthesis illustrates some of the characteristics of such a curve. A, the initial slope of the curve, B, the linear range of photosynthesis, C, the compensation point, D, the saturation intensity, and E, the maximum photosynthetic rate (modified from Rabinowitch, 1951).

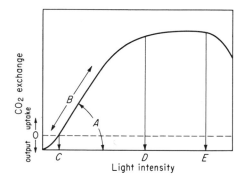

synthesis of an individual leaf is saturated at that amount or less.

Boysen-Jensen and Müller (1929) compared the light responses of beech trees grown in full sun with those of beech trees grown in the shade (Fig. 2-12) and found that the intensity at which photosynthesis was saturated was much lower in shade

Fig. 2-11 | Light-intensity curves for a single leaf and a whole plant of *Avena*, showing especially the differences in initial slope, linear range, and saturating intensities (Boysen-Jensen, 1932).

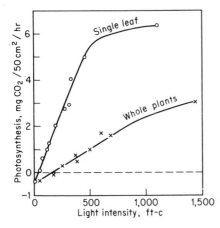

Fig. 2-12 | Light-intensity curves for leaves of *Fagus sylvatica* which are adapted to shade or to full light, showing also the differences in initial slope, linear range, and saturating intensities (Boysen-Jensen and Müller, 1929).

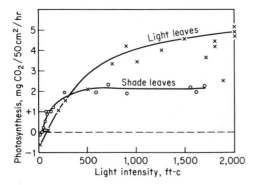

leaves than in sun leaves. In another comparison, Boysen-Jensen (1932) contrasted the responses of tolerant and intolerant species, using *Oxalis* as a tolerant, or shade-loving, species and *Sinapis* as an intolerant, or sun-loving, species. Like the shade leaves, *Oxalis* is saturated at low intensities. These data illustrate how adaptation of a leaf to shade lowers the saturation intensity and usually shortens the linear range of photosynthesis.

More recently, Kramer and Decker (1944) have shown how a tolerant tree such as red oak is saturated in photosynthesis by much lower light intensities than an intolerant tree such as loblolly pine (Fig. 2-13).

The duration of light would be expected to alter the daily amount of photosynthesis, and some data of Went (1957) demonstrate this. Tomato seedlings given different durations of light yielded increases in dry weight which were proportional to the day length (Fig. 2-14). Tomato is not a photoperiod-sensitive species, so this effect was not confounded by alterations in the developmental functions of the plants by day length.

Although the greatest weight increase is shown for the tomato at 24 hr of light, in many circumstances photosynthesis is depressed by continuous illumination. Bohning (1949) described a decline in photosynthesis when continuous light was applied to apple leaves. His results illustrate the rather general finding that leaves which have been adapted to full sunlight are much more resistant to continuous light than shade leaves; the latter show marked inhibitions of photosynthesis after only 48 hr of continuous illumination. Even during one day, photosynthesis may decline with time in the light (e.g., Kozlowski, 1957). In some species continuous light results in extreme chlorosis of the leaves (Withrow and Withrow, 1949), a situation that can be avoided either by daily dark periods or by daily temperature fluctuations (Hillman, 1956).

Photosynthetic rates respond to light intensities on a two-phase curve, being inhibited by intensities above an optimum, as shown in Fig. 2-15 (Myers and Burr, 1940). The inhibitory effects of excessive intensities become accentuated with time of exposure. Steeman-Nielsen (1952*b*) has done some interesting experiments on excessive light intensities with *Cladophora*. Use of an aquatic minimizes temperature complications. His data (Fig. 2-16) show a deterioration of photosynthetic rates in high intensities of light; these linger even when the plants are returned to weak light. Using this technique he could quantify the inhibition effect and show that it was proportional to the duration of the excess light as well as to the intensity of light applied. He concluded that both the light and dark steps of photosynthesis are damaged by excessive light intensities.

Sironval and Kandler (1958) have examined the light-inhibition effects further, and by following time curves they were able to distinguish between an initial "induction" effect, in which photosynthesis was inhibited without chlorophyll bleaching, and a subsequent bleaching effect on chlorophyll itself. These two phases of the damage are illustrated in Fig. 2-17. The induction effect appears to be a photocatalyzed oxidation, requiring oxygen. The bleaching effect is relieved in living cells by elevated CO_2 levels, suggesting that bleaching occurs when the light step of photosynthesis is saturated but the dark reactions cannot proceed for lack of CO_2. These observations reinforce the possibility that the midday slump of photosynthesis may be related to the high light intensities, especially when CO_2 levels are low.

In the past, physiologists have equated the beneficial effects of light with photosynthetic fixation of CO_2, and yet many plants grow more rapidly in short photoperiods, or they may accumulate carbohydrates in storage organs under short photoperiods or low temperatures, conditions

Fig. 2-13 | Light-intensity curves for a tolerant tree species (red oak) and an intolerant species (loblolly pine). Note the low saturation intensity for the oak (Kramer and Decker, 1944).

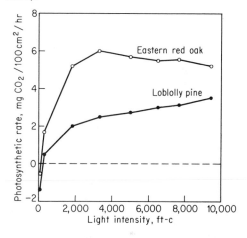

Fig. 2-14 | Increases in the amount of apparent photosynthesis in tomato plants with increasing durations of diurnal light. Photosynthesis is estimated by the increase in dry weight of the plant after 5 days at the indicated photoperiod (Went, 1957).

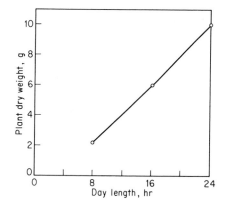

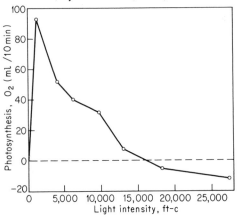

Fig. 2-15 | The inhibition of photosynthesis by excessive light intensities. *Chlorella* cultures exposed to the light intensities indicated for 30 min before the oxygen production was measured (Myers and Burr, 1940).

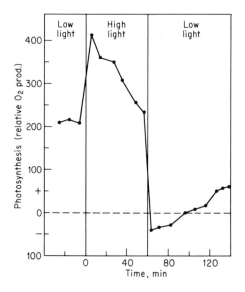

Fig. 2-16 | Inhibitory effects of high light intensity are indicated both by the decline of photosynthesis during a 1-hr exposure to 1,000 ft-c and by the subsequent weak photosynthesis at low intensity (300-ft-c). *Cladophora insignis* cultures (Steeman-Nielsen, 1952*b*).

which would be expected to limit photosynthesis. The fact that the light step in photosynthesis gives rise to phosphorylations suggests that light may provide the plant with energies for synthetic activities within the leaf, such as the conversion of sugars into polysaccharides or fats. The effects of light may include other energy-requiring activities such as nitrogen reduction and chemo-syntheses.

Adaptation to light

Numerous examples of the adaptation of some species or some leaves to higher light intensities have been given. Plants which are adapted to high light intensities are associated with a lower photosynthetic efficiency at low light intensities and hence will do poorly in the shade of other plants. The light-response curves for intolerant species or for sun leaves are quite different from those for tolerant or shade leaves. Referring to the generalized light-response curve shown in Fig. 2-10, in comparison with that shown in Fig. 2-12, it can be seen that adaptation to high light intensity results in a lower initial slope or yield efficiency (A), a longer linear range (B), a higher compensation point (C), and higher saturation intensities and maximal photosynthetic rates (D and E). All these characteristics stem from greater ability of shade leaves to photosynthesize in weak light and a greater ability of sun leaves to utilize higher ranges of light intensities.

To study light adaptation, Wassink et al. (1956) exposed sycamore seedlings to various light intensities during the growth of the leaves (the exposition intensity). After growth was completed, they placed individual leaves in various light intensities for the measurement of photosynthesis (Fig. 2-18). Drawing a light-response curve for each of three exposition intensities, they have illustrated nicely the altered characteristics of light-adapted leaves. Those which

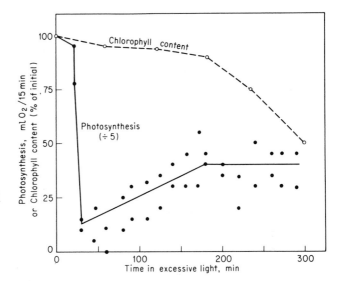

Fig. 2-17 | Detrimental effects of high light intensity evidenced as an immediate drop in photosynthesis and a later bleaching of chlorophyll (Kandler and Sironval, 1959).

matured in high intensities [25,000 ergs/cm^2/sec] exhibit the lower initial slope in the light-response curve, a longer linear range, and higher saturation and maximal photosynthetic rates.

Using this precise manner of experimentation, Wassink et al. (1956) demonstrated that the adaptability to light intensity is obtained only during the growth period of the leaf; after the leaf has matured there is no further adaptation. If light adaptation is a morphological expression, it is logical that once the leaf is structurally mature, further adaptation will not occur. It is common knowledge that when a plant is moved from heavy shade to full sun, the old leaves often deteriorate, and new leaves adapted to the new site must be developed if the plant is to survive.

An extreme case of adaptation to low light intensities occurs in some marine algae which reach photosynthetic saturation at 100 ft-c of light! There are wide differences among species in their ability to adapt to sun and shade conditions (Rabinowitch, 1951), but while these are recognized horti-

Fig. 2-18 | Light-intensity curves for leaves of sycamore which have become adapted to three levels of light intensity. With adaptation to higher intensities, the leaves showed a lower initial slope, longer linear range, and higher saturating intensities (Wassink et al., 1956).

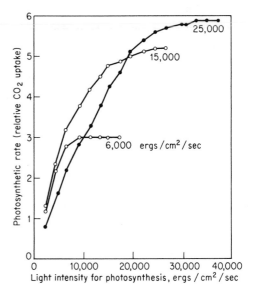

culturally, no physiological explanation has been developed.

Carbon dioxide effects

A surprising feature of the photosynthetic apparatus in leaves is that the physical optima for photosynthesis do not coincide very

Fig. 2-19 | Carbon dioxide curves for the photosynthesis of wheat seedlings at several light intensities. Note that the saturation level is much lower at low light intensity and that the completeness of the saturation effect is likewise most pronounced there (Hoover et al., 1933).

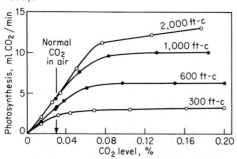

Fig. 2-20 | The stimulative effects of elevated CO_2 levels on the growth of seedlings of wheat, cucumber, and tomato (Lundegårdh, 1924).

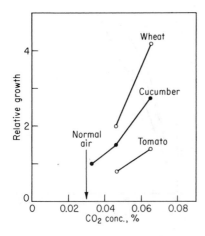

well with the common conditions under which it occurs in the field. The optimal light intensities for plants in general are usually surpassed in full sunlight, and the optimal temperature is ordinarily surpassed in most of the climates of the world. But the optimal carbon dioxide content of air for photosynthesis is far above the usual ambient CO_2 partial pressures. Rabinowitch (1951) has asked whether this discrepancy might reflect a higher CO_2 content of the atmosphere during the earlier phases of photosynthetic evolution.

Whatever the cause, carbon dioxide is apparently the most generally limiting factor in photosynthesis in the field. Sample response curves to varying CO_2 levels shown in Fig. 2-19 (Hoover et al., 1933) illustrate that the slope of the photosynthetic-response curve to increased CO_2 levels is greater for high light intensities than for low. The imposition of any physical limitation would shorten the linear-response range, but the light limitation is especially critical in interaction with CO_2. These data indicate that the most common CO_2 level in air (0.03 to 0.035 per cent) is well below the optimum for wheat leaves experiencing 2,000 ft-c of light. In full sunlight (12,000 to 15,000 ft-c), the atmospheric CO_2 level profoundly limits photosynthesis. It is clear that small changes in atmospheric concentrations can cause large changes in rates of photosynthesis in the field.

Apparently some species are better adapted to low CO_2 concentrations than others. Lundegårdh (1924) compared the CO_2 concentration curves for wheat, cucumber, and tomato (Fig. 2-20) and obtained striking differences between these species.

The relative adaptation to CO_2 has been examined in alpine species on the grounds that they might have a greater efficiency of CO_2 utilization; the weight of CO_2 gas causes its accumulations in the lowlands, leaving markedly lower levels at high altitudes. Decker (1959) has done some interesting experiments comparing a clone of

Mimulus which grows in the lowlands with one growing at high altitudes. He measured photosynthetic rates (CO₂ fixation) as a function of CO₂ concentration at three temperatures (Fig. 2-21) and found that both types of *Mimulus* yielded the same response to the treatments. The evidence did not support the concept of an improved CO₂ absorption system for the alpine plant. His data also show the decrease in apparent photosynthesis at any one CO₂ concentration with increased temperatures above 20°C, with the concomitant increased respiratory rate and hence the higher compensation point.

The great sensitivity of photosynthesis to CO₂ levels results in some marked changes in photosynthetic function in the field. There are diurnal variations in the CO₂ content of air, and these impose similar diurnal variations in photosynthesis (Huber, 1958a). The local gradients of CO₂ content in dense stands of vegetation impose limitations on photosynthetic activity. As the CO₂ content decreases, the green leaf approaches a limit for assimilation, until finally the feeble fixation only matches the production of respiratory CO₂, and beyond that point the illuminated plant is unable to remove net amounts of CO₂ from the air. This phenomenon is illustrated in some experiments of Gabrielsen (1948), in which photosynthesizing plants were enclosed in a tight chamber and the depletion of CO₂ was followed in time (Fig. 2-22). The photosynthesizing leaves reduced the CO₂ level to approximately 0.01 per cent or a little less, but beyond that there was no further depletion. It must be concluded that the respiratory production of CO₂ equaled the ability of the leaves to fix it photosynthetically.

The localized depletion of CO₂ can easily occur under conditions which permit the layering of air over the surface of the leaf. Large increases in photosynthesis can be obtained with air movement, probably reflecting the limitation of photosynthesis by

Fig. 2-21 | Testing for differences in CO₂ responses for the photosynthesis of alpine and nonalpine clones of *Mimulus*. Single pairs of leaves were compared at each CO₂ concentration at 2,000 ft-c and at three temperatures, but no appreciable difference in the responses of the two clones was found (Decker, 1959).

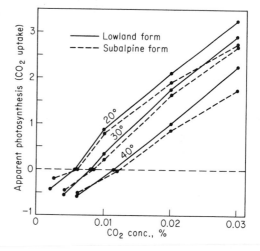

Fig. 2-22 | Photosynthesis in leaves of *Sambucus nigra* can remove CO₂ from the air only to a level of about 0.01 per cent. The plants were illuminated with 1,000 ft-c in a container with either normal air or CO₂ depleted air. In the latter case the leaves lost CO₂ until the 0.01 value of air was achieved (Gabrielsen, 1948).

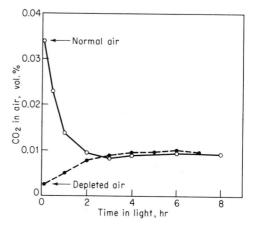

Fig. 2-23 | The inhibition of photosynthesis by high concentrations of CO_2 in cultures of *Chlorella* (Steeman-Nielsen, 1953).

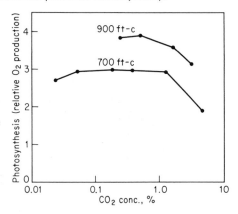

Fig. 2-24 | The extent of opening of the stomata can markedly limit photosynthesis. Oat plants were given 2,000 ft-c of light, and the stomatal apertures were measured by microscopic examination (Stålfelt, 1935).

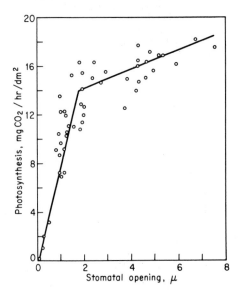

air layering and the localized depletion of CO_2 at the actual surface of the leaf in still air. Went (1957) has illustrated this by comparing photosynthetic rates of plants in still air in an artificial wind. He obtained a 20 per cent increase in CO_2 fixation upon introducing turbulence and a prompt drop when the turbulence was withdrawn. Air layering around large flat leaves may be considerably more acute than around thinly divided leaves. Gessner (1938) observed that the photosynthetic rate of plants with broad leaves was greatly enhanced by air turbulence, while in plants with finely divided leaves it was not appreciably increased.

An excessive supply of CO_2 can limit photosynthesis (de Saussure, 1804). Steeman-Nielsen (1953) has described quantitative experiments on this with *Chlorella* (Fig. 2-23). Under the test conditions, *Chlorella* experienced an optimum photosynthetic rate with 0.05 per cent CO_2 and was inhibited by levels above about 1.0 per cent depending somewhat on the light intensity. Photosynthetic inhibitions by high CO_2 levels have been reported in aerial plants at levels as high as 20 per cent (Livingston and Franck, 1940) and as low as 2.5 per cent (Ballard, 1941). The actual concentration at which inhibition begins changes considerably with other physical variables such as light intensity and temperature. Stålfelt (1960) interprets the CO_2 inhibition as a consequence of an increased acidity of the mesophyll and perhaps a narcotic effect on the metabolic function of the cells. In some plants it may also result from the closure of the stomata in response to the elevated CO_2 level.

The stomata provide the principal means of entry of CO_2 into the leaves of higher plants, and so their degree of opening can have a great influence on photosynthesis (Maskell, 1927). The entry of CO_2 through the epidermal or surface cells is only about one-hundredth as effective as entry through opened stomata (Stålfelt, 1935). The extent of closure of stomata can limit photosynthetic rates (Fig. 2–24). High CO_2 levels can cause the closure of stomata and hence a suppression of photosynthesis; conversely, low partial presures of CO_2 can accentuate the opening of stomata (Scarth and Shaw, 1951), which may improve gas exchange in leaves under conditions of deficient CO_2 supply.

The possibility of improving photosynthesis in crops through CO_2 fertilization has interested agriculturists for many years (cf. Lundegårdh, 1924, in Fig. 2-20), and some reports show exciting increases in plant growth, while others demonstrate only inhibitions with added CO_2. There is great potential for the use of CO_2 fertilization in high-value crops, but the means of consistently obtaining such beneficial effects remain uncertain. The acute importance of air circulation to prevent layering around the leaves, combined with the detrimental effects of excessive concentrations of CO_2 and the varying CO_2 optima with changes in temperature or light intensity, has so far baffled those who have attempted to use such a technique.

The magnitude of the mechanical problem of obtaining the necessary supply of CO_2 has been pointed up by Norman (1962). The plant must "process" a very large volume of air to obtain the necessary carbon source for photosynthesis. For example, an acre of corn which yields 100 bu must assimilate 20,000 lb of CO_2, an amount which is contained in no less than 21,000 tons of air. Since the plant can remove only about one-half of the CO_2 from air, the corn plants must process twice that amount, or 42,000 tons, in the growing season. Corn will develop a leaf area equal to about 3.5 times the ground area (leaf area index), so each square foot of foliage must process about 475 ft³ of air during the season, or about 5 ft³/day. The immensity of the engineering problem seems reason enough for CO_2 being such a limiting factor in photosynthesis.

Chlorophyll content

Even though chlorophyll is an essential ingredient for photosynthesis, the abundance of this pigment exerts a surprisingly weak quantitative influence on photosynthesis in the field. Deficiencies in some inorganic nutrients can bring about limitations of photosynthesis through large-scale depression of the chlorophyll content of leaves (e.g., Kennedy, 1940), and the effect may be magnified through decreases in leaf area. Deficiencies of sulfur, nitrogen, iron, and magnesium may lead to chlorosis and then to chlorophyll limitations on photosynthesis.

The relatively weak influence of chlorophyll content on photosynthetic rates was shown long ago by Willstätter and Stoll (1918) with elm leaves. Their data, repeated in Table 2, compare equal quantities of leaves containing normal and less than one-tenth normal chlorophyll contents. The amounts of CO_2 fixed per hour by these leaves, however, were only about 15 per cent lower in the chlorophyll-deficient leaves. They suggested that under the deficiency conditions there was somehow an increased utilization rate for the chlorophyll molecules present.

Willstätter and Stoll (1918) were interested in the fact that the photosynthetic rates did not correlate with chlorophyll contents (Fig. 2-25). The peak in photosynthesis of ash leaves in the early spring occurs when chlorophyll contents are relatively low, and a peak in chlorophyll content in mid-

Table 2 | *The photosynthetic fixation of CO_2 by equal quantities of elm leaves with normal and deficient cholorophyll contents (Willstätter and Stoll, 1918).*

	Chlorophyll, mg	CO_2 fixed/hr	CO_2 fixed/hr/g chlorophyll
Normal	13.00	0.89	6.8
Chlorotic	0.95	0.75	78.9

summer is not associated with a peak in photosynthesis. The decline of chlorophyll in autumn is associated with a photosynthetic decline. The apparent increased effectiveness of chlorophyll under conditions of deficiencies of the pigment may be explained as a corollary of the nonlimitation by the light step of photosynthesis except at low light intensities. Under field conditions the light intensities are ordinarily so high that they do not limit photosynthetic rates, and the response curve to increases in light is not linear. Thus with a deficient chlorophyll content and a presumed lower efficiency of the light step per unit of incident light, photosynthetic rates would not be proportionally inhibited. At low light intensities, on the other hand, chlorophyll deficiencies would be expected to limit photosynthesis.

There are several reports of depressed chlorophyll content associated with lower photosynthetic rates. Some of these are experiments which were carried out under low light intensities, and hence the observed chlorophyll limitation would not necessarily apply to field conditions. In other cases the chlorophyll deficiency is brought about through a mineral deficiency or other toxic situation under which the lowering of photosynthetic rates would not necessarily be attributed to the chlorophyll deficiency.

The fact that chlorophyll synthesis proceeds rapidly in light (e.g., Koski, 1950) and that chlorophyll degradation does also (Holden, 1961) suggests that the pigment is in a dynamic state in the green leaf. Estimates of the rate of chlorophyll synthesis made from measurements of the rate of incorporation of radioisotopes indicate that synthesis is greater by far in young expanding leaves and declines markedly with leaf age (Sironval et al., 1961).

Temperature effects

The changes of photosynthesis with temperature are complex, but in view of the involvement of both light-driven and enzymatic reactions, such complexities are not unexpected. The light step, being a physical reaction (at least initially), will have a temperature coefficient (Q_{10}) near 1.0, and the dark step or any of the associated enzymatic processes will have a Q_{10} above 2.0. The Q_{10} of photosynthesis will vary according to which steps are rate-limiting. Most reports indicate Q_{10} values for photosynthesis of between 1.0 and 2.7, though a few are higher (Rabinowitch, 1956).

The photosynthetic rates over a temperature range are illustrated by data of Stålfelt (1937) in Fig. 2-26. Not only does the rate of fixation of CO_2 rise with increased temperature, but the steepness of the rise is greatest at temperatures just above freezing and then is moderated at higher temperatures. These changes in slope, which reflect changes in Q_{10}, are especially evident after the apparent photosynthetic rates have been corrected for respiratory activity. The high-

Fig. 2-25 | Seasonal changes in photosynthesis of sycamore do not reflect the seasonal changes in chlorophyll content of the leaves until autumn, when both photosynthesis and chlorophyll decline (Willstätter and Stoll, 1918).

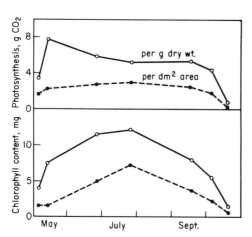

est Q_{10} values are obtained at lowest temperature ranges because under such circumstances the enzymatic processes are most limiting; hence temperature increases will accelerate photosynthesis in the same manner as they would enzymatic processes alone. At temperatures near 20°C, the light step is more likely to be limiting. At higher temperatures, further increases in photosynthesis are not obtained, or actual inhibitions may set in with the intervention of physical limitations such as inadequate CO_2 exchange or enzyme inactivation by the heat.

The temperature responses of photosynthesis also vary with CO_2 availability. At low CO_2 partial pressures, the Q_{10} is low because the diffusion of CO_2 is a physical process with a low Q_{10}. At high CO_2 partial pressures, some very high Q_{10} values for photosynthesis have been reported—4.0 and higher (Emerson and Green, 1934; Rabinowitch, 1956).

The photosynthetic Q_{10} also varies with light intensity (Emerson and Green, 1934), being low when light intensities are very low because under these circumstances the overall rate assumes the same Q_{10} as the light step itself.

Photosynthesis may proceed slowly even at subfreezing temperatures, with compensation points for some evergreens below −6°C (Freeland, 1944). It has been noted that evergreen plants moved into standard conditions during winter months are quite ineffective in photosynthesis (McGregor, 1958; Saeki and Nomoto, 1958, in Fig. 2-8). We can deduce that leaves can adapt to low temperatures and that in this state they have a less effective utilization of light when moved into warm temperatures.

Water effects

Water is of considerable importance as an ecological factor in photosynthesis through its control of stomatal opening and its effects on wilting of leaves. Photosynthesis is proportional to stomatal opening under many conditions (Fig. 2-24) and hence is sensitive to changes in water relations which will affect the stomatal function. The midday slump in photosynthesis has been ascribed in part to a shortage of water with the consequent partial closure of stomata.

Wilting of leaves results in a marked depression of photosynthesis. Schneider and Childers (1941), who followed this response in apples, reported that after wilting developed, photosynthesis dropped to about 15 per cent of its former level. Restoration of normal water supply did not restore photosynthetic rates until 2 to 7 days later, suggesting that some structural damage resulted from the wilting.

Ashton (1956) followed the photosyn-

Fig. 2-26 | The changes in photosynthesis with temperature can be calculated by measuring the apparent photosynthesis in light and the respiration in darkness and correcting accordingly. Note the steep rise with temperature at the lowest temperature ranges. *Sphagnum* in 750 ft-c (Stålfelt, 1937).

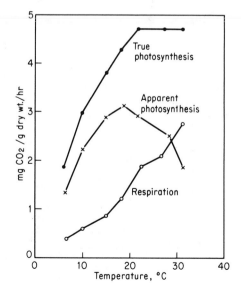

thetic rates of sugarcane plants under various regimes of water shortage and found that at soil tensions near the permanent wilting point there were greatly exaggerated midday slumps in photosynthesis. His data illustrate well the gradual recovery of full photosynthetic rates in the week following wilting.

Age effects

As individual leaves age, their ability to photosynthesize depreciates considerably. This has been shown most often with perennial leaves such at those of conifers (Freeland, 1952) and palms (Nixon and Wedding, 1956). In these instances, photo-synthetic rates are highest at the time of leaf maturation or shortly thereafter, and they gradually decline during successive years (Fig. 2-27). Even the leaves of annuals show this decline with age (Fig. 2-9), and it has been suggested that the deterioration of the anabolic activities contributes to the senescence of the leaf (Das and Leopold, 1964; see Figs. 12-2 and 12-3). This deterioration may occur in the chloroplasts, for the chloroplast preparations from leaves of increasing age show decreasing capacities for the photolysis of water (Clendenning and Gorham, 1950; Miller, 1960).

The aging of entire plants may be reflected in a decline in photosynthetic capacity (Singh and Lal, 1935). Some calculations of the declining total increment of dry matter in stands of Scotch pine older than 30 years indicate likewise that tree populations may experience such a senescent decline (Hellmers and Bonner, 1959).

It can be seen, then, that the photosynthetic operation of green leaves is commonly limited by the environmental features of light intensity and CO_2 availability. Probably temperature and water are less extensive limitations. The ability of the plant to respond to these environmental factors is modified in a less specific way by such variables as plant nutrition, gas-exchange characteristics, age of the leaves, and senescence of the plant.

Fig. 2-27 | The decline in photosynthetic activity with leaf age in date palm (Nixon and Wedding, 1956) and some conifers (Freeland, 1952).

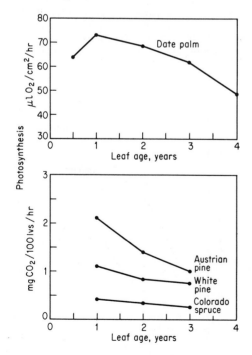

GENERAL REFERENCES

Gaffron, H. 1960. Energy storage: photosynthesis, pp. 3–247. In F. C. Steward (ed.), *Plant Physiology*. Academic Press Inc., New York.

Rabinowitch, E. I. *Photosynthesis*. Interscience Publishers, Inc., New York. Vol. 1 (1945); Vol. 2, Part 1 (1951); and Vol. 2, Part 2 (1956).

REFERENCES CITED

Arnon, D. I. 1958. Chloroplasts and photosynthesis. *Brookhaven Symp. Biol.*, 11:181–231.

Ashton, F. M. 1956. Effects of a series of cycles of low and high soil water on the rate of apparent photosynthesis in sugarcane. *Plant Physiol.*, 31:266–274.

Aufdemgarten, H. 1939. Zur Kenntnis der sogenannten Induktionsvorgange bei der Kohlensaureassimilation. *Planta*, 29:643–678.

Ballard, L. A. T. 1941. The depressant effect of carbon dioxide upon photosynthesis. *New Phytologist*, 40:276–289.

Blackman, F. F. 1905. Optima and limiting factors. *Ann. Botany (London)*, 19:281–295.

Bohning, R. H. 1949. Time course of photosynthesis in apple leaves exposed to continuous illumination. *Plant Physiol.*, 24:222–240.

Boysen-Jensen, P. 1932. *Die Stoffproduktion der Pflanzen.* Gustav Fischer Verlag KG, Jena.

———— and D. Müller. 1929. Die maximale Ausbeute und der tägliche Verlauf der Kohlensaureassimilation. *Jahrb. Wiss. Bot.*, 70:493–502.

Brown, H. T., and F. Escombe. 1905. Researches on some physiological processes of green leaves with special reference to the interchange of energy between the leaf and its surroundings. *Proc. Roy. Soc. (London)*, B,76:29–112.

Chapman, H. W. 1951. Absorption of CO_2 by leaves of the potato. *Am. Potato J.*, 28:602–615.

Clendenning, K. A., and P. R. Gorham. 1950. Photochemical activity of isolated chloroplasts in relation to their source and previous history. *Can. J. Res.*, C,28:114–139.

Das, T. M., and A. C. Leopold. 1964. Physiological changes with leaf senescence. (Unpublished.)

Decker, J. P. 1959. Some effects of temperature and carbon dioxide concentration on photosynthesis of *Mimulus*. *Plant Physiol.*, 34:103–106.

Emerson, R., and W. Arnold. 1932. The photochemical reaction in photosynthesis. *J. Gen. Physiol.*, 16:191–205.

———— and L. Green. 1934. Manometric measurements of photosynthesis in the marine alga *Gigartina*. *J. Gen. Physiol.*, 17:817–841.

Freeland, R. O. 1944. Apparent photosynthesis in some conifers during the winter. *Plant Physiol.*, 19:179–185.

————. 1952. Effect of age of leaves upon the rate of photosynthesis in some conifers. *Plant Physiol.*, 27:685–690.

Gabrielsen, E. K. 1948. Threshold value of carbon dioxide concentration in photosynthesis of foliage leaves. *Nature*, 161:138–139.

Gaffron, H. 1960. Energy storage: photosynthesis, pp. 3–247. In F. C. Steward (ed.), *Plant Physiology*. Academic Press, Inc., New York.

Gessner, F. 1938. Die Beziehung zwischen Lichtintensität und Assimilation bei submersen Wasserpflanzen. *Jahrb. Wiss. Bot.*, 86:491–526.

Guttenberg, H. von, and H. Buhr. 1935. Studien über die Assimilation und Atmung mediterraner Maschiapflanzen wahrend der Regen und Frachenzeit. *Planta*, 24:163–265.

Harder, R. 1933. Über die Assimilation der Kohlensaure bei konstanten Aussenbedingungen. II. Das Verhalten von Sonnen –und Schattenpflanzen. *Planta*, 20:699–733.

Hellmers, H., and J. Bonner. 1959. Photosynthetic limits of forest tree yields. *Proc. Soc. Am. Foresters*, 32–35.

Hill, R. 1937. Oxygen evolved by isolated chloroplasts. *Nature*, 139:881–882.

Hillman, W. S. 1956. Injury of tomato plants by continuous light and unfavorable photoperiodic cycles. *Am. J. Botany*, 43:89–96.

Holden, M. 1961. The breakdown of chlorophyll by chlorophyllase. *Biochem. J.*, 78: 359–364.

Hoover, W. H., E. S. Johnston, and F. S. Brackett. 1933. Carbon dioxide assimilation in a higher plant. *Smithsonian Inst. Misc. Collections*, 87:1–19.

Huber, B. 1958a. Recording gaseous exchange under field conditions, pp. 187–195. In K. V. Thimann (ed.), *The Physiology of Forest Trees*. The Ronald Press Company, New York.

Huber, B. 1958b. Anatomical and physiological investigations on food translocation in trees, pp. 367–400. In K. V. Thimann (ed.), *The Physiology of Forest Trees*. The Ronald Press Company, New York.

Kandler, O., and C. Sironval. 1959. Photooxidation processes in normal green *Chlorella* cells. II. Effects on metabolism. *Biochim. Biophys. Acta*, 33:207–215.

Kennedy, S. R., Jr. 1940. The influence of magnesium deficiency, chlorophyll concentration, and heat treatments on the rate of photosynthesis of *Chlorella*. *Am. J. Botany*, 27:68–73.

Koski, V. M. 1950. Chlorophyll formation in seedlings of *Zea mays*. *Arch. Biochem. Biophys.*, 29:339–343.

Kozlowski, T. T. 1957. Effect of continuous high light intensity on photosynthesis of forest tree seedlings. *Forest Sci.*, 3:220–224.

Kramer, P. J., and J. P. Decker. 1944. Relation between light intensity and rate of photosynthesis of loblolly pine and certain hardwoods. *Plant Physiol.*, 19:350–358.

Kramer, P. J., and T. T. Kozlowski. 1960. *Physiology of Trees*. McGraw-Hill Book Company, New York. 642 pp.

Kursanov, A. L. 1933. Über den Einfluss der Kohlenhydrate auf den Tagesverlauf der Photosynthese. *Planta*, 20:535–548.

Livingston, R., and J. Franck. 1940. Assimilation and respiration of excised leaves at high concentrations of carbon dioxide. *Amer. J. Botany*, 27:449–458.

Lundegårdh, H. 1924. *Der Kreislauf der Kohlensaure in der Natur*. Gustav Fischer Verlag KG, Jena.

McGregor, W. H. D. 1958. Seasonal changes in the rates of photosynthesis and respiration of loblolly and white pine. Ph.D. Diss., Duke Univ. (cited by Kramer and Kozlowski, 1960).

Maskell, E. J. 1927. Experimental researches on vegetable assimilation and respiration. XVIII. The relation between stomatal opening and assimilation. *Proc. Roy. Soc. (London)*, B,102:488–533.

Miller, J. H. 1960. Effect of growth conditions and the stage of leaf development on the Hill reaction in homogenates in *Pisum* leaves. *Am. J. Botany*, 47:532–540.

Myers, J., and G. O. Burr. 1940. Studies on photosynthesis: some effects of light of high intensity on *Chlorella*. *J. Gen. Physiol.*, 24:45–67.

Nixon, R. W., and R. T. Wedding. 1956. Age of date leaves in relation to efficiency of photosynthesis. *Proc. Am. Soc. Hort. Sci.*, 67:265–289.

Norman, A. G. 1962. The uniqueness of plants. *Am. Scientist*, 50:436–449.

Rabinowitch, E. I. 1951. *Photosynthesis*. Interscience Publishers, Inc., New York. Vol. 2, Part 1.

———. 1956. *Photosynthesis and Related Processes*. Interscience Publishers, Inc., New York. Vol. 2, Part 2.

Saeki, T., and N. Nomoto. 1958. On the seasonal change of photosynthetic activity of some deciduous and evergreen broadleaf trees. *Botan. Mag. (Tokyo)*, 71:235–241.

San Pietro, A. 1958. Photochemical reduction of triphosphopyridine nucleotide by chloroplasts. *Brookhaven Symp. Biol.*, 11:262–270.

Saussure, de, T. 1804. *Recherches chimiques sur la vegetation*. Nyon, Paris.

Scarth, G. W., and M. Shaw. 1951. Stomatal movement and photosynthesis in *Pelargonium*. II. Effects of water deficit and chloroform. *Plant Physiol.*, 26:581–597.

Schneider, G. W., and N. F. Childers. 1941.

Influence of soil moisture on photosynthesis, respiration and transpiration of apple leaves. *Plant Physiol.*, 16:565–583.

Shiroya, M., G. R. Lister, C. D. Nelson, and G. Krotkov. 1961. Translocation of C¹⁴ in tobacco at different stages of development. *Can. J. Botany*, 39:855–864.

Singh, B. N., and K. N. Lal. 1935. Investigations of the effect of age on assimilation of leaves. *Ann. Botany (London)*, 49: 291–307.

Sironval, C., and O. Kandler. 1958. Photooxidation processes in normal green *Chlorella* cells. I. The bleaching process. *Biochim. Biophys. Acta*, 29:359–368.

———, W. G. Verly, and R. Marcelle. 1961. Radioisotopic studies of chlorophyll accumulation in soybean leaves. *Physiol. Plantarum*, 14:303–309.

Stålfelt, M. G. 1935. Die Spaltöffnungsweite als Assimilationfaktor. *Planta*, 23:715–759.

———. 1937. Der Gasaustausch der Moose. *Planta*, 27:30–60.

———. 1960. Das Kohlendioxyd. *Handbuch Pflanzenphys.*, 5(2):81–99.

Steeman-Nielsen, E. 1952a. Experimental carbon dioxide curves in photosynthesis. *Physiol. Plantarum*, 5:145–159.

———. 1952b. On detrimental effects of high light intensities on the photosynthetic mechanism. *Physiol. Plantarum*, 5: 334–344.

———. 1953. Carbon dioxide concentration, respiration during photosynthesis, and maximum quantum yield of photosynthesis. *Physiol. Plantarum*, 6:316–332.

Thomas, M. D., and G. R. Hill. 1949. Photosynthesis under field conditions, pp. 19–52. In J. Franck and W. E. Loomis (eds.), *Photosynthesis in Plants*. Iowa State College Press, Ames, Iowa.

Trebst, A. V., H. Y. Tsujimoto, and D. I. Arnon. 1958. Separation of light and dark phases in the photosynthesis of isolated chloroplasts. *Nature*, 182:351–355.

Uhl, A. 1937. Untersuchungen über die Assimilation—Verhaltnisse und die Ursachen ihrer Unterschiede in der Gattung *Pinus*. *Jahrb. Wiss. Bot.*, 85:368–421.

von Wettstein, D. 1958. The formation of plastid structures. *Brookhaven Symp. Biol.*, 11:138–157.

Wassink, E. C., S. D. Richardson, and G. A. Pieters. 1956. Photosynthetic adaptation to light intensity in leaves of *Acer pseudoplantanus*. *Acta Botan. Neerl.*, 5: 247–256.

Went, F. W. 1957. *The Experimental Control of Plant Growth*. Chronica Botanica Co., Waltham, Mass. 336 pp.

Willstätter, R., and A. Stoll. 1918. *Untersuchungen über die Assimilation der Kohlensaure*. Springer-Verlag OHG, Berlin.

Withrow, A. P., and R. B. Withrow. 1949. Photoperiodic chlorosis in tomato. *Plant Physiol.*, 24:657–668.

3 | Organic translocation

Through the productive activities of the photosynthetic apparatus in plants and the consequent formation of starch grains in, or adjacent to, the chloroplasts, a medium for the metabolism and growth of the plant is at hand. In the unicellular plants, the sites of production and utilization are so close that translocation is not a problem; however, as multicellular plants evolved, elevating and specializing the photosynthetic apparatus into aerial leaves, intraplant distances grew, and the organized movement of the products of photosynthesis became a physiological necessity.

Consider the engineering problems involved in the design of such a translocating device. First, it must be capable of moving carbohydrates both up to the stem apex, where growth is most active, and down to the lower stem and roots; in short, it must be bidirectional. Second, it must be able to do this in spite of the fact that water will have to move from root to leaf in the transpiration stream, and so it must be insulated from the water system. Third, it must be able to handle solutions of difficult osmotic qualities, for the molarities of carbohydrates in the translocation stream are quite high—high enough to plasmolyze most plant cells if they were in contact with them. And fourth, it must be capable of mending breaks in the system so that the removal of a leaf or part of a stem does not emasculate the translocation system. If the translocation system utilizes flow under pressure, any break might destroy this internal pressure, with lethal consequences, unless there were a means of plugging the break. These requirements demand a great deal of the translocation-system design; the means by which the design meets these specifications are fascinating, though imperfectly understood.

The phloem translocation system has several other qualities which recommend it: It can handle organic and inorganic materials, carbohydrates, nitrogenous organic materials, and ions. It can serve in part to supply roots with the carbohydrates from which organic nitrogenous materials can be made.

Phloem morphology

In the phloem tissue in which translocation of organic materials principally occurs, there are some rather unexpected and disturbing features from an engineering point of view. The characteristics of the phloem tissue have been slowly elucidated because the sieve cells are generally thin-walled, of poorly defined constituents, and very liable to be altered during the ordinary steps of preserving and sectioning for microscopic examination. They form longitudinal pipe systems comprised of vertical arrays of *sieve elements,* and the cells are separated by *sieve plates* on which there are porous regions called *sieve areas* (Fig. 3-1). These areas of abundant pores permit protoplasmic connections between the cells of the sieve tubes. The attractiveness of these structures for translocation is somewhat tarnished, however, by the fact that each of the pores in the sieve areas becomes encased in a doughnut-shaped callose deposit which enlarges inexorably with age, until as the cell reaches maturity the pore is almost eliminated. The development of callose occurs extremely rapidly during the preparation of sections for examination, and so perhaps the limitations of movement through the sieve plates have been exaggerated (Eschrich, 1963). The contents of the sieve elements seem to be arranged into a cylindrical cytoplasm surrounding a poorly defined vacuolar area, with strands of cytoplasm connecting the contents of adjacent sieve elements through the pores. The nucleus disappears at an early stage in the growth of the sieve element. Slime appears in the vacuolar area as the cell matures, and it accumulates as slime plugs on the sieve plates when the phloem is broken or when cells become old and cease to function. Associated with the sieve elements are the thin-walled nucleated *companion cells,* closely appressed to the sieve elements. Companion cells appear to be metabolically active in a manner suggestive of a fostering of the metabolic requirements of the sieve elements themselves.

The effectiveness of the sieve tubes appears to be short-lived, for after they become full-sized, the callose deposits may grow over the pores of the sieve areas, and slime bodies may accumulate at the basal end of the elements in such quantities that the pores become closed. Growing plants have a rapid system of phloem renewal, however; woody plants produce annual rings of phloem in the bark as complements of the rings of xylem in the wood. At summer's end, the phloem of trees has generally deteriorated so far that there seems to be little effective phloem translocation during the fall and winter months.

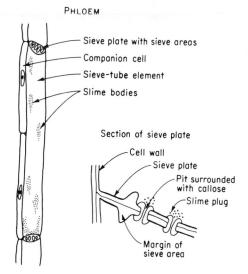

Fig. 3-1 | A diagram of phloem cells, representing a sieve-tube element with sieve plates at each end. The nucleated companion cells are shown appressed to the sieve-tube element. An enlarged detail of the sieve plate in cross section shows the pits which connect adjacent elements (modified from Esau, 1953).

PHLOEM

— Sieve plate with sieve areas
— Companion cell
— Sieve-tube element
— Slime bodies

Section of sieve plate

— Cell wall
— Sieve plate
— Pit surrounded with callose
— Slime plug

— Margin of sieve area

Translocation is hardly restricted to the phloem. Carbohydrates must move through parenchyma cells to pass from the leaf palisade to the phloem, or through ray cells to pass between the bark and the wood of woody stems. The translocation of organic materials in the xylem will be discussed in the next chapter.

Phloem sap

Two methods have been utilized for sampling phloem sap, one involving cuts through the bark or phloem and collection of the liquid that oozes from the severed phloem, and the other involving the collection of exudate from severed aphid stylets. The latter technique was developed by an entomologist (Mittler, 1958) who was interested in learning the nature of the plant sap upon which aphids feed. By the clever device of anesthetizing aphids after they had embedded their stylets into the plant and then severing them from their embedded mouth parts, he was able to obtain phloem sap in convenient droplets for

analysis. Moreover, that these samples were specifically representative of the sieve-tube sap was established by examination of microsections showing that the aphid stylets were each embedded in single sieve-tube elements (Zimmerman, 1961). Samples of such authentic sieve-tube contents have been chromatographed to establish the nature of the solutes therein.

The phloem sap contains about 10 to 25% wt/vol solutes, most of which are carbohydrates. Sucrose is usually the only carbohydrate, and the simpler hexose sugars have not been identified from phloem sap. Higher sugars of the oligosaccharide series (raffinose, stachyose, and verbascose) have been identified in numerous trees including ash, elm, and linden (Zimmerman, 1957a). The sugar alcohols mannitol and sorbitol are also present in some species.

Nitrogenous materials are a lesser constituent of the phloem sap. Ten to twelve amino acids have been chromatographically identified by Mittler (1958). The quantity of amino acids varies markedly with the season, and Mittler has found that peak values are obtained in the spring (0.2 per

Fig. 3-2 | The galactose oligosaccharides. The higher sugars formed by the addition of galactose units onto sucrose are of general occurrence in plants, though apparently not natural metabolic products in animals nor utilizable in animal metabolism. They are nonreducing sugars, including the trisaccharide raffinose (named after the *Raffia* palm), the tetrasaccharide stachyose (named after the artichoke, *Stachys*), and the pentasaccharide verbascose (named after the mullein, *Verbascum*).

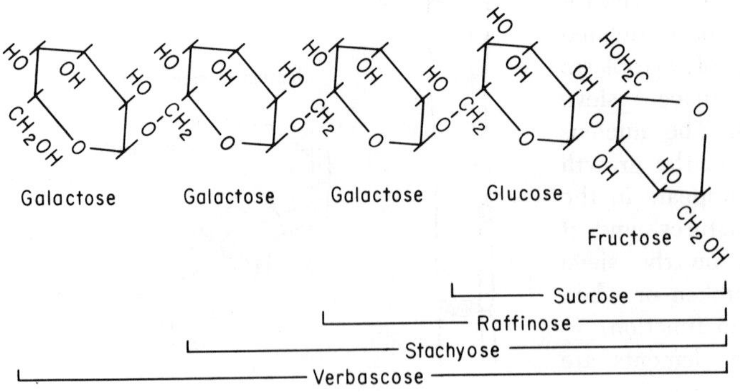

Galactose   Galactose   Galactose   Glucose

Fructose

Sucrose
Raffinose
Stachyose
Verbascose

cent). These fall markedly after leaf growth has been completed (0.03 per cent) and rise again with leaf senescence in the autumn (0.13 per cent). A similar rise in amino acids in the phloem occurs if the leaves are held in darkness (Weatherley et al., 1959). Only traces of protein nitrogen are found in the phloem sap (Ziegler, 1956).

Small amounts of inorganic ions, especially phosphorus, are found in phloem sap.

Translocation rates

Measurements of translocation using dyes, easily detectable ions, or radioactive isotopes indicate velocities ranging from 5 to 100 cm/hr. Reports of much higher rates probably involve movement in the xylem stream or intercellular spaces.

The rate of translocation into pumpkin

fruits has been calculated by Colwell (1942) and Crafts and Lorenz (1944) by simply measuring the rates of increase in dry weight of the fruit. By this device it was possible to estimate the translocation rate in terms of the amount of organic substance moved and the cross-sectional area of the phloem through which it moved. The values plotted in Fig. 3-3 indicate that maximal growth of the fruit occurs about 18 days after fruit set, reaching 1.6 g dry weight per hr. Simultaneous measurements of the amounts of phloem tissue in the fruit pedicel show continuing increases during the fruit growth period, with a 7-mm² cross-sectional area reached after 30 days. The concentration of organic substances was approximately 20 per cent, from which one can calculate the velocity at which the phloem sap must move to achieve the weight increases in the fruit. The calculated

Fig. 3-3 | During the growth of a pumpkin fruit, the translocation rate —calculated from the increase in weight of the fruit and the sieve-tube area—peaks when the fruit is about half grown and the cross-sectional area is still quite small. Assuming 20 per cent solutes in the phloem, the velocity of translocation is calculated to be in the range of 160 cm/hr during the peak in translocation (Crafts and Lorenz, 1944).

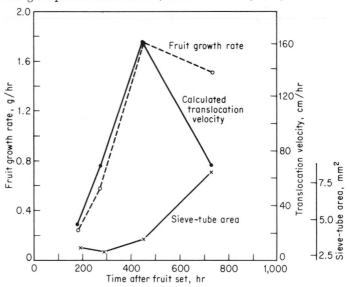

velocities reached 160 cm/hr for the time of maximal growth rate. This is somewhat high in comparison with velocities measured by introduction of tagged materials, but not excessive. If the cross-sectional area of the phloem is reduced to only the lumina of the sieve tubes, the phloem sap must move at the rate of 3,000 cm/hr. Considering the limiting apertures in the pores of the sieve areas, there the rate of movement must be at the velocity of 60,000 cm/hr (Swanson, 1959)!

These calculations are based on the assumption that the phloem moves organic substances by an actual flow of sap. These assumptions may need to be modified to account for the translocation in plants.

With the diurnal changes in photosynthetic sources of organic materials, one might expect a diurnal pattern of movement. Mason and Maskell (1928) found that the carbohydrate content of cotton stems peaked during the later part of the day. A dynamic picture of diurnal changes, drawn by Huber et al. (1937), shows that in trees there is a flow of a concentration peak down the stem. The peak moves down the plant at a velocity of about 3 m/hr and is followed by a diurnal trough down the stem at about the same rate. This phenomenon is illustrated in Fig. 3-4, which shows the changing position of the sucrose peak in a white ash tree (Zimmerman, 1958a). In this case the movement is at the rate of about 10 cm/hr. The diurnal pulsing flow resembles a peristaltic surge carrying food materials down the stems of the trees each night.

Nelson et al. (1958, 1959) have reported some extraordinarily rapid rates of translocation of carbon from $C^{14}O_2$ applied to soybean leaves, with small amounts of label moving 2,000 or even 5,000 cm/hr. It is difficult to imagine how these movements could occur in the phloem system; it seems more likely that the labeled gas moves in the extensive gaseous phase of the interspaces (Barber et al., 1962) and is then fixed into organic materials.

Fig. 3-4 | The sucrose content of phloem exudate from the white ash tree shows diurnal peak in the evening, and the peak moves down the stem during the night, traversing 8 m in about 8 hr (Zimmerman, 1958a).

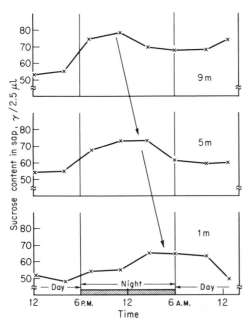

Patterns of translocation

Early experiments on phloem transport were necessarily done with colored dyes or other detectable exogenous materials, but more recently, with the advent of radioactive tracers, movement can be studied using the natural materials in plants. With radioactive CO_2, one can trace photosynthates as they move from the leaf to the growing point or to the root. The pattern of flow out of the leaf is strongly altered by the location of the leaf; for example, photosynthate will move from an upper leaf preferentially into the growing apex, or from lower leaves to the lower stem and roots (Chajlakjan and Butenko, 1957). Essentially no tracer moves from one leaflet to another or from one leaf to an older leaf (Aronoff, 1955), and disruption of the phloem of the leaf providing the photosynthate will terminate any flow. The presence of growing points appears to have a strong mobilizing effect on the translocatable carbohydrates.

The diffusion of a solute through a water channel such as the phloem would be expected to be logarithmic, as is evident in the formula

$$\text{Diffusion constant} = \frac{\text{distance}^2}{\text{time}}$$

Plotting the distribution of a solute as it moves along the phloem should give a straight line in a logarithmic plot, and this would be expected whether the phloem sap were flowing or not.

Horwitz (1958) has developed some mathematical models for the distribution of solutes along the stem, assuming that movement is in a flowing stream of water. In a representative model (Fig. 3-5) he assumes that there is a limited amount of exchange of the solute through the vascular walls, and one can alternatively make parallel assumptions about the exchange of water. The model plotted in Fig. 3-5 seems to fit nicely the distribution patterns of phloem solutes, with a slightly sagging curve for shorter periods of time, becoming more strictly linear as the front advances along the stem.

A comparison of Horwitz's model with the actual distribution of radioactivity along a grape stem after labeled CO_2 had been applied to the leaf is shown in Fig. 3-6 (Swanson and El-Shishiny, 1958). Each of the three sugars examined was distributed logarithmically down the stem.

Biddulph and Cory (1957) compared the distribution patterns for labeled water, sugar, and phosphorus after application to a bean leaf (Fig. 3-7). Plotted on a log scale, their data follow roughly the same

Fig. 3-5 | Calculations of the distribution pattern of a nutrient along the stem, assuming a diffusion-flow type of movement, would predict approximately a logarithmic decline with distance. The curve would progress along the stem with successive time intervals. This model assumes a liquid flow through a pipe with no net loss of water through the walls and some exchange of nutrient solutes through the walls (Horwitz, 1958).

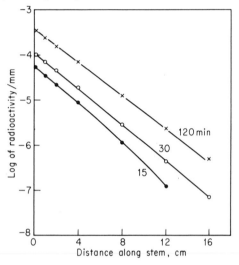

Fig. 3-6 | After radioactive CO_2 has been fixed into the leaf of a grape cane, the radioactivity in the bark was determined for the various sugar fractions and was found to decline with distance in approximately a logarithmic manner (Swanson and El-Shishiny, 1958).

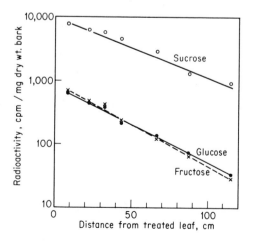

Fig. 3-7 | The simultaneous translocation of three tracers out of the bean leaf. Radioactive water, sucrose, and phosphate were added to comparable leaves and were analyzed in the stem after 30 min of translocation. Note the log scale (Biddulph and Cory, 1957).

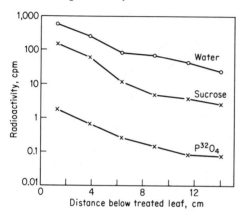

pattern, but the steeper slopes for sucrose and phosphorus suggest that they move less rapidly than water. The interesting phenomenon of different solutes traveling in the phloem at different rates is not surprising; Horwitz (1958) points out that the rate of movement can vary not only with the rate of water flow but also with the cross-sectional area of the vascular system which is accessible to it and with the diffusion constant for the solute. Biddulph and Cory (1957) suggest that the walls of the vascular elements may partition different materials in a manner similar to the partitioning in chromatography, resulting in different rates of solute movement. They set up model chromatographic systems to simulate the differences in phloem movement of sugars and phosphates.

A detailed study of the pattern of sucrose movement down the stems of willow plants has been made by Canny (1961), and he has slightly revised the picture of the logarithmic pattern of translocation. Exposing

Fig. 3-8 | After radioactive CO_2 had been fixed into a willow leaf, the distribution of the radioactivity of the phloem sap was determined. On the left one can see the exponential rise in radioactivity of the sap at a point 3 cm below the leaf. On the right one can see the exponential distribution of radioactivity between about the sixth and twelfth centimeters of stem after 6 hr of translocation (Canny, 1961).

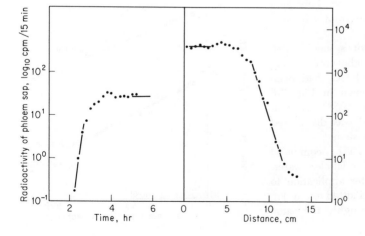

leaves to $C^{14}O_2$ and then tracing the pattern of its translocation in time, he has followed the amounts of radioactivity passing an individual point on the stem and the amounts in successive positions down the stem. Some of his data, plotted in Fig. 3-8, show again the general log type of distribution along the front of translocation. One can also see that the regions near the source of sucrose may be saturated and hence show a plateau of radioactivity. Canny used such data to recalculate the velocity of phloem transport and arrived at the value of about 2 cm/hr for his plant material.

The translocation of organic materials out of leaves does not proceed in a simple gradient away from the leaves but follows definite patterns. Two characteristics may be noted: a tendency toward preferential translocation down the leaf and stem and a preferential translocation along the vascular orthostichy toward mobilization centers. The preferential downward movement has been dramatically shown by Hartt et al. (1963) in sugarcane leaves and stems. Exudate studies of tree stems have also indicated a preferential downward movement (Zimmerman, 1962). The movement toward mobilizing centers such as expanding leaves and stem tips or toward flowers and fruits will be discussed separately in Chap. 5, but mention of the phenomenon will indicate an active role of the region toward which translocation is proceeding and the determination of patterns of flow partly on that basis.

Temperature effects

There has been considerable disagreement in the past about the effects of temperature on translocation. Some evidence indicated that this function had a Q_{10} of less than unity, that is, that translocation might proceed better at lower temperatures than at higher. Several participants to the argument provided conclusive evidence that instead

the Q_{10} is close to that for most biological reactions, translocation rates increasing with temperature up to between 20 and 30°C. Sample data from two experiments (Fig. 3-9) show that the same shape of temperature-response curve is obtained whether one applies the differential temperatures to the entire plant or to the petiole through which translocation is occurring (Swanson and Bohning, 1951; Hewitt and Curtis, 1948). In each of these experiments, the indirect measurement by weight changes was used, but the more refined techniques of isotope labeling have confirmed the nature of the temperature effect (Swanson and Whitney, 1953).

The translocation form

Several facts support the belief that sucrose is commonly the principal transported form

Fig. 3-9 | The effects of temperature on translocation of carbohydrate from bean leaves. In curve A the temperature treatment is restricted to the petiole of the leaf (Swanson and Bohning, 1951), and in curve B the entire plant is given the temperature treatment (Hewitt and Curtis, 1948).

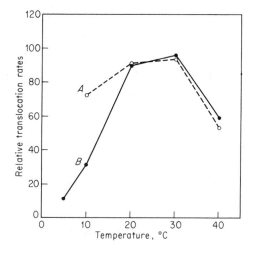

of carbohydrate. It is this sugar which shows the greatest diurnal variation in stems (Mason and Maskell, 1928) and is ubiquitous in phloem sap. Zimmerman (1958*a*) has developed the idea that in some cases the higher oligosaccharides are the principal transported form. Not only are they found in the sap, but they quickly disappear when leaves cease to provide a carbohydrate supply for translocation. The translocation of the higher sugars has certain inherent advantages, for the osmotic value of the oligosaccharides does not go so high per hexose unit of carbohydrate, and a given amount of sap flow would result in a delivery rate proportional to the molarity; hence a given molarity of stachyose would contain twice as many hexose units as sucrose.

Vernon and Aronoff (1952) indicate that

Fig. 3-10 | Changes in sugar content of the phloem sap of white ash trees during the autumn. It is evident that when the leaves yellow, the stachyose and raffinose contents fall off, and there is an associated rise in sucrose content (Zimmerman, 1958*b*).

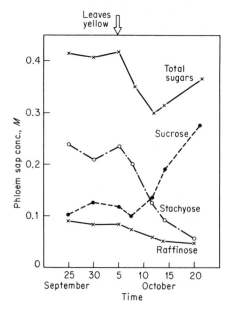

sucrose is the principal translocated carbohydrate in soybeans. Plotting the log of the ratio of radioactivity in the leaf source and in the stem as a function of distance, they found that sucrose had a consistently logarithmic gradient of change in label with distance, which suggests that it was the material transported. Glucose and fructose showed a much more erratic decrement in radioactivity with distance, indicating that they were less prominent in the translocation stream or were formed outside the phloem.

The fact that the simple hexose sugars are not found in analyses of authentic phloem sap makes it unlikely that they are important in phloem translocation.

The forms in which organic nitrogenous materials are transported in the phloem have received less attention. Many different amino acids and sometimes peptides are found in the phloem of most plants. There are exceptions, however; Engard (1939) found only nitrate nitrogen in the phloem of raspberry. There is some evidence that young leaves may produce more amino acids from photosynthesis than older leaves (Nelson et al., 1961) and that with the more youthful condition there may be more amino acid translocation (Shiroya et al., 1961).

To study the changes of phloem sap with leaf fall, Zimmerman (1958*b*) has followed quantitatively the carbohydrate contents of phloem of white ash trees during the autumn. He finds that when leaves yellow and lose their photosynthetic capacities, there is a sharp drop in the carbohydrate content of the phloem (Fig. 3-10). This drop is largely a reflection of changes in stachyose, although a small drop in raffinose occurs also. After leaf senescence, when there is probably little phloem translocation, most of the sap carbohydrate is in the form of sucrose.

If the decline in oligosaccharides is a consequence of the loss of the photosynthetic sources, defoliation should result in the same

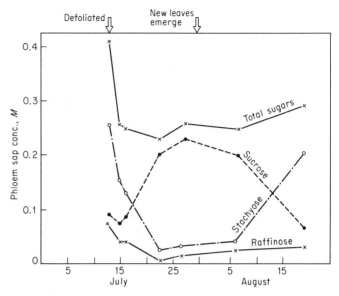

Fig. 3-11 | Changes in sugar content in sap of white ash when the leaves are removed. As in Fig. 3-10, there is a drop in the content of the oligosaccharides, and the sucrose content rises until new leaves emerge about 2 weeks later (Zimmerman, 1958*b*).

changes. Zimmerman (1958*b*) found that this was so (Fig. 3-11), for defoliation imposed an immediate drop in total sugars from phloem exudate, largely because of loss of stachyose. There was a rise in sucrose content at the same time. It appears that as long as sugars are provided by the leaves, the higher sugars such as stachyose and raffinose are formed in the phloem, but when the source is removed, chiefly sucrose remains. This is consistent with the theory that the higher sugars are the translocated form of carbohydrate in the white ash tree.

The mass flow theory

The famous theory that phloem translocation occurs by mass flow was advanced in 1930 by Münch, after extensive studies of the nature of the phloem contents of trees.

This theory assumes that the phloem is a closed system into which carbohydrates are being added by photosynthetic leaves, producing a gradient in osmotic values of the sap between leaves and other plant parts; the associated turgor forces drive the phloem sap away from the leaves. The familiar diagram used to illustrate the mechanism is repeated in Fig. 3-12, which shows two reservoirs *A* and *B*, representing the phloem in the leaf and root regions, respectively, connected by a closed pipe: the phloem sieve tubes. Increases in carbohydrate content in the leaf (*A*) increase the osmotic value there, followed by some water uptake —an osmotic gradient and turgor increase which can be relieved by the removal of solutes in the growing region (*B*) or by the removal of water in *B*, either of which will result in the movement of solutes in the direction of *A* to *B*. If water is removed with carbohydrates at *B* as a result of the turgor increase, the water may return through the xylem. Movement by mass flow, then, depends on the overall movement of the phloem sap as a consequence of the introduction of carbohydrates of the leaves.

If the mass flow theory is to work, several physical conditions must be met in the phloem system. When translocation occurs, there must be a decreasing molar gradient

away from the leaves, a semipermeability in the lateral walls of the sieve tubes, and an easy permeability along the length of the sieve tubes. Finally, there should be a way for water to return from a growing storage organ. Let us look at the evidence for these requirements.

Molar gradients in phloem exudates down the stems of trees have been precisely determined by Zimmerman (1957*b*), as illustrated in Fig. 3-13. Over a distance of 8 m of tree trunk, there was a drop in sap molarity of approximately 20 per cent, and the same drop was obtained for each of the sap sugars as for the overall concentration of sugars. Is this gradient a consequence of leaf activity? If so, then in the absence of leaves the gradient should disappear, and in fact it did when the leaves fell off normally in the autumn (Fig. 3-14). The same loss of gradient occurred when the leaves were removed mechanically during the growing season. The nitrogenous materials in phloem sap apparently do not show such a gradient; they occasionally are more abundant toward the base of the tree than above. The same is true for the phosphate content of phloem sap, but the overall osmotic value of the sap would determine

Fig. 3-12 | Diagrammatic model representing the Münch mass flow system, showing a closed system (the phloem) in which a rise in the sugar content at *A* (the leaves) would create a gradient in concentration such that there would be a mass flow of solution toward point *B* (the stem apex, root or fruit). The increase in osmotic value would lead to the entry of water at *A* and its loss at *B*, and the water would then return through the xylem system (right to left).

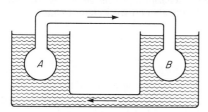

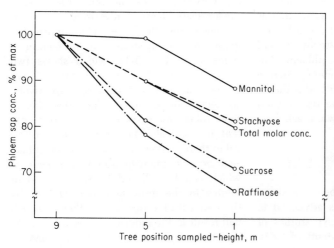

Fig. 3-13 | There are gradients in sugar content down the stem of a white ash tree in July, when phloem translocation is active, and the gradient is evident not only as total sugar content of the phloem sap but also as the content of three separate sugars and mannitol (Zimmerman, 1957*b*).

flow, and that does have a gradient in the proper direction for flow in trees.

Are the lateral walls of the phloem semipermeable so that the osmotic or carbohydrate components of the sap do not leak out of the sieve tubes? Using data from white ash trees, Zimmerman (1957*b*) found that after an initial cut is made into the phloem, the exudate becomes gradually more dilute. If sugars could move freely through the lateral walls of the sieve tubes, there would not be such a dilution of the exudate. This observation is consistent with the idea that water can move slowly through the lateral walls but that carbohydrate contents cannot. Further support for this is the fact that a cut into the phloem of a tree results in sharp losses in turgor or head in the phloem sap above and below the cut but does not cause measurable changes in turgor or head lateral to the cut. Incidentally, after leaf fall in the autumn the sap-dilution effect of Zimmerman's is no longer obtained. This may be a consequence of loss of turgor force with the termination of leaf activity.

Are the sieve tubes permeable longitudinally? The observation noted above that pressure drops occur above and below a cut demonstrates longitudinal permeability. A further dramatic illustration of this quality is found in a report by Zimmerman (1961) of defoliation of one side of an ash tree resulting in gross changes in the phloem sap only on the treated side of the tree. In Fig. 3-15, it is seen that on the north (defoliated) side of the tree there is a sharp difference in the total molarity of the phloem exudate, coincident with sharp changes in the raffinose, stachyose, mannitol, and sucrose contents. Similar patterns were obtained for each level of the tree trunk examined. Clearly, then, changes in the sap content are reflected vertically along the phloem, without appreciable effects being felt laterally.

The large accumulation of materials in the growing fruit implicates a sizable vol-

Fig. 3-14 | There is no gradient in total sugar content of white ash phloem in October after leaf fall, and the decreasing gradient of sucrose and mannitol is neutralized by an increasing gradient of oligosaccharides (Zimmerman, 1957*b*).

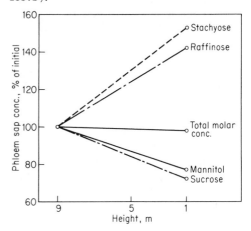

Fig. 3-15 | When the leaves have been removed from the north side of a white ash tree, there is a sharp drop in the oligosaccharides in the phloem sap on that side and an increase in sucrose and mannitol instead. The samples were taken at a height of 1 m and 17 days after defoliation (Zimmerman, 1961).

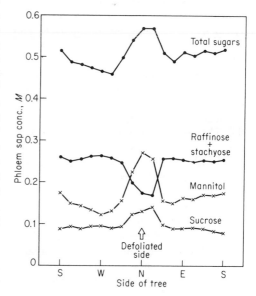

ume of water for mass flow. In a provocative paper, Clements (1940) reports that he measured the growth of sausage-tree fruits and calculated that the deposition of dry matter in the fruit would require an enormous flow of water in a mass flow system, as much as 2 to 5 liters of water per fruit per day. These calculations would lead one to expect a veritable fountain of water returning in the xylem from the fruit, but severing the xylem in pedicels of young fruits did not reveal a water flow. This challenge to the mass flow theory may be tentatively accounted for on the basis of two items: (1) The calculated water movement was based on phloem-sap concentrations of 0.1 to 0.03 M, and in fact the sap is usually five or ten times more concentrated than that; and (2) during the first half of the fruit growth period, when enlargement is proceeding most rapidly, the gain in dry weight is almost exactly matched by increases in volume, suggesting that a return flow of water would be expected only during the last half of the fruit growth period. Clements's paper, however, emphasizes the aspect of a return flow in the xylem associated with mass flow in the phloem, a subject that has received little attention.

Dopp (1938) attempted to sever the xylem strands coming out of squashes and some other fruits and found that such cuts immediately terminated growth of the fruits. He implies that the xylem is a major translocation site for materials going into the fruits, but his experiments did not include controls to compare the effects of severing the phloem; his xylem cuts could have damaged phloem also and could have interfered with the return flow of water through the xylem as readily as with the presumed flow toward the fruit.

The peanut is a novel case with respect to the flow of xylem sap out of the fruits. The underground peanut fruit is particularly susceptible to deficiency of some inorganic nutrients unless they can be taken up by the fruit. Harris (1949) has noted that supplying inorganic nutrients to the roots will not satisfy the nutritive needs of the fruit, an observation consistent with the presumption that the flow of xylem sap is out of the fruit and that hence a nutrient translocated in the xylem must be taken up by the fruit itself.

If the mass flow theory is valid, phloem translocation can proceed in only one direction in any given sieve tube. Several interesting studies have been made on simultaneous translocation in opposite directions. A provocative experiment by Chen (1951) measured the simultaneous movement of radioactive carbohydrate down the stem of geranium and of radioactive phosphate up the same stem. An upper leaf was exposed to radioactive CO_2 in the light, and a lower leaf was treated with radioactive phosphate. The phloem was separated from the stele to limit lateral exchange between the two tissues, and after 5 hr the distribution of the two types of isotopes was examined. The results (Fig. 3-16) indicate that there was in fact simultaneous flow in both directions. Proponents of the mass flow theory have rationalized this experiment by suggesting that there could still have been exchange between the xylem and phloem, so that the phosphate could have moved to the upper node in the xylem. The issue has not been resolved.

Simultaneous translocation in opposite directions in the geranium has been reexamined by Bauer (1953), using fluorescein as the translocated material, and his evidence suggested that the upward movement may occur in separate phloem sieve tubes from the downward movement.

A proposal that transport could occur in both directions through the same sieve tube was made by Thaine (1961, 1962), who suggested that strands passed through the sieve plates serving as tubes through which flow could occur in both directions. He could actually observe upward and downward movement through the strands. Esau et al. (1963) established that the strands were not in the sieve tubes but instead were in the adjacent parenchyma cell walls and that the movement Thaine observed was a streaming of cytoplasm in the parenchyma cells. There does not, therefore, seem to be any structural basis for simultaneous translocation in both directions in the same sieve elements.

The mass flow theory has been criticized on the basis that various organic nutrients may be translocated at different rates and with different distributional patterns (Nelson and Gorham, 1959a). The involvement of partitioning in the different rates of translocation of various solutes has been suggested by Biddulph and Cory (1957). Actual differences in the patterns of distribution of added solutes are not readily explained, though the plants translocating various applied solutes are necessarily different individual plants. The characteristic patterns of distribution of inorganic nutrients are well known and are assumed to be due to differences in accumulation activities by the plant cells rather than to the pattern of translocational flow (see Chap. 4).

For flow to occur, it is presumed that osmotic events would create a pressure in the phloem system which would actuate the movement of sap. The application of pressures to the cut ends of stem sections can cause the flow of phloem sap. Weatherley et al. (1959) obtained phloem flow out of an aphid stylet when pressures were applied to the entire cut end of the stem, though the xylem probably transmitted the largest part of the pressure. Peel and Weatherley (1963) further noted that the flow was prevented by elevating the osmotic values with sugar additions.

A final criterion of the feasibility of the mass flow theory is the establishment that phloem sap actually flows in the intact sieve tube. Ziegler and Vieweg (1961) have provided ingenious evidence that such flow does in fact occur. They pulled bundles of sieve tubes out of *Heracleum* petioles for short spans, leaving the bundles still at-tached at each end. Applying heat by a light beam to a localized area of the phloem, they could measure the velocity of movement of the sap as the progress of the warmth of the heated sap, utilizing paired thermocouples located at intervals along the bundle. So sensitive were the thermocouples that they could elevate the temperature of the sap just 1° and detect the movement, showing flow rates of 35 cm/hr.

Limitations of the mass flow theory

The assembled evidence indicates that the basic requirements for mass flow may be met in the plant, but the theory has many limitations. First, still unexplained is the means by which the leaves can pump sugars into the closed phloem system, a step which

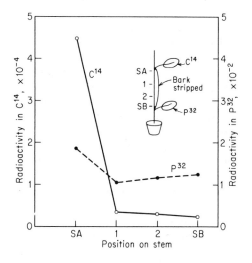

Fig. 3-16 | Experiments with geranium to show translocation in both directions in the phloem. $C^{14}O_2$ was fixed into the upper leaf (SA), and $P^{32}O_4$ was added to the lower leaf (SB) with the bark stripped away from the wood in between. After 5 hr the distribution of each was measured, and the P^{32} had moved into the upper leaf, while the C^{14} had moved down in the bark in small quantities. Radioactivities as cmp/100 mg of bark (Chen, 1951).

must take place against a concentration gradient. Second, while there are concentration gradients down trees during the time of phloem translocation, the gradients are quite small, amounting to about 0.3 atm/m of stem. Crafts (1931) has estimated the need for as much as 20 atm/m to effectively move the phloem sap by mass flow. Third, there is the problem of the means by which the sieve tubes can pass the sap along at sufficient rates; it appears morphologically that the sieve plates would be a serious hindrance. Fourth, the flow of sap at rather high osmotic concentrations implies that the sieve elements would not be disturbed by such traffic, and yet Currier et al. (1955) found that sieve elements can be plasmolyzed by sugar solutions of the same osmotic values. And fifth, such a mechanical theory does not indicate any role for metabolic inhibitors, and yet several lines of evidence indicate that inhibitors or lack of oxygen may limit translocation in the phloem.

Kursanov (1961) rejects the mass flow concept on the basis that respiratory activity of the vascular tissues is essential for translocation in the phloem. Instead of considering the sieve tubes to be passive carriers of an osmotically driven flow, he believes that active work must be done in transit. Kursanov and Brovchenko (1961) found that application of ATP stimulated translocation of sugars out of leaves, ADP or AMP being ineffective. Furthermore, translocation is sometimes inhibited by metabolic inhibitors, as is seen in the work of Willenbrink (1957), who applied cyanide to localized areas of geranium petioles and inhibited the movement of fluorescein, amino acids, or photosynthates. Inhibitions of metabolic activities of the companion cells or other components of the vascular system may be responsible for this effect, or alternatively the inhibitor could be moving into the leaf and there inhibiting the entry of the organic materials into the phloem.

At about the same time that Willenbrink

was carrying on inhibitor studies, Ziegler (1956) observed that while only sucrose may be found in the sieve-tube sap, hexoses are abundant in other leaf tissues, implying that there might be a synthetic step involved in the sugar entry into the phloem. He stained leaf material for phosphatase activity and found that the phosphatase was markedly more active along the margins of the vascular strands than elsewhere in the leaf. Companion cells and xylem ray cells are also rich in this enzyme in the spring, when sugars are being moved from the rays to the phloem. By analogy with the sucrose-secreting nectaries of flowers, which are also very rich in phosphatase, Ziegler suggested that sugars are secreted into the phloem by a phosphorylation step which produces sucrose. This would permit active transport into the sieve tube against a concentration gradient and would also be sensitive to metabolic inhibitors.

At about the same time, Barrier and Loomis (1957) studied the entry and translocation of phosphate and 2,4-D in bean leaves and noted that radioactive phosphate accumulated markedly along the margins of the veins in leaves. This accumulation did not occur if the leaves were kept darkened; it would be restored if they were removed to the light or if sugars were added. They concluded that there might be a loading effect of phosphate along the vascular strands and that this somehow involved sugars. It is enticing to believe that these two observations relate to the same physiological process and that phosphates and sugars are involved together in the entry of sugars into the phloem.

Ulrich (1962) examined the effect of ATP in stimulating translocation in geranium leaves and found that such stimulation was obtained only when the ATP was applied to the leaf areas in which materials were entering the phloem system. He suggests that the ATP effect Kursanov (1961) observed was an energizing effect on the loading of organic materials into the phloem rather than on the movement within the phloem.

It is interesting that when larger sugars (raffinose, stachyose, and verbascose) are the translocated forms, entry of sugar into the sieve tubes may involve the synthesis of oligosaccharides from the sucrose in the sap, implying that galactose may be the principal sugar entering. Zimmerman (1958*b*) has never found galactose free in the phloem sap and suggests that a *trans*-galactosidase attached to the sidewalls of the sieve elements and the companion cells could be responsible for the loading and unloading of galactose without its appearing free in the sieve sap. The larger sugars would allow the translocation of larger amounts of sugar per unit of liquid moving in a mass flow situation, which might relieve somewhat the apparent wide discrepancy between the amount of molar gradient down tree stems and the amount needed to move the appropriate amount of sugar.

If sugars are secreted into the phloem, their secretion into the nectaries of flowers is an interesting analogy. Lüttge (1961) has found that like the phloem, the nectar is principally sucrose and is secreted by the nectary against the concentration gradient. Only traces of glucose and fructose are found in nectar, and those in essentially equal amounts. Some amino acids enter the nectary, the amounts varying widely with the species. Lüttge showed that there is an active uptake of labeled phosphate by the secretion cells, implying a role of phosphorylation in the secretory step. Another phloem analogy is found in the observation that nectar itself could plasmolyze the nectary cells under some conditions.

The protoplasmic streaming theory

Dissatisfied with the mass flow scheme, Curtis (1935) suggested as an alternative that translocation could occur via protoplasmic streaming. This idea has the merit of being able to account more readily for simultaneous translocation in opposite directions and would account for the inhibitory effects of metabolic poisons, for cyclosis is very sensitive to metabolic inhibitions and oxygen deficiency.

The rates of cyclosis are somewhat less than the range of the velocities of translocation. Most reports rate cyclosis at 1 to 5 cm/hr, which is lower than the usual phloem translocation velocities of 5 to 100 cm/hr. The amounts of solutes which could be moved by this system appear somewhat limited. No more than one-quarter of the sugars in the streaming sieve cells could be translocated at full velocity, so this theory faces a discouraging statistic in the large total amounts of sugars that are translocated. In short, to obtain the same rates as translocation by mass flow, this system would have to be at least four times as efficient per sieve tube, and the necessary speed of movement of solutes through the sieve plates discourages this speculation. It is interesting that cyclosis has never been observed in mature sieve tubes. It has been noted readily in companion cells, so that if it occurred at any dramatic rates in sieve tubes, it would no doubt have been detected.

The interfacial flow theory

After Münch (1930) suggested the mass flow theory, van der Honert (1932) proposed an interesting alternative. Noting that translocation was much faster than what diffusion rates could account for and that delivery rates of the sugars were high considering the size of the sieve tubes, it occurred to him that materials could move by interfacial flow without an appreciable movement of water. He demonstrated this by using a trough containing ether and water as immiscible solvents and by adding potassium oleate to the trough at one end. The fat moved along the interface between the two solvents at a rate which was 70,000 times faster than diffusion and with scarcely any solvent movement. The rates observed are entirely adequate to account for translocation, but since sucrose or oligosaccharides are the principal translocated forms and are so readily soluble in the aqueous cytoplasm and sap of the sieve tubes, it is unlikely that an effective interface for their movement could be developed in the sieve tubes.

Activated diffusion

After some detailed experiments on the rates of translocation, Mason et al. (1936) were impressed by the fact that movement of solutes can be expressed as a logarithmic function with distance (a feature that would be expected of simple diffusion) but that the velocities are much higher than diffusion would ordinarily permit. They calculated the rate of diffusion that would be expected if there were no hindrance by the solvent, that is, as if the solutes were diffusing in a gas medium. The velocities under this hypothetical situation were just within the range of those observed for translocation. They suggested, then, that diffusion could be the essential feature of translocation but that metabolic activities permitted the removal of the solvent hindrance. This concept of an activated diffusion as the translocation system has not yet acquired experimental support with respect to movement in the sieve tubes. However, an interesting possible application of this point of view may be the movement of materials through parenchyma cells.

Lateral translocation of organic materials in stems does not occur through sieve tubes but takes place essentially across parenchyma cells. The same is true of the movement across leaf mesophyll to the border of the sieve-tube system and of the movement across the leaves of insectivorous plants such as *Drosera*. These types of translocation share distinctive properties, including rates of translocation which are slower than those in the phloem—more nearly approaching the rates of diffusion. They do not appear to be associated with the flow of water or with osmotic gradients or protoplasmic streaming. Yet these types of translocation are clearly sensitive to inhibition with metabolic poisons and are also sensitive to lowered oxygen tensions. Since the rates of movement are near those expected for diffusion phenomena and are dependent on metabolic activities, the term *activated diffusion* has been applied here (Arisz, 1952).

In the leaves of *Drosera*, translocation of various organic substances has been studied with respect to the locus of the movement, and it is found that while some materials move in the cytoplasm, others move from the vacuole of one cell to the next. These leaves also translocate some ions and organic nitrogenous materials readily, but not sugars (Arisz, 1952).

General comments

The translocation system does work, and it does appear to fulfill the functional requirements of the plant. Organic materials can move up or down, independent of the water stream, insulated from the cells of the plant, and in a system capable of mending breaks. The direction of flow correlates well with sites of utilization, such as toward growing points and roots, but there is as yet no satisfactory explanation of how the flow is steered through the plant. The accumulation of organic materials in fruits and storage organs must involve some mobilization force which the mass flow theory assumes but does not explain. The capacity for mending breaks in the phloem tube system appears to be a function of the sieve plates and the associated slime plugs, though the function of these structures in permitting or stopping flow is not thoroughly understood. Huber (1958) pointed out that there has been an elaboration and increased development of sieve plates with evolutionary advance of the higher plants, suggesting that there must be useful functions for such structures. The most likely positive value of the sieve plates may be in sealing the phloem pressure system when breaks occur.

Considerable evidence suggests that boron may facilitate sugar translocation (Gauch and Dugger, 1953), but sieve tubes in which sugars are actively moving contain very small amounts of boron (cf. Ziegler, 1956)—too little to support the suggestion that sugars may be translocated as a boron complex. It is still possible that boron may be involved with the entry of sugars into the phloem system.

GENERAL REFERENCES

Crafts, A. S. 1961. *Translocation in Plants.* Holt, Rinehart and Winston, Inc., New York, 182 pp.

Esau, K. 1961. *Plants, Viruses, and Insects.* Harvard University Press, Cambridge, Mass. 103 pp.

Kursanov, A. L. 1963. Metabolism and the transport of organic substances in the phloem. *Advan. Bot. Res.,* 1:209–278.

Swanson, C. A. 1959. Translocation of organic solutes, pp. 481–545. In F. C. Steward (ed.), *Plant Physiology.* Academic Press, Inc., New York.

Zimmerman, M. H. 1961. Movement of organic substances in trees. *Science,* 133:73–79.

REFERENCES CITED

Arisz, W. H. 1952. Transport of organic compounds. *Ann. Rev. Plant Physiol.,* 3:109–130.

Aronoff, S. 1955. Translocation from soybean leaves. II. *Plant Physiol.,* 30:184–185.

Barber, D. A., M. Ebert, and N. T. S. Evans. 1962. The movement of O^{15} through barley and rice plants. *J. Exptl. Botany,* 13:397–403.

Barrier, G. E., and W. E. Loomis. 1957. Absorption and translocation of 2,4-dichlorophenoxyacetic acid and P^{32} in leaves. *Plant Physiol.,* 32:225–231.

Bauer, L. 1953. Zur Frage der Stoffbewegungen in der Pflanze mit besonderer Berucksichtigung der Wanderung von Fluorochromen. *Planta,* 42:367–451.

Biddulph, O., and R. Cory. 1957. An analysis of translocation in the phloem of the bean plant using THO, P^{32}, and C^{14}. *Plant Physiol.,* 32:608–619.

Canny, M. J. 1961. Measurements of the velocity of translocation. *Ann. Botany (London),* 25:152–167.

Chajlakjan, M., and R. Butenko. 1957. Movement of assimilates of leaves to shoots under differential photoperiodic conditions of leaves. *Compt. Rend. Acad. URSS,* 4:450–462.

Chen, S. L. 1951. Simultaneous movement of P^{32} and C^{14} in opposite directions in phloem tissue. *Am. J. Botany,* 38:203–211.

Clements, H. F. 1940. Movement of organic solutes in the sausage tree. *Plant Physiol.,* 15:689–700.

Colwell, R. N. 1942. Translocation in plants with special reference to the mechanism of phloem transport. Ph.D. Diss., Univ. of California (cited by Crafts and Lorenz, 1944).

Crafts, A. S. 1931. Movement of organic materials in plants. *Plant Physiol.,* 6:1–41.

——— and O. A. Lorenz. 1944. Fruit growth and food transport in cucurbits. *Plant Physiol.,* 19:131–138.

Currier, H. B., K. Esau, and V. I. Cheadle. 1955. Plasmolytic studies of phloem. *Am. J. Botany,* 42:68–81.

Curtis, O. F. 1935. *The Translocation of Solutes in Plants.* McGraw-Hill Book Company, New York.

——— and D. G. Clark. 1950. *An Intro-*

duction to Plant Physiology. McGraw-Hill Book Company, New York. 752 pp.

Dopp, W. 1938. Beitrage zur Frage der Stoffwanderung in den Siebrohren. *Jahrb. Wiss. Bot.*, 87:679–705.

Engard, C. J. 1939. Translocation of nitrogenous substances in the Cuthbert raspberry. *Botan. Gaz.*, 101:1–34.

Esau, K. 1953. *Plant Anatomy.* John Wiley & Sons, Inc., New York. 735 pp.

———, E. M. Engleman, and T. Bisalputra. 1963. What are transcellular strands? *Planta*, 59:617–623.

Eschrich, W. 1963. Beziehungen zwischen dem Auftreten von Callose und der Feinstruktur des primaren Phloems bei *Cucurbita ficifolia. Planta*, 59:243–261.

Gauch, H. G., and W. M. Dugger, Jr. 1953. The role of boron in the translocation of sucrose. *Plant Physiol.*, 28:457–466.

Harris, H. C. 1949. Effect on the growth of peanuts of nutrient deficiencies in the root and pegging zone. *Plant Physiol.*, 24:150–161.

Hartt, C. E., H. P. Kortschal, A. J. Forbes, and G. O. Burr. 1963. Translocation of C^{14} in sugarcane. *Plant Physiol.*, 38:305–318.

Hewitt, S. P., and O. F. Curtis. 1948. The effect of temperature on loss of dry matter and carbohydrate from leaves by respiration and translocation. *Am. J. Botany*, 35:746–755.

Honert, T. H. van der. 1932. On the mechanism of transport of organic materials in plants. *Proc. Koninki. Ned. Akad. Wetenschap.*, 35:1104–1112.

Horwitz, L. 1958. Some simplified mathematical treatments of translocation in plants. *Plant Physiol.*, 33:81–93.

Huber, B. 1958. Anatomical and physiological investigations on food translocation in trees, pp. 367–400. In K. V. Thimann (ed.), *The Physiology of Forest Trees.* The Ronald Press Company, New York.

———, E. Schmidt, and H. Jahnel. 1937. Untersuchungen über den Assimilatström.

Tharandt. Forstl. Jahrb., 88:1017–1048 (cited by Huber, 1958).

Kursanov, A. L. 1961. The transport of organic substances in plants. *Endeavour*, 20:19–26.

——— and M. I. Brovchenko. 1961. Effect of ATP on the entry of assimilates into the conducting system of sugar beets. *Fiziol. Rast.*, 8:211.

Lüttge, V. 1961. Über die Zusammensetzung des Nektars und den Mechanismus seiner Sekretion. I. *Planta*, 56:189–212.

Mason, T. G., and E. J. Maskell. 1928. Studies on the transport of carbohydrates in the cotton plant. I. *Ann. Botany (London)*, 42:189–253.

———, E. J. Maskell, and E. Phillis. 1936. Further studies on transport in the cotton plant. III. *Ann. Botany (London)*, 50:23–58.

Mittler, T. E. 1958. Studies on the feeding and nutrition of *Tuberolachnus.* II. *J. Exptl. Biol.*, 35:74–84.

Münch, E. 1930. *Die Stoffbewegungen in der Pflanze.* Gustav Fischer Verlag KG, Jena.

Nelson, C. D., H. Clauss, D. C. Mortimer, and P. R. Gorham. 1961. Selective translocation of products of photosynthesis in soybean. *Plant Physiol.*, 36:581–588.

——— and P. R. Gorham. 1959a. Translocation of C^{14} labelled amino acids and amides in the stems of young soybean plants. *Can. J. Botany*, 37:431–438.

——— and ———. 1959b. Physiological control of the distribution of translocated amino acids and amides in young soybean plants. *Can. J. Botany*, 37:439–447.

———, H. J. Perkins, and P. R. Gorham. 1958. Note on a rapid translocation of photosynthetically assimilated C^{14} out of the primary leaf of the young soybean plant. *Can. J. Biochem. Physiol.*, 36:1277–1279.

———, ———, and ———. 1959. Evidence for different kinds of concurrent translocation of photosynthetically assimilated C¹⁴ in the soybean. *Can. J. Botany*, 37:1181–1189.

Peel, A. J., and P. E. Weatherley. 1963. Studies in sieve-tube exudation through aphid mouthparts. II. Effects of pressure gradients. *Ann. Botany (London)*, 27: 197–212.

Shiroya, M., G. R. Lister, C. D. Nelson, and G. Krotkov. 1961. Translocation of C¹⁴ in tobacco at different stages of development. *Can. J. Botany*, 39:855–864.

Swanson, C. A. 1959. Translocation of organic solutes, pp. 481–545. In F. C. Steward (ed.), *Plant Physiology*. Academic Press, Inc., New York.

——— and R. H. Bohning. 1951. The effect of petiole temperature on the translocation of carbohydrate from bean leaves. *Plant Physiol.*, 26:557–564.

——— and E. D. H. El-Shishiny. 1958. Translocation of sugars in the Concord grape. *Plant Physiol.*, 33:33–37.

——— and J. B. Whitney. 1953. Studies on the translocation of foliar applied P³² and other radioisotopes in bean plants. *Am. J. Botany*, 40:816–823.

Thaine, R. 1961. Transcellular strands and possible movement in mature sieve tubes. *Nature*, 192:772.

———. 1962. A translocation hypothesis based on the structure of plant cytoplasm. *J. Exptl. Botany*, 13:152–160.

Ulrich, W. 1962. Der Einfluss der ATP auf den Fluorescein transport in Siebröhren. *Planta*, 57:713.

Vernon, L. P., and S. Aronoff. 1952. Metabolism of soybean leaves. IV. Translocation. *Arch. Biochem. Biophys.*, 36:383–398.

Weatherley, P. E., A. J. Peel, and G. P. Hill. 1959. The physiology of the sieve tube. *J. Exptl. Botany*, 10:1–16.

Willenbrink, J. 1957. Über die Hemmung des Stofftransports in den Siebröhren durch lokale Inaktivierung verschiedener Atmungsenzyme. *Planta*. 48:269–342.

Ziegler, H. 1956. Leitung und Sekretion der Assimilate. *Planta*, 47:447–500.

——— and G. H. Vieweg. 1961. Der Experimentelle Nachweis einer Massenströmung im Phloem von *Heracleum mantigazzianum* Somm. et Lev. *Planta*, 56:402–408.

Zimmerman, M. H. 1957a. Translocation of organic substances in trees. I. The nature of the sugars in the sieve tube exudate of trees. *Plant Physiol.*, 32:288–291.

———. 1957b. Translocation of organic substances in trees. II. On the translocation mechanism in the phloem of white ash. *Plant Physiol.*, 32:399–404.

———. 1958a. Translocation of organic substances in trees. III. The removal of sugars from sieve tubes in the white ash. *Plant Physiol.*, 33:213–217.

———. 1958b. Translocation of organic substances in the phloem of trees, pp. 381–400. In K. V. Thimann (ed.), *The Physiology of Forest Trees*. The Ronald Press Company, New York.

———. 1961. Movement of organic substances in trees. *Science*, 133:73–79.

———. 1962. Translocation of organic substances in trees. V. Experimental double interruption of phloem in white ash. *Plant Physiol.*, 37:527–530.

4 | Inorganic translocation

In dealing with the translocation of inorganic substances through plants, we consider another major structural unit of the plant, the xylem trachea. At least a general picture of these structures would be useful in approaching the subject.

The xylem trachea constitute an apparently inert plumbing system. They are tubes through which water courses with a minimum of metabolic involvement. Two types of conducting elements are found (Fig. 4-1): the tracheids, which have sievelike openings into adjacent cells, and the vessels, in which virtually the entire end walls are gone. The vertical files of cells thus constitute a continuous conduction tube. The walls and end plates of tracheids contain pits, areas without secondary wall thickenings and with only a thin mantle of the primary wall stretched over the openings. These pits permit the movement of xylem sap both vertically and laterally between tracheids. Vessels ordinarily also have pits located along the lateral walls, but as already mentioned, the end walls have instead relatively large holes or perforations through which the xylem sap can readily flow.

Lateral translocation of materials into and out of the xylem trachea occurs through the ray cells, which pierce laterally through the xylem tissues of woody plants and continue through the phloem. In many instances these ray cells are oriented radially, in line with their function of lateral movement of materials. Large numbers of paired pits on the walls between xylem trachea and ray cells aid in the ready exchange of solutes.

In the gymnosperms there can be a closure of the valvelike torus in the tracheid pits. In angiosperms tracheal closure may be accomplished through the invasion of the trachea by the adjacent ray cells. These ingrowths, or tyloses, along with the accumulation of oils, gums, resins, and tannins in the older wood, plug the trachea. At the same time, the closure of the trachea renders them less accessible to fungal invasion and strengthens the structural qualities of the woody stem.

Mention has been made of the increasing need for translocation of materials as the size of the organism increases, and it is interesting to note that longer tracheids are formed as a tree becomes larger (Bailey, 1958). This increase (Fig. 4-2) continues in coniferous woods until the plant loses vigor with old age.

The entry of inorganic materials into the xylem from the soil appears to be most active in the root tips, experiments with isotopes having shown the uptake from the soil solution to be principally in the terminal centimeters of root tip. The ions are then translocated from the tip into the xylem. The interesting question of how much of the root is accessible to the soil solution without entering into biological reactions is outside the scope of our attention here, but it might be noted that ions in the soil solution seem to have free access to only a part of the root cross section. For example, a comparison of the free entry of phosphate into intact barley roots with entry into excised barley roots (Jacobson et al., 1958) suggests that the intact root has an inaccessible space of about the same volume as the stele of the root. Evidence indicates that entry of solutes into the xylem is metabolically regulated and does not occur freely from the soil solution in large amounts.

The xylem sap

Once a substance is inside the xylem, it is relatively unhindered in its movement through the plant, and some surprisingly large molecules can enter the xylem from the soil solution. This aspect of translocation has become increasingly interesting as applications of agricultural chemicals to the soil have become so widespread (Chap. 24).

The solution inside the xylem is considerably more dilute than phloem sap, being

Fig. 4-1 | Conducting cells in the xylem, showing a tracheid (left) with its pitted walls and ends and a vessel element (right) with its pitted sidewalls but open ends. The nucleated ray parenchyma cells are shown with their pitted connections with the vessel element (modified from Esau, 1953).

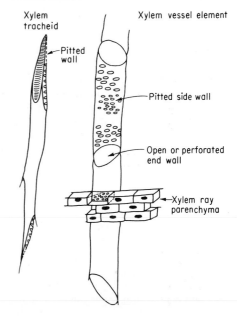

Fig. 4-2 | The tracheid cells formed in the xylem of conifer wood are markedly longer in older, taller trees, averaging around 1 mm in length in seedlings and over 4 mm in length in 120-year-old trees (Bailey, 1958).

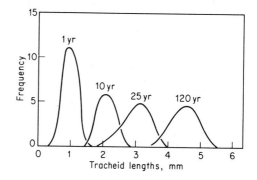

ordinarily constituted of about 0.1 to 0.4 per cent solutes. About one-third of these are minerals, and the other two-thirds are organic material. The organic constituents generally include sugars, organic acids, alkaloids, lactones, and often large amounts of organic nitrogenous materials.

The xylem sap can be sampled for analysis by applying suction to sections of stem or root and then making repeated cuts from the distal end of the piece while the suction is being applied. Bollard (1953) has used this method to follow the changes in xylem sap of apple branches throughout the year. He found a great increase in the amount of organic nitrogenous materials in the sap during the period of blooming, paralleling the high level of organic nitrogen in phloem sap. This peak falls off during the summer and maintains a low value during the winter months (Fig. 4-3). By comparison, the sugar content of the xylem sap falls essen-

tially to zero during the flowering time (Anderssen, 1929, with pears) and then rises in late summer and winter.

Bollard (1958) separated the nitrogenous constituents of the sap of diverse trees and found complicated mixtures of amino acids and amides. Amino acids are the most common nitrogen components. A small group of trees has citrulline as the principal nitrogen form in the xylem sap—an odd substance in that it is not found as a component of any plant proteins as far as is known. Another small group of species contains principally the ureides allantoin and allantoic acid. Their role in plants is as unclear as that of citrulline, though in animal metabolism the ureides are known to be products of purine metabolism. These amides, citrulline and the ureides, are appropriate for the translocation of nitrogen, being very rich in nitrogen on a molar basis. The efficiency of allantoin as a nitrogen carrier is attested to by the fact that most dogs and many animals excrete nitrogen in this form in their urine.

The nitrogenous materials of tree sap increase greatly at flowering in both xylem and phloem, but the second surge in nitrogen accumulation in the phloem at the time of leaf senescence (Mittler, 1958) is not reflected in the xylem.

The nitrogenous constituents of xylem sap may be of major importance in the distribution of such materials through the plant. The roots are often the principal site of nitrate-reducing activity (Thomas, 1927) or of biosynthesis of complex nitrogenous materials (e.g., Dawson, 1941, 1942).

In addition to the carbohydrate and nitrogenous components, there are numerous inorganic nutrients, especially sulfur, potassium, magnesium, calcium, phosphorus, and iron in the xylem sap. Of these, the metals are almost entirely in the form of chelates (Stewart, 1963). Some metals may be chelated with organic acids, as for example iron (Tiffin and Brown, 1962). Some may be chelated with sugars, as for example iron and fructose or calcium and lactose (Char-

Fig. 4-3 | Seasonal changes in the xylem-sap constituents of some rosaceous trees. The nitrogen content of the sap of apple is very high at the time of flowering and then declines to low levels for the remainder of the year (Bollard, 1953). The sugar content of pear sap falls precipitously at the time of flowering and then rises gradually in summer and fall (Anderssen, 1929).

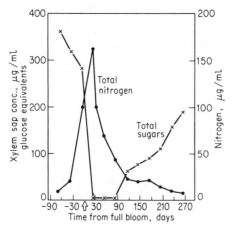

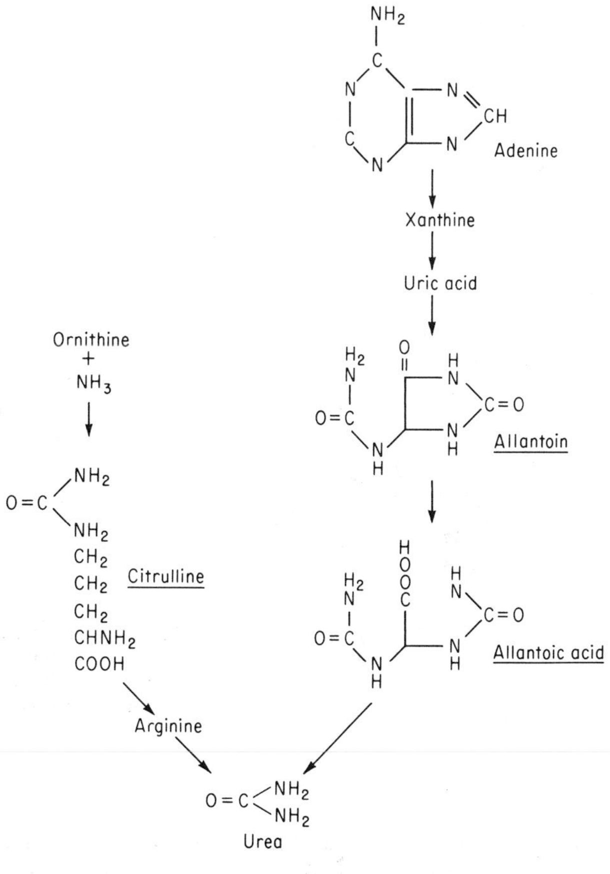

Fig. 4-4 | Citrulline and the ureide nitrogen carriers. Although they are major nitrogenous components of xylem sap of some species, little is known of their metabolic role in plants. In animals, citrulline is considered to be a probable intermediate in the ornithine cycle through which ammonia is fixed into urea; it was named after the watermelon (*Citrullus*). The ureides are also intermediates in the formation of urea in animal metabolism. Repeated oxidations of purines lead to allantoin and allantoic acid formation.

ley et al., 1963; Charley and Saltman, 1963). Winter (1952) has suggested that one beneficial effect of organic soils may be the provision of generous amounts of natural chelating agents which facilitate the movement of cations through the xylem without precipitation. Among the metals, potassium is apparently not chelated. Among the anions, sulfur apparently moves as the sulfate, and phosphorus may move in the xylem as a phosphoryl choline (Bollard, 1960).

The seasonal changes in some of the common inorganic nutrients in the xylem sap of apple have been followed by Bollard (1958; Fig. 4-5). The most dramatic changes were found for potassium, which reached a peak in the early summer. Phosphorus and magnesium attained small peaks in the early summer. All these nutrients remained relatively low during the later growing season and were very low when the tree was dormant. It does not appear that the content of these ions in the xylem is seasonally related to transpiration, either directly or conversely, even though the transpiration rate will profoundly affect the amount of sap traversing the tissues.

Comparison of the xylem-sap constituents between successive annual rings of woody plants shows that the greatest concentration of solutes occurs in the first, or most recent,

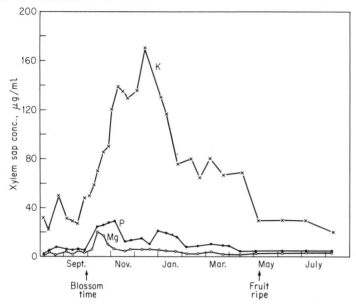

Fig. 4-5 | Seasonal changes in nutrients in the xylem sap of apple trees. The contents of potassium, phosphorus, and magnesium all rise during early summer (October and November in South Africa), though the rise in potassium content is much the most pronounced (Bollard, 1958).

annual ring, suggesting that this may be the most important region for the translocation of solutes in the xylem.

Xylem translocation

The xylem translocation of nutrients might be expected to follow kinetic patterns similar to translocation in the phloem, but there have been no successful demonstrations of the logarithmic distribution of materials moving in the xylem. The same nutrients which follow the mathematical models described in Chap. 3 when moving in the phloem do not apparently do so when moving in the xylem.

When an isotope is applied to the root system, an upward distribution through the plant may be obtained which is highly divergent from the pattern of water flow. For example, radioactive phosphate will accumulate in various leaves at differing rates, depending on the age of the leaves. Biddulph (1951) has measured the amounts of phosphorus accumulating in bean leaves after 4 days. His data (Fig. 4-6) show that the phosphate accumulates almost exponentially in successively higher leaves. We can deduce that movement of this nutrient is not by a simple mechanical system, the accumulation in the leaves not being proportional to transpiration. Instead there must be some diversion or sorting mechanism involved in the distribution of the nutrient. Old leaves do not accumulate phosphorus; in fact, they export it in large amounts. This will be discussed in more detail in Chap.

5. Biswas and Sen (1959) have shown that the preferential accumulation of labeled phosphorus and sulfate from the roots to the young leaves is erased if the apex of the plant is removed: Decapitated plants develop equal distribution of label in all leaves. The distribution of nutrients from the root system, then, is clearly a function of both an upward flow of xylem sap and some sorting device which either permits the nutrient to reside in the leaf or restricts such residence.

The distribution patterns of various nutrients in the leaves show many variations. Some collect in young leaves, as is the case with phosphorus; some collect in older leaves, as for example, calcium; and others collect along leaf veins (iron) or in hydathodes (cobalt). These distribution patterns must be consequences of sorting mechanisms in the plant which respond to chemical properties of the ions.

In the past there has been an argument about whether upward translocation of ions occurred in the xylem or in the phloem, and definitive data on this issue have been obtained with the advent of isotope tracer methods. For example, as shown in Fig. 4-7, Stout and Hoagland (1939) established that radioactive phosphate applied to the roots of *Salix* appeared to be only in the xylem in stem regions where the bark was separated from the wood. During upward translocation, the isotope abounded in the xylem in all parts of the stem, whereas it was present in the bark only in regions in which there was immediate contact with the wood. The bulk of the isotope in the bark was probably the product of lateral movement from the xylem. The lower graph of Fig. 4-7 is taken from data of Biddulph and Markle (1944), who applied radioactive phosphate to a leaf of cotton and again separated the bark from the wood in an intermediate section of the stem. In this case (downward translocation), the isotope was abundant in the bark in all parts of the

stem, whereas it was present in the xylem only in regions quite near the point of application. The data imply that the translocation out of the leaf is essentially restricted to the phloem.

The rates of translocation in the xylem are greatly influenced by the rate of transpiration, for the xylem-sap nutrients are moving in the transpirational medium. Thus it is not surprising to find reports of translocation rates of materials in the xylem as high as 900 cm/hr, though under moderate transpirational conditions the rates of movement are not appreciably unlike those in the phloem—10 to 100 cm/hr.

Fig. 4-6 | The accumulation of P^{32} in various leaves of bean seedlings 4 days after the addition of $P^{32}O_4$ to the nutrient solution. The old leaves at the base of the plant receive very little of the nutrient, and the young, expanding fifth leaf receives by far the most (Biddulph, 1951).

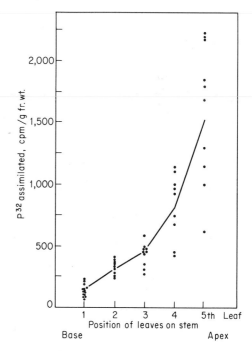

Factors in translocation

In addition to the strong influence of transpiration on translocation in the xylem, numbers of internal and external factors can be recognized. Internally, the pathway of translocation is profoundly affected by the orthostichy of the vascular system. Where there are direct vascular connections the ions will flow readily, and where vascular connections are poor the ions will move very little. Thus ions entering a given side of a plant will move more readily either up or down that same side in preference to crossing to another side. Where there are vascular connections across a tree or grass stem, translocation will more readily cross the plant.

Another internal factor may be that of metabolic involvement in translocation. A dramatic illustration is seen in the data of Hanson and Biddulph (1953), who measured the uptake of rubidium and of phosphate through the roots of bean seedlings. They found a diurnal variation in the readiness with which these ions were translocated out of the roots, and they correlated the changes with diurnal changes in light. Thus in Fig. 4-8 it is seen that the translocation was slow during the night and rose rapidly with the advent of light each morning. Hanson and Biddulph found that the rise in translocation could be moved to earlier hours of the night by exposing the plants to light and that the light treatment was associated with a large increase in sugar content of the roots. Sugar supplied instead of light did not entirely replace light in stimulating translocation. In some experiments they observed that the rise in translocation preceded somewhat the advent of light in the morning, which suggests that the translocation response is not a direct consequence of either the light or the sugar level in the roots. Perhaps the diurnal changes in translocation may be a reflection of the rhythmic opening of the stomata, resulting in transpiration and therefore in xylem flow.

Fig. 4-7. | A comparison of the translocation of P^{32} upward from the root and downward from the leaf. In each case the bark was stripped from the wood between the leaf and the base of the plant to limit crossing of the tracers between phloem and xylem. (*a*) Upward translocation in willow after 5 hr of root uptake (Stout and Hoagland, 1939); (*b*) downward translocation in cotton after 1 hr of uptake by the leaf (Biddulph and Markle, 1944).

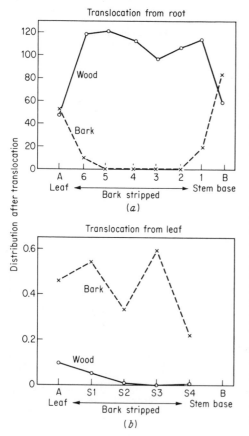

The profound effects of temperature on the translocation of sugars through plants have been mentioned in Chap. 3. A definitive study of the comparable effects of temperature on inorganic translocation was carried out by Swanson and Whitney (1953). They enclosed sections of stem or petiole in temperature-controlled jackets and made comparable measurements for a number of radioactive ions applied either to a leaf above the jacketed section or to the roots below. In each case the amount of isotope passing through the temperature-controlled section was used as a measure of translocation. Comparisons of phosphate, potassium, cesium, and calcium in the downward stream from a leaf showed the same temperature sensitivity as carbohydrate moving in the phloem: a marked increase with increasing temperatures, until a peak was obtained at 25 to 35°C (Fig. 4-9). The relatively immobile calcium was insensitive to the temperature differences. A direct comparison of upward and downward translocation was made with radioactive phosphate, with results shown in Fig. 4-10. Translocation out of a leaf was highly sensitive to temperature, but that upward from the roots was quite insensitive to stem temperature. If the upward translocation from the roots occurs principally through a non-metabolic system of xylem, one would expect it to be insensitive to stem temperatures. The xylem translocation thus stands in stark contrast to the phloem translocation of the same nutrient.

The same premise would lead one to expect that steam-killing a section of stem would not alter upward xylem translocation, and in fact this was shown to be so by some experiments of Swanson and Whitney (1953).

In speaking of upward translocation of inorganic materials, we have been referring principally to translocation from roots up through the xylem. In addition, however, there is an upward translocation in the phloem, especially when the ions have been applied to the leaf. Like carbohydrates, the inorganic nutrients moving out of a leaf are translocated both upward and downward at about the same rates (e.g., Biddulph and Markle, 1944). All the characteristics of phloem transport would be expected to apply to such upward translocation of the inorganic nutrients.

In discussing the patterns of ions translocated from the roots into the leaves, it was noted that older leaves accumulated much less phosphate than younger ones (Fig. 4-6); this is consonant with the fact that older leaves are known to export large amounts of carbohydrate, nitrogen, potassium, and phosphorus as they age. This tendency to export phosphorus has been measured quantitatively by Koontz and Biddulph (1957) by the simple device of applying equal amounts of isotope to leaves of different ages. Their results (Fig. 4-11) show the relatively larger amounts of P^{32} translocated out of the older primary leaf of bean seedlings, compared with the amounts translocated out of the first and second trifoliate leaf. Notably,

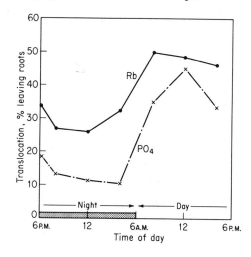

Fig. 4-8 | Translocation of rubidium and phosphate out of bean roots shows a diurnal variation, being faster with commencement of the light period (Hanson and Biddulph, 1953).

the direction of transport varied with the leaf location, the lower leaf exporting large amounts of P[32] to the root system and the uppermost leaf exporting essentially none.

Retranslocation

The above experiments of Koontz and Biddulph (1957) demonstrate clearly the ca-

Fig. 4-9 | The effects of temperature on translocation of cesium, phosphorus, and potassium out of bean leaves are very great. Calcium translocation is poor and is quite insensitive to temperature. The temperature treatments were restricted to the petioles of treated leaves; about 5μC was applied to each leaf. The Ca values are multiplied by 10 (Swanson and Whitney, 1953).

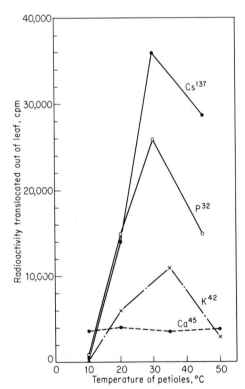

pacity of leaves to export inorganic materials —an ability which has enormous significance in the development of intact plants. The export of materials from older leaves, or the retranslocation of these materials, supplies the growing parts of the plant with a large proportion of its inorganic nutrients during the later stages of growth. When small grains such as wheat and oats have reached 25 per cent of full size, their net uptake of nitrogen and phosphorus is 90 per cent completed, and so for the last 75 per cent of their growth, the plants must be supplied with these elements principally by retranslocation. Petrie et al. (1939) have shown that as much as 85 per cent of the nitrogen and up to 90 per cent of the phosphorus in leaves of wheat, for example, are retranslocated out of the leaves as they approach senescence.

The magnitude of retranslocation is also illustrated by some data of Williams (1938), who plotted the distribution of nitrogen in oat plants as a function of age. Figure 4-12 shows that when the inflorescence appears, extensive amounts of nitrogen are exported from the roots and leaves, while accumulation of nitrogen into the inflorescence proceeds. At a slightly later stage, the stems too provide an apparent source of nitrogen for the inflorescence, and a decline in stem nitrogen takes place.

Little is understood about retranslocation phenomena, except in a descriptive sense. Besides the large increases in retranslocation from a leaf with age, some influence of growing points on this process can be recognized. Apparently vegetative apices, and also flowers or fruits, can somehow have a mobilizing effect on nutrients in the older leaves, roots, and stem (Petrie et al., 1939; Burström, 1948). This phenomenon is discussed further in Chap. 5.

There is a marked selectivity between ions for retranslocation. Some interesting experiments on the ability of different ions to be retranslocated have been done by Biddulph et al. (1958), who compared the distribution patterns of the relatively mobile phosphorus, the relatively immobile calcium, and the intermediately mobile sulfate. Solutions of these tracers were applied briefly to the roots of bean plants, and then the distribution patterns in the leaves were followed at intervals by autoradiography. Striking differences in retranslocation were found; phosphorus accumulated in the primary leaf up to 6 hr after exposure, and then the radioactivity in this leaf declined steadily as the ion was retranslocated toward the growing point and young, developing leaves. In direct contrast, calcium accumulated in the primary leaf for about 6 hr after exposure, and then no detectable decline in the radioactivity of the primary leaf was observed—that is, no apparent retranslocation of the calcium occurred. The sulfate was retranslocated to an extent comparable with the phosphorus (Fig. 4-13).

The suggestion has been made that the inability of the plant to retranslocate calcium has made necessary a means of disposing of this ion, a matter which is accomplished by the formation of insoluble oxalate crystals (Biddulph, 1959). The converse argument could be defended, however, that calcium is not retranslocated because of its ability to form insoluble salts such as oxalates.

Lateral translocation

In the discussion, we have mentioned xylem translocation (principally upward) and phloem translocation (upward or downward), but little has been said about the ability of materials to move laterally. There is abundant evidence which indicates that some transfer of materials between the xylem and phloem does occur, and the laterally oriented ray tissues appear to be well adapted for lateral translocation. Few real measurements of this phenomenon have been made, though. Biddulph and Cory (1957) noted that when isotopic phosphate

Fig. 4-10 | The translocation of phosphorus downward from the bean leaf is temperature-sensitive, whereas the translocation upward from the root is not (Swanson and Whitney, 1953).

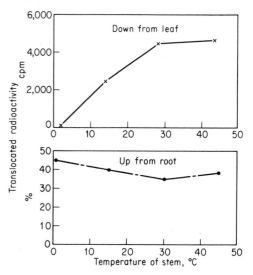

Fig. 4-11 | The translocation of phosphorus[32] out of bean leaves varies with the age of the leaf to which it is applied. Equal amounts of NaH_2PO_4 were applied to different leaves, and the translocation into three separate divisions of the plant (A, B, and C) was measured after 24 hr. Note the relatively large amounts translocated out of the oldest leaf (Koontz and Biddulph, 1957).

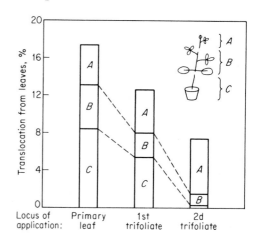

and tritium water were applied to leaves, 24 per cent of the P^{32} and 31 per cent of the THO were subsequently found in the stem xylem.

The apparent capacity for lateral translocation has inevitably led to the suggestion that there could be actual circulations of materials in plants—ions moving up the xylem, across the rays or parenchyma, and back down the phloem and then repeating this cycle. This cyclic movement appears possible, but there seems little reason to expect repeating cycles to occur in the excursions of materials through plants.

Conclusion

The distinction between organic and inorganic translocation almost disappears when close comparisons are made; many erstwhile inorganic nutrients apparently move in the translocation systems as organic forms or as chelates with organic materials. There is not even a reasonable distinction between

the kinetics of those that do move in the inorganic form (sulfate, potassium) and those that do not. The characteristics of movement are more precisely identifiable with the tissue in which translocation is occurring.

Three general types of factors regulating translocation can be recognized: First, the movement of the solvent (phloem or xylem sap) is a major factor; second, features of the solute can modify its ability to move with the solvent (these include its solubility, its diffusion characteristics, its partitioning properties with the cell walls or other nonmoving components, and any tendency to be removed by surrounding tissues); and third, there is a metabolic involvement most evident in the directive activities of the plant apex, in the retranslocation from older leaves, and in the mobilizing forces in general.

The weak effects of temperature on xylem translocation contrast strongly with phloem translocation, implying a lack of metabolic influences on the actual flow processes in the xylem. Though metabolic activities may direct the destination of the nutrients in the xylem, or even their availability for translocation, they do not seem to be involved in the actual flow.

Fig. 4-12 | The distribution of nitrogen components in the oat plant during growth, showing the loss of nitrogen from the leaves and stem into the inflorescence in the last 50 days (Williams, 1938).

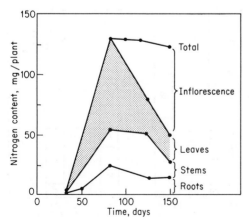

GENERAL REFERENCES

Biddulph, O. 1959. Translocation of inorganic solutes, pp. 553–603. In F. C. Steward (ed.), *Plant Physiology.* Academic Press, Inc., New York.

Bollard, E. G. 1958. Nitrogenous compounds in tree xylem sap, pp. 83–94. In K. V. Thimann (ed.), *The Physiology of Forest Trees.* The Ronald Press Company, New York.

———. 1960. Transport in xylem. *Ann. Rev. Plant Physiol.,* 11:141–166.

Crafts, A. S. 1961. *Translocation in Plants.* Holt, Rinehart and Winston, Inc., New York. 182 pp.

Fig. 4-13 | The retranslocation of sulfur[35] out of the primary leaves of bean. The tracer was applied to the root nutrient medium for 1 hr, and the distribution is shown after 0, 6, 12, 24, 48, and 96 hr (Biddulph et al., 1958). Almost all the tracer has been retranslocated out of the primary leaf after 24 hr.

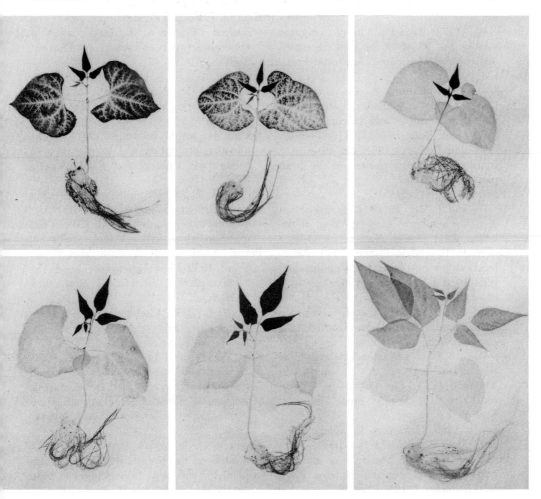

REFERENCES CITED

Anderssen, F. G. 1929. Some seasonal changes in the tracheal sap of pear and apricot trees. *Plant Physiol.*, 4:459–476.

Bailey, I. W. 1958. The structure of tracheids in relation to the movement of liquids, suspensions and undissolved gases, pp. 71–82. In K. V. Thimann (ed.), *The Physiology of Forest Trees*. The Ronald Press Company, New York.

Biddulph, O. 1951. The translocation of minerals in plants, pp. 261–278. In E. Truog (ed.), *Mineral Nutrition of Plants*. The University of Wisconsin Press, Madison, Wis.

————. 1959. Translocation of inorganic solutes, pp. 553–603. In F. C. Steward (ed.), *Plant Physiology*. Academic Press, Inc., New York.

————, S. Biddulph, R. Cory, and H. Koontz. 1958. Circulation patterns for phosphorus, sulfur and calcium in the bean plant. *Plant Physiol.*, 33:293–300.

———— and R. Cory. 1957. An analysis of translocation in the phloem of the bean plant using THO, P^{32} and C^{14}. *Plant Physiol.*, 32:608–619.

———— and J. Markle. 1944. Translocation of radiophosphorus in the phloem of the cotton plant. *Am. J. Botany*, 31:65–70.

Biswas, V. B., and S. P. Sen. 1959. Translocation and utilization of sulfate and phosphate in the pea plant. *Indian J. Plant Physiol.*, 2:1–8.

Bollard, E. G. 1953. The use of tracheal sap in the study of apple tree nutrition. *J. Exptl. Botany*, 4:363–368.

————. 1958. Nitrogenous compounds in tree xylem sap, pp. 83–94. In K. V. Thimann (ed.), *The Physiology of Forest Trees*. The Ronald Press Company, New York.

————. 1960. Transport in xylem. *Ann. Rev. Plant Physiol.*, 11:141–166.

Burström, H. 1948. The rate of nutrient transport to swelling buds of trees. *Physiol. Plantarum*, 1:124–135.

Charley, P., and P. Saltman. 1963. Chelation of calcium by lactose: its role in transport mechanisms. *Science*, 139:1205–1206.

————, B. Sarkar, C. F. Stitt, and P. Saltman. 1963. Chelation of iron by sugars. *Biochim. Biophys. Acta*, 69:313–321.

Dawson, R. F. 1941. The localization of the nicotine synthetic mechanism in the tobacco plant. *Science*, 94:396–397.

————. 1942. Accumulation of nicotine in reciprocal grafts of tomato and tobacco. *Am. J. Botany*, 29:66–71.

Esau, K. 1953. *Plant Anatomy*. John Wiley & Sons, Inc., New York. 735 pp.

Hanson, J. B., and O. Biddulph. 1953. The diurnal variation in the translocation of minerals across bean roots. *Plant Physiol.*, 28:356–370.

Jacobson, L., R. J. Hannapel, and D. P. Moore. 1958. Non-metabolic uptake of ions by barley roots. *Plant Physiol.*, 33:278–282.

Koontz, H., and O. Biddulph. 1957. Factors affecting absorption and translocation of foliar applied phosphorus. *Plant Physiol.*, 32:463–470.

Mittler, T. E. 1958. Studies on the feeding and nutrition of *Tuberolachnus*. II. Nitrogen and sugar composition of phloem sap and honeydew. *J. Exptl. Biol.*, 35:74–84.

Petrie, A. H. K., R. Watson, and E. D. Ward. 1939. Physiological ontogeny in the tobacco plant. I. *Australian J. Exptl. Biol. Med. Sci.*, 17:93–122.

Stewart, L. 1963. Chelation in the absorption and translocation of mineral elements. *Ann. Rev. Plant Physiol.*, 14:295–310.

Stout, P. R., and D. R. Hoagland. 1939. Upward and lateral movement of salt in certain plants as indicated by radioactive isotopes of potassium, sodium and phosphorus absorbed by roots. *Am. J. Botany*, 26:320–324.

Swanson, C. A., and J. B. Whitney. 1953. Studies on the translocation of foliar applied P^{32} and other radioisotopes in bean plants. *Am. J. Botany*, 40:816–823.

Thomas, W. 1927. The seat of formation of amino acids in *Pyrus malus* L. *Science,* 66:115–116.

Tiffin, L. O., and J. C. Brown. 1962. Iron chelates in soybean exudate. *Science,* 135: 311–313.

Williams, R. F. 1938. Physiological ontogeny in plants and its relations to nutrition. IV. The effect of phosphorus supply on the total-, protein-, and soluble-nitrogen contents, and water content of the leaves and other plant parts. *Australian J. Exptl. Biol. Med. Sci.,* 16:65–83.

Winter, A. G. 1952. Untersuchungen über die Aufnahme von Penicillin und Streptomycin durch die Wurzeln von *Lepidium sativum* L. and ihre Bestandigkeit in natürlichen Boden. *Z. Botan.,* 40:153–172.

5 | Mobilization

The translocation of organic and inorganic materials is frequently considered to be a movement of substances from regions of higher to regions of lower concentrations— either lower concentrations of solutes (as in mass flow) or of solvents (as in the movement in the transpiration stream). However, numerous observations in Chaps. 3 and 4 imply that such a concentration gradient does not apply in many instances of translocation in plants. The preferential accumulations of phosphorus in young leaves would be an obvious example.

The large accumulations of carbohydrates or fats in such storage organs as fruits and tubers are considered to be a consequence of the activities of enzymes which convert the soluble translocated carbohydrates into insoluble forms, thus creating a gradient for further accumulation (cf. review of Wanner, 1958). Accumulations can be generally correlated with the activity of enzymes which synthesize such relatively insoluble materials as starches, fats, and proteins; conversely, the export of materials from storage organs can be correlated with the activity of hydrolyzing enzymes such as amylase. A basis for the control of the enzymes which may control mobilization actions remains obscure.

Mobilization centers

The mobilization of nutrients into flowers, fruits, tubers and bulbs, and apical regions of the plant has been known for many years. To illustrate the mobilization by fruits, the weight increases of barley grains are plotted in Fig. 5-1a, from which it is evident that the increases are at least partly at the expense of the dry weights of leaves (Archbold and Mukerjee, 1942). This accumulation, which is principally into the endosperm, gives way at germination to a mobilization by the embryo, as in Fig. 5-1b (Folkes et al., 1952). The embryo mobilization is clearly at the expense of the endosperm.

70

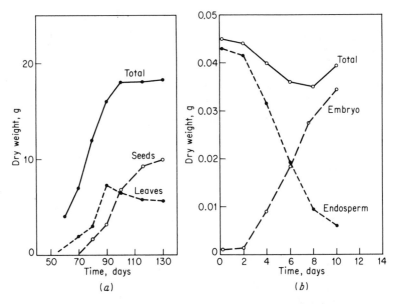

Fig. 5-1 | Some examples of mobilization in barley. (*a*) During the growth of the plant, materials are mobilized into the developing grain largely at the expense of the leaves (Archbold and Mukerjee, 1942); (*b*) during the germination of the seed, materials are mobilized into the developing embryo at the expense of the endosperm (Folkes et al., 1952).

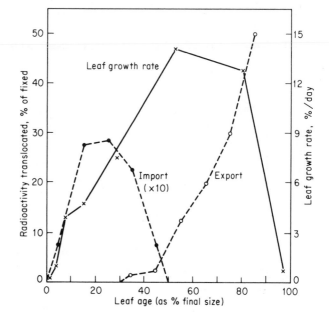

Fig. 5-2 | Translocation into and out of a soybean leaf as a function of stage of development. During early expansion, translocation is all import, as shown by radioactivity translocated from older leaves. As the leaf reaches full size, translocation is all export, as shown by label moving out. Labeled CO_2 given for 2 hr in light, counted after 6 weeks (Thrower, 1962).

Fig. 5-3 | The movement of P³² from leaf tip
to base shows mobilization effect by rust lesions.
Red bobs wheat leaves given 2 microliters
P³²O₄, 2 cm from the tip; lesions of *Puccinia
recondita* at base. Leaves scanned consecutively
in time (Johnson, 1964).

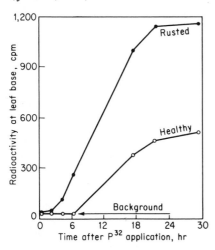

Fig. 5-4 | Diurnal changes in total sugars in
the sap of cotton plants, comparing the changes
in the leaf, bark, and boll. The increase of leaf
sugar in the afternoon is followed generally by
a rise in the bark and boll. (Mason and Maskell,
1928).

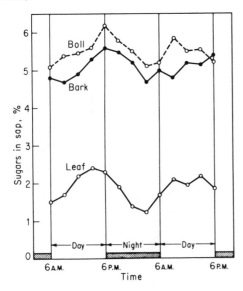

The data in Fig. 5-2 illustrate mobilization
by young, expanding leaves and show that
radioactive photosynthates are preferentially
accumulated into soybean leaves during the
early growth, an action which declines as
maximal growth rate is reached. Export of
photosynthates then becomes increasingly
greater as the growth rate falls to a low level
(Thrower, 1962). As in the developing endosperm, then, mobilization can be into or
out of the leaf, depending on its stage of
development.

Many other cases of mobilization could
be cited, including that out of the fruit hull
into the cotyledons of peanuts and beans or
the filling of some potato tubers at the expense of others on the same plant.

Pathogens may cause mobilizations of nutrients to the infection lesions, presumably
providing nutrients in this way. Yarwood
and Jacobson (1955) noted that radioactive
phosphate applied to a healthy bean leaf
was preferentially moved into a rust-infected
region of another leaf. Shaw et al. (1954)
reported that rusted regions of a leaf showed
increased dry weight, starch accumulations,
and increased abilities for uptake of radioactive phosphate. Johnson (1964) further
illustrated the mobilization effect by showing that leaves with rust lesions at their
bases mobilized P³² from more apical regions markedly better than uninfected leaves
(Fig. 5-3).

Mobilization concepts

The concept of translocation as a flow
toward sinks of different sizes has been
popular for many years. The active dispo-
sition of nutrients in a storage form would
constitute a mobilization sink. Mason and
Maskell (1928) did much to develop the
sink concept in plant translocation, after
making some precise measurements of the
carbohydrate fractions in leaves, stems, and
fruits of cotton plants at various times during the day. Some of their data (Fig. 5-4)

show that the rise of sugar content during the day in the leaves is reflected in a rise in the content in bark and in bolls of the cotton. The diurnal increase is not dissimilar to a puffing action in the inflation of a balloon. With each day there is a repeated new increment of carbohydrates in the leaves, reflected then in an addition to the mobilizing sink.

The flow of assimilates into regions where they are being most rapidly used is another type of mobilization; Fig. 5-2 illustrates one example. In some experiments of Chajlakjan and Butenko (1957) on the flow of radioactive carbon after fixation in the green leaf, the greatest movement was into the apical regions of the stem and the rapidly expanding leaves; somewhat lesser amounts went into the root regions of the plant, and essentially none into the mature leaves. The upper leaves export their carbon to the apex and other upper leaves, and those in the lower part supply the roots more generously (e.g., Shiroya et al., 1961; also see Fig. 4-11).

Mobilization may involve some sort of pulling forces acting on the translocation systems. Many early studies implied that movement may be against an apparent concentration gradient; for example, the data of Mason and Maskell (1928) in Fig. 5-4 show higher total sugars in the cotton fruit than in the leaves. Crowther (1934) observed that in cotton there was also an export of nitrogenous compounds from the leaves into the fruits, and this almost entirely depleted the leaves (Fig. 5-5). Burström (1948) noted that the mobilization of phosphorus into swelling tree buds in the spring occurred at rates actually more rapid than the apparent flow of water into the buds. The action of pulling forces in mobilization is more directly seen in the patterns of translocation of radioactive solutes. Nelson and Gorham (1959) found that the movement of radioactive aspartic acid down a soybean stem followed a logarithmic curve if the roots were intact, but if they

were removed or chilled the downward movement was sharply curtailed.

There is evidence to indicate that mobilization may involve yielding activities as well as pulling forces. Rinsing leaves with water can elute considerable amounts of organic and inorganic constituents (Tukey et al., 1957), and old leaves yield much more than young ones—a difference of about 60 per cent. The translocation of organic and inorganic nutrients out of older leaves was observed by Mason et al. (1936) and numerous others, and the data in Figs. 4-11 and 4-13 illustrate this tendency. There seems to be a basis for suspecting, therefore, that mobilization events can also involve the tendencies of an organ to give up its nutrients.

Factors in mobilization

In some early work, Mothes (1928) observed that the loss of nitrogenous materials from aging tobacco leaves could be pre-

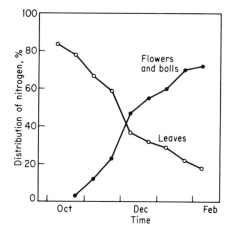

Fig. 5-5 | The nitrogen components of cotton flowers and bolls increase in midsummer (November in South Africa), and there is an associated decrease in nitrogen in the leaves (Crowther, 1934).

Fig. 5-6 | By topping tobacco plants, the mobilization of nitrogenous materials from the leaves into the fruits is avoided. The leaves of topped plants still lose nitrogenous materials somewhat, however, apparently to the stem and roots (Watson and Petrie, 1940).

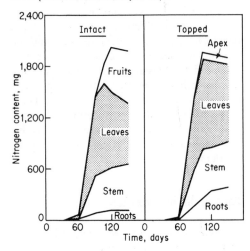

Fig. 5-7 | Demonstration of the mobilizing action of developing fruits of *Calonyction*. (*a*) An intact fruit; (*b*) an aborted fruit on a cutting by itself does not show degeneration of the fleshy peduncle; (*c*) an aborted fruit on a cutting with an intact fruit shows an exhaustion of the fleshy peduncle (Marré, 1948*b*).

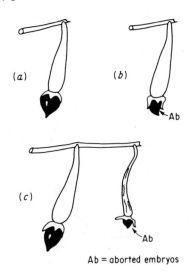

Ab = aborted embryos

vented by topping the plant. After taking more elaborate data on the subject, Petrie et al. (1939) reasserted that topping would greatly reduce the export of nitrogenous materials, and they described this as a sink effect—the fruits forming a large depot in which these nutrients accumulated. The effects of topping are illustrated in Fig. 5-6 (Watson and Petrie, 1940).

It is remarkable that with topping and removal of the fruits as a nutrient sink, the roots take up much of the leaf nitrogen. Thus the leaves of topped plants still export some of their nitrogen, though markedly less than they would if the flowers and fruits were on the plants.

That the roots may draw nutrients from the leaves might be deduced from the observation of Pristupa and Kursanov (1957) that C^{14} fixed photosynthetically in the leaves of pumpkins was most readily translocated into the roots at night—further evidence for a diurnal flow into the roots— and that this flow was markedly depressed by a nitrogen deficiency in the nutrient solution. If the roots were then supplied with additional NH_4NO_3, the flow of C^{14} into the roots was restored.

The mobilization effect of developing fruits and flowers has been examined in an interesting fashion by Marré (1948*a*, 1949). He found that the growth of the ovary and stamens was associated with a relatively high concentration of starches in the peduncle. If he removed the ovaries or the stamens, the starches in the peduncle were degraded and disappeared. The developing fruit seems to be a positive mobilizing force, for in *Calonyction* the receptacle and peduncle became much enlarged and fleshy during fruit growth, but the accumulated materials were translocated away if the ovary was damaged during growth. If a cutting was made to include two developing fruits, as represented in Fig. 5-7, this loss of the storage materials in the peduncle of an aborted ovary was rapid and complete. If a cutting included only one fruit, the abortion of its ovary did not result in loss of the peduncle tissues. There seems to be a positive mobilizing force in an intact fruit.

The mobilization action of fruits is further illustrated by some experiments with tomato by McCollum and Skok (1960). Whole plants were exposed to $C^{14}O_2$ in the light, and fruits were analyzed for radioactivity 1 day later. The data in Fig. 5-8 indicate that the young fruits exerted by far the strongest mobilizing action, reaching a level of radioactivity more than sevenfold that recorded for the donor leaves. Older fruits approaching the mature, green stage were less effective mobilizing centers, and then a brief rise in mobilization occurred as the ripening process began before the mobilization action fell to almost zero. McCollum and Skok suggested that the rise in mobilization as ripening started might be due to utilization of the leaf sugars for the formation of the carotenoid pigments in the fruit.

What environmental factors can be recognized as modifying the mobilizing activities? Vickery et al. (1937) noted that tobacco leaves held in darkness lost their nitrogenous constituents rapidly, whereas leaves given daily light periods were relatively stable. Perhaps light can fortify the mobilizing activities of leaves. Nutrient deficiencies to the plant can increase the export of nitrogenous materials from leaves (Williams, 1955). In some recent experiments, Engelbrecht and Mothes (1960) have shown that heat treatment of tobacco leaves results in loss of color of the treated area. That this response involves a loss in mobilizing pull is indicated by the experiments in which radioactive amino acids were applied to the heated leaf area; after a few days the radioactivity had been translocated across the leaf to the untreated area.

In contrast to the demobilizing effects of heat, Engelbrecht and Mothes (1960) found that kinetin applied to a portion of a tobacco leaf would have strong mobilizing effects. If an excised leaf were treated with kinetin in a localized area, this area would remain green, while the untreated portion would turn yellow. That nutrients were being mobilized from the untreated into the treated area was shown (Mothes et al., 1959) by the fact that radioactive amino acids applied to one part of a leaf would be mobilized effectively into the kinetin-treated area (Fig. 5-9). This effect was found whether isotopes of carbon or of nitrogen were used in the amino acids.

The kinetin effect is further illustrated by following the nitrogenous constituents of tobacco leaves with kinetin treatment. It is evident from Fig. 5-10 that in time severed leaves lose large amounts of their protein nitrogen and that the soluble degradation products accumulate in the midrib of the leaf. If kinetin has been applied to one-half of the leaf blade, instead of the accumulation of solubles in the midrib there is

Fig. 5-8 | The translocation of C^{14} from tomato leaves into fruits of various stages of development, showing a strong mobilization into young fruits up to 20 days old and a declining mobilization by older fruits, except for a brief period at the mature green stage (McCollum and Skok, 1960).

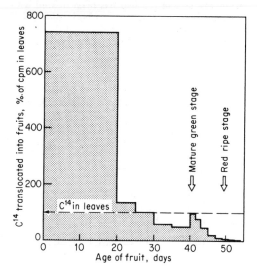

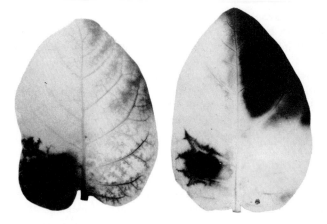

Fig. 5-9 | Autoradiograph showing the mobilization of radioactive glycine in *Nicotiana rustica* leaves by kinetin treatment. Each leaf was treated in the lower left quarter with radioactive glycine and in the upper right corner with kinetin. The leaf on the left is a young leaf showing little mobilization by kinetin, and the one at the right 'is an old leaf showing strong mobilization (Mothes, 1960).

Fig. 5-10 | The changes in soluble and insoluble nitrogen fractions of tobacco leaves after excision. Left: the initial distribution in left and right halves of the blade and in the midrib. Middle: after 9 days, considerable loss of the protein nitrogen (shaded bars) has occurred in the blades, and solubles (unshaded bars) have accumulated in the midrib. Right: after 9 days, when one side of the leaf has been treated with kinetin, there is an increase in both soluble and protein nitrogen in the treated side at the expense of the untreated parts (Mothes et al., 1959).

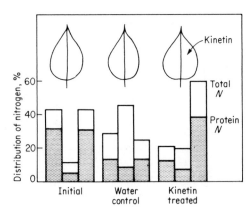

an accumulation of nitrogen in the treated leaf part. Measurements of the treated and untreated sides showed that kinetin treatment resulted in an enhancement of chlorophyll content, protein synthesis, and nucleic acid content of the leaf. As the protein was degraded in the leaf, the soluble products actually accumulated in the midrib, even though there was no further depot to which they could be translocated. This effect suggests that nitrogenous materials are being pushed out of the senescing leaf.

Chibnall (1939) long ago described the yellowing of aging tobacco leaves as a degradation of protein components of the leaf, and even before that Michael (1936) showed that the extent of yellowing of the leaf could be used as an index of the declining protein content during the aging of leaves.

It appears that there are shifting patterns of mobilization in the plant, with one part actively accumulating assimilates for a time and then yielding to mobilizations by other parts of the plant. There seems to be clear evidence for believing that the mobilization effects may be brought about by active accumulative activities of local parts of the plant, and furthermore there may be forces causing the release or demobilization of materials in some parts of the plant. Applications of kinetin and some related compounds can bring about a mobilization of nutrients in a manner suggestive of the mobilization by apices, flowers, fruits, and other centers; the interesting possibility appears, then, that the correlative movement of materials from one part to another may be regulated at least in part by growth substances.

GENERAL REFERENCES

Mothes, K. 1961. Der Beitrag der Kinetinforschung zum Verstandnis pflanzlicher Korrelationen. *Ber. Deut. Botan. Ges.*, 74:24–41.

Wanner, H. 1958. Mobilizierung der Kohlenhydrate bei der Keimung. *Handbuch Pflanzenphys.*, 6:935–951.

Williams, R. F. 1955. Redistribution of mineral elements during development. *Ann. Rev. Plant Physiol.*, 6:25–42.

REFERENCES CITED

Archbold, H. K., and B. N. Mukerjee. 1942. Physiological studies in plant nutrition. XII. Carbohydrate changes in the several organs of the barley plant during growth. *Ann. Botany (London)*, 6:1–14.

Burström, H. 1948. The rate of nutrient transport to swelling buds of trees. *Physiol. Plantarum*, 1:124–135.

Chajlakjan, M., and R. Butenko. 1957. Movement of assimilates of leaves to shoots under differential photoperiodic conditions of leaves. *Compt. Rend. Acad. URSS*, 4:450–462.

Chibnall, A. C. 1939. *Protein Metabolism in the Plant*. Yale University Press, New Haven, Conn. 306 pp.

Crowther, F. 1934. Studies in growth analysis of the cotton plant under irrigation in the Sudan. I. *Ann. Botany (London)*, 48: 877–913.

Engelbrecht, L., and K. Mothes. 1960. Kinetin als Faktor der Hitzresistenz. *Ber. Deut. Botan. Ges.*, 73:246–257.

Folkes, B. F., A. J. Willis, and E. W. Yemm. 1952. The respiration of barley plants. VII. The metabolism of nitrogen and respiration in seedlings. *New Phytologist*, 51:317–341.

Johnson, L. B. 1964. Nutrient mobilization by *Puccinia recondita*. Ph.D. Diss., Purdue Univ.

McCollum, J. P., and J. Skok. 1960. Radiocarbon studies on the translocation of organic constituents into ripening tomato fruits. *Proc. Am. Soc. Hort. Sci.*, 75:611–616.

Marré, E. 1948a. Regolazione ormonale del ricambio dell' amido nella pianta. I. Funzione amilofissatrice del seme. *Boll. Soc. Ital. Biol. Sper.*, 24:1–4.

———. 1948b. Hormone regulation of starch metabolism in the higher plant. II. The starch fixing and starch mobilizing action of the seed in the competition between neighboring fruits. *Boll. Soc. Ital. Biol. Sper.*, 24:602–605.

———. 1949. Growth hormones and carbohydrate metabolism in the higher plant. I. Starch fixing action of auxin after castration or removal of the developing seeds. *Boll. Soc. Ital. Biol. Sper.*, 25:331–334.

Mason, T. G., and E. J. Maskell. 1928. Studies on the transport of carbohydrates in the cotton plant. I. *Ann. Botany (London)*, 42:189–253.

———, E. J. Maskell, and E. Phillis. 1936. Further studies on transport in the cotton plant. III. *Ann. Botany (London)*, 50: 23–58.

Michael, G. 1936. Über die Beziehungen zwischen Chlorophyll und Eiweissabbau im vergilbenden Laubblatt von *Tropaeolum*. *Z. Botan.*, 29:385–425.

Mothes, K. 1928. Die Wirkung des Wassermangels auf den Eiweissumsatz in hoheren Pflanzen. *Ber. Deut. Botan. Ges.*, 46: 59–67.

———. 1960. Über das Altern der Blätter

und die Moglichkeit ihrer Wiederverjungung. *Naturwissenschaften,* 47:337–350.

——, L. Engelbrecht, and O. Kulajewa. 1959. Über die Wirkung des Kinetins auf Stickstoffverteilung und Eiweisssynthese in isolierte Blättern. *Flora (Jena),* 147: 445–464.

Nelson, C. D., and P. R. Gorham. 1959. Physiological controls of the distribution of translocated amino acids and amides in young soybean plants. *Can. J. Botany,* 37: 439–447.

Petrie, A. H. K., R. Watson, and E. D. Ward. 1939. Physiological ontogeny in the tobacco plant. I. *Australian J. Exptl. Biol. Med. Sci.,* 17:93–122.

Pristupa, N. A., and A. L. Kursanov. 1957. Descending flow of assimilates and its relation to the absorbing activity of roots. *Fiziol. Rast.,* 4:417–424 (AIBS translation).

Shaw, M., S. A. Brown, and D. R. Jones. 1954. Uptake of radioactive carbon and phosphorus by parasitized leaves. *Nature,* 173:768–769.

Shiroya, M., G. R. Lister, C. D. Nelson, and G. Krotkov. 1961. Translocation of C^{14} in tobacco at different stages of development. *Can. J. Botany,* 39:855–864.

Thrower, S. L. 1962. Translocation of labelled assimilates in the soybean. II. The pattern of translocation in intact and defoliated plants. *Australian J. Biol. Sci.,* 15:629–649.

Tukey, H. B., Jr., S. H. Wittwer, and H. B. Tukey. 1957. Leaching of carbohydrates from plant foliage as related to light intensity. *Science,* 126:120–121.

Vickery, H. B., G. W. Pucher, A. J. Wakeman, and C. S. Leavenworth. 1937. Chemical investigations of the tobacco plant. VI. Chemical changes in light and darkness. *Conn. Agr. Expt. Sta. New Haven Bull.,* 399:757–828.

Wanner, H. 1958. Mobilisierung der Kohlenhydrate bei der Keimung. *Handbuch Pflanzenphys.* 6:935–951.

Watson, R., and A. H. K. Petrie. 1940. Physiological ontogeny in the tobacco plant. IV. *Australian J. Exptl. Biol. Med. Sci.,* 18:313–339.

Williams, R. T. 1955. Redistribution of mineral elements during development. *Ann. Rev. Plant Physiol.,* 6:25–42.

Yarwood, C. E., and L. Jacobson. 1955. Accumulation of chemicals in diseased areas of leaves. *Phytopathology,* 45:43–48.

Part II | GROWTH

The discussion of the assimilative activities of plants started with the plant considered as a complete biological entity. We shall now examine some of the mechanisms that may be involved in achieving the grown structure.

Growth of the single-celled organism is complicated enough, involving the processes of cell enlargement and organelle production, but with the development of multicellular plants complexity is increased with the additional problems of coordination of the actions of various cells in the organism. Lack of coordination and specialization of cell activities results in only a colony of cells without the special advantages of the multicellular organism. There are two evident types of mechanisms which can be employed to bring about coordination in the plant: systems of chemical messengers which direct cells to carry out various functions and systems of field or physical forces. The former class includes the plant hormones, and the latter might involve electrical gradients over the entire plant, or metabolic, pressure or gas-exchange gradients. Other types of cellular control mechanisms may exist, but at present we are unaware of them.

Little is known about field forces which may be involved in the multicellular plant organization; however, much information has been accumulated about hormone systems and chemical control mechanisms. Considering the present state of knowledge, therefore, most of our attention will be directed to these hormonal and chemical control systems in order to develop a logical picture of how cells are regulated in growth and differentiation.

The end product of these controls is a complex plant organism with localized regions of growth and with specialized regions for photosynthetic activities, translocation of materials, accumulation of the necessary raw materials, or differentiation into reproductive or other specific functions.

Chemicals which may participate in the control of growth are called *growth regula-*

tors. Plant physiologists have been able to recognize four types: auxins, gibberellins, kinins, and inhibitors. The term *auxin* includes two types of materials: the growth hormones, which are natural plant constituents and which regulate cell enlargement in the manner of indoleacetic acid, and the natural or synthetic materials, which can also stimulate cell enlargement in the manner of indoleacetic acid but which are not natural components of the growth-regulating system in the plant. The *gibberellins* also regulate growth, but through a type of action which is distinctive; it seems likely, however, that gibberellin growth effects require the presence of auxin. The *kinins* regulate growth at least in part by stimulating cell division, an effect not clearly separate from the previous two categories, for kinins may require auxin for their action, and either auxins or gibberellins may themselves stimulate cell division. The *inhibitors* include a wide array of chemical entities which may inhibit growth or development functions or may inhibit some component reaction relating to the growth regulators. Inhibitors are at present a poorly defined group of growth regulators.

6 | Auxins*

The discovery of auxins was the outcome of experiments designed to explain a correlation effect: phototropism. Darwin (1897) found that the tip of a grass coleoptile is essential to the tropistic response of the whole coleoptile, and Paàl (1919) concluded that a "correlation carrier" was supplied by the tip and that changes in its movement accounted for the curvature. Went (1928) actually found such a substance in diffusates from coleoptile tips and was able to explain both the correlative nature of the tropistic response and the endogenous control of growth rates on the basis of this substance, auxin.

Kögl et al. (1934) described indoleacetic acid as an auxin, and this chemical was purified from plant materials by Kögl and Kostermans (1934) and by Thimann (1935). The subsequent study of auxins has been dominated by interest in its control over growth. Went (1928) proposed that "Ohne Wuchsstoff, kein Wachstum" (without auxin, no growth). The term *growth hormone* became synonymous with auxin, and the studies of the mechanism of auxin action have been mainly studies of the effects of auxin on cell enlargement. This hormone, auxin, is certainly intimately involved in the catalysis of cell enlargement in stems and coleoptiles; however, its role as a stimulant of growth in other organs such as roots, leaves, and fruits is still uncertain.

Since the search for auxin was initially a study of tropistic curvature of coleoptiles, it is appropriate that the first good bioassay for it should utilize the stimulation of curvature of coleoptiles. The data in Fig. 6-1 show the quantitative curvature which develops when auxin is applied onto one side of the decapitated *Avena* coleoptile. The precision of the response depends on the polar transport of the auxin down the coleoptile on the treated side and the preferential stimulation of growth there.

* Parts of this chapter are adapted from Leopold (1964).

When pieces of coleoptile or stem are immersed in an auxin solution, quantitative stimulations of elongation are obtained as shown in Fig. 6-2 (Galston and Hand, 1949; Galston and Baker, 1951*b*). These large stimulations are roughly proportional to the log of the concentration of auxin, and etiolated stems are more sensitive than green ones.

Inhibitory growth responses to auxin are very general. Roots are particularly sensitive to auxins; an example of the quantitative inhibitions obtained is shown in Fig. 6-3.

In addition to their abilities to regulate growth, auxins may participate in the regulation of correlation events in the plant. Their central role in the tropisms is one such correlation effect, and they play an important part in the phenomenon of apical dominance (Thimann and Skoog, 1934) and are a major control of abscission (La Rue, 1936). Closely allied to the correlation effects is the auxin role in the differentiation of organs and tissues, including effects on the induction of root initiation (Thimann and Went, 1934) and on the differentiation of xylem (Jacobs, 1954; Wetmore, 1955).

The tropistic stimulation shown in Fig. 6-1 is a classic illustration of one of the correlation influences of auxin; the ability of auxin to inhibit the enlargement of the lateral bud in the phenomenon of apical dominance is illustrated in Fig. 6-4 (Thimann and Skoog, 1934); and the quantitative ability of auxin to induce rooting in the basal ends of cuttings is shown in Fig. 6-5 (Biale and Halma, 1937).

Fig. 6-1 | The unilateral application of auxin to decapitated oat-coleoptile tips produces quantitative curvature responses away from the treated side. This technique provides a means of quantitative bioassay for auxin (Went and Thimann, 1937).

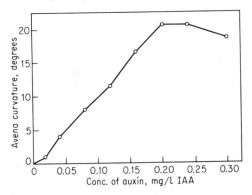

Fig. 6-2 | Sections of pea stem show quantitative stimulations of growth when floated on auxin solutions. Sections from etiolated plants are more responsive than those from green plants and are commonly used as an auxin bioassay (Galston and Hand, 1949; Galston and Baker, 1951*b*).

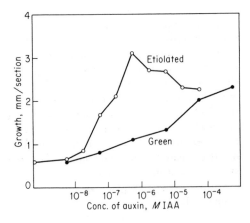

Synthetic auxins

The range of chemical materials which possess growth-stimulating abilities in the manner of indoleacetic acid is too extensive for treatment here, but some of the most common materials used in physiological experimentation or agricultural application are listed in Fig. 6-6. The abilities of various indole compounds to produce growth and formative effects were reported almost simultaneously from several laboratories (Kögl et al., 1934; Haagen-Smit and Went, 1935; Zimmerman et al., 1936). Activities of the naphthalene acids were observed by Zimmerman et al. (1936) and of the naphthoxy acids by Irvine (1938) and Zimmerman and Hitchcock (1941). The great activity of some phenoxyacetic acids in causing formative effects was realized during the early period of World War II (Zimmerman and Hitchcock, 1942), and for a time the research on this class of auxins was carried on under military secrecy. The strong activity of the benzoic acids was not discovered until 1950 (Bentley, 1950). Among the most active of these four types of common auxins, toxicity and persistence increase generally in the series of indoles, naphthyls, phenoxys, and benzoic auxins. Their usefulness in agricultural applications reflects these properties. The indoles and naphthyls are used principally for rooting and fruit set, the phenoxys are fine herbicides and modifiers of fruit growth and ripening, and the benzoics are herbicides (cf. reviews of Leopold, 1955, 1958; Audus, 1959).

The interesting question of the relation of structure to activity of the auxins has received much attention, in the expectation of shedding some light on the nature of the auxin action. Three general features of the molecule are ordinarily needed for auxin activity. These include an aromatic ring, an acidic side chain, and some spatial relationship between the two (Koepfli et al., 1938). There are exceptions to each of these requirements, so the generalizations are each insecure; and surprisingly, the extensive literature on the problem of auxin structure and activity has not led to any definitive information about what the auxin molecule does or where it acts at the molecular level.

The phenoxyacetic acids may be used to illustrate the three general features

Fig. 6-3 | Auxin responses of intact pea roots show quantitative inhibitions of growth (Åberg and Jonsson, 1955).

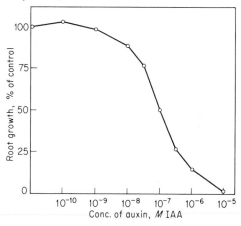

Fig. 6-4 | Decapitation of green seedlings of *Vicia faba* causes rapid growth of the lateral bud; auxin solution applied to the severed stem suppresses the lateral bud. Auxin was an extract of *Rhizopus sinuis* and was applied for 8 days (Thimann and Skoog, 1934).

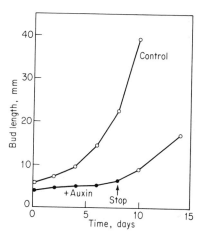

Fig. 6-5 | Treatment of citrus cuttings with auxin produces a quantitative rooting stimulation (Biale and Halma, 1937).

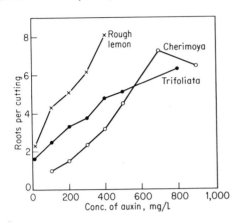

needed for auxin activity. Starting with 2,4-D (2, 4-dichlorophenoxyacetic acid) as a highly active auxin, chlorination in both ortho positions depresses the activity to a low level for 2,6-dichlorophenoxyacetic acid. The free ortho position on the aromatic ring is important for activity. If there is no carboxyl group in the side chain, activity is lost, as in 2,4-dichloroanisole. The spatial configuration between the ring and side chain is another critical feature, as illustrated by the absence of activity in the levo form of 2,4-dichlorophenoxypropionic acid in contrast to the good activity in the dextro form (cf. review of Muir and Hansch, 1955).

Fig. 6-6 | Examples of commonly used auxins, including some indole acids, naphthalene acids, phenoxy acids, and benzoic acids.

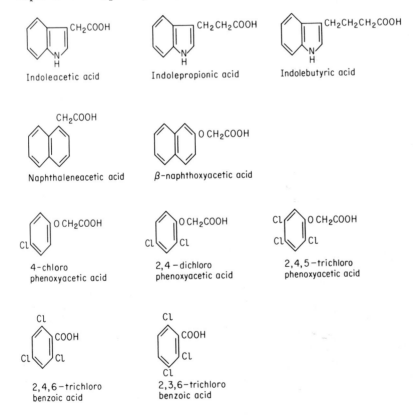

While this wide range of chemical materials can evoke the auxin effects on growth, a much smaller group can exert the auxin influences on correlative effects. This is apparently due to the differences in the structural requirements for growth stimulation and for movement in the polar transport system. Few synthetic auxins are transported by this means; naphthaleneacetic acid is the most familiar (Went and White, 1939; Leopold and Lam, 1961). Other auxins may be transported by this system very slowly or not at all (McCready, 1963).

Natural occurrence

The stimulation of coleoptile or stem growth by auxin has been the most common basis for measuring the amount of auxin in extracts or diffusates from plant parts. Two principal assay methods have been widely used: the straight-growth tests, in which the simple elongation of coleoptile or stem sections in a test solution is measured (Fig. 6-2), and the curvature test, in which coleoptiles are given a unilateral treatment of auxin in an agar block and the stimulation of growth on the treated side results in a growth curvature (Fig. 6-1). The straight-growth tests are handicapped by having only a logarithmic sensitivity to concentrations of auxin, and the curvature test is limited by being sensitive only to auxins which are actively transported in a polar manner by the coleoptile tissue. Prior to about 1952, most workers used the curvature test as a bioassay, and since indoleacetic acid is almost unique in this transport characteristic, nearly all isolations from plants led to the identification of indoleacetic acid. Since the advent of paper chromatography, however, the straight-growth assay has become widely accepted as it adapts more readily to the bioassay of chromatographs. With this assay technique, evidence of other growth-stimulating compounds has been found in plants, and the concept of the

nature of endogenous auxin has become considerably more complicated.

Indole auxins. Indoleacetic acid (IAA) is present in diverse plant tissues. Most identifications have been based on chromatographic behavior and color tests (cf. review of Bentley, 1958), although the isolation of crystalline material has been used in several instances for identification of this auxin (Kögl et al., 1934; Thimann, 1935; Haagen-Smit et al., 1946; Redemann et al., 1951). Indoleacetic acid occurs commonly, but there are numerous growing tissues in which it has not been identified (cf. Bentley, 1958, 1961).

Indoleacetaldehyde was identified as an auxin-active material in plants by Larsen in 1944. This compound is active in the stimulation of growth by its ready conversion into indoleacetic acid, and the extent to which it stimulates growth can be correlated with the conversion to the acid (Larsen, 1951; Bentley and Housley, 1952). It is generally regarded as the immediate precursor of indoleacetic acid on the pathway of biosynthesis from tryptophan (cf. Gordon and Nieva, 1949; Gordon, 1956).

Indoleacetonitrile has been isolated from numerous species, especially among the Cruciferae (Jones et al., 1952; Henbest et al., 1953). If one uses a bioassay tissue which can convert this compound into indoleacetic acid, auxin-stimulation effects are observed (cf. Fig. 6-7). The coleoptiles of most small grains convert it into the acid readily. An enzyme capable of doing this interesting conversion has been separated by Thimann and Mahadevan (1958). The pathway of formation of the nitrile is a puzzle, as it does not appear to be a natural intermediate in the synthesis of indoleacetic acid from tryptophan. Its formation from a glucoside oil, glucobrassicin, has been demonstrated by Gmelin and Virtanen (1961).

Indolepyruvic acid was reported to have been identified in corn by Stowe and Thimann (1953), but Bentley et al. (1956) denied the claim on the basis that this acid

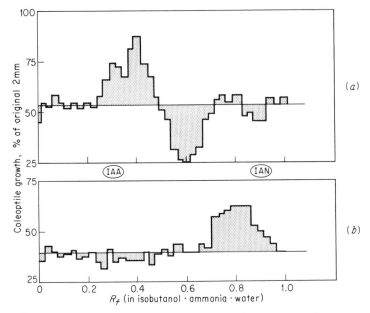

Fig. 6-7 | A representative bioassay of extracted auxins using the oat-coleoptile-section test suggests the presence of acidic auxins (*a*), one of which has the R$_f$ of IAA, and a neutral auxin (*b*) with an R$_f$ similar to indoleacetonitrile. The R$_f$ values for authentic samples are indicated by ovals. Extracts from currant fruits; acid fraction separated with ether from bicarbonate water phase and chromatographed separately (Wright, 1956).

is converted into indoleacetic acid and some other indole derivatives in ammonia, which Stowe and Thimann used for its chromatographic separation. Evidence from Dannenburg and Liverman (1957) and Kaper and Veldstra (1958) that indolepyruvic acid is more stable in plant extracts than in solutions from the crystalline material suggests a resolution of the difference. Chromatographic evidence for the occurrence of this compound in several species (Vlitos and Meudt, 1954; Bitancourt et al., 1954; Blommaert, 1954) and several enzymatic considerations (reviewed by Gordon, 1961) implicate indolepyruvic acid as a common intermediate in the biosynthesis of indoleacetic acid from tryptophan.

Ethyl indoleacetate has been identified in apple and corn extracts (Redemann et al.,

1951; Teubner, 1953), but the utilization of ethanol in making the plant extracts suggests that the esters could have been artifacts of the experimental technique (Henbest et al., 1953). The use of more refined techniques has reaffirmed, however, that the ester does exist in corn as well as in willow and tobacco (Schwarz and Bitancourt, 1957; Hinsvark et al., 1954).

Indoleacetamide, which has been identified chromatographically from tissues treated with auxin (Andreae and Good, 1957), shows good auxin activity in the straight-growth test. However, Zenk (1961) found that the amide is formed from the indoleacetic acid glucoside during extraction if ammonium hydroxide is employed in the separation method, and the amide may not be a natural plant consituent.

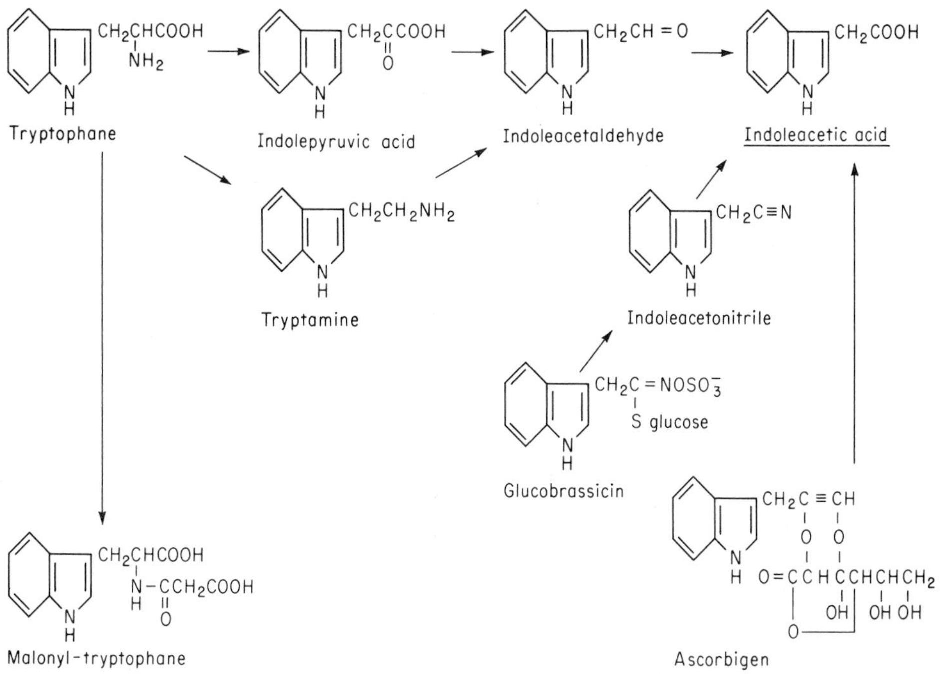

Fig. 6-8 | Some reactions which relate to the biosynthesis of indoleacetic acid from tryptophan and other indole compounds.

The investigation of indole auxins has revealed several compounds with auxin activity in plants, but in each case the growth-stimulating activity could be due to the conversion into indoleacetic acid.

The enzyme systems for conversion of tryptophan to indoleacetic acid occur generally in plants and are especially active in regions of high metabolic activity such as meristems, expanding leaves, fruits, and roots.

The most general path for the conversion involves the formation of indolepyruvic acid as an intermediate, through an oxidative deamination, or deamination, or a phenolic deamination (involving chlorogenic acid or other ortho phenol). Alternatively, the conversion may go through tryptamine by a decarboxylation and then deamination by amine oxidase. Either way indoleacetaldehyde is the immediate precursor of indoleacetic acid, and several oxidative enzymes may complete the final conversion to indole-

acetic acid (Gordon, 1961).

Indoleacetic acid may be formed from the nitrile by nitrilase (Thimann and Mahadevan, 1958). The nitrile in turn may be formed from the thioglucoside, glucobrassicin, or its relative neoglucobrassicin (Gmelin and Virtanen, 1961, 1962).

Another glycoside type of precursor may be ascorbigen, which yields indoleacetic acid and ascorbic acid on hydrolysis (Kutacek et al., 1960).

Tryptophan may also be diverted to form malonyl tryptophan (Good and Andreae, 1957), which may limit auxin biosynthesis (Zenk, 1963).

Nonindole auxins. In addition to the indole auxins, chromatography of extracts has separated numerous growth stimulators which do not give the characteristic color reactions for indole compounds. Reports of these auxins have been compiled by Bentley (1958, 1961), but none of the compounds has been identified. After reviewing the publications on this subject, Bentley concluded that there are auxins in plants which are not indole compounds, though she also suggested that small changes in the indole ring could account for the lack of indole color reactions without removing the capacity of the substance to stimulate growth. For example, hydroxyindoleacetic acid does not give the Salkowsky color reaction for indoles; it is known to be active as an auxin (Thimann, 1958a; Nitsch and Nitsch, 1958; Bulard and Leopold, 1960), and there is some evidence for the occurrence of both the 5-hydroxy and the 2-hydroxy derivatives of indoleacetic acid in plants (Udenfriend et al., 1956; Klämbt, 1959). Indole auxins could masquerade as nonindoles by forming additional products, by combining in dimers as Bentley (1958) has suggested, or by forming complexes or bound forms. Masking substances on the paper chromatograph can also interfere with the development of indole color tests (Shibaoka and Imaseki, 1957). Numerous technical difficulties have beset the identification of any nonindole

auxins, but there is a widespread belief that they do occur in plants. Since the evidence for the existence of these auxins rests on the straight-growth tests, which are responsive to numerous other substances (gibberellins, antibiotics, metals, chelating agents, and even some organic acids), caution seems in order here until the nonindole auxins have been characterized and identified.

Auxin derivatives

For a chemical material to serve as a hormone, the organism must be able to dispose of it after the hormone reaction is completed.

The plant has several options available for the disposal of indoleacetic acid (IAA): It can be converted into several types of complexes, bound onto some sites in the cytoplasm, or enzymatically degraded.

There are three types of complexes into which IAA may enter. First, it may form a peptide, indoleacetyl aspartate. This compound was first detected as a product of metabolism when IAA was added to pea roots (Andreae and Good, 1955; Fig. 6-9) or other tissues (Good et al., 1956), and it has since been found to occur naturally in plants (Klämbt, 1960). Another type of product which may be formed is glycosides of IAA. Indoleacetic acid arabinose was detected in corn by Shantz and Steward (1957), and indoleacetic acid glucose was detected by Zenk (1961, 1962) and by Klämbt (1961); the formation of the glucoside can account for more than half of the IAA entering the tissues of many species (Zenk, 1963). A third possible complex which IAA can form is with ortho phenols such as chlorogenic acid. Evidence that such a complex might be formed in plants was presented by Tomaszewski (1959, 1961), and in vitro formation of complexes with several ortho phenols was carried out by Leopold and Plummer (1961), though they have not been identified in plants.

In plant tissues auxin may be bound to

Fig. 6-9 | As indoleacetic acid is taken up by pea-root tissue, the initial rise of free IAA is soon transformed into indoleacetyl aspartate. Pea roots in $10^{-4}M$ IAA (Andreae and van Ysselstein, 1960).

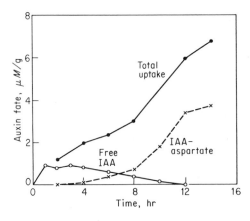

some cytoplasmic entity. Bound auxin is analogous in many ways to the storage forms of some of the animal hormones such as the neurohumors. Its occurrence was first suggested by Thimann and Skoog (1940), who found that auxin was released from plant tissues by proteolytic enzyme action. A bound form was separated from wheat endosperm by Gordon (1946). The fact that auxin was released by gentle hydrolysis or by treatment of the alkaline solutions led him to suggest that it was adsorbed onto protein surfaces. More recent evidence for the binding of auxin onto cytoplasmic proteins has been brought forward by Freed et al. (1961), who also consider the binding to be an adsorptive action. Zenk (1963) has found that the product of an enzymatic binding of IAA onto protein is much more stable than an adsorption complex, as evidenced by the fact that it can be removed only by hydrolysis of the protein.

Bound auxin considerably complicates auxin determinations in plant tissues. Van Overbeek et al. (1947) felt that the continued release of auxin from pineapple tissue during successive extractions (Fig. 6-10) was due to the continued release of auxin from a bound form.

Auxin degradation

Thimann (1934) noted that some plant tissues could cause the disappearance of natural auxins, and an enzyme preparation which carries out the oxidative degradation of IAA was separated from peas by Tang and Bonner (1947). Since that time, a number of such enzymes have been separated and partly characterized, but a unified concept of indoleacetic oxidase (as it is termed) has not emerged. Preparations from different plants have very different characteristics. Tang and Bonner suggested that the pea enzyme was an iron enzyme, probably a peroxidase; Wagenknecht and Burris (1950) thought that it was a copper enzyme; and Galston et al. (1953) believed it was a peroxidase linked to a flavin. Since the enzyme is activated by light, they proposed that the flavin activated the peroxidase. In IAA oxidase preparations from other species, however, there seemed to be no peroxidase or phenolase (Sequeira and Steeves, 1954). An ability of tyrosinase to destroy IAA has been described by Briggs and Ray (1956).

Although the general nature of the enzyme is not clear, the oxidation of IAA re-

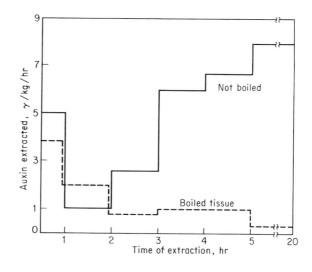

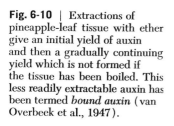

Fig. 6-10 | Extractions of pineapple-leaf tissue with ether give an initial yield of auxin and then a gradually continuing yield which is not formed if the tissue has been boiled. This less readily extractable auxin has been termed *bound auxin* (van Overbeek et al., 1947).

Fig. 6-11 | The degradation of indoleacetic acid by indoleacetic oxidase from beans involves nearly equivalent amounts of CO_2 produced and of O_2 consumed, though the ratio of the two (RQ) seems to be initially above unity (Wagenknecht and Burris, 1950).

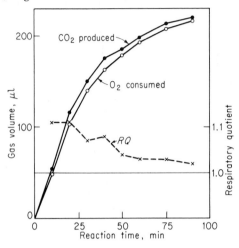

sults in the evolution of CO_2 and the consumption of O_2 in nearly identical amounts, as shown in Fig. 6-11 (Wagenknecht and Burris, 1950).

The enzyme system from peas depends on two types of cofactors, manganese ions and phenolics. After some confusion, the manganese was shown to be responsible for the basic oxidation step; that is, manganic ions can directly oxidize IAA with the production of CO_2 (Waygood et al., 1956). It was further established that the phenolics served as oxidation carriers for the reoxidation of Mn^{++}; this apparently accounts for the fact that several reports show slightly more rapid exchange of CO_2 than O_2, as can be seen in Fig. 6-11.

The ability of light to activate the oxidation was noted by Tang and Bonner (1947) and later confirmed by experiments of Galston and Baker (1951 a,b; Fig. 6-12). The light effect was explained as the removal of an inhibitor which could be dialyzed from the enzyme. Galston and Baker proposed that the light acted through an activation of flavin, but in later experiments Waygood et al. (1956) attributed the light effect simply to the removal of a flavin inhibition of the oxidation. Nevertheless, light can activate the enzymatic destruction of IAA in plants (Fang and Butts, 1957).

The products of auxin oxidation are not known. There is some evidence for the formation of indolealdehyde by action of the pea enzyme, but this may account for only a small fraction of the IAA destroyed (Racusen, 1955), and the enzyme from other sources may not form the aldehyde (Stutz, 1957). Many studies of the products have been made (cf. Ray, 1958; Galston and Hillman, 1961), but of the several compounds usually formed, none have been identified with certainty. The progress curves for the degradation suggest interconversions of the successive intermediates as implied by the data in Fig. 6-13 (Pilet, 1960), contributing to the difficulties in establishing the identities of the products.

Fig. 6-12 | The disappearance of indoleacetic acid from a solution containing indoleacetic oxidase from peas is markedly more rapid in light than in dark, though dialysis of the enzyme will speed the reaction as readily as light. This led to the suggestion that light served to remove an inhibitor of the enzyme (Galston and Baker, 1951a).

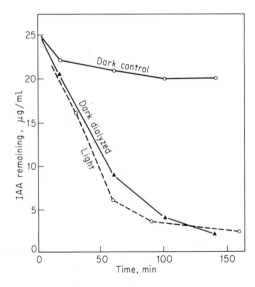

The presence of enzymes which can destroy IAA does not mean that the hormone is disposed of through such channels, and there is considerable disagreement about whether IAA oxidase is significant in plant development. Some circumstantial evidence implies that it is. For example, Konishi (1956) found that the slow growth of rosette stems was associated with a high IAA oxidase activity (Fig. 6-14). Kamerbeek (1956) has inversely correlated growth rates with peroxidase contents for several plants, but the evidence is far from unanimous (Platt, 1954).

In short, it can be said that the plant has enzymes capable of disposing of IAA by several means, but the relative importance of the formation of complexes, the formation of bound auxin, and the degradation of auxin in the plant is not known.

Relation to growth

If auxin functions in the control of growth in stem tissues, it should show some kinetic relation to the locus and time of growth activity in the plant. A general relationship of auxin to growth has been shown in many tissues in a variety of ways. Some results of Scott and Briggs (1960; Fig. 6-16) show that the growth rate in pea stems dwindles from the apex toward the base of the plant as does the auxin content, though more gradually. The correlation with time is illustrated by some data of Hatcher (1959; Fig. 6-17). The auxin content in apple twigs rises in the spring as growth gets under way, and it subsequently declines through the growing season; trailing after it is a decline in the growth rate until autumn. Another type of correlation is that in magnitude; for example, branches which will develop into "long shoots" form large and continuing supplies of auxin; those which will be "short shoots" develop a diminutive supply, as illustrated in Fig. 6-18 (Gunckel and Thimann, 1949).

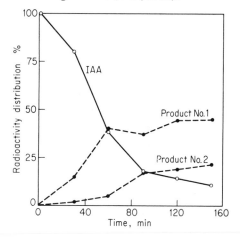

Fig. 6-13 | As an indoleacetic acid solution is attacked by indoleacetic oxidase from *Lens* roots, the disappearance of the IAA is associated with the appearance of at least two other products separable by paper chromatography. The rise in product 2 after 60 min suggests successive degradations (Pilet, 1960).

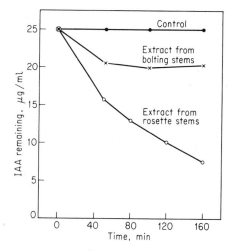

Fig. 6-14 | A comparison of the indoleacetic oxidase activity from stems of *Silene* which are rosette or bolting indicates that the rapid growth in the bolting stems may be related to the lower activity of the enzyme which degrades auxin (Konishi, 1956).

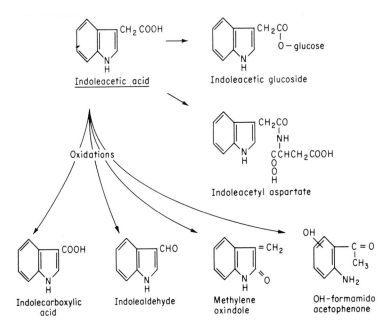

Fig. 6-15 | The plant can dispose of indoleacetic acid by the formation of derivatives such as the glycosides, or the peptide indoleacetyl aspartate, or by the degradation of the acid through cleavage of side chain or indole ring.

Fig. 6-16 | A comparison of the distribution of growth activity down a pea stem and the distribution of diffusible auxin (Scott and Briggs, 1960).

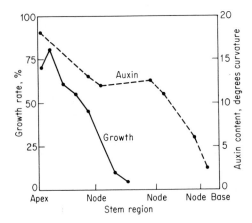

Correlations between auxin content of tissues and growth rates have frequently been made, but there are many instances in which no such correlation was found. In the data for pea stems (Fig. 6-16), Scott and Briggs (1960) observed a slight decline in diffusible auxin down the stem over the region of declining growth rate, but extractable auxin showed no appreciable change over the whole region from the rapidly growing stem apex to the point where growth had essentially stopped. They deduced that the auxin which was obtained from peas by diffusion was more relevant to the growth-regulating action than that which was obtained by extraction. These results vary according to the plant tissue. Went (1942) reported that in oat coleoptiles the extractable auxin correlated well with growth rate, whereas the diffusible

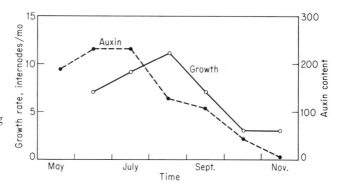

Fig. 6-17 | A comparison of the distribution of growth of apple stems through the growing season and the content of diffusible auxin from the first five nodes (Hatcher, 1959).

auxin correlated instead with the tropistic reactions. This sufficiently illustrates that the means of sampling the auxin content of a tissue will influence what correlations will be obtained and that it is not possible to generalize that diffusible auxins are relevant to growth activities or that extractable auxins are relevant to some other types of activities in plants.

Auxin often occurs most abundantly in the most actively growing tissue; this may be so even in tissues in which it apparently does not stimulate growth. In roots, for instance, Pilet (1951) found that extractable auxin is most abundant about 2 to 10 mm from the tip of the *Lens* root and that the most active growth is about 2 mm from the tip (Fig. 6-19). Furthermore, with increasing age of the plant, the subterminal auxin content continues to rise in time in a manner suggestive of the increasing root growth rate. Very young *Lens* roots give small positive growth responses to added auxins; older roots are not stimulated. The amount of auxin which is found by extraction of the roots greatly inhibits growth if applied to other roots (Audus, 1959).

Thimann (1937) proposed that roots have a lower threshold of auxin sensitivity and that their natural auxin content is above the optimum for growth. Thus, the removal of the root tip as the source of auxin should increase the root growth, and in

fact, Cholodny (1924) succeeded in showing such an increase. Yet many recent investigators have been unable to obtain promotions of root growth following decapitation (Gorter, 1932; Younis, 1953; Vardar and Tozun, 1958). This creates considerable doubt about the role that auxin might play in stimulating root growth.

The situation in fruits presents another relevant illustration of auxin production which may or may not be associated with

Fig. 6-18 | Markedly more auxin is diffusible from buds of *Ginkgo* which will develop into long shoots than from those which will not elongate, remaining as short shoots (Gunckel and Thimann, 1949).

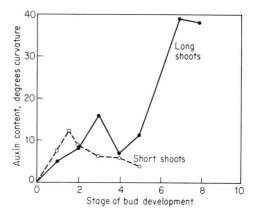

growth. Several workers have shown that as some fruits enter rapid phases of growth, there is a preceding surge in auxin production (Nitsch, 1950; Wright, 1956). In other species auxin production may occur only during the first phases of fruit growth (Nitsch et al., 1960; Crane et al., 1959), or it may not be related to any stage of fruit growth at all (Stahly and Thompson, 1959; Coombe, 1960).

The evidence on the auxin contents of various tissues as they may relate to growth rates generally supports the concept of auxin as a growth hormone in stems and coleoptiles, but in roots and fruits the role of auxin is less certain. Auxin occurrence is usually associated with growing tissues, and in some of these it causes large growth stimulations.

Fig. 6-19 | The auxin extractable with chloroform from *Lens* roots is most abundant in the regions at, or shortly behind, the region of most rapid growth (Pilet and Meylan, 1953).

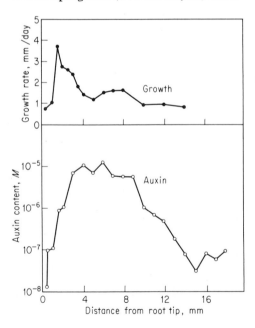

Auxin sources

The ability of auxin (or at least indoleacetic acid) to move through many plant tissues in a polar manner results in its physiological influences over a wider range of locations than those in which it is formed. The usual sites of auxin formation in vascular plants are meristems and enlarging tissues. The classic case of hormone synthesis in the apex of the grass coleoptile, implied by the experiments of Darwin (1897) and specifically suggested by Paàl (1919), was experimentally proved by Went (1928) to explain the physiological mechanism of tropistic movements in plants. The apex is the principal site of auxin formation in the coleoptile, and the polar transport of the hormone down the coleoptile provides the stimulus for growth in the regions below the tip. In dicotyledons the meristematic apex is usually the main locus of auxin production, and its removal results in depressed auxin levels and depressed growth in tissues below the apex. If one plots the amount of auxin as it relates to the distance from the coleoptile apex, one usually obtains a declining curve similar to that shown in Fig. 6-16 and roughly parallel to the declining gradient of growth rate. There are some interesting variants of this situation; Mirov (1941) found that in pine shoots auxin occurrence is much greater at the more basal parts of the new growth than at the apical; Gunckel and Thimann (1949) reported that in *Ginkgo* the early stages of stem growth seem to be supplied with auxin from the apical meristem but that as growth progresses, a larger supply is formed in the more basal internodes in a manner similar to that in pine.

Embryos are another type of meristem which often produce large amounts of auxin. Nitsch (1950) and Luckwill (1949) have shown that embryos are a principal site of auxin production in strawberry and apple fruits during fruit growth. In seeds, too, the embryo is a major source of the hormone (Hemberg, 1955).

Expanding tissues are common sources of auxin; the lengthening internodes of *Ginkgo* and expanding cells in the tip of the oat coleoptile are good examples. During the enlargement of leaves of higher plants, there is generally a large production of auxin (e.g., Goodwin, 1937; Wetmore and Jacobs, 1953; Shoji et al., 1951). There is a similar auxin production during the expansion of fern pinnae (Steeves and Briggs, 1960; Fig. 6-20). The auxin production by leaves is especially interesting since the effects of auxin on growth of the leaf blade are generally small (Miller, 1951; Kuraishi, 1959). This is another example of the production of auxin in a tissue without its apparently playing a major role in stimulating growth of the tissue. It should be noted, though, that auxin produced in the leaf may have extensive correlation effects—hormonal effects on more or less remote tissues.

Auxins are frequently provided for plants by parasitic or symbiotic organisms. Root growth is stunted by auxin-producing mycorrhizae (MacDougal and Dufrenoy, 1944), the formation of nodules on legumes is associated with auxin-forming *Rhizobium* (Thimann, 1936*b*; Kefford et al., 1960), and some plant swellings are associated with invasion by auxin-producing pathogens (Wolf, 1952, 1956; Pilet, 1952; Hirata, 1954). Other pathogens apparently reduce the auxin content of host tissues (e.g., Sequeira and Steeves, 1954; Shaw and Hawkins, 1958; Oaks and Shaw, 1960).

Transport

A striking feature of auxin as a hormonal control within plants is that it may be transported through plant tissues with a characteristic polarity; thus its influences on growth and development are reflections of the polar pattern of its distribution.

The polar feature of auxin transport is best known in the stems and coleoptiles of higher plants. Here auxin moves from the apical regions with a more or less strict polarity in a physiologically basipetal direction. Polar transport is most active near the stem or coleoptile tips, and it declines with distance down the plant (van der Weij, 1932; Jacobs, 1950*a*). In green plants this gradient in polar transport is especially pronounced, giving way in some cases to almost equal transport upward and downward at the base of the stem and the root (Leopold and Guernsey, 1953). In the root the polar feature is erratic; there is commonly a preferential transport away from the root tips, while transport of auxin occurs up or down with equal facility in many older roots (Gorter, 1932). In leaves the basipetal polarity during the early growth loses its directional quality as the leaf matures (Mai, 1934).

Fig. 6-20 | The auxin diffusible from the expanding fronds of the fern *Osmunda cinnamomea* is most abundant at the time of most rapid growth or shortly thereafter (Steeves and Briggs, 1960).

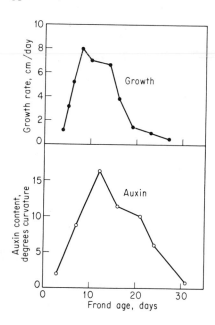

Fig. 6-21 | The velocity of the transport of auxin through tissues can be measured as the time of the first arrival of detectable auxin through 5-mm pieces of tissue; here the velocities are compared for corn coleoptile (1.5 cm/hr), oat coleoptile (1.2 cm/hr), and sunflower stem (0.7 cm/hr) (data of Hertel, 1962, and van der Weij, 1932).

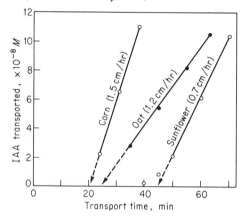

Fig. 6-22 | The ability of bean stems to transport auxin basipetally declines in a gradient down the stem. Stem sections 5 mm long transported for 3 hr from 2-mg/liter IAA donor blocks. Only small amounts of auxin moved acropetally (Jacobs, 1950*a*).

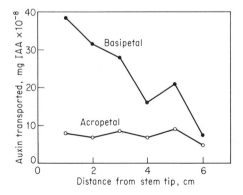

The polarity of auxin transport is not restricted to seed plants. It has been found in ferns (Steeves and Briggs, 1960) and in the horsetails and liverworts (Hertel, 1962). From the evidence it appears that the characteristic of polar auxin transport is widespread in the plant kingdom.

The velocity of the polar transport of auxin is between 0.5 and 1.5 cm/hr. A simple method of measuring velocity, developed first by van der Weij (1932), involves determination of the amount of auxin transported through sections of coleoptile cylinders at various time intervals and then extrapolation of the curve to find the time at which the first auxin must have come through. Velocity determinations obtained in this way for some representative tissues are presented in Fig. 6-21, from which it is evident that transport is somewhat more rapid in corn coleoptiles (Hertel, 1962) than in oat (van der Weij, 1932) or sunflower stems (Leopold and Lam, 1961). Cell length is greater in corn than in oat or sunflower, and the lesser number of cell walls to be traversed in corn may be related to the greater velocity of transport (Hertel, 1962).

The ability of stems to transport auxin changes markedly with age. Figure 6-22 indicates such a gradient of transport ability down the stem of seedlings (Jacobs, 1950*a*). The decreasing activity may be related to increasing age of the cells and to increasing distance from the growing point (Leopold and Lam, 1962). In leaves there is perhaps an even greater loss of transport effectiveness as the leaf reaches full size (Mai, 1934). During the early stages in the ontogeny of a stem there can be increases in the transport ability which may be related to interesting physiological events. For example, Jacobs (1950*b*) found that the stem tissue in the hypocotyl hook of bean seedlings was ineffective in the transport of auxin, thus limiting the auxin supply to the stem immediately below. Konishi (1956) measured the transport of IAA and of naphthaleneacetic acid through spinach stems and found that transport was poor in the rosette periods of growth but good in the bolting stages. A similar lack of transport in the nonelongating stems of loblolly pine was reported by Brown (1958) and Brown and Wetmore (1959).

A useful material for experimentation on auxin transport is 2,3,5-triiodobenzoic acid, which strongly inhibits transport (Niedergang-Kamien and Skoog, 1956). The movement of auxin basipetally or acropetally through stems, roots, and petioles is sensitive to this inhibitor, indicating that movements in both directions involve active transport (Hertel, 1962; Leopold, 1963b). Even the lateral movement of auxin which follows geotropic stimulation of coleoptiles is sensitive to inhibition, and hence it is apparently an active transport (Hertel and Leopold, 1963).

There is good evidence that auxin transport is an active transport. It is specific for indoleacetic acid and only a few of the synthetic auxins (Went and White, 1939; Leopold and Lam, 1961; McCready, 1963); it depends on metabolic forces, as evidenced by its sensitivity to metabolic inhibitors (du Buy and Olson, 1940; Niedergang-Kamien and Leopold, 1957) and low oxygen levels (Gregory and Hancock, 1955); its velocity is greater than that which can be accounted for by diffusion; and it can proceed against a concentration gradient (van der Weij, 1932). Using triiodobenzoic acid as a transport inhibitor, Hertel (1962) found that the movement of auxin out of tissues was preferentially inhibited and deduced that the transport of auxin was a secretive process. The polarity of transport might seem, therefore, to be a consequence of some polar orientation of a secretive apparatus in the cell (cf. review of Leopold, 1963b).

As a feature of plant development, the active transport of auxin is especially interesting because it causes more or less polar distribution of auxins through plant organs,

providing a basis for hormonal influences on a wide array of correlation effects—effects imposed by one part of the plant on another part.

Auxin effects

The best-known stimulations by added or exogenous auxins are the elongation of stems and coleoptiles. The concentrations of auxin which stimulate growth are in the same range as the endogenous auxin concentrations, and so the concept that auxin controls this type of growth is natural and logical. Another type of growth stimulated by auxins is cell enlargement by nonpolar swelling, which occurs in potato and artichoke tubers, in callus cells in tissue cultures, and in some fruit growth. Whether auxin occurs in concentrations needed for stimulating growth of these nonpolar tissues is not yet convincingly established. In many cases there is a lack of correlation between growth and the amount of auxin in these less polar types of tissues.

A scheme for the comparison of the auxin responses of various organs was developed by Thimann (1937), who pointed out that stems, buds, and roots each show a two-phase type of growth response to auxins, with promotions at lower concentrations and inhibitions at higher ones (Fig. 6-23). Stems have the highest optimum auxin concentration for growth, and so auxin levels which promote stem growth may inhibit bud or root growth. A dramatic illustration of Thimann's principle published by Furuya and Soma (1957) shows such ranges for the auxin promotions and inhibitions of stems and roots in the same plant material. Their data suggest that intermediate regions between the stem and root tips have auxin sensitivities which are intermediate with respect to concentrations which stimulate or inhibit growth. Other growth functions can be added to this two-phase response scheme, including the stimulations and inhibitions of flower development (Leopold and Thimann, 1949).

While the two-phase type of auxin-response curve for growth of various tissues seems to be general, there is an interesting question about the significance of auxins in the growth stimulations of roots and leaves which show only small stimulations. Is auxin a growth hormone for these organs? Inhibitory effects of auxin are extremely potent, especially in roots, but the promotive actions are relatively small, ranging from about 10 to 30 per cent, and are limited to special cases. Torrey (1956) has appropriately stated that "there exists an urgent need for clear indisputable evidence for or against the direct involvement of endogenous auxin in the control of root elongation." The same need exists for other poor auxin responders such as leaves, some fruits, and storage organs.

In addition to the effects on growth, auxin participates widely in the overall organization of plant processes, including the regulation of differential growth rates (i.e., the tropisms and apical dominance) and

the regulation of differentiation phenomena, such as the organization of xylem strands differentiating in enlarging leaf primordia or the differentiation of roots at the base of a cutting or at other barriers to its polar transport. In abscission phenomena, auxin may be involved in the differentiation of a separation layer and the new growth on the proximal side of the separation zone, which may push off the abscising leaf (Scott et al., 1948). Since these correlation effects all involve more than the auxin hormone system, they will be discussed in Chap. 10 and are mentioned here only to emphasize the multiple effects of auxin in the organization of the growing plant.

Antiauxins

The discovery of antiauxins holds great promise for the elucidation of auxin phenomena. These chemicals, which can prevent the action of auxin in plants, were first noted by Skoog et al. (1942), who found that γ-phenylbutyric acid could suppress the auxin stimulations of growth. Funke and Söding (1948) described a material extracted from plants which inhibited growth and yielded auxin upon hydrolysis. Tonzig (1950) suggested that ascorbic acid might antagonize auxin action by interfering with its presumed action on enzymes, and Larsen (1951) described extractable materials which interfered with auxin action. Among the synthetic materials, van Overbeek et al. (1951) found that *trans*-cinnamic acid inhibitions of growth could be entirely reversed with auxin applications, and they suggested that it was an antiauxin. Leopold and Klein (1952) described a reversal of maleic hydrazide inhibition with auxin and a reversal of auxin inhibitions with maleic hydrazide.

The concept was considerably clarified by McRae and Bonner (1953*a,b*), who suggested that antiauxins should specifically interfere with the molecular function of the

Fig. 6-23 | Schematic representation of the growth responses of roots, buds, and stems to a range of auxin concentrations, each organ having a promotive and an inhibitory range (Thimann, 1937).

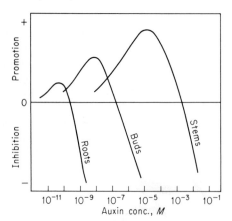

auxin and hence should be chemicals which closely resembled auxins in structure but which lacked some of the requirements for auxin activity. They proposed that in view of the three structural requirements for auxin, there might be three types of anti-auxins: chemicals which lacked an adequate ring nucleus, those which lacked an adequate side chain, and those which lacked the proper spatial relationship between the two. In addition, they thought some chemicals might have the structural requirements for auxin function but, because of their low reactivity, would act as antiauxins by interfering with the function of more reactive auxins (Fig. 6-24).

As examples of these antiauxin classes, McRae and Bonner (1953*a,b*) demonstrated that 2,6-dichlorophenoxyacetic acid was an excellent inhibitor of auxin effects, presumably because it lacked an adequate ring, owing to the diortho substitutions; that 2,4-dichloroanisole was inhibitory since it lacked the carboxyl for an adequate side chain; and that 2,4-dichlorophenoxy*iso*-butyric acid was inhibitory presumably be-

Fig. 6-24 | If one assumes that antiauxins are chemicals which closely resemble auxins but lack one essential structural requirement, there may be antiauxins which lack an adequate ring (because of substitutions of both ortho positions or saturation of the ring near the side chain), which lack an adequate side chain, which lack the proper spatial relationship of the two (due to steric hindrance of *iso*butyric or other bulky side chain), or which have only very weak auxin activity.

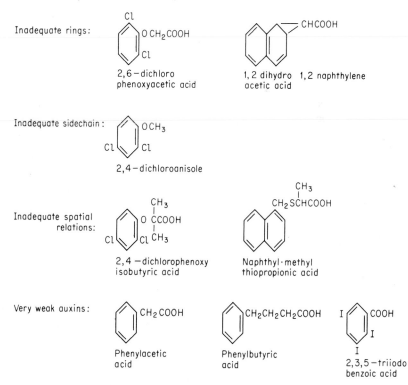

Inadequate rings:

2,6-dichloro phenoxyacetic acid

1,2 dihydro 1,2 naphthylene acetic acid

Inadequate sidechain:

2,4-dichloroanisole

Inadequate spatial relations:

2,4-dichlorophenoxy isobutyric acid

Naphthyl·methyl thiopropionic acid

Very weak auxins:

Phenylacetic acid

Phenylbutyric acid

2,3,5-triiodo benzoic acid

cause of the stearic interference of the excessively substituted side chain. They established kinetic evidence that these chemicals directly compete with auxin for a growth-stimulating site, using the Lineweaver-Burk type of analysis involving a double inverse plot of concentration against velocity. This is shown for 2,4-D *iso*butyric acid in Fig. 6-25. In the double inverse plot, the fact that the curves with and without inhibitor approach the same maximum velocity (on the ordinate) is consistent with the supposition that the substrate (auxin) and the inhibitor are directly competing for the same site of action.

Fig. 6-25 | Analysis of the inhibition of auxin-stimulated growth of oat coleoptiles can be made with the double inverse plot method (below), showing that the antiauxin 2,4-dichlorophenoxy*iso*butyric acid (1 mg/liter) may act in the manner of a competitive inhibitor with the auxin 2,4-D. The unchanged intercept on the ordinate (V_{max}) may indicate competitive action by the inhibitor (McRae and Bonner, 1953*a*).

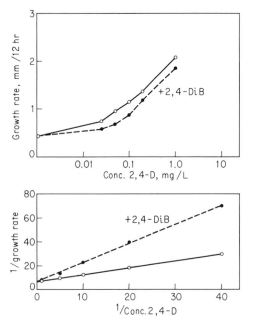

The list of antiauxins has been increased to include compounds with partly saturated rings (Kefford, 1959) and various bulky side chains (Åberg, 1953).

Not only do antiauxins seem to inhibit the growth responses to auxins in a competitive manner, but they have promotive effects on root growth which are suggestive of auxin antagonisms (Åberg, 1952). They also relieve the auxin inhibitions of root growth. Bonner (1949) induced flowering in *Xanthium* with 2,4-dichloroanisole and triiodobenzoic acid at near-threshold photoperiods—conditions under which auxin markedly inhibits flowering.

Unfortunately, the antiauxin concept has been weakened since its emergence. In the first place, several chemicals which should be expected to have antiauxin properties do not. These include the 2,6-substituted benzoic acids, which are auxins instead of antiauxins, and skatole, the indolic equivalent of dichloroanisole, which lacks antiauxin properties (Thimann, 1958*a*). Secondly, the diortho substances such as 2,6-D are slightly active as auxins (Thimann, 1952). This was unexpected because of their inadequate ring structure. Thirdly, experiments with root promotions by the antiauxins show occasional surprising parallels with auxins. Both compounds have similar effects on cell-wall tensility, and either can reverse the promotion effects of an antiauxin (Burström, 1955). The most damaging blow came when Osborne et al. (1954, 1955) found that by substitutions onto the side chain of the 2,6-substituted phenoxy acid antiauxins, these compounds could be converted into auxins nearly as active as 2,4-D. Thus the concept of antiauxins interfering with the three basic structural requirements for auxin activity is regrettably untenable.

The way in which the antiauxins interfere with auxin action should offer potential means for greatly improving the understanding of the action of auxin, but at present the situation remains clouded.

Mechanism of action

Growth promotions. The ultimate step of growth by cell enlargement is a coincident enlargement of the protoplast by water uptake and a yielding of the cell wall. Experimental evidence indicates that the stimulatory action of auxin softens the cell wall by increasing its plasticity (e.g., Heyn, 1931; Tagawa and Bonner, 1957; Cleland, 1958). With a softening of the wall, there ensues a swelling of the cell by simple osmotic water uptake until the restraining forces of the wall balance the osmotic values of the cytoplasm.

That auxin does cause a softening of the cell wall was shown in 1931 by Heyn in simple experiments on the changing physical properties of coleoptiles following auxin treatments. Bending a coleoptile with a standardized force and measuring its distortion and recovery after removal of the force yielded measurements of plastic and elastic values for the cells (Heyn, 1931, 1940; Tagawa and Bonner, 1957). The technique is illustrated in Fig. 6-26. Auxin treatment of the coleoptiles increases the plastic bending of the tissues to a degree which parallels the stimulating effects on growth. This parallelism is illustrated in some data of Bonner (1960) shown in Fig. 6-27. Brauner and Hasman (1947) obtained similar results measuring plasticity by stretching cylinders of potato tissue.

Walls of the young growing cells may be cemented together by pectin chains made firm by cross-linkages of bivalent cations such as calcium. Bennet-Clark (1956) suggested that auxins may remove calcium linkages, thus softening the cell wall and encouraging growth. However, when radioactive calcium was incorporated into the cell walls and then auxin was applied, neither Thimann and Takahashi (1961) nor Cleland (1960a) could show that any calcium was lost from the walls or shifted from one pectin fraction to another. Yet the strong inhibitions of growth and espe-

Fig. 6-26 | As a means of measuring the plasticity and elasticity of oat coleoptiles, the tissue can be held horizontally and deflected by hanging a weight on it; the degree of restoration following removal of the weight can be taken as a measure of elasticity, and the unrecovered deflection as a measure of plasticity (Tagawa and Bonner, 1957).

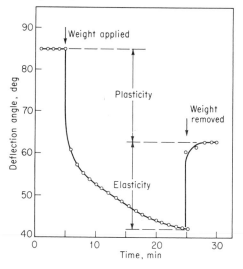

Fig. 6-27 | Using the measure of plasticity shown in Fig. 6-26, the oat coleoptile is seen to respond to auxin treatments with an increase in plasticity which is similar in magnitude to the increase in growth (Bonner, 1960).

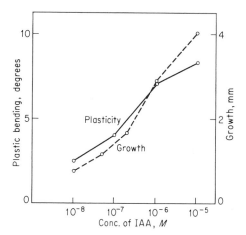

cially of the cell-softening processes by calcium (Cooil and Bonner, 1956; Tagawa and Bonner, 1957) make the calcium linkages between the wall pectins an attractive site for auxin attack. Masuda (1960) suggested alternatively that auxin may bring about an increase in available RNA, which may then bind calcium ions, making them less effective in cementing the wall pectins. The wall plasticity can be measurably increased by adding calcium binders, such as oxalic acid or chelating agents (Bennet-Clark, 1956).

The effectiveness of calcium in binding the cell-wall substances also depends on the availability of free carboxyl groups on the pectic substances; hence there is an interest in enzymatic systems which may either methylate the carboxyls or remove methyl groups. The enzyme which causes the methylation of pectins is not known, but Ordin et al. (1955) found that auxin increases the incorporation of the methyl group from methionine into cell-wall pectins. Cleland (1960*b*) demonstrated that such methylation was inhibited by ethionine, and the lack of a similar inhibition of auxin growth promotions made him doubt that methylation effects were the basis of auxin actions (Cleland, 1963). The removal of methyl esters is modified by auxin: Osborne (1958) showed that pectin methylesterase activity was markedly increased by auxin, and Yoda (1958) demonstrated that esterase increase closely matched the stimulation of growth by the auxin treatment. Glasziou (1957) suggested that auxin may bring about the binding of the esterase onto the cell wall, improving its effectiveness against the pectin esters of the wall even without a net change in activity. This attractive idea has been dimmed somewhat by Jansen et al. (1960), who found that most of the esterase in coleoptiles is associated with the cell wall and that the extent of the association is not altered by auxin.

Ginzburg (1958) has developed the possibility that in addition to the pectic substances, protein materials contribute heavily to the structural properties of the walls of young cells. The extent to which auxin may be involved in proteinaceous aspects of wall structure is not known, though there is good evidence that it can greatly alter both protein turnover and synthesis (Thimann and Loos, 1957).

A second part of the growth reaction, distinguishable from cell-wall plasticization, is a synthesis of new cell-wall materials. Several reports indicate that auxin treatments increase cell-wall components, including cellulose and hemicellulose in pea stems (Christiansen and Thimann, 1950) and hemicelluloses and pectins in oat coleoptiles (Bayley and Setterfield, 1957). Albersheim and Bonner (1959) reported large increases in the synthesis of both cold- and hot-water-soluble pectic substances with auxin treatment, along with increases in the incorporation of radioactivity from glucose substrate. Whether cell-wall synthesis is a part of the basic growth stimulus by auxin is unclear. Numerous investigators have failed to detect cell-wall synthesis associated with growth stimulations of oat (Bennet-Clark, 1956; Ordin and Bonner, 1957) or corn coleoptiles (Davison, 1957).

A third component of the growth reaction is the osmotic uptake of water, which maintains a swelling force against the softening cell wall. Early reports indicated that this might involve a metabolic uptake of water (Bonner et al., 1953), but more recent evidence supports the viewpoint that water-uptake activities are osmotic in nature and not driven by metabolic activity. Two lines of evidence support this osmotic mechanism: Increases in the osmotic values of the ambient solution result in exponential depressions of cell enlargement (Ordin et al., 1955), and as growth proceeds there may be an actual dilution of the osmotic components associated with water uptake (Hackett, 1952). Such a dilution would be expected if growth were initiated by a softening of the wall followed by osmotic entry of water. If this dilution proceeds unchecked, growth will be checked; in experiments with oat coleoptiles, sucrose is a convenient source of renewed osmotic substance for the cytoplasm (Ordin et al., 1955).

The permeability of the cell to water remains unchanged with auxin treatment. This has been determined with heavy-water equilibration experiments by Thimann and Samuel (1955) and Ordin and Bonner (1956).

A dynamic experiment on the action of auxin involves presenting the tissue with some auxin but suspending the growth response temporarily with cold anaerobic conditions or a high osmotic medium. Auxin effects on the cell wall may proceed even though cell enlargement is suspended. The cell-wall effects can then be estimated by allowing the tissues to resume growth and then measuring the relative rate of enlargement of auxin-pretreated and nontreated pieces. This type of experiment was carried out first by Thimann (1954a) using potato disks. Cold entirely suspended both cell enlargement and cell-wall changes; mannitol suspended enlargement but permitted a loosening of the cell wall in response to the applied auxin. Further refining the techniques, Cleland and Bonner (1956) concluded that the softening effect was proportional to the duration of the auxin treatment (Fig. 6-28). This experiment provides evidence that auxin primarily brings about a softening of the cell wall but incorporates some uncertainties with respect to effects of the mannitol on the properties of both the cytoplasm and the cell wall (Bayley and Setterfield, 1957).

Fig. 6-28 | In an effort to assess the effects of auxin on the cell wall without growth, auxin applied to oat coleoptiles in a hypertonic concentration of mannitol can be seen to result in a greater subsequent ability for stretching in growth (*a*), and this increased stretchability may increase with greater duration of auxin exposure (*b*) (Cleland and Bonner, 1956).

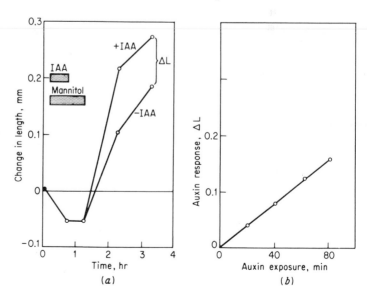

The concept that auxin softens the cell wall, permitting a passive osmotic uptake of water which expands the cell wall, is very attractive. It is not understood how this action may relate to changes in pectic or other structural components of the cell wall.

Growth inhibitions. Since inhibitory auxin effects in plants may be widespread, it is unfortunate that little information is available on the mechanisms by which inhibitions may be obtained. Two important suggestions have been made to explain auxin inhibitions, one by Burström (1955) that auxin catalyzes a hardening of the cell wall and one by Skoog et al. (1942) and later by Foster et al. (1952) that auxin interferes with its own action when two molecules become attached to two points of attachment presumed to be necessary for auxin stimulations.

There is little evidence on the possible hardening of the cell wall in tissues such as the oat coleoptile. The reports of auxin increasing cell-wall plasticity in coleoptiles do not carry the effects into the higher concentration ranges, and experimental evidence does not indicate that high auxin concentrations might decrease plasticity. However, Bonner (1935) found that auxin stimulated a hardening of cellulose in the cell wall of coleoptiles, and increased cellulose synthesis in other tissues has been occasionally reported (Christiansen and Thimann, 1950; Davison, 1957; Burström, 1958). In roots, where auxin inhibitions of growth are exceedingly strong, high auxin concentrations markedly inhibit the formation of cellulose, but the inhibition of growth is not correlated with this effect (Burström, 1958a). Yet Burström (1955) finds that in roots, auxins bring about a foreshortening of cell elongation. He divides the auxin effects into two sectors, one a promotion of the plastic softening of the cell wall similar to the promotive auxin effects on coleoptiles and the other a shortening of the period of actual cell elongation. The latter effect would constitute the inhibitory act of the auxin. Most important in this concept is the separation of the promotion and the inhibitory effects into separate processes with dissimilar responses to auxin.

Skoog et al. (1942) and Foster et al. (1952) approach the inhibition problem from a different point of view, starting with the concept that auxin may act by attaching to some (enzymatic) entity in the cell. In stimulating growth, it may become attached at two positions—hence the dual requirement for an aromatic ring and an acidic side chain for auxin activity. If two auxin molecules become attached at the same site, one molecule on each of the two positions, they would mutually inhibit by preventing the complete double attachment. This situation is represented diagrammatically in Fig. 6-29. The concept is based on inhibition as a modification of the auxin function involved in the growth stimulation.

Growth reactions are generally stimulated by low concentrations of auxin and inhibited by higher ones (Figs. 6-2, 6-23, and 6-29). The two-phase action is not restricted to growth responses but occurs again in geotropic responses in a manner seemingly distinct from any overall growth inhibition (Anker, 1955), in the differentiation of roots (Zimmerman and Hitchcock, 1942), in the inhibition of buds (Skoog, 1939), in the development of flowers (Leopold and Thimann, 1949), and in abscission responses to auxin (Biggs and Leopold, 1958). Might the inhibition effects be extensions of the same action of auxin which invoked the promotion effects, or alternatively might they be related to separate actions? The general occurrence of the two-phase type of response curve makes the former possibility attractive. The self-inhibition scheme used to describe coleoptile growth responses (Foster et al., 1952) is based on such an assumption. But Marinos (1957) showed that the inhibitory auxin concentrations used in the oat-coleoptile experiments may be attributed to toxic responses, including a disruption of the normal cell permeability

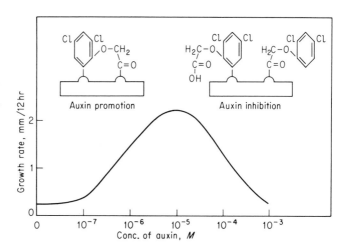

Fig. 6-29 | The self-inhibition concept of auxin-inhibitory actions considers the promotive act to be due to the completion of two attachments of the molecule to reaction sites and the inhibitory act to be due to the completion of each of the two attachments by different auxin molecules; hence the blockage of growth (adapted from Foster et al., 1952).

and a leaching of materials from the cells. Yet Bonner and Foster (1955) showed that their coleoptiles were still capable of maximal auxin stimulation after 6 hr in inhibitory auxin concentrations. The physiological dependability of the auxin inhibitions of coleoptile growth could be debated from either side of the question.

Several lines of evidence make the concept of separate inhibitory actions attractive. Inhibitions are most readily obtained in tissues which are not appreciably promoted by auxins, as in roots and many lower plants. In fact, the inhibitions of roots generally occur at auxin concentrations 10,000 or 100,000 times more dilute than those which promote stem growth (cf. Fig. 6-23). If these inhibitions are attributed to a greater sensitivity of roots to auxin, perhaps there should be a greater promotive response to auxin after the tissue has been washed extensively in a manner which would elute the auxin from the root. In addition, while the structural specificity for inhibition of roots is similar to that for promotion of stems, there is no evidence of similar structural specificity for the *promotive* effects of auxins on roots. Lastly, the concept of a separate inhibitory action is directly supported by the fact that in

two instances auxin inhibitions have been separable in time from promotions. Burström (1958a) separated in time the promotive effects on root growth from the inhibitory effects; similarly, Rubinstein and Leopold (1963) found that the inhibition of abscission represents an effect on an initial stage and that the promotion effects are on a later stage, though both promotive and inhibitory effects have similar structural requirements for auxin action (Chatterjee and Leopold, 1962).

Hellström (1953) noted that the concentration effects of auxins on root inhibition (Fig. 6-3) are strikingly similar to adsorption isotherm curves. This led him to suggest that auxin may be adsorbed onto some entities in the plant, where it produces an inhibition effect. The action of mixtures of auxins and antiauxins can similarly be interpreted as adsorptive competitions, and the differences in activity of auxins on a molar basis can be interpreted as differences in their physical adsorptive properties (Linser, 1956; Kaindl, 1956). The adsorption concept assumes that there are separate adsorptive sites for promotive and inhibitory actions of the growth substances and for growth and differentiation effects (Bottelier, 1959).

Freed et al. (1959) described several 2,4-D effects which suggested an adsorptive action. A physicochemical theory by Veldstra (1956) attempted to account for the molecular-structure requirements for auxin activity on the basis of molecular properties which are compatible with the adsorptive mechanism of attachment.

Conclusion

Three major features of auxins stand out strikingly: (1) the diversity of their effects, (2) the diversity of other chemical controls which may be interwoven with the auxin effects, and (3) the systemic patterns of the auxin effects.

1. The diverse effects of auxins are readily apparent in the large and expanding list of growth and differentiation activities which are influenced by endogenous auxins or modified by exogenous auxins. In addition to cell elongation, tropisms, xylem and root differentiation, apical dominance, and abscission processes, there are other effects on flower initiation and development, pollen-tube growth, fruit set and fruit growth, the formation of compression wood in conifers, tuber and bulb formation, and seed germination. Almost every dynamic part of plant growth and development seems to be affected by auxin. In the individual cell there are effects on the plasticity and elasticity of the wall, on cytoplasmic viscosity, on protoplasmic streaming, on respiration rates, on metabolic pathways, on changes in oxidative states, on the contents of nucleic acids, and on the activities of many enzymes.

Allied with the diversity of physiological effects of auxins is a diversity of molecular species which can bring about the responses. The fact that indoleacetic acid can share its biological effectiveness with such diverse chemicals as naphthaleneacetic acid, 2,4-dichlorophenoxyacetic acid, 2,3,6-trichlorobenzoic acid, and a host of others attests to the wide range of compounds which can act as auxins in plants. Most auxins are able not only to stimulate growth of stems and coleoptiles but also to alter differentiation, abscission, and other developmental effects. The systemic correlative effects are not shared by all auxins, for the restricted ability of many to move in the auxin-transport system limits their participation in normal correlation effects. They are readily swept along in the stream of phloem translocation, but such movement does not conform to the polar qualities of the hormone-transport system.

2. The diversity of chemical agents which may participate in growth regulation is a strikingly repetitive theme. Cell enlargement may be directed by gibberellins, auxins, kinins, and various inhibitors; there are strong growth-promoting effects of chelating agents, fatty acids, and even organic acids. When auxin was first discovered, Went (1928) stated the dictum "Ohne Wuchsstoff, kein Wachstum." Now there is evidence that such a concise, all-or-none dependence on auxin is not a general characteristic of cell enlargement (cf. Kefford and Goldacre, 1961). Many cells do not appear to need auxin for growth. The auxin influences on physiological and developmental processes generally require other substances as cofactors—including the other factors for cell division, cell enlargement, xylem differentiation, root initiation, and apical dominance. The chemicals regulating growth and development are manifold.

3. The systemic patterns of auxin effects in the plant, representing the correlation effects on growth and differentiation, reveal auxin as a chemical messenger influencing many patterns of plant development. A system of chemical messengers is a principal ingredient for the creation of a multicellular organism out of what would otherwise be only a multicellular colony, and auxin is the outstanding known participant in such a control system.

GENERAL REFERENCES

Audus, L. J. 1959. *Plant Growth Substances.* Leonard Hill, Ltd., London. 553 pp.

Bentley, J. A. 1961. Chemistry of the native auxins. *Handbuch Pflanzenphys.*, 14:485–500.

Galston, A. W., and W. S. Hillman. 1961. The degradation of auxin. *Handbuch Pflanzenphys.*, 14:647–670.

Gordon, S. A. 1961. The biogenesis of auxin. *Handbuch Pflanzenphys.*, 14:620–646.

Leopold, A. C. 1955. *Auxins and Plant Growth.* University of California Press, Berkeley, Calif. 354 pp.

Linser, H., and O. Kiermayer. 1957. *Methoden zur Bestimmung pflanzlicher Wuchsstoffe.* Springer-Verlag, Vienna. 181 pp.

Pilet, P. E. 1961. *Les Phytohormones de Croissance.* Masson et Cie, Paris. 774 pp.

REFERENCES CITED

Åberg, B. 1952. On the effects of weak auxins and antiauxins upon root growth. *Physiol. Plantarum*, 5:305–319.

———. 1953. On the interaction of 2,3,5-triiodobenzoic acid and maleic hydrazide with auxins. *Physiol. Plantarum,* 6:277–291.

——— and E. Jonsson. 1955. Studies on plant growth regulators. XI. Experiments with pea roots, including some observations of the destruction of indoleacetic acid by different types of roots. *Kgl. Lantbruks-Hogskol. Ann.*, 21:401–416.

Albersheim, P., and J. Bonner. 1959. Metabolism and hormonal control of pectic substances. *J. Biol. Chem.*, 234:3105–3108.

Andreae, W. A., and N. E. Good. 1955. The formation of indoleaspartic acid in pea seedlings. *Plant Physiol.*, 30:380–382.

——— and ———. 1957. Studies on 3–indoleacetic acid metabolism. IV. Conjugation with aspartic acid and ammonia as processes in the metabolism of carboxylic acids. *Plant Physiol.*, 32:566–572.

——— and M. W. van Ysselstein. 1960. Studies of indoleacetic acid metabolism. VI. Indoleacetic acid uptake and metabolism by pea roots and epicotyls. *Plant Physiol.*, 35:225–232.

Anker, L. 1955. The auxin concentration rule for the geotropism of *Avena* coleoptiles. *Acta Botan. Neerl.*, 5:335–341.

Audus, L. J. 1959. *Plant Growth Substances.* Leonard Hill, Ltd., London. 553 pp.

Bayley, S. T., and G. Setterfield. 1957. The influence of mannitol and auxin on growth of cell walls in *Avena* coleoptiles. *Ann. Botany (London)*, 21:633–641.

Bennet-Clark, T. A. 1956. Salt accumulation and mode of action of auxin, pp. 284–294. In R. L. Wain and F. Wightman (eds.), *Chemistry and Mode of Action of Plant Growth Substances.* Butterworth Scientific Publications, London.

Bentley, J. A. 1950. Growth-regulating effect of certain organic compounds. *Nature*, 65:449.

———. 1958. The naturally-occurring auxins and inhibitors. *Ann. Rev. Plant Physiol.*, 9:47–80.

———. 1961. Chemistry of the native auxins. *Handbuch Pflanzenphys.*, 14:485–500.

———, K. R. Farrar, S. Housley, G. F. Smith, and W. C. Taylor. 1956. Some chemical and physiological properties of 3-indolylpyruvic acid. *Biochem. J.*, 64:44–49.

——— and S. Housley. 1952. Studies on plant growth hormones. I. *J. Exptl. Botany*, 3:393–405.

Biale, J. B., and F. F. Halma. 1937. The use of heteroauxin in rooting of subtropicals. *Proc. Am. Soc. Hort. Sci.*, 35:443–447.

Biggs, R. H., and A. C. Leopold. 1958. The two-phase action of auxin on abscission. *Am. J. Botany*, 45:547–551.

Bitancourt, A. A., K. Schwartz, and R. Dierberger. 1954. La nature des auxines des tumeurs vegetales. *Compt. Rend. Soc. Biol. (Paris)*, 148:822–825.

Blommaert, K. L. J. 1954. Growth and inhibiting substances in relation to the rest period of the potato tuber. *Nature*, 174:970.

Bonner, J. 1935. Zum Mechanismus der Zellstreckung auf grund der Micellarlehre. *Jahrb. Wiss. Bot.*, 82:377–412.

———. 1949. Further experiments on flowering in *Xanthium*. *Botan. Gaz.*, 100:625–627.

———. 1960. The mechanical analysis of auxin-induced growth. *Z. Schweiz. Forstv.*, 30:141–159.

———, R. S. Bandurski, and A. Millerd. 1953. Linkage of respiration to auxin-induced uptake. *Physiol. Plantarum*, 6:511–522.

——— and R. J. Foster. 1955. The growth-time relationships of the auxin-induced growth in *Avena* coleoptile sections. *J. Exptl. Botany*, 6:293–302.

Bottelier, H. P. 1959. On the relation between auxin concentration and effect in different tests. *Proc. Koninkl. Ned. Akad. Wetenschap.*, C, 62:493–504.

Brauner, L., and M. Hasman. 1947. Weitere Untersuchungen über die anomale Komponente des osmotischen Potentials lebenden Pflanzenzellen. *Rev. Fac. Sci. Forest. Univ. Istanbul*, B,12:210.

Briggs, W. R., and P. M. Ray. 1956. An auxin inactivation system involving tyrosinase. *Plant Physiol.*, 31:165–167.

Brown, C. L. 1958. Studies in the auxin physiology of longleaf pine seedlings, pp. 511–525. In K. V. Thimann (ed.), *The Physiology of Forest Trees*. The Ronald Press Company, New York.

——— and R. H. Wetmore. 1959. Auxin transport in the long shoots of pine. *Am. J. Botany*, 46:586–590.

Bulard, C., and A. C. Leopold. 1960. Activité auxinique de l'acide 5-hydroxyindolacetique. *Compt. Rend. Soc. Biol. (Paris)*, 154:1432–1434.

Burström, H. 1955. Activity of plant growth regulators. *Ann. Appl. Biol.*, 42:158–161.

———. 1958a. The influence of growth regulators on the composition of the cell wall. *Kgl. Fysiograf. Sallskap. Lund Forh.*, 28:53–64.

———. 1958b. Influence of plasmolysis and inhibitors on the sucrose inversion of wheat. *Physiol. Plantarum*, 11:771–781.

Chatterjee, S., and A. C. Leopold. 1962. Auxin structure and abscission activity. *Plant Physiol.*, 38:268–273.

Cholodny, N. 1924. Über die hormonale Wirkung der Organspitze bei der geotropischen Krümmung. *Ber. Deut. Botan. Ges.*, 42:356–362.

Christiansen, G. S., and K. V. Thimann. 1950. The metabolism of stem tissue during growth and its inhibition. I. Carbohydrates. *Arch. Biochem.*, 26:230–247.

Cleland, R. 1958. A separation of auxin-induced cell wall loosening into its plastic and elastic components. *Physiol. Plantarum*, 11:599–609.

———. 1960a. Effect of auxin upon loss of calcium from cell walls. *Plant Physiol.*, 35:581–584.

———. 1960b. Auxin-induced methylation in maize. *Nature*, 185:44.

———. 1961. The relation between auxin and metabolism. *Handbuch Pflanzenphys.*, 14:754–783.

———. 1963. Independence of effects of auxin on cell wall methylation and elongation. *Plant Physiol.*, 38:12–18.

——— and J. Bonner. 1956. The residual effect of auxin on the cell wall. *Plant Physiol.*, 31:350–354.

Cooil, B. J., and J. Bonner. 1956. The nature of growth inhibition by calcium in the *Avena* coleoptile. *Planta*, 48:696–723.

Coombe, B. G. 1960. Relationship of growth and development to changes in sugars, auxins and gibberellins in fruit of seeded and seedless varieties of *Vitis*. *Plant Physiol.*, 35:241–250.

Crane, J. C., M. V. Bradley, and L. C. Luckwill. 1959. Auxins in parthenocarpic and non-parthenocarpic figs. *J. Hort. Sci.*, 34:142–153.

Dannenburg, W. N., and J. L. Liverman.

1957. Conversion of tryptophan to indole-acetic acid by watermelon tissue slices. *Plant Physiol.*, 32:263–268.

Darwin, C. 1897. *The Power of Movement in Plants*. D. Appleton & Company, Inc., New York.

Davison, R. M. 1957. Studies on cell elongation with respect to geotropic effects. Ph.D. Diss., Univ. of London (cited by Cleland, 1961).

du Buy, H. G., and R. A. Olson. 1940. The relation between respiration, protoplasmic streaming, and auxin transport in the *Avena* coleoptile. *Am. J. Botany*, 27: 401–414.

Fang, S. C., and J. S. Butts. 1957. Studies of carboxyl labeled indoleacetic acid in plants. *Plant Physiol.*, 32:253–259.

Foster, R. J., D. H. McRae, and J. Bonner. 1952. Auxin induced growth inhibition: a natural consequence of two point attachment. *Proc. Natl. Acad. Sci. U.S.*, 38:1014–1022.

Freed, V. H., F. J. Reithel, and L. F. Remmert. 1961. Some physicochemical aspects of synthetic auxins with respect to their mode of action, pp. 289–303. In R. M. Klein (ed.), *Plant Growth Regulation*. Iowa State University Press, Ames, Iowa.

Funke, H., and H. Söding. 1948. Über das Wuchsstoff-Hemmstoffsystem der Hafer-Koleoptile und der Kartoffelknolle. *Planta*, 36:341–370.

Furuya, M., and K. Soma. 1957. The effects of auxins on the development of bean embryos cultivated *in vitro*. *J. Fac. Sci. (Tokyo)*, 7:163–198.

Galston, A. W., and R. S. Baker. 1951a. Studies on the physiology of light action. III. Light activation of a flavoprotein enzyme by reversal of the naturally occurring inhibition. *Am. J. Botany*, 38:190–195.

——— and ———. 1951b. Studies on the physiology of light action. IV. Light enhancement of auxin-induced growth in green peas. *Plant Physiol.*, 26:311–317.

———, J. Bonner, and R. S. Baker. 1953. Flavoprotein and peroxidase as components of the indoleacetic acid oxidase system of peas. *Arch. Biochem. Biophys.*, 49:456–470.

——— and M. E. Hand. 1949. Studies on the physiology of light action. I. Auxin and the light inhibition of growth. *Am. J. Botany*, 36:85–94.

——— and W. S. Hillman. 1961. The degradation of auxin. *Handbuch Pflanzenphys.*, 14:647–670.

Ginzburg, B. Z. 1958. Evidence for a protein component in the middle lamella of plant tissue. *Nature*, 181:398–400.

Glasziou, K. T. 1957. The effect of indolylacetic acid on the binding of pectin methylesterase to the cell walls of tobacco pith. *Australian J. Biol. Sci.*, 10: 337–341.

Gmelin, R., and A. I. Virtanen. 1961. Glucobrassicin: the precursor of indolylacetylnitrile, ascorbigen and SCN in *Brassica oleracea*. *Suomen Kemistilehti*, 34:15–18.

——— and ———. 1962. Neoglucobrassicin, ein zweiter SCN-Precursor vom Indoltyp in *Brassica*-Arten. *Acta Chem. Scand.*, 16:1378–1384.

Good, N. E., and W. A. Andreae. 1957. Malonyltryptophan in higher plants. *Plant Physiol.*, 32:561–566.

———, W. A. Andreae, and M. W. H. Ysselstein. 1956. Studies on 3-indoleacetic acid metabolism. II. Some products of the metabolism of exogenous indoleacetic acid in plant tissue. *Plant Physiol.*, 31:231–235.

Goodwin, R. H. 1937. The role of auxin in leaf development in *Solidago* sp. *Am. J. Botany*, 24:43–50.

Gordon, S. A. 1946. Auxin-protein complexes of the wheat grain. *Am. J. Botany*, 33: 160–169.

———. 1956. Auxin biosynthesis: a cytoplasmic locus of radiation damage, pp. 44–47. In *Progress in Radiobiology*, Oliver and Boyd, Ltd., London.

————. 1961. The biogenesis of auxin. *Handbuch Pflanzenphys.*, 14:620–646.

———— and F. S. Nieva. 1949. Biosynthesis of auxin in the vegetative pineapple. I. *Arch. Biochem.*, 20:356–366.

Gorter, C. J. 1932. Groeistofproblemen bej Wortels. Ph.D. Diss., Univ. of Utrecht.

Gregory, F. G., and C. R. Hancock. 1955. The rate of transport of natural auxin in woody shoots. *Ann. Botany (London)*, 19:451–465.

Gunckel, J. E., and K. V. Thimann. 1949. Studies of development in long shoots and short shoots of *Ginkgo biloba* L. III. Auxin production in shoot growth. *Am. J. Botany*, 36:145–151.

Haagen-Smit, A. J., W. B. Dandliker, S. H. Wittwer, and A. E. Murneek. 1946. Isolation of indoleacetic acid from immature corn kernels. *Am. J. Botany*, 33:118–119.

———— and F. W. Went. 1935. A physiological analysis of the growth substance. *Proc. Koninkl. Ned. Akad. Wetenschap.*, 38:852–857.

Hackett, D. P. 1952. The osmotic change during the auxin-induced water uptake by potato tissue. *Plant Physiol.*, 27:279–284.

Hatcher, E. S. J. 1959. Auxin relations of the woody shoot. *Ann. Botany (London)*, 23:409–423.

Hellström, N. 1953. An attempt to explain the interaction of auxin and anti-auxin in root growth by an adsorption mechanism. *Acta Chem. Scand.*, 7:461–468.

Hemberg, T. 1955. Studies on the balance between free and bound auxin in germinating maize. *Physiol. Plantarum*, 8:418–432.

Henbest, H. B., E. R. H. Jones, and G. F. Smith. 1953. Isolation of a new plant-growth hormone, 3-indolylacetonitrile. *J. Chem. Soc.*, 776:3796–3801.

Hertel, R. 1962. Der Auxintransport in der Koleoptile von *Zea mays*. Ph.D. Diss., Ludwig Maximillian Univ., Munich. 72 pp.

———— and A. C. Leopold. 1963. Versuche zur Analyse des Auxintransports in der Koleoptile von *Zea mays*. *Planta*, 59:535–562.

Heyn, A. N. J. 1931. Der Mechanismus der Zellstreckung. *Rec. Trav. Bot. Neerl.*, 28:113–244.

————. 1940. The physiology of cell elongation. *Botan. Rev.*, 6:515–574.

Hinman, R. L., C. Bauman, and J. Lang. 1961. The conversion of indoleacetic acid to 3·methylene oxindole in the presence of peroxidase. *Biochem. Biophys. Res. Commun.*, 5:250–254.

Hinsvark, O. N., W. H. Houff, S. H. Wittwer, and H. M. Sell. 1954. The extraction and colorimetric estimation of indoleacetic acid and its esters in developing corn kernels. *Plant Physiol.*, 29:107–108.

Hirata, S. 1954. Studies on the phytohormone in the malformed portion of the diseased plants. I. The relation between the growth rate and the amount of free auxin in the fungous galls and virus-infected plants. *Ann. Phytopathol. Soc. Japan*, 19:33–38.

Irvine, V. C. 1938. Studies in growth promoting substance related to x-radiation and photoperiodism. *Univ. Colorado Studies*, 26:69–70.

Jacobs, W. P. 1950a. Auxin transport in the hypocotyl of *Phaseolus vulgaris*. *Am. J. Botany*, 37:248–254.

————. 1950b. Control of elongation in the bean hypocotyl by the ability of the tip to transport auxin. *Am. J. Botany*, 37:551–555.

————. 1954. Acropetal auxin transport and xylem regeneration: a quantitative study. *Am. Naturalist*, 88:327–337.

Jansen, E. F., R. Jang, P. Albersheim, and J. Bonner. 1960. Pectic metabolism of growing cell walls. *Plant Physiol.*, 35:87–97.

Jones, E. R. H., H. B. Henbest, G. F. Smith, and J. A. Bentley. 1952. 3-Indolylacetonitrile: a naturally occurring plant growth hormone. *Nature*, 169:485.

Kaindl, K. 1956. The action-concentration

curves of mixtures of growth promoting and growth inhibiting substances, pp. 159–164. In R. L. Wain and F. Wightman (eds.), *Chemistry and Mode of Action of Plant Growth Substances.* Butterworth Scientific Publications, London.

Kamerbeek, G. A. 1956. Peroxydase content of dwarf types and giant types of plants. *Acta Botan. Neerl.,* 5:257–263.

Kaper, J. M., and H. Veldstra. 1958. On the metabolism of tryptophan by *Agrobacterium tumefaciens. Biochim. Biophys. Acta,* 30:401–420.

Kefford, N. P. 1959. Extension growth activities of some cyclopropane derivatives, a new class of antiauxin. *Australian J. Biol. Sci.,* 12:257–262.

———, J. Brockwell, and J. A. Zwar. 1960. The symbiotic synthesis of auxin by legumes and nodule bacteria and its role in nodule development. *Australian J. Biol. Sci.,* 13:456–467.

——— and P. L. Goldacre. 1961. The changing concept of auxin. *Am. J. Botany,* 48:643–650.

Klämbt, H. D. 1959. 2-OH Indoleessigsaure in pflanzliches Indolederivat. *Naturwissenschaften,* 46:649.

———. 1960. Indol-3-acetylasparginsaure, ein naturlich vorkommenden Indolderivat. *Naturwissenschaften,* 17:398.

———. 1961. Wachsstumsinduktion und Wuchsstoffmetabolismus in Weizencoleoptilzylinder. II. *Planta,* 56:618–631.

Koepfli, J. B., K. V. Thimann, and F. W. Went. 1938. Phytohormones: structure and physiological activity. *J. Biol. Chem.,* 122:763–780.

Kögl, F., A. J. Haagen-Smit, and H. Erxleben. 1934. Über ein neues auxin ("Heteroauxin") aus Harn. XI. *Z. Physiol. Chem.,* 228:90–103.

——— and D. G. F. R. Kostermans. 1934. Hetero-auxin als Stoffwechselprodukt niederer pflanzlicher Organismen. XIII. *Z. Physiol. Chem.,* 228:113–121.

Konishi, M. 1956. Studies on development of flowering stalks in long-day plants in relation to auxin metabolism. *Mem. Coll. Agr. Kyoto Univ. Botan. Ser.,* 3:1–70.

Kuraishi, S. 1959. Effect of kinetin analogs on leaf growth. *Sci. Papers Coll. Gen. Educ. Univ. Tokyo,* 9:67–104.

Kutacek, M., C. Prochazka, and D. Grunberger. 1960. Biosynthesis of ascorbigen, indoleacetonitrile, indolecarboxylic acid from tryptophan-3C^{14} in *Brassica oleracea. Nature,* 187:61–62.

Larsen, P. 1944. 3-Indole acetaldehyde as a growth hormone in higher plants. *Dansk Botan. Ark.,* 11:1–132.

———. 1951. Enzymatic conversion of indole acetaldehyde and naphthalene acetaldehyde to auxins. *Plant Physiol.,* 26:697–707.

La Rue, C. D. 1936. Effect of auxin on abscission of petioles. *Proc. Natl. Acad. Sci. U.S.,* 22:254–259.

Leopold, A. C. 1955. *Auxins and Plant Growth.* University of California Press, Berkeley, Calif. 354 pp.

———. 1958. Auxin uses in the control of flowering and fruiting. *Ann. Rev. Plant Physiol.,* 9:281–310.

———. 1963a. Kinins and the regulation of leaf aging, pp. 705–718. *Colloq. Reg. Nat. Croiss. Veg.*

———. 1963b. The polarity of auxin transport. *Brookhaven Symp. Biol.,* 16:218–234.

———. 1964. Plant hormones, pp. 1–66. In G. Pincus and K. V. Thimann (eds.), *The Hormones.* Academic Press, Inc., New York.

——— and F. S. Guernsey. 1953. Auxin polarity in the *Coleus* plant. *Botan. Gaz.,* 115:147–154.

——— and W. H. Klein. 1952. Maleic hydrazide as an anti-auxin. *Physiol. Plantarum,* 5:91–99.

——— and S. L. Lam. 1961. Polar transport of three auxins, pp. 411–418. In R. M. Klein (ed.), *Plant Growth Regulation.* Iowa State University Press, Ames, Iowa.

——— and ———. 1962. The auxin transport gradient. *Physiol. Plantarum*, 15: 631–638.

———— and T. H. Plummer. 1961. Auxin-phenol complexes. *Plant Physiol.*, 35: 589–592.

———— and K. V. Thimann. 1949. The effect of auxin on flower initiation. *Am. J. Botany*, 36:342–347.

Linser, H. 1956. Chemical configuration and action of different growth substances and inhibitors, pp. 141–158. In R. L. Wain and F. Wightman (eds.), *Chemistry and Mode of Action of Plant Growth Substances.* Butterworth Scientific Publications, London.

Luckwill, L. C. 1949. Fruit drop in the apple in relation to seed development. *Ann. Appl. Biol.*, 36:567–568.

McCready, C. C. 1963. Movement of growth regulators in plants. I. Polar transport of 2,4-D. *New Phytologist*, 62: 3–18.

MacDougal, D. T., and J. Dufrenoy. 1944. Mycorrhizal symbiosis in *Aplectrum, Corallorhiza* and *Pinus. Plant Physiol.*, 19:440–465.

McRae, D. H., and J. Bonner. 1953*a*. Chemical structure and anti-auxin activity. *Physiol. Plantarum*, 6:485–510.

———— and ————. 1953*b*. Diortho substituted phenoxyacetic acids as anti-auxins. *Plant Physiol.*, 27:834–838.

Mai, G. 1934. Korrelationsuntersuchungen an entspreiteten Blattstielen mit lebender Orchideenpollinien als Wuchstoffquelle. *Jahrb. Wiss. Bot.*, 79:681–713.

Marinos, N. G. 1957. Responses of *Avena* coleoptile sections to high concentration of auxin. *Australian J. Biol. Sci.*, 10:147–163.

Masuda, Y. 1960. Physiological significance of ribonucleic acid in the growth promoting action of auxin. *J. Inst. Polytech. Osaka City Univ.*, 11:1–23.

Miller, C. O. 1951. Investigations on the physiology of leaf expansion. Ph.D. Diss., Ohio State Univ.

Mirov, N. T. 1941. Distribution of growth hormone in shoots of two species of pine. *J. Forestry*, 39:457–464.

Muir, R. M., and C. Hansch. 1955. Chemical constitution as related to growth regulator action. *Ann. Rev. Plant Physiol.*, 6: 157–176.

Niedergang-Kamien, E., and A. C. Leopold. 1957. Inhibitors of polar auxin transport. *Physiol. Plantarum*, 10:29–38.

———— and F. Skoog. 1956. Studies on polarity and auxin transport in plants. I. Modification of polarity and auxin transport by triiodobenzoic acid. *Physiol. Plantarum*, 9:60–73.

Nitsch, J. P. 1950. Growth and morphogenesis of the strawberry as related to auxin. *Am. J. Botany*, 37:211–215.

———— and C. Nitsch. 1958. Activité de quelques composes indoliques sur la test mesocotyle. *Bull. Soc. Botan. France*, 105: 482–490.

————, C. Pratt, C. Nitsch, and N. J. Shanlis. 1960. Natural growth substances in Concord and Concord seedless grapes. *Am. J. Botany*, 47:566–576.

Oaks, A., and M. Shaw. 1960. An indole-acetic acid oxidase system in the mycelium of *Milampsora lini* (Pers) Lev. *Can. J. Botany*, 38:761–767.

Ordin, L., and J. Bonner. 1956. Permeability of *Avena* coleoptile sections to water measured by diffusion of deuterium hydroxide. *Plant Physiol.*, 31:53–57.

———— and ————. 1957. Effect of galactose on growth and metabolism of *Avena* coleoptile sections. *Plant Physiol.*, 32: 212–215.

————, R. Cleland, and J. Bonner. 1955. Influence of auxin on cell wall metabolism. *Proc. Natl. Acad. Sci. U.S.*, 41: 1023–1029.

Osborne, D. J. 1958. Changes in the distribution of pectin methylesterase across leaf abscission zones of *Phaseolus vulgaris. J. Explt. Botany*, 9:446–457.

————, G. E. Blackman, S. Novoa, F. Sudzuke, and R. G. Powell. 1955. The physiological activity of 2,6-substituted phenoxyacetic acids. *J. Exptl. Botany,* 6: 392–408.

———, G. E. Blackman, R. G. Powell, F. Sudzuke, and S. Novoa. 1954. Growth-regulating activity of certain 2,6-substituted phenoxyacetic acids. *Nature,* 174: 742.

Overbeek, J. van, R. Blondeau, and V. Horne. 1951. Transcinnamic acid as an anti-auxin. *Am. J. Botany,* 38:589–595.

———, E. S. Vasquez, and S. A. Gordon. 1947. Free and bound auxin in the vegetative pineapple plant. *Am. J. Botany,* 34:266–270.

Paàl, A. 1919. Über phototropische Reizleitung. *Jahrb. Wiss. Bot.,* 58:406–458.

Pilet, P. E. 1951. Contribution a l'étude des hormones de croissance (auxines) dans la racine de *Lens culinaris. Mem. Soc. Vaudoise Sci. Nat.,* 10:137–244.

———. 1952. Probleme hormonal concernant l'*Endophyllum sempervivi* parasite du *Sempervivum tectorum. Bull. Soc. Botan. Suisse,* 62:269–274.

———. 1960. Le catabolisme auxinique. *Bull. Soc. Franc. Physiol. Vegetale,* 6: 119–137.

——— and S. Meylan. 1953. Polarité électrique, auxines et physiologie des racines du *Lens culinaris Medikus. Bull. Soc. Botan. Suisse,* 63:430–465.

Platt, R. S. 1954. The inactivation of auxin in normal and tumorous tissue. *Colloque Internat. Physiol. Cultures Tissus Vegetaux (Briaçon),* pp. 349–359.

Racusen, D. 1955. Formation of indole-3-aldehyde by indoleacetic oxidase. *Arch. Biochem.,* 58:508–509.

Ray, P. M. 1958. Destruction of auxin. *Ann. Rev. Plant Physiol.,* 9:81–118.

Redemann, C. T., S. H. Wittwer, and H. M. Sell. 1951. The characterization of indole-3-acetic acid and its esters. *J. Am. Chem. Soc.,* 73:2957.

Rubinstein, B., and A. C. Leopold. 1963. Analysis of the auxin control of bean leaf abscission. *Plant Physiol.,* 38:262–267.

Schwarz, K., and A. A. Bitancourt. 1957.

Paper chromatography of unstable substances. *Science,* 126:607–608.

Scott, F. M., M. R. Schroeder, and F. M. Turrell, 1948. Development of abscission in the leaf of Valencia orange. *Botan. Gaz.,* 109:381–411.

Scott, T. K., and W. R. Briggs. 1960. Auxin relationships in the Alaska pea. *Am. J. Botany,* 47:492–499.

Sequeira, L., and T. A. Steeves. 1954. Auxin inactivation and its relation to leaf drop caused by the fungus *Omphalia flavida. Plant Physiol.,* 29:11–16.

Shantz, E. M., and F. C. Steward. 1957. The growth stimulating substances in extracts of immature corn grain: a progress report. *Plant Physiol.,* 32:viii.

Shaw, M., and A. R. Hawkins. 1958. The physiology of host-parasite relations. *Can. J. Botany,* 36:1–16.

Shibaoka, H., and H. Imaseki. 1957. Identification of growth inhibitors in *Helianthus* leaves. *Botan. Mag. (Tokyo),* 70: 362.

Shoji, K., F. T. Addicott, and W. A. Swets. 1951. Auxin in relation to leaf blade abscission. *Plant Physiol.,* 26:189–191.

Skoog, F. 1939. Experiments on bud inhibition with indoleacetic acid. *Am. J. Botany,* 26:702–707.

——— and C. O. Miller. 1957. Chemical regulation of growth and organ formation in plant tissues cultured *in vivo. Symp. Soc. Exptl. Biol.,* 11:118–131.

———, C. L. Schneider, and P. Malan. 1942. Interactions of auxins in growth and inhibition. *Am. J. Botany,* 29:568–576.

Stahly, E. A., and A. H. Thompson. 1959. Auxin levels of developing Halehaven peach ovules. *Maryland Agr. Expt. Sta. Bull.,* A-104. 22 pp.

Steeves, T. A., and W. R. Briggs. 1960. Morphogenetic studies on *Osmunda cinnamomea* L.: the auxin relationship of expanding fronds. *J. Exptl. Botany,* 11: 45–67.

Stowe, B. R., and K. V. Thimann. 1953.

Indolepyruvic acid in maize. *Nature*, 172: 764.

Stutz, R. E. 1957. The indoleacetic acid oxidase of *Lupinus albus. Plant Physiol.*, 32:31–39.

Tagawa, T., and J. Bonner. 1957. Mechanical properties of the *Avena* coleoptile as related to auxin and to ionic interactions. *Plant Physiol.*, 32:207–212.

Tang, Y. W., and J. Bonner. 1947. The enzymatic inactivation of indoleacetic acid. I. *Arch. Biochem. Biophys.*, 13:11–25.

Teubner, F. G. 1953. Identification of the auxins present in apple endosperm. *Science*, 118:418.

Thimann, K. V. 1934. Studies on the growth hormone of plants. VI. The distribution of the growth substances in plant tissues. *J. Gen. Physiol.*, 18:23–34.

——. 1935. On the plant growth hormone produced by *Rhizopus suinus. J. Biol. Chem.*, 109:279–291.

——. 1936*a.* Auxins and the growth of roots. *Am. J. Botany*, 23:561–569.

——. 1936*b.* On the physiology of the formation of nodules on legume roots. *Proc. Natl. Acad. Sci. U.S.*, 22:511–514.

——. 1937. On the nature of inhibitions caused by auxin. *Am. J. Botany*, 24:407–412.

——. 1952. The role of ortho substitutions in the synthetic auxins. *Plant Physiol.*, 27:392–404.

——. 1954*a.* Growth in plant tissues. *Am. Scientist*, 42:589–606.

——. 1954*b.* Correlations of growth by humoral influences. *Proc. Intern. Botan. Congr. 8th*, 11:114–128.

——. 1958*a.* Auxin activity of some indole derivatives. *Plant Physiol.*, 33:311–321.

——. 1958*b.* Inter-relations between plants and bacteria: the borderland between epiphytism, parasitism and symbiosis. *Trans. Bose Res. Inst. (Calcutta)*, 22:69–75.

—— and G. M. Loos. 1957. Protein synthesis during water uptake by tuber tissue. *Plant Physiol.*, 32:274–279.

—— and S. Mahadevan. 1958. Enzymatic hydrolysis of indoleacetonitrile. *Nature*, 181:1466–1467.

—— and E. W. Samuel. 1955. The permeability of potato tissue to water. *Proc. Natl. Acad. Sci. U.S.*, 41:1029–1033.

—— and F. Skoog. 1934. Inhibition of bud development and other functions of growth substances in *Vicia faba. Proc. Roy. Soc. (London)*, B, 114:317–339.

—— and ——. 1940. The extraction of auxin from plant tissues. *Am. J. Botany*, 27:951–960.

—— and N. Takahashi. 1961. Interrelationships between metallic ions and auxin action, pp. 363–380. In R. M. Klein (ed.), *Plant Growth Regulation.* Iowa State University Press, Ames, Iowa.

—— and F. W. Went. 1934. On the chemical nature of the root-forming hormone. *Proc. Kon. Akad. Wetensch.*, Amsterdam, 37:456–459.

Tomaszewski, M. 1959. Chlorogenic acid phenolase as a system inactivating auxin isolated from some leaves of some *Prunus* species. *Bull. Acad. Polon. Sci.*, 7:127–130.

——. 1961. A relationship between the phenol-phenolase system and the processes of respiration, formation of lignin and auxin inactivation. *Arboretum Kornickie*, 6:169–226.

Tonzig, S. 1950. The significance of ascorbic acid in plants. *Proc. Intern. Botan. Congr. 7th*, 755–756.

Torrey, J. G. 1956. Physiology of root elongation. *Ann. Rev. Plant Physiol.*, 7:237–266.

Udenfriend, S., E. Titus, H. Weissbach, and R. E. Peterson. 1956. Biogenesis and metabolism of 5-hydroxyindole compounds. *J. Biol. Chem.*, 219:335–344.

Vardar, Y., and B. Tozun. 1958. Role played by decapitation in growth and differentiation of *Lens culinaris* roots. *Am. J. Botany*, 45:714–718.

Veldstra, H. 1956. On form and function of plant growth substances, pp. 117–133. In R. L. Wain and F. Wightman (eds.), *Chemistry and Mode of Action of Plant Growth Substances*. Butterworth Scientific Publications, London.

Vlitos, A. J., and W. Meudt. 1954. The role of auxin in plant flowering. III. Free indole acids in short-day plants grown under photoinductive and nonphotoinductive daylengths. *Contrib. Boyce Thompson Inst.*, 17:413–417.

Wagenknecht, A. C., and R. H. Burris. 1950. IAA inactivating enzymes from bean roots and pea seedlings. *Arch. Biochem. Biophys.*, 25:30–53.

Waygood, E. R., A. Oaks, and G. A. Maclachlan. 1956. On the mechanism of indoleacetic acid oxidation by wheat leaf enzymes. *Can. J. Botany*, 34:54–59.

Weij, H. G. van der. 1932. Der Mechanismus des Wuchsstofftransportes. *Rec. Trav. Bot. Neerl.*, 29:379–496.

Went, F. W. 1928. Wuchsstoff und Wachstum. *Rec. Trav. Bot. Neerl.*, 25:1–116.

———. 1935. Hormones involved in root formation. *Proc. Intern. Botan. Congr. 6th*, 2:267–269.

———. 1942. Growth, auxin and tropisms in decapitated *Avena* coleoptiles. *Plant Physiol.*, 17:236–249.

——— and K. V. Thimann. 1937. *Phytohormones*. The Macmillan Company, New York. 294 pp.

——— and R. White. 1939. Experiments on the transport of auxin. *Botan. Gaz.*, 100:465–484.

Wetmore, R. H. 1955. Differentiation of xylem in plants. *Science*, 121:626–627.

——— and W. P. Jacobs. 1953. Studies on abscission: the inhibiting effect of auxin. *Am. J. Botany*, 40:272–276.

Wolf, F. T. 1952. The production of indoleacetic acid by *Ustilago zeae* and its possible significance in tumor formation. *Proc. Natl. Acad. Sci. U.S.*, 38:106–111.

———. 1956. The production of indole acetic acid by the cedar apple rust fungus, and its identification by paper chromatography. *Phytopathol. Z.*, 26:219–223.

Wright, S. T. C. 1956. Studies of fruit development in relation to plant hormones. III. Auxins in relation to fruit morphogenesis. *J. Hort. Sci.*, 31:196–211.

Yoda, S. 1958. Auxin action and pectic enzyme. *Botan. Mag. (Tokyo)*, 71:207–213.

Younis, A. F. 1953. Experiments on the growth and geotropism of roots. I. Technique for achieving regular growth, and a study of the effects of decapitation and reheading on the growth of *Vicia faba* roots. *J. Exptl. Botany*, 5:357–372.

Zenk, M. H. 1961. Indoleacetylglucose: a new compound in the metabolism of indoleacetic acid in plants. *Nature*, 191:493–494.

———. 1962. Aufnahme und Stoffwechsel von Naphthylessigsaure durch Erbsenepictoyle. *Planta*, 58:75–94.

———. 1963. Isolation, biosynthesis and function of indoleacetic acid conjugates, pp. 241–250. *Colloq. Reg. Nat. Croiss. Veg.*

——— and G. Müller. 1963. In vivo destruction of exogenously applied indoleacetic acid as influenced by naturally occurring phenolic acids. *Nature*, 200:761–763.

Zimmerman, P. W., and A. E. Hitchcock. 1941. Formative effects induced by naphthoxyacetic acid. *Contrib. Boyce Thompson Inst.*, 12:1–14.

——— and ———. 1942. Substitued phenoxy and benzoid acid growth substances and the relation of structure to physiological activity. *Contrib. Boyce Thompson Inst.*, 12:321–343.

———, A. E. Hitchcock, and F. Wilcoxen. 1936. Several esters as plant hormones. *Contrib. Boyce Thompson Inst.*, 8:105–112.

7 | Gibberellins

About the same time that auxins were recognized as chemical constituents of plants, work in Japan led to the discovery of another group of growth substances, the gibberellins. Kurosawa (1926) was studying a disease of rice plants caused by the fungus *Gibberella fujikoroi* which caused a characteristic excessive growth of the rice plant. He found that extracts of the fungus applied to the intact plant could bring about the growth stimulations. The separation of this growth regulator closely preceded the first separation of auxin from plants in 1928. The heat-stable substance eluded purification for several years, partly because of the presence in the extract of an inhibiting substance, fusarinic acid (cf. Chap. 9), but in 1935, Yabuta crystallized the compound and named it *gibberellin*. While the auxins were widely heralded through the next two decades, the research on gibberellins proceeded in Japan almost unnoticed by the Western world.

In the early 1950s there was a sudden widespread interest in the gibberellins. In addition to the Japanese work headed by Hayashi and Sumiki, active centers of interest sprang up in England under Brian and in the United States under Stodola and others. The unusual ability of gibberellin (GA) to stimulate plant growth (Fig. 7-1) finally attracted the attention of physiologists, and soon the molecular structures of several gibberellins were clarified (Cross, 1954). Nine separate gibberellins have been isolated, six from the fungus and three others from higher plants. One GA is found in both the fungus and in higher plants (Cross et al., 1961).

Gibberellin was discovered because of its ability to increase growth in plants, and in this quality its effects are more impressive than those of auxins. Application of gibberellin to grasses such as rice causes both leaf and stem elongation. In the broad-leaved plants, the stimulations of stem growth are dramatic. A cabbage may elongate to a height of 6 ft, and a bush bean may become a climbing pole bean (Fig. 7-2). The stimulative effects on stems are more pronounced with intact plants than with excised pieces. However, the stimulative effects on leaves are often greater for excised than for intact ones.

Whether the gibberellin effect is due to a stimulation of cell division or of cell enlargement has been extensively debated. Early investigators found no particular increase in cell size and deduced that the stimulation was one of cell division (Sawada and Kurosawa, 1924). Careful quantitative studies on bolting in *Hyoscyamus* confirmed the fact that the principal effect on growth is a stimulation of cell division in the region immediately below the stem apex (Sachs et al., 1959; Fig. 7-3). On the other hand, Hayashi et al. (1953) found that cell enlargement was also stimulated, and Haber and Luippold (1960), by irradiating seeds at a dosage which prevented mitosis, obtained large gibberellin promotions which must have been due exclusively to cell enlargement (Fig. 7-4).

Not only is gibberellin an effective growth stimulant when applied to intact plants, but it is also a natural plant component participating in the endogenous control of growth activities and a variety of developmental activities including dormancy, flowering, and responses to light and temperature.

Occurrence

Gibberellins are diterpenoids. Diterpenes, aliphatic acids which usually have three rings, are common constituents of the resins of conifers; diterpenoids, which usually have four rings, are common plant constituents, especially as glycosides. Steviol, a diterpenoid with four rings, is an active gibberellin in some tests (Ruddat et al., 1963). The gibberellins which have been identified are all five-ringed diterpenoids (Fig. 7-5). GA_9 may be considered the basic structural unit, the other eight being substituted derivatives. Gibberellic acid, GA_3, is the most abundant fungal product and the most active in many bioassays. Like the auxins, all gibberellins are acids; the array shown in Fig. 7-5 ranges from the most oxidized on the left to the most reduced on the right, and from the most polar (because of added OH groups) at the top to the least polar at the bottom.

The history of the separation and identification of gibberellin is complex (Stodola, 1958). GA_1 was probably the first to be identified in fungal extracts (Yabuta and Hayashi, 1939; Takahashi et al., 1957) and in higher plants (MacMillan and Suter, 1958). Gibberellic acid (GA_3) was isolated in 1954 by Cross, who was attempting to repeat the isolation of GA_1 reported by the Japanese workers. Since that time GA_5, GA_6, and GA_8 have been identified in flowering plants (MacMillan et al., 1961; West and Reilly, 1961), and GA_2, GA_4, GA_7, and

Fig. 7-1 | Applications of gibberellin to meteor peas result in large stimulations of the growth of the plant; as little as 0.1 μg per plant causes a doubling of plant height in 22 days (Brian and Hemming, 1955).

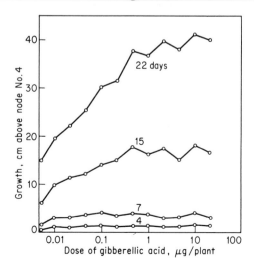

Fig. 7-2 | Application of 20 μg of gibberellin to a bean plant (var.
Contender) results in large stimulation of growth and a change from bush to
vine habit (Wittwer and Bukovac, 1957*a*).

GA$_9$ from the fungus, in addition to GA$_3$ and GA$_1$ mentioned above (Cross et al., 1961).

Gibberellin detection and assays are usually based on their stimulative effects on plant growth. The three most common assay methods involve the stimulation of growth of dwarf corn, the promotion of the stem growth of dwarf peas, and the promotion of elongation of rice seedlings. The assay using dwarf corn was developed by Phinney et al. (1957). It involves the application of a gibberellin solution to the first leaf of the dwarf corn seedling and the measurement of the stimulation of elongation of the next internode or leaf sheath. Representative results of such an assay are shown in Fig. 7-6 (Smith and Rappaport, 1961). The assay using dwarf peas was developed by McComb and Carr (1958) and is illustrated in Fig. 7-7. In each case only minute quantities of growth substance are needed to produce measurable growth responses. In the rice-seedling assay (Hashimoto and Yamaki, 1960), whole seedlings are placed in a dish with gibberellin solution, and the growth promotion of the next enlarging leaf is measured (Fig. 7-8). This figure also compares the relative activities of some of the gibberellins on rice; as in many tests, the gibberellic acid (GA$_3$) is one of the most active materials. In this test GA$_1$ is also highly active; in others the relative activities may be interchanged (e.g., Wittwer and Bukovac, 1962; Nitsch and Nitsch, 1962a).

The gibberellin contents of plants were originally studied in relation to the presence of the fungus *Gibberella*. Subsequently, extracts of developing bean fruits showed strong growth stimulations in intact plants (Mitchell et al., 1951), and examination of such extracts established the fact that gibberellins occurred naturally in the plant (West and Phinney, 1958; Murakami, 1959). Radley (1958) followed changes in the gibberellin content of seeds and fruits and showed that this growth substance in-

Fig. 7-3 | The growth stimulation resulting from gibberellin application to *Hyoscyamus* is associated with a large increase in the frequency of mitoses in the region just below the apical meristem. GA (25 μg) applied at 0 and 24 hr (Sachs et al., 1959).

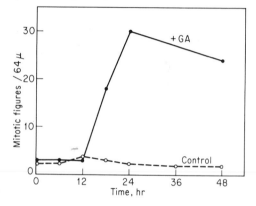

Fig. 7-4 | Gibberellin can stimulate growth through an exclusive effect on cell enlargement. Wheat seedlings were given 612 kr of x-ray, which entirely prevents subsequent cell division. They are shown to still respond to gibberellin application ($3 \times 10^{-4}M$) (Haber and Luippold, 1960).

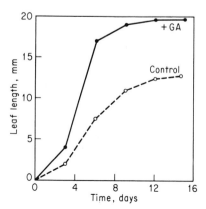

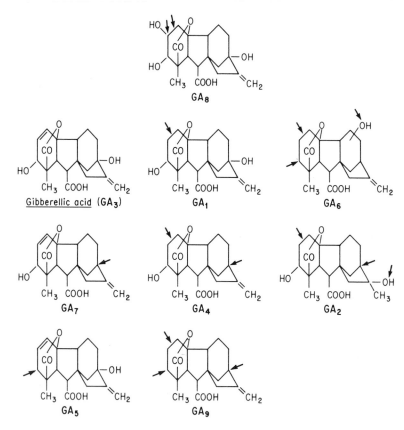

Fig. 7-5 | The structures of the nine known gibberellins. Each difference from the structure of gibberellic acid is indicated by an arrow. The compounds are arranged with the most unsaturated on the left and the most polar at the top (adapted from Cross et al., 1961, and MacMillan et al., 1961).

creased and then decreased during fruit development. Some data for the changes in amount of gibberellin in the developing fruits of *Pharbitis* are shown in Fig. 7-9. It is evident that the gibberellin content was highest shortly before the period of greatest fruit growth rate (Murakami, 1961). We can deduce that there are mechanisms for both the biosynthesis and the natural removal of this type of growth substance, but presently little is known of such mechanisms.

The occurrence of gibberellins in the maturing seed suggested to Corcoran and Phinney (1962) that they are somehow involved in seed-maturation processes. Gibberellins are also present in the germinating seedling, as is shown in the data of Wheeler (1960) in Fig. 7-10. Murakami (1961) found that gibberellin content declined considerably during the first 2 weeks after germination of *Pharbitis*. The data in Fig. 7-10 also suggest that gibberellins may be most abundant in rapidly growing tissues such as the expanding cotyledon or leaf.

Some of the most dramatic effects of gibberellin are on the growth of dwarf mutants. Phinney (1956) reported that gibberellin applications restored some dwarf corn mutants to standard or normal size (Fig. 7-11). Brian and Hemming (1955) obtained large growth promotions in dwarf pea plants with gibberellin applications, and 11 different varieties responded to giberellin in proportion to the extent of their dwarfing tendencies (Fig. 7-12). Auxin treatments had essentially no effect in relieving the dwarfing tendencies of the peas.

Ogawa (1962*b*) compared the gibberellin contents of dwarf seedlings and non-dwarf seedlings of *Pharbitis* and found that the normal seedlings showed large amounts of two chromatographically separable gibberellins but that the dwarf variety contained only a small amount of each (Fig. 7-13).

Dormancy may be associated with a low gibberellin content in seeds and tubers. Gibberellin treatments break dormancy, and the natural gibberellin content rises with emergence from the dormant condition (Smith and Rappaport, 1961; Naylor and Simpson, 1961).

Unlike auxin, there does not seem to be any polarity of gibberellin movement in the plant (Kato, 1958*b*). Movement in the vascular system may be in the phloem or the xylem (Zweig et al., 1961) and is not appreciably inhibited by the auxin-transport inhibitor, triiodobenzoic acid (Kentzer and Libbert, 1961). These are preliminary statements about movement of exogenously applied gibberellin; the natural movement of endogenous gibberellins is not known.

It appears likely that gibberellin may occur in plants in some bound or modified form. McComb (1961) found an increase in gibberellin activity in an extract from runner beans following action by a proteolytic enzyme, and he felt that there might be a binding of gibberellins to proteins. Lazer et al. (1961) and Hayashi et al.

(1962) also suggested that gibberellins might be bound or otherwise altered in the plant. Using extracts from neutral fractions of potato peels they observed a gradual conversion of the neutral materials into an active acidic material.

The growth rates of seeds and seedlings are sometimes better correlated with gibberellin than with auxin contents. Murakami

Fig. 7-6 | The quantitative response of dwarf corn (D_5) to gibberellic acid applied to the first leaf ligule (Smith and Rappaport, 1961).

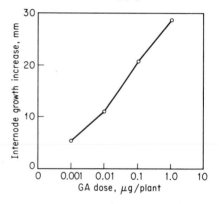

Fig. 7-7 | The quantitative response of meteor dwarf peas to gibberellic acid applied as a droplet to the third node. Plants measured after 6 days (McComb and Carr, 1958).

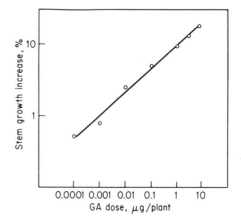

Fig. 7-8 | Quantitative responses of rice seedlings to four gibberellins. The seedlings were in dishes containing the solutions being tested. Growth measured after 6 days (Hashimoto and Yamaki, 1960).

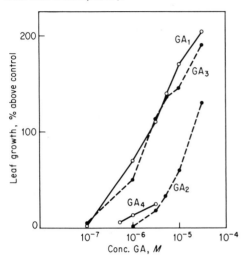

Fig. 7-9 | The gibberellin content of the developing seed of *Pharbitis* reaches a peak shortly before the seed reaches maximal fresh weight. Gibberellin assayed by rice seedlings applied to chromatograms of extract (Murakami, 1961).

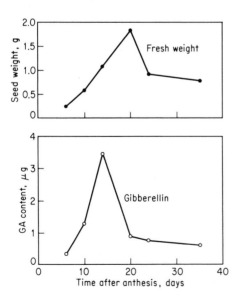

(1959) has suggested that gibberellins are essential for all plant cell growth; there seems no doubt that these natural substances do regulate plant growth in some situations, but it seems hasty to propose an absolute control at this time on the basis of the current information.

Developmental roles

Gibberellin seems to be involved in the phenomena of dormancy, flowering, and fruiting and in some correlation events, in addition to its role in dwarfism.

Gibberellin treatments can overcome some types of dormancy (Kahn et al., 1957), and as seeds emerge from the dormant condition there may be a natural rise in endogenous gibberellin contents (Naylor and Simpson, 1961; Smith and Rappaport, 1961). (See Chap. 19.)

Gibberellin treatments can induce flowering of some photoperiodically sensitive and some cold-requiring plants (Lang, 1956a, b; Lang et al., 1957), as will be discussed in Chap. 13. Subsequently it has been shown that the induction of flowering may bring about a natural rise in the endogenous gibberellin content (Lang and Reinhard, 1961; Fig. 13-34). A striking ability of gibberellin applications to alter the sex of flowers has been reported by Mitchell and Wittwer (1962).

The ability of gibberellin applications to bring about fruit set (Weaver, 1958; Gustafson, 1960; Prosser and Jackson, 1959; Crane et al., 1960) raises the question of whether endogenous gibberellins might be involved in that developmental step. Shastry and Muir (1963) found that treatment of tomato flowers with gibberellin caused a large increase in diffusible auxin, which might itself be responsible for the setting action. Gibberellins have been extracted from newly set fruits and from pollen (Coombe, 1960; Weaver, 1961). The rich supplies of gibberellins in developing fruits and seeds provided the initial sources from which endogenous gibberellins were first studied in plants.

The involvements of gibberellins in correlation effects are not clear. Associated with the stimulations of stem growth, gibberellin treatments may suppress the growth of lateral branches (Lona and Bocchi, 1956; Brian et al., 1959a; Bradley and Crane, 1960). Whether this inhibition is caused by the gibberellin itself or by auxin in the more active apex is not known. Tissue-culture experiments have shown that gibberellin can suppress both bud and root formation (Murashige, 1961).

With auxins. Physiologists tended initially to ascribe gibberellin growth-stimulatory actions to an interaction with auxin, which had become firmly established among physiologists as the growth hormone in plants. Proposals were made that gibberellins increased the auxin content of tissues or enhanced auxin effectiveness by increasing the active sites upon which it might act or that gibberellin had effects on growth quite separate from the auxin-regulated steps.

Pilet (1957) reported that gibberellin suppressed the activity of indoleacetic oxidase, but Kato and Katsumi (1959) and Kögl and Sterna (1960) did not note any such suppressive effects. In a clever experiment, Kefford (1962) prevented IAA oxidase from acting and found that the growth response to gibberellin was not suppressed under such conditions. Several workers reported that gibberellin applications increased endogenous auxin contents (Phillips et al., 1959) and that the auxin increases were strikingly parallel to the growth responses obtained (Kuraishi and Muir, 1962; Fig. 7-14). Yet gibberellin can still promote growth when supraoptimal auxin concentrations are supplied (Hillman and Purves, 1961), and the numerous effects of gibberellin which do not parallel auxin effects make it clear that gibberellin stimulations are not strictly a consequence of an increased auxin content. In fact, the effects of auxin on the cell wall are opposite those of gibberellin, according to Yoda and Ashida (1960).

The early reports that auxin and gibberellins act synergistically in stimulating growth (Brian, 1958; Galston and Warburg, 1959) implied that gibberellin might somehow increase the availability of sites for auxin function. That possibility, too, is denied by the evidence of differences between the types of growth responses of gibberellin and auxin. Kato (1961) and Hillman and Purves (1961) established that the inhibitions by antiauxins were not alleviated by gibberellins as they were by auxins—

Fig. 7-10 | The gibberellin contents of bean seedlings at various times after germination, showing a peak of gibberellin in the cotyledons, followed by a peak in the first leaf at the time of greatest leaf growth rate. Extracts of Canadian wonder bean assayed by the growth of bean leaf disks (Wheeler, 1960).

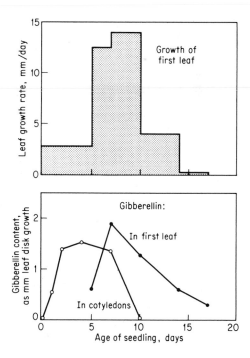

Fig. 7-11 | Gibberellin applications to dwarf corn (D₁) cause it to grow like standard corn. Left to right: standard control, standard with gibberellin applied (60 μg per plant), dwarf control, dwarf with gibberellin applied (Phinney, 1956).

Fig. 7-12 | Comparing the responses of 11 pea varieties to gibberellic acid, one finds that the varieties with the lowest natural growth rate (i.e., the most dwarfed) give the greatest growth response to the gibberellin. Auxin is essentially without effect on the growth rates of these plants. Each datum represents the response of one variety either to 100 mg/liter GA or to 20 mg/liter IAA (Brian and Hemming, 1955).

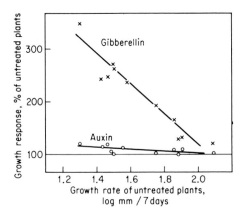

strong evidence that the gibberellins do not act on the same system as auxins.

The contrasting actions of gibberellins and auxins can be seen by comparing their effects on plants. Both stimulate growth, but only gibberellins restore growth in dwarfs. Only auxins seem to be generally able to inhibit growth. Among the correlation effects, both may suppress lateral-bud development, but only auxins exert the polar effects on rooting and abscission. Among the developmental effects, both may cause fruit set, but the stimulations of flowering and dormancy control are almost unique to the gibberellins. It seems reasonable to assume that the gibberellins and the auxins have distinctive, separate actions on growth systems.

With growth inhibitors. Brian (1958) suggested that gibberellin might alleviate the action of some growth inhibitors, and Kato (1958a) reported that the inhibition of pea-stem sections by coumarin was alleviated by adding gibberellin. Similarly,

Phillips (1961) reported that the dormancy of lettuce seed imposed by treatment with naringenin was overcome by additions of gibberellin. Wareing and Villiers (1961) found that the end of dormancy of *Fraxinus* buds was not associated with the disappearance of the growth inhibitors present but that instead a natural growth promoter accumulated, neutralizing the effects of the inhibitors. This natural promoter was perhaps not identical with gibberellin, but it had properties very suggestive of it.

With metabolism. In 1940, Hayashi reported that gibberellins produced stimulatory effects on the malting processes in grains. This was studied in detail by Paleg (1960, 1961), who reported that endosperm tissues of oats showed large increases in hydrolytic activities following treatment with gibberellin. In Fig. 7-15, the decrease in endosperm dry weight is shown to be accounted for by the release of large amounts of sugars and proteins. Paleg (1961) found that gibberellin causes the formation of hydrolytic enzymes in the endosperm and that the embryo may naturally provide this hydrolytic activity through the release of gibberellins during germination. Radley (1959) showed that the malting process also involves the natural accumulation of gibberellins by the malting grains. The manner by which gibberellin may enhance the activity of the hydrolytic enzymes is particularly interesting.

Light. Gibberellin can have effects, some of which are parallel and some opposite to those of light. Specifically, the ability of either light or gibberellin to relieve the dormancy of some seeds (e.g., Kahn et al., 1957) contrasts sharply with the ability of gibberellin to overcome the inhibitions of growth imposed by light.

The antagonism between gibberellin and light effects was described by Lockhart (1956). Light inhibits the growth of etiolated peas, and gibberellin applications promote growth to about the same extent (Fig. 7-16). Using the stem-bending technique

Fig. 7-13 | The gibberellin contents of normal and dwarf varieties of *Pharbitis nil* (Tendan and Kidachi) relate to their dwarfing habits. The normal variety contains a relatively large supply, and the dwarf a small supply. Extracts chromatographed and assayed with rice-seedling test; two active R_f zones are plotted separately (Ogawa, 1962b).

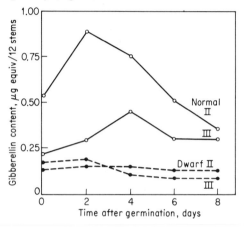

Fig. 7-14 | The application of various concentrations of gibberellin to sunflower seedlings results in plant-height increases which are paralleled by increases in diffusible auxin obtainable by 2-hr diffusion from the stems. *Avena* curvature assay (Kuraishi and Muir, 1962).

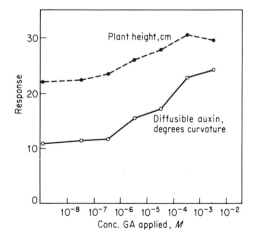

Fig. 7-15 | Pieces of Prior barley seed placed on a solution of gibberellin ($2 \times 10^{-6}M$) experience a rapid loss of components as indicated by the loss of dry weight. The loss, like the losses during normal germination, consist mostly of the release of sugars and, to a lesser extent, of protein materials (Paleg, 1961).

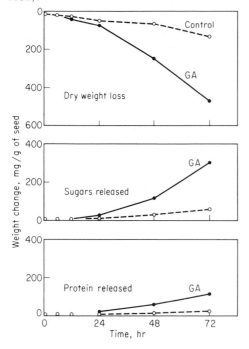

Fig. 7-16 | A comparison of the gibberellin responses of etiolated pea seedlings (Morse Progress) and seedlings grown under red light shows a greater stimulation of stem length obtainable with the seedlings grown in red light (Lockhart, 1956).

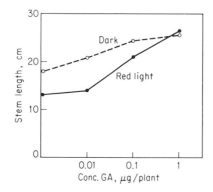

of Tagawa and Bonner (1957), Lockhart (1960) showed that red light caused a depression of cell-wall plasticity and elasticity and that gibberellin could restore the plasticity and elasticity (though cf. Yoda and Ashida, 1960). Hillman (1959) and Mohr and Appuhn (1962), on the other hand, found that even with abundant gibberellin, seedling stems were inhibited by red light, indicating that the light and the gibberellin responses were quite separate.

Burström (1960) suggested that the light inhibition of root growth might be specifically related to the presence of Fe^{++} ions and that the inhibition was related to the formation of chlorophyll; gibberellin relieved the inhibition of root growth by Fe^{++} and also depressed chlorophyll formation in the light.

The dwarf varieties of plants are commonly the best responders to applied gibberellins, and Gorter (1961) related the dwarfism feature to a light and gibberellin interaction. She found that in the absence of light, dwarf and normal peas grew at the same rates and that light preferentially inhibited the dwarfs, which were then most readily stimulated by gibberellins. She suggested, therefore, that dwarfism involved a light-imposed limitation of growth. Although her results tend to support Lockhart's idea of light-gibberellin antagonism, Lockhart (1956) reported that his dwarf peas responded to gibberellin either in light or in darkness.

Considering the cases in which light and gibberellins have parallel effects (as in the stimulation of seed germination or of long-day photoperiodic phenomena), Brian (1958) suggested that light promotes the formation of gibberellin in the plant. Some evidence for this was obtained by Chajlakjan and Lozhnikova (1961) and through more precise chromatographic experiments by Lang and Reinhard (1961). It appears that light may increase the gibberellin content of plants.

Low temperature. In many developmental events, gibberellin applications can stimulate changes usually obtained with low temperatures. The first of these to be discovered was the stimulation of flowering in cold-requiring plants such as the biennials (Lang, 1956a). Gibberellin applications also replaced the cold requirement for breaking dormancy in buds (Donaho and Walker, 1957) and for preventing dwarfing in peach seedlings (Flemion, 1959). The gibberellin substitution for cold experiences is not universal (cf. Moore and Bonde, 1958), but it can substitute for a variety of such requirements.

Antigibberellins

Agricultural enterprises have recently developed an array of growth-inhibiting chemicals which are suggestive of antigibberellins. Amo-1618 (a quaternary ammonium salt of piperidine carboxylate) markedly inhibits stem elongation (Wirwillie and Mitchell, 1950), and its action is prevented by the application of gibberellin (Sachs et al., 1960; Downs and Cathey, 1960). Phosphon (a chlorinated phosphonium salt) is also an effective growth inhibitor which is reversible with gibberellin (Lockhart, 1962). CCC (a chlorinated choline) likewise strongly inhibits growth, and its action is prevented by the application of gibberellin (Wittwer and Tolbert, 1960). The mutual antagonism is not restricted to the growth effects, for CCC can impose dormancy on lettuce seeds. This effect is overcome with gibberellin, as is the inhibition of flowering of long-day plants (Wittwer and Tolbert, 1960).

If these inhibitors are acting competitively with gibberellins at a common site, one would hope that they might be structurally similar to the gibberellins in some respects. Since they are not, Tolbert (1961) has suggested caution in considering them as true antigibberellins.

Corcoran et al. (1961) have reported that there may be inhibitors in the plant

which act in an antagonistic way to gibberellins. An illustration of such a plant-extract effect is given in Fig. 7-17. (See also Fig. 9-8).

Conclusion

The gibberellins are natural growth-regulating substances in plants and are also involved in the development of pathological symptoms. They occur naturally in plants, and their presence appears to correlate well with some aspects of growth and development.

The effectiveness of gibberellins in regulating growth and the limited evidence of their quantitative changes in growing tissues suggest that they are components of the natural growth-regulating system in higher plants. They appear to be involved in some types of dwarfism and in the determination of general plant form such as the bush vs. vine habit. Their stimulative effects may be most pronounced on stems, but under some circumstances they may

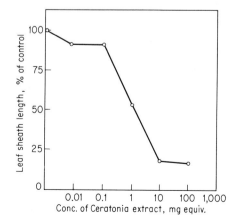

Fig. 7-17 | An acetone/water extract from the fruits of *Ceratonia* contains materials which can suppress the responsiveness of the D_1 dwarf corn to applied gibberellin (0.5 μg per plant) (Corcoran et al., 1961).

also stimulate leaf, flower, and fruit growth.

The gibberellins can trigger several developmental events which are ordinarily under environmental control, including flowering, breaking of dormancy, and other temperature- and photoperiod-controlled steps. The implication is that the gibberellins are involved in the regulatory systems which are responsible for the developmental responses of the plant to environmental cues.

GENERAL REFERENCES

Knapp, R. (ed.). 1962. *Eigenschaften und Wirkungen der Gibberelline.* Springer-Verlag, Berlin. 275 pp.

Merritt, J. M., et al. 1961. Gibberellins. *Advan. Chem. Ser.*, 28. 167 pp.

Phinney, B. O., and C. A. West. 1961. Gibberellins and plant growth. *Handbuch Pflanzenphys.*, 14:1185–1227.

Stodola, F. H. 1958. *Source Book on Gibberellin, 1828–1957.* U.S. Department of Agriculture, Peoria, Ill. 450 pp.

Stowe, B. B., and T. Yamaki. 1959. Gibberellins: Stimulants of plant growth. *Science*, 129:807–816.

REFERENCES CITED

Bradley, V., and J. C. Crane. 1960. Gibberellin-induced inhibition of bud development in some species of *Prunus. Science*, 131:825–826.

Brian, P. W. 1958. Role of gibberellin-like hormones in regulation of plant growth and flowering. *Nature*, 181:1122–1123.

——— and H. G. Hemming. 1955. The effect of gibberellic acid on shoot growth of pea seedlings. *Physiol. Plantarum*, 8:669–681.

———, H. G. Hemming, and D. Lowe. 1959a. The effect of gibberellic acid on shoot growth of cupid sweet peas. *Physiol. Plantarum*, 12:15–29.

———, J. H. Petty, and P. T. Richmond. 1959b. Extended dormancy of deciduous woody plants treated in autumn with gibberellic acid. *Nature*, 184:69.

Burström, H. 1960. Influence of iron and gibberellic acid on the light sensitivity of roots. *Physiol. Plantarum*, 13:597–615.

Chajlakjan, M., and N. V. Lozhnikova. 1961. Gibberellin-like substances in higher plants and their effect on growth and flowering. *Fiziol. Rast.*, 7:432–438.

Coombe, B. G. 1960. Relationship of growth and development to changes in sugars, auxins, and gibberellins in fruit of seeded and seedless varieties of *Vitis. Plant Physiol.*, 35:241–250.

Corcoran, M. R., and B. O. Phinney. 1962. Changes in amount of gibberellin in developing seed of *Echinocystis, Lupinus* and *Phaseolus. Physiol. Plantarum*, 15:252–262.

———, A. West, and B. O. Phinney. 1961. Natural inhibitors of gibberellin-induced growth. *Advan. Chem. Ser.*, 28:152–158.

Crane, J., P. Primer, and R. Campbell. 1960. Gibberellin induced parthenocarpy in *Prunus. Proc. Am. Soc. Hort. Sci.*, 75:129–137.

Cross, B. E. 1954. Gibberellic acid. I. *J. Chem. Soc.*, 1954, 4670–4676.

———, J. F. Grove, P. McCloskey, J. MacMillan, J. S. Moffatt, and T. P. C. Mulholland. 1961. The structures of the fungal gibberellins. *Advan. Chem. Ser.*, 28:3–17.

Donaho, C. W., and D. R. Walker. 1957. Effect of gibberellic acid on breaking of rest period in Elberta peach. *Science*, 126:1178–1179.

Downs, R. J., and H. M. Cathey. 1960. Effects of light gibberellin and a quaternary ammonium compound on the growth of dark-grown red kidney beans. *Botan. Gaz.*, 121:233–237.

Flemion, F. 1959. Effect of temperature, light and gibberellin on stem elongation in dwarfed peach and *Rhodotypos. Contrib. Boyce Thompson Inst.*, 20:57–70.

Galston, A. W., and H. Warburg. 1959. An analysis of auxin-gibberellin interaction in pea stem tissue. *Plant Physiol.*, 34:16–22.

Gorter, C. J. 1961. Dwarfism of peas and the action of gibberellic acid. *Physiol. Plantarum*, 14: 332–343.

Gustafson, F. G. 1960. Influence of gibberellic acid on setting and development of fruits in tomato. *Plant Physiol.*, 35:521–523.

Haber, A. H., and H. J. Luippold. 1960. Effects of gibberellin on gamma-irradiated wheat. *Am. J. Botany*, 47:140–144.

Hashimoto, T., and T. Yamaki. 1960. Comparative effectiveness of gibberellins A_1, A_2, A_3, and A_4, with special reference to that of A_4. *Botan. Mag.* (*Tokyo*), 73:64–68.

Hayashi, T. 1940. Biochemical studies on "bakanae" fungus of rice. 6. Effect of gibberellin on the activity of amylase in germinated cereal grains. *J. Agr. Chem. Soc. Japan*, 16:531–538.

———, S. Blumenthal-Goldschmidt, and L. Rappaport. 1962. Acid and neutral gibberellin-like substances in potato tubers. *Plant Physiol.*, 37:774–780.

———, Y. Takijima, and Y. Murakami. 1953. The biochemistry of bakanae fungus. 28. The physiological action of gibberellin. IV. *J. Agr. Chem. Soc. Japan*, 27:672–675.

Hillman, W. S. 1959. Interaction of growth substances and photoperiodically active radiations on the growth of pea sections, pp. 181–196. In R. B. Withrow (ed.), *Photoperiodism*. American Association for the Advancement of Science, Washington, D.C.

——— and W. K. Purves. 1961. Does gibberellin act through an auxin-mediated mechanism? pp. 589–600. In R. M. Klein (ed.), *Plant Growth Regulation*. Iowa State University Press, Ames, Iowa.

Kahn, A. J., A. Goss, and D. E. Smith. 1957. Effect of gibberellin on germination of lettuce seed. *Science*, 125:645–646.

Kato, J. 1958*a*. Studies on the physiological effect of gibberellin. II. On the interaction of gibberellin with auxins and growth inhibitors. *Physiol. Plantarum*, 11:10–15.

———. 1958*b*. Nonpolar transport of gibberellin through pea stem and a method for its determination. *Science*, 128:1008–1009.

———. 1961. Physiological action of gibberellin with special reference to auxin, pp. 601–609. In R. M. Klein (ed.), *Plant Growth Regulation*. Iowa State University Press, Ames, Iowa.

——— and M. Katsumi. 1959. Studies on the physiological effect of gibberellin. V. Effect of gibberellic acid and gibberellin A on the activity of indoleacetic acid oxidase. *Mem. Coll. Sci. Univ. Kyoto*, 26:53–60.

Kefford, N. P. 1962. Auxin-gibberellin interactions in rice coleoptile elongation. *Plant Physiol.*, 37:380–386.

Kentzer, T., and E. Libbert. 1961. Blockade des Gibberellinsaure-Transports in Hypocotylsegmenten durch Trijodbenzoesaure zugleich ein neuer Agarblocktest auf Gibberellin. *Planta*, 56:23–27.

Kögl, F., and J. Sterna. 1960. Wirkungsbezieungen zwischen Indoleessigsaure und Gibberellinsaure. *Naturwissenschaften*, 4:90.

Kuraishi, S., and R. M. Muir. 1962. Increase in diffusible auxin after treatment with gibberellin. *Science*, 137:760–761.

Kurosawa, E. 1926. Experimental studies on the secretion of *Fusarium heterosporum* on rice plants. *Trans. Nat. Hist. Soc. Formosa*, 16:213–227.

Lang, A. 1956*a*. Induction of flower formation in biennial *Hyoscyamus* by treatment with gibberellin. *Naturwissenschaften*, 12:284–285.

———. 1956*b*. Gibberellin and flower formation. *Naturwissenschaften*, 23:544.

——— and E. Reinhard. 1961. Gibberellins and flower formation. *Advan. Chem. Ser.*, 28:71–79.

————, J. A. Sandoval, and A. Bedri. 1957. Induction of bolting and flowering in *Hyoscyamus* and *Samolus* by a gibberellin-like material from a seed plant. *Proc. Natl. Acad. Sci. U.S.,* 43:960–964.

Lazer, L., A. M. Dalgiel, W. E. Boumgartner, R. V. Dahlstrom, and B. J. Morton. 1961. Determination of residual tritium-labeled gibberellic acid in potatoes, grapes and products. *Advan. Chem. Ser.,* 28:116–121.

Lockhart, J. A. 1956. Reversal of the light inhibition of pea stem growth by the gibberellins. *Proc. Natl. Acad. Sci. U.S.,* 42:841–848.

————. 1960. Intracellular mechanism of growth inhibition by radiant energy. *Plant Physiol.,* 35:129–135.

————. 1962. Kinetic studies of certain anti-gibberellins. *Plant Physiol.,* 37:759–764.

Lona, F., and A. Bocchi. 1956. Caratteristiche d' accrescimento e sviluppo di alcune razze invernali di cereali trattate con acido gibberellico. *Riv. Intern. Agr.* 6.

McComb, A. J. 1961. Bound gibberellin in mature runner bean seeds. *Nature,* 192:575–576.

———— and D. J. Carr. 1958. Evidence from a dwarf pea bioassay from naturally occurring gibberellins in the growing plant. *Nature,* 181:1548–1549.

MacMillan, J., J. C. Seaton, and P. J. Suter. 1961. Isolation and structures of gibberellins from higher plants. *Advan. Chem. Ser.,* 28:18–24.

———— and P. J. Suter. 1958. The occurrence of gibberellin A_1 in higher plants: isolation from the seed of runner bean (*Phaseolus multiflorus*). *Naturwissenschaften,* 45:46.

Mitchell, J. W., D. P. Skaggs, and W. P. Anderson. 1951. Plant growth-stimulating hormones in immature bean seeds. *Science,* 114:159–161.

Mitchell, W. D., and S. H. Wittwer. 1962. Chemical regulation of flower sex expression and vegetative growth in *Cucumis sativa. Science,* 136:880–881.

Mohr, H., and V. Appuhn. 1962. Die Steurung der Hypocotylwachstums von *Sinapis alba* durch Licht und Gibberellinsaure. *Planta,* 59:49–67.

Moore, T. C., and E. K. Bonde. 1958. Interaction of gibberellic acid and vernalization in the dwarf telephone pea. *Physiol. Plantarum,* 11:752–759.

Murakami, Y. 1959. The occurrence of gibberellins in mature dry seeds. *Botan. Mag. (Tokyo),* 72:438–442.

————. 1961. Paper chromatographic studies on change in gibberellins during seed development and germination in *Pharbitis. Botan. Mag. (Tokyo),* 74:241–242.

Murashige, T. 1961. Suppression of shoot formation in cultured tobacco cells by gibberellic acid. *Science,* 134:280.

Naylor, J. M., and G. M. Simpson. 1961. Dormancy studies in seed of *Avena fatua.* 2. A gibberellin sensitive inhibitory mechanism in the embryo. *Can. J. Botany,* 39:281–295.

Nitsch, J. P., and C. Nitsch. 1962a. Activités comparées de neuf gibberellines sur trois tests biologiques. *Ann. Physiol. Vegetale,* 4:85–97.

———— and ————. 1962b. Composés phenoliques et croissance vegetale. *Ann. Physiol. Vegetale,* 4:211–225.

Ogawa, Y. 1962a. Über die photoperiodische Empfindlichkeit der Keimpflanzen von *Pharbitis nil* Chois. mit besonderer Berucksichtigung auf dem Wuchsstoffgehalt der Kotyledonen. *Botan. Mag. (Tokyo),* 75: 92–101.

————. 1962b. Quantitative difference of gibberellin-like substances in normal and dwarf varieties of *Pharbitis nil* Chois. *Botan. Mag. (Tokyo),* 75:449–450.

————. 1962c. Weitere Untersuchungen über die Wirkung von Gibberellinahnlichen Substanzen auf die Blutenbildung von *Pharbitis nil. Plant Cell Physiol. (Tokyo),* 3:5–21.

Paleg, L. G. 1960. Physiological effects of gibberellic acid. II. *Plant Physiol.*, 35: 902–906.

———. 1961. Physiological effects of gibberellic acid. III. *Plant Physiol.*, 36:829–837.

Phillips, I. D. J. 1961. Induction of light requirement for germination of lettuce seed by naringenin and its removal by gibberellic acid. *Nature*, 192:240–241.

———, A. J. Vlitos, and H. Cutler. 1959. The influence of gibberellic acid upon the endogenous growth substances of the Alaska pea. *Contrib. Boyce Thompson Inst.*, 20:111–120.

Phinney, B. O. 1956. Growth response of single-gene dwarf mutants in maize to gibberellic acid. *Proc. Natl. Acad. Sci. U.S.*, 42:185–189.

———, C. A. West, M. Ritzel, and P. M. Neely. 1957. Evidence for "gibberellin-like" substances from flowering plants. *Proc. Natl. Acad. Sci. U.S.*, 43:398–404.

Pilet, P. E. 1957. Action des gibberellins sur l'activité auxines-oxydasique de tissus cultives *in vitro*. *Compt. Rend. (Paris)*, 245:1327–1328.

Prosser, M. V., and G. A. D. Jackson. 1959. Induction of parthenocarpy in *Rosa arvensis* buds with gibberellic acid. *Nature*, 184:180.

Radley, M. 1958. The distribution of substances similar to gibberellic acid in higher plants. *Ann. Botany (London)*, 22:297–307.

———. 1959. The occurrence of gibberellin-like substances in barley and malt. *Chem. Ind.*, 1959:877–878.

Ruddat, M., A. Lang, and E. Mosettig. 1963. Gibberellin activity of steviol, a plant terpenoid. *Naturwissenschaften*, 50: 23.

Sachs, R. M., C. F. Bretz, and A. Lang. 1959. Shoot histogenesis: the early effects of gibberellin upon stem elongation in two rosette plants. *Am. J. Botany*, 46:376–384.

———, A. Lang, C. F. Bretz, and J. Roach.

1960. Shoot histogenesis: subapical meristematic activity in a caulescent plant and the action of gibberellic acid and AMO-1618. *Am. J. Botany*, 47:260–266.

Sawada, K., and E. Kurosawa. 1924. On the prevention of the bakanae disease of rice. *Exptl. Sta. Bull. Formosa*, 21:1–19.

Sastri, A. A., and R. M. Muir. 1963. Gibberellin: effect on diffusible auxin in fruit development. *Science*, 140:494–495.

Smith, O. E., and L. Rappaport. 1961. Endogenous gibberellins in resting and sprouting potato tubers. *Advan. Chem. Ser.*, 28:42–48.

Stodola, F. H., 1958. *Source Book on Gibberellin, 1828–1957*. U.S. Department of Agriculture, Peoria, Ill. 450 pp.

Tagawa, T., and J. Bonner. 1957. Mechanical properties of the *Avena* coleoptile as related to auxin and to ionic interactions. *Plant Physiol.*, 32:207–212.

Takahashi, N., Y. Seta, H. Kitamura, and Y. Sumiki. 1957. A new gibberellin, gibberellin A4. *Bull. Agr. Chem. Soc. Japan*, 21:396–398.

Tolbert, N. E. 1961. Structural relationships among chemicals which act like antigibberellins. *Advan. Chem. Ser.*, 28:145–151.

Wareing, P. F., and T. A. Villiers. 1961. Growth substance and inhibitor changes in buds and seeds in response to chilling, pp. 95–107. In R. M. Klein (ed.), *Plant Growth Regulation*. Iowa State University Press, Ames, Iowa.

Weaver, R. J. 1958. Effect of gibberellic acid on fruit set and berry enlargement in seedless grapes of *Vitis vinifera*. *Nature*, 181:851–852.

———. 1961. Growth of grapes in relation to gibberellin. *Advan. Chem. Ser.*, 28:89–108.

West, C. A., and B. O. Phinney. 1958. Gibberellins from flowering plants. I. Isolation and properties of a gibberellin from *Phaseolus vulgaris* L. *J. Am. Chem. Soc.*, 81:2424.

——— and T. Reilly. 1961. Properties of

gibberellins from flowering plants. *Advan. Chem. Ser.,* 28:37–41.

Wheeler, A. W. 1960. Changes in leaf growth substance in cotyledons and primary leaves during the growth of dwarf bean seedlings. *J. Exptl. Botany,* 11:217–226.

Wirwillie, J. W., and J. W. Mitchell. 1950. Six new plant growth inhibiting compounds. *Botan. Gaz.,* 111:491–494.

Wittwer, S. H., and M. J. Bukovac. 1957*a.* Gibberellins: new chemicals for crop production. *Michigan State Univ. Agr. Expt. Sta. Quart. Bull.,* 39:469–494.

———— and ————. 1957*b.* Gibberellin and higher plants. III. Induction of flowering in longday annuals grown under short days. *Michigan State Univ. Agt. Expt. Sta. Quart. Bull.,* 39:661–672.

———— and ————. 1962. Exogenous plant growth substances affecting floral initiation and fruit set, pp. 65–88. In S. G. Younkin (ed.), *Plant Science Symposium on Fruit Set.* Campbell Soup Co., Camden, N.J.

———— and N. E. Tolbert. 1960*a.* 2-Chloroethyl trimethylammonium chloride and related compounds as plant growth substances. V. Relation to auxin and gibberellin. *Plant Physiol.,* 35:871–877.

———— and ————. 1960*b.* (2 Chloroethyl) trimethylammonium chloride and related compounds as plant growth substances. III. *Am. J. Botany,* 47:560–565.

Yabuta, T. 1935. Biochemistry of the "bakanae" fungus of rice. *Agr. Hort. (Tokyo),* 10:17–22.

———— and T. Hayashi. 1939. Biochemical studies on "bakanae" fungus of the rice. II. Isolation of "gibberellin," the active principle which makes the rice seedlings grow slenderly. *J. Agr. Chem. Soc. Japan,* 15:257–266.

Yoda, S., and J. Ashida. 1960. Effects of gibberellin and auxin on the extensibility of the pea stem. *Plant Cell Physiol. (Tokyo),* 1:99–105.

Zweig, G., S. Yamaguchi, and G. W. Mason. 1961. Translocation of C^{14}-gibberellin in red kidney bean, normal corn, and dwarf corn. *Advan. Chem. Ser.,* 28:122-134.

8 | Kinins

In the discussion of the auxin and gibberellin growth substances, emphasis has been placed on cell enlargement as the basic unit of growth. The logical need for the existence of a control system for cell division led Wiesner (1892) to suggest long ago that there might be such a chemical control in plants. In a startling projection into experimental approaches which were to follow 30 years later, Haberlandt (1913) found that diffusates from phloem tissues could induce cell division in potato parenchyma. Crushed cells yielded a material which provoked cell division around a wound, and rinsing the region of the crushed cells eluted the stimulus away (Haberlandt, 1921). Bonner and English (1938) found that an alcoholic extract of bean fruits yielded a substance which caused localized cell enlargement and division on bean pods, from which they isolated a fatty acid, traumatin ($C_{12}H_{20}O_4$). Using modern tissue-culture techniques, Jablonski and Skoog (1954) essentially redid Haberlandt's experiment. They demonstrated that a piece of vascular tissue cultured on top of pith tissue could bring about division in the pith cells, which would otherwise not divide. In 1955, Miller et al. separated from yeast DNA an active stimulant of cell division which they named *kinetin* and then (Miller et al., 1955, 1956) identified it as 6-furfuryl aminopurine. The ability of this purine to cause cell divisions is illustrated in Fig. 8–1.

The generic name *kinin* was proposed for chemical substances which stimulated cell division or cytokinesis. Unfortunately, the animal physiologists at the same time proposed the term *kinin* to refer to a class of polypeptides which irritate smooth muscles and nerve endings in the manner of various stings and venoms (cf. Collier, 1962)—biological products of a completely different sort.

The purines and other plant kinins began to receive attention in the physiological literature in the 1940s. Van Overbeek et al.

Fig. 8-1 | The effectiveness of kinetin in inducing cell division in tobacco-pith-tissue cultures. The kinetin concentrations were present in the medium for 7 days in the presence also of 2 mg/liter of indoleacetic acid (Skoog and Miller, 1957).

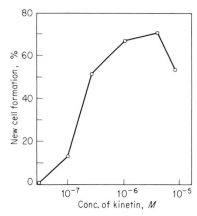

Fig. 8-2 | Some natural and synthetic materials reported to have kinin activities, illustrating the wide range of chemical types—purines and aromatic and nonaromatic compounds.

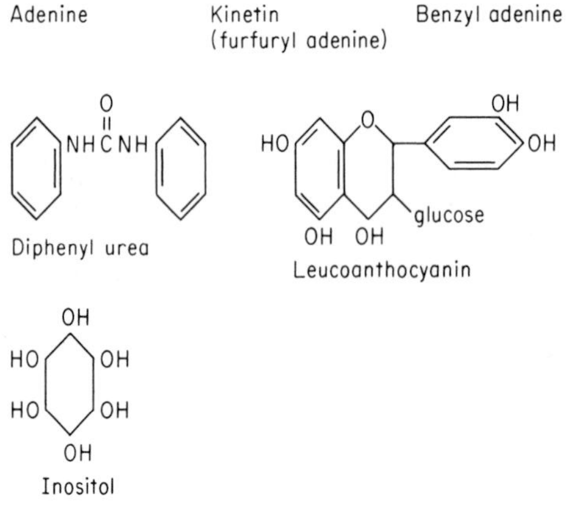

Adenine

Kinetin (furfuryl adenine)

Benzyl adenine

Diphenyl urea

Leucoanthocyanin

Inositol

(1941, 1942) found that coconut milk contained some materials which greatly promoted the growth of embryos in tissue cultures. In Steward's laboratory a refined method of studying the requirements for growth substances in cultures was developed using carrot-root tissue (Steward and Caplin, 1952; Caplin and Steward, 1952), and the analysis of the components of coconut milk which began at that time has continued for over ten years.

Skoog and Tsui (1948) found that the purine adenine was quite effective in promoting the differentiation of buds on tobacco-pith-tissue cultures. After the isolation of kinetin, the bud-forming ability of that substituted purine was found to be even greater (Skoog and Miller, 1957).

In addition to their effects on cell division and bud differentiation, kinetin and the coconut-milk factors have a variety of other growth effects. These include stimulations of leaf growth (a cell-enlargement phenomenon; Miller, 1956), release of lateral buds from apical dominance (Thimann and Wickson, 1957), and release of lettuce seeds from dormancy in the manner of red light (Miller, 1958). Furthermore, Mothes (1960) has demonstrated the ability of kinetin application to stimulate the mobilization of nutrients in leaves.

Thus is repeated the theme that a substance separated from plant cells because of its effectiveness in a relatively concise growth phenomenon is found to be capable of diverse physiological controls in addition to the one for which it was originally investigated.

Isolation and detection

With such an array of physiological effects, kinins can be measured by various bioassays and techniques. Auxin assays most frequently involve the straight-growth test or the *Avena* curvature test, but kinins are assayed in almost as many types of tests as there are laboratories working on them. The cell-division tests of Steward employ principally carrot-root-tissue culture, and the tests of Skoog use tobacco-pith-tissue culture. The ability of kinins to induce bud formation is the basis of another assay used by Skoog and Miller (1957), and their ability to promote leaf enlargement has resulted in another test (Miller, 1956), utilizing excised leaf disks treated with kinetin (Kuraishi, 1959; Fig. 8-3). Kinins maintain the green coloration in leaves against the development of senescence, and this characteristic has been used as an assay by Osborne and McCalla (1961; Fig. 8-4). Many other tests have been developed (McLane and Murneek, 1952; Skinner et al., 1956; Skinner, 1959; Nitsch and Nitsch, 1961*b*), but no bioassay is entirely specific for the kinins, whether it is for cell division, leaf growth, or leaf senescence; all these are affected to some extent by growth substances other than the known kinins. This makes the quantitative analysis of natural kinins extremely complex and introduces many difficulties in the purification and identification of plant kinins.

Research on the specific chemical substance which may regulate cell division and other activities attributed to the kinins has produced some diverse results. Kinetin was isolated from nucleic-acid preparations from yeast, fish, and animal glands, suggesting the possibility that the purine type of substance might not be identical with the endogenous plant kinins. More recently several reports of purine materials found in growing plant tissues make it clear that the purines have a place among the endogenous kinins (Shantz and Steward, 1957; Miller, 1961*a*, *b*; Letham, 1963; Beauchesne and Goutarel, 1963). Based on the present evidence it seems that the native purine kinins may not be furfuryladenine, but many may be closely allied amino-substituted adenines.

The richest sources from which kinins have been isolated are fruits and endosperm tissues. Coconut milk is the most famous of

Fig. 8-3 | Stimulations of the enlargement of leaf disks have been used as an assay for kinins. These data are for radish leaf disks in the light, 20 hr (Kuraishi, 1959).

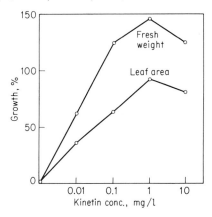

Fig. 8-4 | The ability of kinins to suppress the loss of chlorophyll from darkened disks of mature green leaves has also been used as an assay. In this case, *Xanthium* leaf disks were floated on kinetin solutions for 48 hr, and then the chlorophyll was extracted with 80 per cent ethanol and measured at 665 mμ. The initial chlorophyll content before the disks were placed in darkness is indicated by the arrow (Osborne and McCalla, 1961).

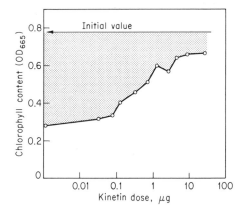

these (Steward and Caplin, 1952; Mauney et al., 1952). Corn endosperm has yielded growth substances active in tissue cultures (Haagen-Smit et al., 1945; Caplin and Steward, 1952; Netien and Beauchesne, 1954). McLane and Murneek (1952) found that content of the active material in corn increases abruptly after fertilization of the embryo and endosperm (Fig. 8-5). Other fruits from which kinins have been isolated include the plum, apple, tomato, chestnut, and banana (cf. Steward and Shantz, 1959*b*).

Vegetative tissues have yielded some kinins (Letham and Bollard, 1961; Zwar and Skoog, 1963), and tumorous tissues appear to be promising sources for kinin separation (Braun and Naf, 1954; Wood, 1963).

The identities of the kinins are confused. Research in Steward's laboratory indicates that as any one fraction of the coconut milk is purified, it loses its activity unless tested in combinations with other active fractions. Steward and Shantz (1959) have divided the active materials into three fractions: (1) compounds which are nitrogen sources, including amino acids, urea, allantoin, and others (Shantz and Steward, 1959*a*); (2) a neutral fraction which is not active itself but which is highly synergistic with the third; and (3) an "active" fraction which is a composite of numerous materials. One of these appears to be diphenyl urea (Shantz and Steward, 1955), which does not have striking stimulative effects itself but which is distinctly active when added in the presence of casein hydrolysate or other coconut-milk fractions. Table 3 shows that when diphenyl urea is added to the basic medium, the growth of carrot tissues is only slightly increased but that when it is added in combination with casein hydrolysate, it causes a doubling of the number of cells.

Further components of the third, or "active," fraction of coconut milk are inositol and sorbitol (Pollard et al., 1961). These compounds have only small activity themselves but have much greater effects when added with other components, reminiscent of the synergistic effects of inositol with the other B vitamins in animal nutrition.

Complex interactions are not restricted to coconut milk; similar requirements for multiple factors have been reported for fractionations from corn endosperm (Beauchesne, 1957) and *Aesculus* endosperm.

Fig. 8-5 | The kinin content of corn kernels is high in the first few days after fertilization and then proceeds to decline, as evidenced by the stimulatory effects of extracts on the growth (3 days) of excised corn embryos (McLane and Murneek, 1952).

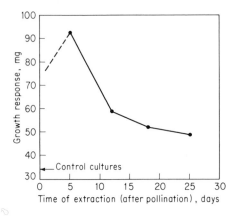

Table 3 | *Effect of diphenyl urea, coconut milk, and casein hydrolysate on growth of carrot-tissue cultures (Steward and Shantz, 1956).*

	Fresh weight, mg	Cell no., x10³
Basal medium	7.2	45
Basal + 2 ppm DPU	9.4	50
Basal + casein hydrolysate	29.4	201
Basal + casein hydrolysate + 2 DPU	56.8	508
Basal + casein hydrolysate + 10% CCM	294	2,662

The latter has yielded another active compound, a leucoanthocyanin (Steward and Shantz, 1956).

A specific interaction between the kinins and auxin should be mentioned. The growing tissues used as sources of extractable kinins consistently contain large amounts of auxin, and it is clear that auxins greatly magnify the kinin effects (Shantz et al., 1955).

Growth effects

Added kinins increase mitosis in roots (Guttman, 1956) and encourage mitosis in cultured flower anthers (Vasil, 1957; Walker and Dietrich, 1961), but the overall plant responses to kinins have been much less dramatic than those to auxins or gibberellins.

One of the most striking effects of the kinins is on differentiation. It has been noted that adenine can induce differentiation of buds on callus cultures (Skoog and Tsui, 1948, 1951) and that kinetin is much more effective in this differentiation effect (Skoog and Miller, 1957). Torrey (1958) found that roots of some types of *Convolvulus* which have strong tendencies to regenerate buds when disturbed are relatively rich in endogenous kinins. Vardjan and Nitsch (1961) followed the growth-substance changes during regeneration of chicory-root cuttings (Fig. 8-6). They found that at the base of the cutting, where roots are differentiated, the auxin content is high and the kinin content low—the conditions which favor the differentiation of roots (Skoog and Tsui, 1948). At the apex of the cutting, the kinin concentration is much higher initially, as would be appropriate for the region of bud differentiation.

Kinins are strong promoters of bud growth, thus modifying apical dominance. Thimann and Wickson (1957) obtained bud-growth promotion in pea-stem cuttings even when auxin was supplied in amounts which would normally inhibit bud growth. This kinin modification of apical dominance was confirmed in other tissues by von Maltzahn (1959).

Kinins also stimulate leaf enlargement. Leaves of etiolated seedlings often do not enlarge in the absence of light, and kinetin and other purines appear to increase the effectiveness of light. This effect, discovered simultaneously by Kuraishi and Okumura (1956) and by Scott and Liverman (1956), is illustrated in Fig. 8-3. Kuraishi and Okumura (1961) later separated from coconut milk a material which was similarly effective in promoting leaf enlargement.

The applications of kinins to plants can modify many developmental activities in-

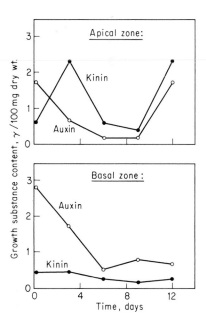

Fig. 8-6 | A comparison of the kinin and auxin content of root cuttings of *Chichorium* during regeneration. The apical part of the cutting shows the greatest kinin content, and the basal part the greatest auxin content, as asayed by the leaf disk and mesocotyl tests, respectively (Vardjan and Nitsch, 1961).

cluding dormancy (Miller, 1956; Ogawara and Ono, 1961), polarity of growth (Sommer, 1961), and flowering (Nakayama et al., 1962). These various effects repeatedly imply some relationship between kinins and light. Thus kinetin may increase the effectiveness of light in seed germination (Miller, 1956), leaf enlargement (Scott and Liverman, 1956), stem elongation (Fries, 1960), or bud formation (Szweykowska, 1963).

Kinin action

The assays used in the studies of kinins are highly heterogeneous, and the action of kinins on cells and tissues seems to be extremely varied. The heterogeneous nature of the molecules active in cell division ranges from the simple purines such as kinetin and benzyladenine to the startlingly different inositol and leucoanthocyanin

Fig. 8-7 | Cell division in synchronized cultures of *Chlorella* is inhibited by 1 per cent CO_2. Bicarbonate ($10^{-3}M$) can neutralize the inhibition. Treatments were applied at 7 hr. All cells in control divided by 16 hr, when these data were taken (Sorokin, 1962*b*).

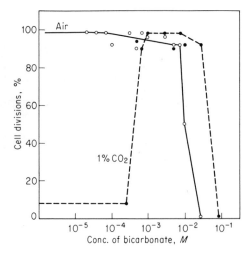

(Fig. 8-2). This makes the prospect of finding straightforward action of the kinins as a group appear highly unlikely.

The assignment of kinins with the regulation of cell divisions is sometimes difficult to defend. Auxins can induce cell divisions in many situations (Levan, 1939); the requirement for auxins as cofactors of the cell-division actions of both the purine kinins and the coconut-milk factors again implicates the auxins in the control of this physiological function. Gibberellins, too, can induce cell divisions (Sachs et al., 1959). In short, Wiesner's (1892) idea of a chemical that would control cell division therefore appears too simple to match the facts. Instead, as Steward and Shantz (1959*a*) pointed out, it is more reasonable to assume that the control of cell division encompasses many chemical factors, and if in a test situation one of these is insufficient, its addition will indicate cell-division stimulatory properties for that factor.

The ability of cells to undergo division can be markedly altered by the acidity and the presence of CO_2. Using synchronized cultures of *Chlorella*, Sorokin (1962*a,b*) found that mitoses which were normally completed by all the cells after 16 hr in darkness were in fact entirely prevented by 1 per cent CO_2 (Fig. 8-7). The inhibition was alleviated by concentrations of bicarbonate which neutralized the acidifying tendencies of the CO_2. The sensitivity of mitosis to acid pH is a reminder that the cell-division factors are the only known class of growth substance which is not acidic. The role of acidity of the cell microenvironment as a determinant of cell division remains to be clarified.

The numerous types of substances which may regulate mitosis could be a consequence of numerous steps which can be regulated. Patau et al. (1957) suggested that kinins and auxins may affect distinctive mitotic steps, including the doubling of the DNA content of the nucleus, the steps of mitosis itself (prophase, metaphase, anaphase, and telophase), and then cytokinesis. Their evidence indicates that auxin may share in the control of the nuclear increase in DNA and of the mitotic stages but that kinetin may preferentially regulate the cell-division or cytokinesis step.

This scheme of Patau et al. (1957) permits a more rational arrangement of some otherwise confusing information. The fact that auxin can stimulate mitosis without cytokinesis (Naylor et al., 1954) is consistent with the later finding that auxin can encourage the DNA doubling step, and to a lesser extent the mitotic steps, but not cytokinesis (Patau et al., 1957). McMann (1960) showed that kinetin could cause a decrease in mitotic figures, whereas auxin could increase their frequency. This is consistent with the interpretation that the kinin stimulation of cytokinesis could "use up" the available cells which had already doubled their nuclear contents and that auxins could make more of these available but without the capability of stimulating the progress into cytokinesis.

Some experiments by Torrey (1961) illustrate the ability of kinetin specifically to stimulate the cytokinesis step. He found that kinetin applied to root-tissue cultures would preferentially encourage cytokinesis in cells which had already undergone endomitosis. By altering the cell-division factors added to tissue cultures, he was able preferentially to stimulate cytokinesis in the 2N, the 4N, or the 8N cells. The kinetin concentration, too, altered the types of cells stimulated to cytokinesis; lower concentrations stimulated diploid cells, and higher concentrations stimulated tetraploid cells (Fig. 8-8).

Kinins cause marked alterations in the protein and nucleic acid components of tissues, an effect which could be a basic part of the kinin effects on cell division (Guttman, 1956) as well as on growth and mobilization actions. The increases in proteins and nucleic acids in kinin-treated leaves have been illustrated by Mothes's school (Mothes et al., 1959; Mothes, 1960).

Some comparative data published by Parthier and Wollgiehn (1961) are illustrated in Fig. 8-9. It appears that protein content and RNA and DNA contents are all increased markedly by kinetin treatment.

The application of kinins to leaves causes a mobilization of nutrients into the treated area (Mothes et al., 1959). The mobilization effect may be related to the effects on protein and nucleic-acid contents and to the development of senescence of the leaves (see Chap. 12) but does not apparently involve any cell-division activities. Figures 5-9 and 5-10 show that kinetin applications could defer the decline in leaf proteins with aging and could lead to the accumulation of labeled nutrients in the treated leaf sectors. As a further illustration, Fig. 8-10 (Mueller, 1964) shows the mobilization of labeled phosphorus into a kinetin-treated zone in a corn leaf. The occurrence of kinins in regions of strong mobilization activities such as flowers and young fruits suggests that they may be involved in the endogenous mechanisms of mobilization phenomena (Leopold, 1963). The ability to draw nu-

Fig. 8-8 | In root-tissue cultures, where there may accumulate various levels of polyploidy, kinetin may have a preferential effect in causing cell division among the 2N or the 4N cells, depending upon the concentration of kinetin applied (Torrey, 1961).

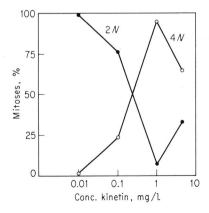

Fig. 8-9 | The application of kinetin to leaf disks of *Nicotiana* can increase the incorporation of C¹⁴ from glycine into protein, RNA, and DNA fractions. Shaded bars represent the disks treated with kinetin (30 mg/liter); cpm × 10³ for protein and × 10² for the nucleic acids (Partheir and Wollgiehn, 1961).

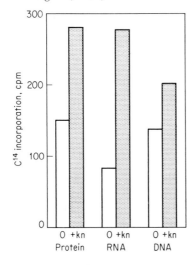

Fig 8-10 | A localized application of kinetin (30 mg/liter) to corn leaves results in a mobilization of radioactivity from $P^{32}O_4$ applied near the leaf tip. Scanning the same leaf at intervals reveals the accumulation at the position of kinetin application (Mueller, 1964).

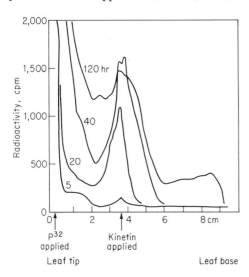

trients to a localized area and there elevate the protein and nucleic acid contents is an appropriate characteristic for cell-division factors.

Conclusion

In discussing the kinins, it has been emphasized that in comparison with the auxins and gibberellins, more diverse types of chemicals can have cell-division effects. Furthermore, the kinins as a group can alter many other growth functions including leaf growth, apical dominance, and various light responses. These growth responses may be entirely independent of any cell-division stimulations, but this is not surprising in view of the known effects of the kinins in elevating the levels of protein, DNA, and RNA in the cells. In short, the kinins appear to be a loose group of substances which occur in plants and which can participate in many aspects of growth and development.

A sharp contrast between the kinins and the other growth substances is seen in the fact that the kinins are not acidic in reaction, in contrast to the acid auxins and gibberellins. Woolley (1957) suggested that the mobile plant hormones may be acidic because with the acidic nature of plant cell walls alkaline materials would be much less mobile. In the kinins we see an extreme case of nonmobility in this nonacidic plant growth substance.

GENERAL REFERENCES

Miller, C. O. 1961. Kinetin and related compounds in plant growth. *Ann. Rev. Plant Physiol.*, 12:395–408.

Skoog, F., and C. O. Miller. 1957. Chemical regulation of growth and organ formation in plant tissues cultured *in vivo*. *Symp. Soc. Exptl. Biol.*, 11:118–131.

Steward, F. C., and E. Shantz. 1959. The chemical regulation of growth. *Ann. Rev. Plant Physiol.*, 10:379–404.

REFERENCES CITED

Beauchesne, G. 1957. *Compt. Rend.* (*Paris*). 244:112. (In Steward and Shantz,1959*b*.)

———— and R. Goutarel. 1963. Isolement d'une kinine à partir du maïs immature et determination de sa formule chimique, pp. 119–122. *Colloq. Reg. Nat. Croiss. Veg.*

Bonner, J., and J. English. 1938. A chemical and physiological study of traumatin, a plant wound hormone. *Plant Physiol.*, 13: 331–348.

Braun, A. C., and U. Naf. 1954. A non-auxinic growth-promoting factor present in crown gall tumor tissue. *Proc. Soc. Exptl. Biol. Med.*, 86:212–214.

Caplin, S. M., and F. C. Steward. 1952. Investigations on the growth and metabolism of plant cells. II. *Ann. Botany* (*London*), 16:219–234.

Collier, H. O. J. 1962. Kinins. *Sci. Am.*, 207:111–118.

Fries, N. 1960. The effect of adenine and kinetin on growth and differentiation of *Lupinus. Physiol. Plantarum*, 13:468–481.

Guttman, R. 1956. Effects of kinetin on cell division with special reference to initiation and duration of mitosis. *Chromosoma*, 8:341–350.

Haagen-Smit, A. J., R. Siar, and G. Wilson. 1945. A method for the culturing of excised, immature corn embryos *in vitro*. *Science*, 101:234.

Haberlandt, G. 1913. Zur Physiologie der Zellteilung. *Sitz. Ber. k. preuss. Akad. Wiss.*, 1913:318–345.

————. 1921. Wundhormone als Erreger von Zellteilungen. *Beitr. Allg. Bot.*, 2:1–53.

Jablonski, J. R., and F. Skoog. 1954. Cell enlargement and cell division in excised tobacco pith tissue. *Physiol. Plantarum*, 7:16–24.

Kuraishi, S. 1959. Effect of kinetin analogs on leaf growth. *Sci. Papers Coll. Gen. Educ. Univ. Tokyo*, 9:67–104.

———— and F. S. Okumura. 1956. The effect of kinetin on leaf growth. *Botan. Mag.* (*Tokyo*), 69:817–818.

———— and ————. 1961. A new green leaf growth stimulating factor, phyllococosine, from coconut milk. *Nature*, 189: 148–149.

Leopold, A. C. 1963. Kinins and the regulation of leaf aging. *Colloq. Reg. Nat. Croiss. Veg.*, 101–103.

Letham, D. S. 1963. Isolation of a kinin from plum fruitlets and other tissues. *Colloq. Reg. Nat. Croiss. Veg.*

———— and E. G. Bollard. 1961. Stimulator of cell division in developing fruits. *Nature*, 191:1119–1120.

Levan, A. 1939. The effect of colchicine on meiosis in *Allium. Hereditas*, 25:9–26.

McLane, S. R., and A. E. Murneek. 1952. The detection of syngamin, an indigenous plant hormone, by culture of immature corn embryos. *Univ. Missouri Res. Bull.*, 496:1–91.

McMann, M. A. 1960. Certain mitotic effects of kinetin, gibberellic acid, indole acetic acid and maleic hydrazide on the root of *Allium cepa. Nature*, 185:44–45.

Mauney, J. R., W. S. Hillman, C. O. Miller, F. Skoog, R. A. Clayton, and F. M. Strong. 1952. Bioassay, purification and properties of a growth factor from coconut. *Physiol. Plantarum*, 5:485–497.

Miller, C. O. 1956. Similarity of some kinetin and red light effects. *Plant Physiol.*, 31:318–319.

————. 1958. The relationship of the kinetin and red-light promotions of lettuce seed germination. *Plant Physiol.*, 33:115–117.

————. 1961*a*. Kinetin and related compounds in plant growth. *Ann. Rev. Plant Physiol.* 12:395–408.

————. 1961*b*. A kinetin-like compound in maize. *Proc. Natl. Acad. Sci. U.S.*, 47: 170–174.

————, F. Skoog, F. S. Okumura, M. H. von Saltza, and F. M. Strong. 1955. Structure and synthesis of kinetin. *J. Am. Chem. Soc.*, 77:2662–2663.

————, ————, ————, ————, and ————. 1956. Isolation, structure and synthesis of kinetin, a substance promoting cell division. *J. Am. Chem. Soc.,* 78:1375–1380.

———, F. Skoog, M. H. von Saltza, and F. M. Strong. 1955. Kinetin: a cell division factor from deoxyribonucleic acid. *J. Am. Chem. Soc.,* 77:1392.

Mothes, K. 1960. Über das Altern der Blatter und die Möglichkeit ihrer Wiederverjungung. *Naturwissenschaften,* 47:337–350.

———, L. Engelbrecht, and O. Kulajewa. 1959. Über die Wirkung des Kinetins auf Stickstoffverteilung und Eiweisssynthese in isolierte Blättern. *Flora (Jena),* 147: 445–464.

Mueller, K. 1964. Kinetin action and senescence. Doctoral Diss., Ludwig Maximillian Univ., Munich.

Nakayama, S., H. Tobita, and F. S. Okumura. 1962. Antagonism of kinetin and far-red light or IAA in flowering in *Pharbitis. Phyton (Buenos Aires),* 19:43–48.

Naylor, J., G. Sander, and F. Skoog. 1954. Mitosis and cell enlargement without cell division in excised tobacco pith tissue. *Physiol. Plantarum,* 7:25–29.

Netien, G., and G. Beauchesne. 1954. Essai d'isolement d'un facteur de croissance présent dans un extrait laiteaux de caryopses de mais immatures. *Ann. Biol.,* 58: 437–443.

Nitsch, J. P., and C. Nitsch. 1961*a.* Synergistes naturels des auxines et des gibberellines. *Bull. Soc. Botan. France,* 108: 349–362.

——— and ———. 1961*b.* Growth factors in the tomato fruit, pp. 687–705. In R. M. Klein (ed.), *Plant Growth Regulation.* Iowa State University Press, Ames, Iowa.

Ogawara, K., and K. Ono. 1961. Interaction of gibberellin, kinetin and potassium nitrate in germination of light-sensitive tobacco seeds. *Plant Cell Physiol. (Tokyo),* 2:87–98.

Osborne, D. J., and D. R. McCalla. 1961. Rapid bioassay for kinetin and kinins using senescing leaf tissue. *Plant Physiol.,* 36: 219–221.

Overbeek, J. van, M. E. Conklin, and A. F. Blakeslee. 1941. Factors in coconut milk essential for growth and development of *Datura* embryos. *Science,* 94:350–351.

———, ———, and ———. 1942. Cultivation *in vitro* of small *Datura* embryos. *Am. J. Botany,* 29:472–477.

Partheir, B., and R. Wollgiehn. 1961. Über den Einfluss des Kinetins auf den Eiweiss —und Nukleinsäure Stoffwecksel in isolierten Tabakblattern. *Ber. Deut. Botan. Ges.,* 74: 47–51.

Patau, K., N. K. Das, and F. Skoog. 1957. Induction of DNA synthesis by kinetin and indoleacetic acid in excised tobacco pith tissue. *Physiol. Plantarum,* 10:949–966.

Pollard, J. K., E. M. Shantz, and F. C. Steward. 1961. Hexitols in coconut milk: their role in nurture of dividing cells. *Plant Physiol.,* 36:492–501.

Sachs, F. M., C. F. Bretz, and A. Lang. 1959. Short histogenesis: the early effects of gibberellin upon stem elongation in two rosette plants. *Am. J. Botany,* 46: 376–384.

Scott, R. A., Jr., and J. L. Liverman. 1956. Promotion of leaf expansion by kinetin and benzylaminopurine. *Plant Physiol.,* 31:321–322.

Shantz, E. M., and F. C. Steward. 1955. The identification of compound A from coconut milk as 1,3-diphenylurea. *J. Am. Chem. Soc.,* 77:6351–6353.

——— and ———. 1957. The growth stimulating substances in extracts of immature corn grain: a progress report. *Plant Physiol.,* 32:viii.

——— and ———. 1959. Investigations on growth and metabolism of plant cells. VII. Sources of nitrogen. *Ann. Botany (London),* 23:372–390.

———, F. C. Steward, M. S. Smith, and R. L. Wain. 1955. Investigations on the growth and metabolism of plant cells. VI. Growth of potato tuber tissue in culture: the synergistic action of coconut milk and some synthetic growth-regulating compounds. *Ann. Botany (London)*, 19:49–58.

Skinner, C. G. 1959. Stimulation of lettuce seed germination by 6-substituted purines. *Plant Physiol.*, 34:1–3.

———, R. G. Ham, D. C. Fitzgerald, Jr., R. E. Eakin, and W. Shive. 1956. Synthesis and biological activity of some 6-substituted thiopurines. *J. Organ. Chem.*, 21:1330.

Skoog, F., and C. O. Miller. 1957. Chemical regulation of growth and organ formation in plant tissues cultured *in vivo*. *Symp. Soc. Exptl. Biol.*, 11:118–131.

——— and C. Tsui. 1948. Chemical control of growth and bud formation on tobacco stem and callus cultured *in vitro*. *Am. J. Botany*, 35:782–787.

——— and ———. 1951. Growth substances and the formation of buds in plant tissues, pp. 263–298. In F. Skoog (ed.), *Plant Growth Substances*. The University of Wisconsin Press, Madison, Wis.

Sommer, N. F. 1961. Longitudinal and lateral response of etiolated pea sections to indoleacetic acid, gibberellins, kinetins, sucrose and cobalt. *Physiol. Plantarum*, 14:741–749.

Sorokin, C. 1962*a*. Effects of acidity on cell division. *Exptl. Cell Res.*, 27:583–584.

———. 1962*b*. Carbon dioxide and bicarbonate in cell division. *Arch. Mikrobiol.*, 44:219–227.

Steward, F. C., and S. M. Caplin. 1952. Investigations on growth and metabolism of plant cells. *Ann. Botany (London)*, 16:478–489.

———, and E. M. Shantz. 1956. The chemical induction of growth in plant tissue cultures, pp. 165–186. In R. L. Wain and F. Wightman (eds.), *The Chemistry and Mode of Action of Plant Growth Substances*. Academic Press, Inc., New York.

——— and ———. 1959*a*. Biochemistry and morphogenesis: knowledge derived from plant tissue cultures. *Proc. Intern. Congr. Biochem. 4th*, 6:223–236.

——— and ———. 1959*b*. The chemical regulation of growth. *Ann. Rev. Plant Physiol.*, 10:379–404.

Szweykowska, A. 1963. Kinetin-induced formation of gametophores. *J. Exptl. Botany*, 14:137–141.

Thimann, K. V., and M. Wickson. 1957. Experiments on the physiology of apical dominance. *Photo-thermoperiodism Colloq. (Parma)*, 47–50.

Torrey, J. G. 1958. Endogenous bud and root formation by isolated roots of *Convolvulus* grown *in vitro*. *Plant Physiol.*, 33:258–263.

———. 1961. Kinetin as trigger for mitosis in mature endomitotic plant cells. *Exptl. Cell Res.*, 23:281–299.

Vardjan, M., and J. P. Nitsch. 1961. La regeneration chez *Chichorium:* étude des auxines et des kinines endogenes. *Bull. Soc. Botan. France*, 108:363–374.

Vasil, I. K. 1957. Effect of kinetin and gibberellic acid on excised anthers of *Allium cepa*. *Phytomorphology*, 7:138–149.

von Maltzahn, K. E. 1959. Interaction between kinetin and IAA in control of bud reactivation in *Splachnum ampullaceum*. *Nature*, 183:60–61.

Walker, G. W. R., and V. Dietrich. 1961. Kinetin induced meiotic prophase acceleration in *Tradescantia* anthers. *Nature*, 192:889–890.

Wiesner, J. 1892. *Die Elementarstruktur und das Wachstum der lebender Substanz*. A. Hölder, Vienna.

Wood, H. N. 1963. The characterization of naturally occurring kinins from crown gall tumor cells of *Vinca rosea*, pp. 97–102. *Colloq. Reg. Nat. Croiss. Veg.*

Woolley, D. W. 1957. Probable evolutionary relationship of serotonin and indoleacetic acid and some practical consequences thereof. *Nature*, 180:630–633.

Zwar, J. A., and F. Skoog. 1963. Promotion of cell division by extracts from pea seedlings. *Australian J. Biol. Sci.*, 16:129–139.

9 | Inhibitors

It seems reasonable to assume that if there were not means of retarding growth and developmental processes, the resulting uncontrolled growth could be a distinct disadvantage to the plant. There are obvious structural limitations to an unending enlargement of stem internodes, leaves, or in fact nearly any plant part. At certain times the survival of a plant depends on its ability to become dormant or otherwise restrain its growth or reproductive activities. Furthermore, many developmental processes require restrictions on growth. To control or limit growth processes, the plant may utilize the toxic products of metabolism. In many instances, research on the nature of biological controls of growth processes has produced evidence that toxic substances or inhibitors may be involved in the control.

An experimental difficulty in studies of inhibitors is the fact that the presence of toxic substances in plant extracts is not necessarily indicative of their involvement in any growth or developmental process. Cyanide can be extracted from almonds, but this does not indicate that enzyme systems are being inhibited. The presumption that toxic substances in extracts may be involved in the control of a growth or developmental process must be based on evidence that such substances are at least quantitatively related to the process.

The toxic substance should also effectively inhibit the particular growth or developmental process in question. Studies of seed dormancy which use the coleoptile straight-growth test to measure inhibitors from dormant seeds may give results which are not pertinent to dormancy. It is helpful to select an assay which most nearly evokes the type of response in the phenomenon being studied, but physiologists have often used unrelated tests, and the results are difficult to interpret.

In many cases the conventional growth tests have poor sensitivity to the natural inhibitory substances. For example, the oat-coleoptile straight-growth test shows only weak responses to such common inhibitors as ferulic, caffeic, or chlorogenic acid. Consequently, many studies of plant extracts may be misleading in that the assay did not satisfactorily respond to the inhibitors that were present.

Occurrence

Toxic substances and growth inhibitors are ubiquitous in plants, and it is beyond the scope of this text to discuss them all. Instead, examples will be given of some inhibitors found in plants for which there is evidence of participation in some phase of growth or development.

Toxic or inhibitory compounds have been separated from plants for many years. Köckemann (1934) was perhaps the first to implicate these materials in the natural control of a developmental process in plants. Finding inhibitors in seeds, he proposed that such materials might limit the ability of seeds to germinate. Audus (1947) noted that in roots, lactones such as coumarin were sometimes present in quantities which could limit either germination or growth rates. Representative data in Fig. 9-1 show that with the addition of coumarin, either root growth or seed germination could be effectively inhibited.

The regulatory concept of growth inhibitors really gained importance, however, with the discovery by Hemberg (1949*a,b*) that dormant buds of ash and potatoes contained large amounts of inhibitors and that when dormancy was broken, the inhibitor contents declined. By testing the effectiveness of a standard amount of auxin in the *Avena* curvature assay when increasing amounts of the suspected inhibitor were added, Hemberg obtained results (Fig. 9-2) showing a dynamic change in amount of inhibitors associated with the emergence from dormancy.

Since that time, the concept of inhibitors as endogenous controls of growth has been

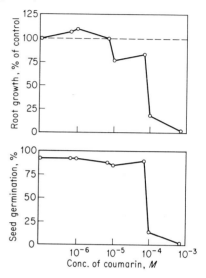

Fig. 9-1 | The inhibitory effects of coumarin on the growth of roots of cress seedlings (above) and on the germination of cress seeds (below) (Audus, 1947).

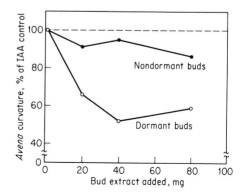

Fig. 9-2 | Measurements of the amount of extractable inhibitors from potato buds indicate relatively large amounts in the dormant buds and little or none in the nondormant buds. Assayed as inhibition of *Avena* curvature test with increasing amounts of bud extract added to auxin in the agar block (as milligram equivalents of peelings extracted). Dormancy was removed by ethylene treatment of the tubers 4 days before extraction (Hemberg, 1949*a*).

applied to a wide range of growth processes. For example, Nitsch (1957) showed that various woody plants which cease growth under short photoperiods experience a pronounced increase in growth inhibitors (Fig. 9-3). Representative of the current method of analysis for growth inhibitors, methanol extracts were chromatographed, and the regions of the paper were then assayed for growth inhibition with oat-coleoptile sections.

Using the chromatographic method of analysis, the idea of Köckemann (1934) has been reexamined. Varga and Ferenczy (1957) have analyzed strawberry fruits for inhibitors which may limit the germination of the achenes. They found (Fig. 9-4) that there was a single inhibitory material detectable by chromatography. Note that they employed a seed-germination assay for their suspected germination inhibitor, albeit a poppy-seed test.

Iwanami (1957*b*) was interested in the possibility that inhibitory substances in the styles of incompatible flowers might contribute to the failure of pollen-tube growth. Using the chromatographic separation of stylar extracts of *Camellia,* he found that pollen seeded onto the moistened chromatographic paper allowed the detection of a pollen-tube growth inhibitor (Fig. 9-5).

Plants can release inhibitors into the ambient soil or solution medium, where they can then cause inhibitions of growth either of the source plants or of competing plants. This aspect of the action of inhibitors emerged in 1928, when Davis identified juglone as the toxic material in roots and branches of walnut. He further showed that this substance was responsible for the inhibitions of growth of other plants near walnut trees. In 1944, Bonner and Galston established that cinnamic acid could account for the inhibitory effects of guayule plants on nearby competitors. Since then many other inhibitors have been found as decomposition products or simply as excreted materials from roots or leaves (cf. review of Bonner, 1950).

Fig. 9-3 | Measurements of the amounts of extractable inhibitors from shoot tips of *Rhus typhina* grown in long days or after 14 short days (10 hr). Methanol extracts were chromatographed in isopropanol/ammonia/water, and the paper was assayed with the oat-coleoptile-section test. Note the large increase in inhibitor content after the short-day treatment. Dotted lines indicate the R_f expected for indoleacetic acid (Nitsch, 1957).

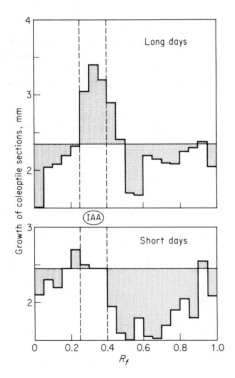

Chemical types of inhibitors

The most common growth inhibitors are aromatic organic materials, although there are also such diverse inhibitors as ascorbic acid (Tonzig and Marré, 1955), some fatty acids (Bentley, 1958; Isogai, 1960), and metallic ions (Burström, 1960). The simple phenyl compounds are most widely represented, including the phenols, the benzoic acids, the longer-chained cinnamic acid series, and the lactones of these—the coumarin series. Among larger molecules are the flavanoid inhibitors and depsids between two acids such as chlorogenic acid. Some representatives of these known classes of natural inhibitors are shown in Fig. 9-6.

The aromatic inhibitors fall into the pharmacologist's category of phenolics, associated most commonly with the plant tannins (cf. review of Bate-Smith, 1959). The phenolics include many substances of potent biological activity, with such diverse properties as estrogenic activities, cathartic actions, musculature controls, and photodynamic and bactericidal actions, in addition to toxic properties (cf. Fairbairn, 1959).

The acidic nature of the phenolics permits the formation of esters with other hydroxyl compounds. Thus the phenols and flavins occur in plants usually as glycoside esters with sugars or as depsid esters between two phenolics, as in chlorogenic acid.

Among the phenolics, the acids are best recognized as plant growth inhibitors. The hydroxybenzoic acids are extremely common plant constituents (Tomaszewski, 1960). The slightly larger cinnamic acid series are also common inhibitors as the free acids (cinnamic, caffeic, coumaric, ferulic) and the closely related internal lactones (coumarin, esculin, scopoletin). The cinnamic acids may be weak auxins in the *cis* configuration or antagonists of auxin in the *trans* form (van Overbeek et al., 1951), and the lactones are commonly synergistic types of inhibitors (Thimann and Bonner, 1949). Chlorogenic acid, a depsid between caffeic and quinic acids, is a common inhibitor which may be classed as the synergistic type, and the more elaborate flavanoids are also sometimes strong synergistic inhibitors (Nitsch and Nitsch, 1961; Nitsch, 1962a).

Special mention should be made of a complex of inhibiting substances first described by Bennet-Clark and Kefford (1953). This appeared as an inhibitory area

on paper chromatograms of plant extracts, running ahead of indoleacetic acid upon development with isopropanol/ammonia/water. The characteristic position of this inhibitor β is shown in Fig. 9-7 (Kefford, 1955a). The inhibitory zones shown in Figs. 9-3 and 9-4 are probably similar materials. Inhibitor β is widespread in plants

Fig. 9-4 | Inhibitors of seed germination in strawberry fruits. Ethanol extracts were chromatographed in isopropanol/ammonia/water, and the paper was assayed with germinating poppy seeds. Note the strong inhibitor at R_f 0.6 to 0.8 (Varga and Ferenczy, 1957).

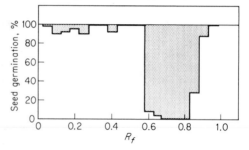

Fig. 9-5 | Inhibitors of pollen-tube growth in *Camellia* stigmas. Alcoholic extracts chromatographed in butanol/ethanol/water and assayed using the growth of *Lilium* pollen on the moistened paper. Note the growth inhibitor in the region of R_f 0.2; the inhibition near the solvent front (R_f 0.8 to 1.0) was due to impurities in the developing solvents (Iwanami, 1957b).

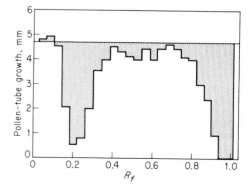

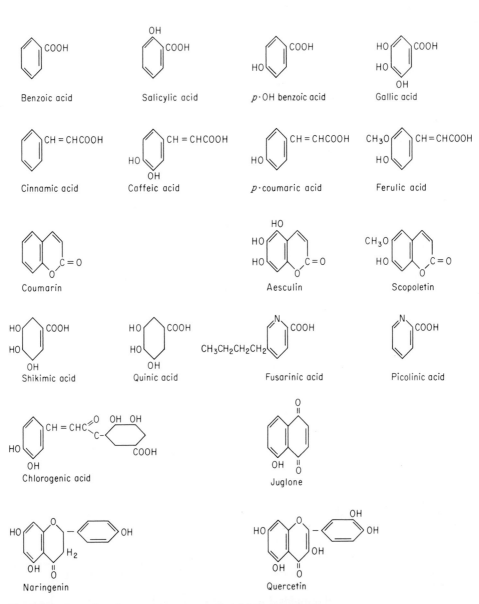

Fig. 9-6 | Examples of some common growth inhibitors in plants. Derivatives of benzoic acid including salicylic, *p*-hydroxy benzoic and gallic acids are very common, especially in ripening fruits. The cinnamic acid derivatives include the cofactors for indoleacetic oxidase, *p*-coumaric acid and ferulic acid. The commonest lactone inhibitors include coumarin, aesculin and scopoletin. Other types include pyridine derivatives (fusarinic and picolinic acids), depsids (chlorogenic acid), quinones (juglone), and flavanoids (naringenin and quercitin).

and has attracted much attention. It has been related with both dormancy and correlation effects; however, it has not yet yielded to identification attempts. Elution of the inhibitory zone from the chromatograph and rechromatography in other solvents has yielded mixtures of acidic and neutral substances (Libbert, 1954). Bentley (1958) has suggested that it may include some toxic fatty acids, but still the nature of inhibitor β remains obscure.

Since most growth inhibitors were worked out by physiologists specifically interested in the auxin regulation of growth, the concepts of growth inhibition and auxin antagonism have become closely intertwined. But it is increasingly clear that some natural growth inhibitors may antagonize the action of gibberellins. The gibberellin-stimulated growth of dwarf pea seedlings can be inhibited by an extract of lima beans (Fig. 9-8). That inhibitors may also antagonize the action of the kinins is implied by the effects of some flavanoids reported by Nitsch (1962*a*) and of some plant extracts reported by Letham (1963). There is a maximum of information available about the actions of inhibitors against auxin stimulations of growth, perhaps reflecting the inclinations of physiologists more than the propensities of natural growth regulators.

Actions of inhibitors

The actions involving auxin systems might be conveniently discussed as actions on auxin oxidase, actions on auxin itself, and synergistic actions, though the three categories overlap.

A relatively simple action which is often invoked to explain the inhibitory effects of various phenolics on plant growth is the activation of indoleacetic oxidase. The oxidative decarboxylation of indoleacetic acid by the pea enzyme requires a phenolic cofactor as an oxidant for the metallic oxidizer (Mn). Goldacre et al. (1953) found

Fig. 9-7 | Growth substances detected from an extract of etiolated sunflower seedlings, showing in addition to the auxin at R_f 0.3 (probably indoleacetic acid) another growth promoter at the starting line—accelerator α—and large amounts of an inhibitor at R_f 0.5 and above—inhibitor β. Ethanol extract chromatographed in isopropanol/ammonia/water (Kefford, 1955*a*).

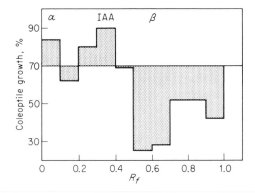

Fig. 9-8 | Evidence for an inhibitor of gibberellin-stimulated growth in extracts of lima beans. Chloroform extract applied to dwarf peas with or without addition of gibberellic acid (15 mμg per plant), showing the inhibition of the stem response to gibberellic acid (Kohler and Lang, 1963).

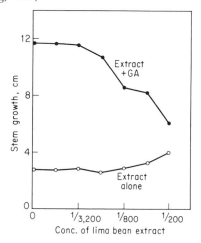

that various substituted phenols would activate indoleacetic oxidase, and Gortner et al. (1958) attributed the activation effect specifically to endogenous ferulic and *p*-coumaric acid in pineapple-leaf tissues. In other tissues other naturally occurring phenolics may be functional (e.g., Mumford et al., 1963), and the net effect of the presence of these chemicals would presumably be a depression of growth. If the action of a growth inhibitor were simply this, one would hope that its addition would restore growth when auxin concentrations were excessive. In roots, auxin levels are considered to be supraoptimal, but root growth promotions are not usually obtained with natural inhibitors (e.g., Pohl and Tegethoff, 1949).

Inhibitors might also be added to the auxin molecule itself, as suggested for *ortho*-phenols by Tomaszewski (1959), or they may compete at the presumed site of auxin action, as suggested for *trans*-cinnamic acid by van Overbeek et al. (1951).

Fig. 9-9 | Apparent synergistic effects of coumarin and indoleacetic acid on the growth of oat-coleoptile sections. All solutions contain sucrose plus 1 mg/liter indoleacetic acid; growth was for 48 hr. At low coumarin concentrations there was an enhancement of growth; at higher concentrations there was an inhibition (Thimann and Bonner, 1949).

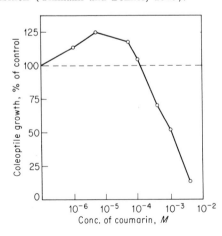

Many natural inhibitors in plant extracts have a synergistic effect on growth, promoting auxin-induced growth at low concentrations and inhibiting at higher concentrations. This complicated effect was noted by Thimann and Bonner (1949) for the lactones such as coumarin (Fig. 9-9). Such synergistic effects are common to many phenols and flavanoids (Nitsch and Nitsch, 1962). It is not uncommon for inhibitors to show synergistic promotive effects at low concentrations, but the basis for such effects is unclear (Thimann, 1956). It has been suggested that synergistic promotions may be due to competition of, for example, auxin and coumarin for inactive sites, causing a greater efficiency of the auxin at very low inhibitor concentrations. Possibly an inhibitor may have more than one way of affecting growth, the alternative effects dominating growth at different inhibitor concentrations. Andreae (1952) found that the lactone scopoletin could inhibit indoleacetic oxidase; thus its promotive effects on growth could be through such an action, in contrast to its inhibitory effects at higher concentrations. Henderson and Nitsch (1962) showed that chlorogenic acid could retard the disappearance of indoleacetic acid in oat internodes, implying again that the promotions at low concentrations could relate to indoleacetic oxidase effects.

Nitsch and Nitsch (1961) discovered that the synergistic promotions of growth by phenolics were obtained only when indoleacetic acid was supplied as the auxin. No promotive effects were found from additions of chlorogenic acid or other phenolics when naphthaleneacetic acid or other auxins were used. This led to the suggestion that synergisms were specifically consequent to the phenolic actions on indoleacetic acid oxidase—perhaps a sparing action on auxin at low phenolic concentrations. Some phenolics simply inhibit growth without any synergistic promotions (e.g., *meta*-phenols, salicylic acid, *p*-coumaric acid, and naringenin), whereas others are synergistic promoters at low concentrations and inhibitors at higher ones (e.g., *ortho*-phenols, polyhydroxy phenols, chlorogenic acid, and quercitin) (Nitsch and Nitsch, 1961, 1962). Zenk and Müller (1963) performed the critical experiment of adding various phenols to coleoptile pieces and measuring the effects on the decarboxylation of labeled indoleacetic acid. The auxin synergists caffeic acid and chlorogenic acid actually suppressed auxin oxidation, and the growth inhibitors *p*-hydroxybenzoic acid and *p*-coumaric acid markedly enhanced auxin oxidation in the tissues. Some of the growth regulating actions of phenolic types of compounds can clearly be attributed, then, to their effects on indoleacetic oxidase.

The synergistic effect depends on the concentration of the phenolic compound and also on the auxin concentration. For example, coumarin itself has probably no activity in the oat straight-growth test, but it has a synergistic action in the presence of 10^{-5} M indoleacetic acid; at higher auxin concentrations the synergism is lost (Fig. 9-10; Gantzer, 1960). Occasionally the reverse is true, and the promotion effect is obtained only without added auxin, but this may be due to the presence of adequate endogenous auxin content in the growing tissue (Barlow et al., 1955; Shibaoka and Imaseki, 1957).

In contrast to the information on inhibitor interactions with auxins which has evolved into the complicated realm of competitions and synergisms, the interactions of inhibitors with other growth regulators have hardly been examined. The stimulations of growth evoked by gibberellins can be inhibited by natural extractable materials, as shown first by Corcoran et al. (1961; Fig. 7-17). In more detailed studies of such inhibitors, Kohler and Lang (1963) separated from lima beans an inhibitor which clearly antagonized gibberellin-induced growth (Fig. 9-8) in a manner suggesting the antagon-

isms of gibberellin already known for some synthetic growth regulators. Kuraishi and Muir (1963) have questioned whether the auxin and gibberellin antagonisms of growth regulators can really be separated, however, for they found that the growth inhibitions imposed by the presumed gibberellin antagonist CCC (see Chap. 7) were reversible with the addition of auxin but not with gibberellin. This observation may be due to the fact that the growth system used was the coleoptile section, which is markedly more sensitive to auxin than to gibberellin.

In addition to the inhibitors of auxin and of gibberellin actions, there is preliminary evidence of an inhibitor of kinin action. Letham (1963) has found an inhibitor of cell division in extracts of developing plum fruitlets.

It would be unreasonable to attempt to account for the actions of growth inhibitors as being due exclusively to their interactions with auxins, gibberellins, or other specific

Fig. 9-10 | The effect of different concentrations of indoleacetic acid on the synergistic promotions with coumarin, showing synergism with $10^{-5}M$ IAA but not with $10^{-4}M$ IAA. Oat-coleoptile sections after 48 hr of growth (Gantzer, 1960).

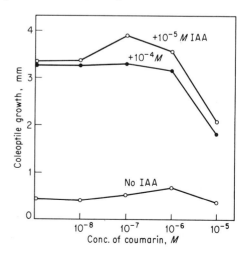

growth regulators. There must also be many types of inhibitors which act through metabolic or other nonhormonal means. These are generally outside the scope of this coverage, but two types of such actions should be mentioned as most relevant to the growth-regulation systems: inhibitors which act as sulfhydryl antagonists and those which act as respiratory uncouplers.

The possibility that auxin regulation of growth may involve specific sulfhydryl requirements has been suggested several times on various bases (Thimann and Bonner, 1949; Thimann, 1951; Marré and Arrigoni, 1955, 1957), and growth inhibitions are frequently relieved by supplying compounds with free sulfhydryl groups (Thimann and Bonner, 1949; Leopold et al., 1952; Elliott and Leopold, 1953; Marré and Arrigoni, 1955; Shibaoka, 1961). Pilet (1957) has implicated the increasing ability of roots to inactivate auxin during aging with the lowering amount of natural free sulfhydryl content of the roots. The inhibitions of growth by ascorbic acid (Tonzig and Trezzi, 1950) have been interpreted as a regulation of the oxidation of sulfhydryl groups (Tonzig and Marré, 1961).

A second type of inhibitor action which may be especially relevant to the growth inhibitors in developmental phenomena is the metabolic uncoupling agent. The classic uncoupling agent is dinitrophenol, which lowers the effectiveness with which respiratory energy can be accumulated as energy-rich phosphoryl esters. The first report of a plant extract which had this inhibitory action was by Millerd et al. (1953), who extracted it from ripening avocado fruits. Inhibitor β, found in many plant tissues and suggested as the inhibitor responsible for dormancy of buds and tubers, is also reported to be an uncoupling agent (Marinos and Hemberg, 1960). The correlation of elevated oxygen consumption (uncoupling effect) with the growth inhibition in oat-coleoptile sections is illustrated in Fig. 9-11. Cinnamic acid and triiodobenzoic acid may also act in part through respiratory uncoupling actions (Nagao and Ohwaki, 1955).

Inhibitors in development

Growth inhibitors may be able to regulate naturally the rate of growth in plant tissues, but most of the published evidence for regulating effects of inhibitors is centered on developmental phenomena. A clear case of an increase in growth inhibitors related to photoperiodism was reported by Kawase (1961) on photoperiod effects of *Betula*. Short days cause a suppression of growth with the subsequent onset of dormancy. The quantitative effects on growth rate and inhibitor content are shown in Fig. 9-12. Konishi (1954) correlated the presence of inhibitors with the rosette stage of growth in spinach and *Silene* plants. The suppression of growth by photoperiods has been at-

Fig. 9-11 | The effects of inhibitor β on growth and respiration of oat-coleoptile sections, showing an increased oxygen consumption (presumably an uncoupling effect) at concentrations of the inhibitor which suppress growth. Inhibitor β eluted from chromatograms of potato extracts; growth measured in 24 hr and respiration in 4 hr (Marinos and Hemberg, 1960).

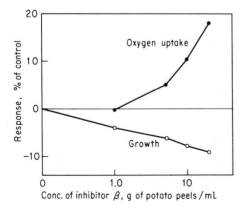

tributed to the formation of inhibitors in the leaves and then the presumed translocation of the inhibitor to the growing point of the stem (Downs and Borthwick, 1956; Phillips and Wareing, 1959). The breaking of dormancy is generally associated with a decrease in the quantity of inhibitor present, whether it is broken by cold (Luckwill, 1952), ethylene (Hemberg, 1949a,b), or gibberellin application (Boo, 1961). Sometimes the inhibitor does not decline as dormancy is broken (cf. Chap. 19).

Inhibitor contents of leaves, stems, fruits, and roots increase with age (Varga and Koves, 1958, 1959). Inhibitor β is considered one of the principal accumulating substances (Varga and Koves, 1959; Pilet, 1963), and in stems and fruits the inhibitors are apparently accumulated from the leaves (Varga and Koves, 1959).

Ballard and Lipp (1959) have described an interesting specificity of inhibitor action. They extracted inhibitors from the seeds of *Echium* and separated them into two fractions by elution from carbon. One fraction inhibited germination of *Echium* seeds, and the other inhibited only that of some other species. Comparing the two fractions on germination of 19 species, they found that some were inhibited only by one, some only by the other and some by both fractions. These experiments indicate the importance of assaying for inhibitors with the same biological material which the inhibitor might affect and also imply an ecological potential for inhibitors which can show selectivity between species.

Environmental factors

The effects of light on growth inhibitors are compound. Although light may overcome the effects of inhibitors in causing seed dormancy, it can cause the formation of inhibitors in leaves, stems, and roots. The increase in growth-inhibitor content of many species under short photoperiods is apparently an expression of the light induction of inhibitor content, for more inhibitor is present in leaves at the end of the light period than at the end of the dark (Phillips and Wareing, 1959). Why the short photoperiod should then result in more inhibitor than the long photoperiod is unknown. Perhaps more precise evidence of the role of light is shown by the experiments of Bayer (1961) and Masuda (1962), who compared the inhibitor contents of seedlings in the etiolated condition and after exposure to light, obtaining marked increases with the light treatment. Zucker and Ahrens (1958) showed that chlorogenic acid formation in tobacco leaves depends on light, and Zucker and Levy

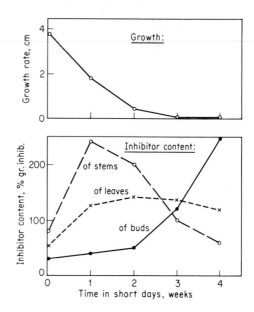

Fig. 9-12 | The relation between growth rates and the accumulation of growth inhibitors in *Betula pubescens* with increasing numbers of short photoperiods (10 hr). Methanol extracts chromatographed in isopropanol/ammonia/water and assayed by oat-coleoptile-section test; the inhibitor content above R_f 0.6 was summed and presented in these data. Note the most rapid accumulation of inhibitor in the stems and leaves, followed by rise of inhibitor in the buds (Kawase, 1961).

(1959) found that both sugar and oxygen levels were critical in chlorogenic acid formation. Both of these may contribute to the light effects. The oxygen requirement might account for the greater formation of chlorogenic·acid in the skins of potatoes than in the interior parenchyma tissues.

Light may be able to overcome some inhibitor actions. This is implied from the fact that it can overcome dormancy, but specific evidences of the light interaction with inhibitors are rare. Nutile (1945) made the original observation that the coumarin inhibition of seed germination was overcome by light. This has been confirmed by Evenari (1957) and contrasted with the effects of dinitrophenol which are not relieved by light. Phillips (1961) has inhibited lettuce seed with naringenin and relieved the inhibition with light.

The abilities of high temperatures to cause growth inhibitions and dormancy have occasionally been attributed to elevated inhibitor contents (Vegis, 1956). The effects of germination inhibitors can be overcome by low temperatures (Evenari, 1957) in a manner paralleling the ability of light to overcome germination inhibitors. Low temperatures can reduce the inhibitor contents, and this is a component part of the improvement of seed germination by "stratification" (Luckwill, 1952), a procedure discussed in more detail in Chap. 19.

Conclusion

Like the kinins, the growth inhibitors in plants display a diversity in molecular species which implies a diversity of physiological mechanisms in which they may participate. The growth inhibitors may play important roles in developmental processes and in the systems by which plants respond to environmental cues. Though their specific actions might not be clear, the growth inhibitors are an integral part of the mechanisms of dormancy in seeds and buds. They

are certainly sensitive to the environmental variables which regulate dormancy, especially light and temperature.

It would be erroneous to identify the growth-inhibitor actions too uniformly with auxin interactions, for evidence points up the existence of inhibitors of the gibberellin-stimulated phases of growth and development and perhaps of the kinin-stimulated phases as well.

The growth inhibitors appear to be basic components of the endogenous controls of plant growth and development.

GENERAL REFERENCES

Audus, L. J. 1959. *Plant Growth Substances,* pp. 384–404. Leonard Hill, Ltd., London.
Bonner, J. 1950. The role of toxic substances in the interactions of higher plants. *Botan. Rev.,* 16:51–65.
Evenari, M. 1949. Germination inhibitors. *Botan. Rev.,* 15:153–194.
———. 1957. The physiological action and biological importance of germination inhibitors. *Symp. Soc. Exptl. Biol.,* 11:21–43.
Hemberg, T. 1961. Biogenous inhibitors. *Handbuch Pflanzenphys.,* 14:1162–1183.

REFERENCES CITED

Andreae, W. A. 1952. Effect of scopoletin on indoleacetic acid metabolism. *Nature,* 170:83.
Audus, L. J. 1947. Effects of certain organic metabolic products on plant nutrition and growth. *Intern. Congr. Pure Appl. Chem. Rept.* XI.
Ballard, L. A. T., and A. E. G. Lipp. 1959. Differential specificity exhibited by two germination inhibitors present in *Echium plantagineum. Australian J. Biol. Sci.,* 12:343–347.
Barlow, H. W. B., C. R. Hancock, and H. J. Lacey. 1955. Some observations on

growth inhibitors extracted from woody shoots. *Ann. Rept. East Malling Res. Sta. Kent*, 1954:115–121.

Bate-Smith, E. C. 1959. Plant phenolics in food, pp. 133–148. In J. W. Fairbairn (ed.), *The Pharmacology of Plant Phenolics*. Academic Press, Inc., New York.

Bayer, M. 1961. Über die Aktivierung des Hemmstoffsystem von *Helianthus* durch kurzfristige Belichtung. *Planta,* 57:258–265.

Bennet-Clark, T. A., and N. P. Kefford. 1953. Chromatography of the growth substances in plant extracts. *Nature,* 171:645–647.

Bentley, J. A. 1958. The naturally-occurring auxins and inhibitors. *Ann. Rev. Plant Physiol.,* 9:47–80.

Bonner, J. 1950. The role of toxic substances in the interactions of higher plants. *Botan. Rev.,* 16:51–65.

———— and A. W. Galston. 1944. Toxic substances from the culture media of guayule which may inhibit growth. *Botan. Gaz.,* 106:185–198.

Boo, L. 1961. The effect of gibberellic acid on inhibitor β complex in resting potato. *Physiol. Plantarum,* 14:676–681.

Burström, H. 1960. Influence of iron and gibberellic acid on the light sensitivity of roots. *Physiol. Plantarum,* 13:597–615.

Corcoran, M. R., C. A. West, and B. O. Phinney. 1961. Natural inhibitors of gibberellin-induced growth. *Advan. Chem. Ser.,* 28:152–158.

Davis, R. F. 1928. The toxic principle of *Juglans nigra* as identified with synthetic juglone and its toxic effects on tomato and alfalfa plants. *Am. J. Botany,* 15:620.

Downs, R. J., and H. A. Borthwick. 1956. Effect of photoperiod upon the vegetative growth of *Weigela florida* var. *variegata. Proc. Am. Soc. Hort. Sci.,* 68:518–521.

Elliott, B. B., and A. C. Leopold. 1953. An inhibitor of germination and of amylase activity in oat seeds. *Physiol. Plantarum,* 6:66–78.

Evenari, M. 1957. The physiological action and biological importance of germination inhibitors. *Symp. Soc. Exptl. Biol.,* 11:21–43.

Fairbairn, J. W. (ed.). 1959. *The Pharmacology of Plant Phenolics*. Academic Press, Inc., New York. 151 pp.

Gantzer, E. 1960. Wirkungen von Cumarin auf Wachstum und Entwicklungsvorgange und seine Wanderungs fahigkeit im Pflanzengewebe. *Planta,* 55:235–253.

Goldacre, P. L., A. W. Galston, and R. L. Weintraub. 1953. The effect of substituted phenols on the activity of the indoleacetic acid oxidase of peas. *Arch. Biochem. Biophys.,* 43:358–373.

Goodwin, R. H., and F. Kavanaugh. 1949. Isolation of scopoletin, a blue fluorescing compound from oat roots. *Bull. Torrey Botan. Club,* 76:255–265.

Gortner, W. A., M. J. Kent, and G. K. Sutherland. 1958. Ferulic and *p*-coumaric acids in pineapple tissue as modifiers of pineapple indoleacetic acid oxidase. *Nature,* 181:630–631.

Hemberg, T. 1949*a*. Significance of growth inhibiting substances and auxins for the rest period of potato. *Physiol. Plantarum,* 2:24–36.

————. 1949*b*. Growth inhibiting substances in buds of *Fraxinus. Physiol. Plantarum,* 2:37–44.

Henderschott, C. H., and D. R. Walker. 1959. Identification of a growth inhibitor from extracts of dormant peach flower buds. *Science,* 130:798–799.

Henderson, J. H. M., and J. P. Nitsch. 1962. Effect of certain phenolic acids on the elongation of *Avena* first internodes in the presence of auxins and tryptophan. *Nature,* 195:780–782.

Isogai, Y. 1960. Studies of the growth agents separated from etiolated bean seedlings. V. Auxin fractions and addendum. *Sci. Papers Coll. Gen. Educ. Univ. Tokyo,* 10:73–85.

Iwanami, Y. 1957*a*. Physiological researches of pollen. XI. Starch grains and sugars in stigma and pollen. *Botan. Mag.* (*Tokyo*), 70:38–43.

———. 1957*b*. Physiological researches of pollen. XIII. Growth inhibition of the pollen tube of *Camellia japonica. Botan. Mag.* (*Tokyo*), 70:144–149.

Kawase, M. 1961. Growth substances related to dormancy in *Betula. Proc. Am. Soc. Hort. Sci.*, 78:532–544.

Kefford, N. P. 1955*a*. The growth substances separated from plant extracts by chromatography, I. *J. Exptl. Botany*, 6: 129–151.

———. 1955*b*. The growth substances separated from plant extracts by chromatography. II. *J. Exptl. Botany*, 6:245–255.

Köckemann, A. 1934. Über eine keimungshemmende Substanz in fleischigen Fruchten. *Ber. Deut. Botan. Ges.*, 52:523–526.

Kohler, D., and A. Lang. 1963. Evidence for substances in higher plants interfering with gibberellin responses. *Plant Physiol.*, 38:555–560.

Konishi, M. 1954. Development of flowering stalks in *Silene armeria* in relation to auxin metabolism. *Proc. Japan Acad.*, 30: 24–29.

Kuraishi, S., and R. M. Muir. 1963. Mode of action of growth retarding chemicals. *Plant Physiol.*, 38:19–24.

Leopold, A. C., F. I. Scott, W. H. Klein, and E. Ramstad. 1952. Chelidonic acid and its effect on plant growth. *Physiol. Plantarum*, 5:85–90.

Letham, D. S. 1963. Regulators of cell division in plant tissues. I. *New Zealand J. Sci.*, 1:336–349.

Libbert, E. 1954. Das Zusammenwirken von Wuchs-und Hemmstoffen bei der Korrelativen Knospenhemmung. *Planta*, 44: 286–318.

Luckwill, L. C. 1952. Growth-inhibiting and growth-promoting substances in relation to the dormancy of apple seeds. *J. Hort. Sci.*, 27:53–67.

Marinos, N. G., and T. Hemberg. 1960. Observations on a possible mechanism of action of the inhibitor β complex. *Physiol. Plantarum*, 13:571–581.

Marré, E., and O. Arrigoni. 1955. Ulteriori ricerche sull'azione inibente dell'auxinanei confronti dell'ossidasi dell'acido ascorbico. *Rendi. Accad. Nazl. Lincei*, 18–8: 539–547.

——— and ———. 1957. Metabolic reactions to auxins. I. Effects of auxin on glutathione and growth. *Physiol. Plantarum*, 10:289–301.

Masuda, Y. 1962. Effect of light on a growth inhibitor in wheat roots. *Physiol. Plantarum*, 15:780–790.

Millerd, A., J. Bonner, and J. B. Biale. 1953. The climacteric rise in fruit respiration as controlled by phosphorylative coupling. *Plant Physiol.*, 28: 521–531.

Mumford, F. E., H. M. Stark, and D. H. Smith. 1963. 4-hydroxybenzlalcohol: a naturally occurring cofactor of indoleacetic oxidase. *Phytochemistry*, 2:215–220.

Nagao, M., and Y. Ohwaki. 1955. The action of trans-cinnamic and 2,3,5-triiodobenzoic acids in the rice seedling. *Sci. Rept. Tohoku Univ.*, 21:96–108.

Nitsch, J. P. 1957. Growth responses of woody plants to photoperiodic stimuli. *Proc. Am. Soc. Hort. Sci.*, 70:512–525.

———. 1962*a*. Action de flavonoides sur la croissance de tissus de *Topinambour* cultives *in vitro*. II. *Bull. Soc. Botan. France*, 109:113–115.

———. 1962*b*. Basic physiological processes affecting fruit development, pp. 5–24. In S. G. Younkin (ed.), *Plant Science Symposium on Fruit Set.* Campbell Soup Co., Camden, N.J.

——— and C. Nitsch. 1961. Synergistes naturels des auxines et des gibberellines. *Bull. Soc. Botan. France*, 108:349–362.

——— and ———. 1962. Composés phenoliques et croissance vegetale. *Ann. Physiol. Vegetale*, 4:211–225.

Nutile, G. E. 1945. Inducing dormancy in lettuce seed with coumarin. *Plant Physiol.*, 20:433–442.

Overbeek, J. van, R. Blondeau, and V.

Horne. 1951. Transcinnamic acid as an anti-auxin. *Am. J. Botany*, 38:589–595.

Phillips, I. D. J. 1961. Induction of light requirement for germination of lettuce seed by naringenin and its removal by gibberellic acid. *Nature*, 192:240–241.

—— and P. F. Wareing. 1959. Studies in dormancy of sycamore. II. The effect of day length on the natural growth-inhibitor content of the shoot. *J. Exptl. Botany*, 10:504–514.

Pilet, P. E. 1957. Distribution of sulfhydryl (−SH) groups, activity of auxin-oxydases and content of auxins in the roots of *Lens. Physiol. Plantarum*, 10:708–727.

——. 1963. Physiologie vegetale: sur deux inhibiteurs radiculaires. *Compt. Rend. Acad. Sci.* (*Paris*), 256:1348–1350.

Pohl, R., and B. Tegethoff. 1949. Der Hemmstoff des Maisscutellums ein Wuchsstoffinaktivator. *Naturwissenschaften*, 10:319.

Shibaoka, H. 1961. Studies on the mechanism of growth inhibiting effect of light. *Plant Cell Physiol.* (*Tokyo*), 2:175–197.

—— and H. Imaseki. 1957. Identification of growth inhibitors in *Helianthus* leaves. *Botan. Mag.* (*Tokyo*), 70:362–369.

Tamari, K., and J. Koji. 1954. Studies on the mechanism of the inhibitory action of fusarinic acid. *J. Biochem.*, 41:143–165.

Thimann, K. V. 1951. The synthetic auxins: relation between structure and activity, pp. 21–36. In F. Skoog (ed.), *Plant Growth Substances*. The University of Wisconsin Press, Madison, Wis.

——. 1956. Promotion and inhibition: twin themes of physiology. *Am. Naturalist*, 90:145–162.

—— and W. D. Bonner. 1949. Inhibition of plant growth by protoanemonin and coumarin and its prevention by BAL. *Proc. Natl. Acad. Sci. U.S.*, 35:272–276.

Tomaszewski, M. 1959. Chlorogenic acid phenolase as a system inactivating auxin isolated from some leaves of some *Prunus* species. *Bull. Acad. Polon. Sci.*, 7:127–130.

——. 1960. The occurrence of *p*-hydroxybenzoic acid and some other simple phenols in vascular plants. *Bull. Acad. Polon. Sci.*, 8:61–65.

Tonzig, S., and E. Marré. 1955. The auxin-ascorbic acid oxidase interaction as related to the physiological activity of auxin. *Istituto Lombardo Rend. Sci.*, 89:243–268.

—— and ——. 1961. Ascorbic acid as a growth hormone, pp. 725–734. In R. M. Klein (ed.), *Plant Growth Regulation*. Iowa State University Press, Ames, Iowa.

—— and F. Trezzi. 1950. Ricerche sulla fisiologia dell' acido ascorbico. III. L'acido ascorbico e la distensione cellulare. *Nuovo Giorn. Botan. Ital.*, 57:535–548.

Varga, M. 1958. Growth inhibiting substances in rice-straw. *Acta Biol.* (*Budapest*), 4:13–16.

—— and L. Ferenczy. 1957. Paperchromatographic examination of inhibiting substances in fleshy fruits. *Naturwissenschaften*, 14:398–399.

—— and E. Koves. 1958. Vorkommen, Verteilung und quantitative Veranderung des β-Inhibitors in den einzelnen Organen der Bohnenpflanze. *Naturwissenschaften*, 45:468–469.

—— and E. Koves. 1959. Distribution and quantitative changes in the β-inhibitor in the various organs of the bean plant during ontogeny. *Acta Biol.* (*Budapest*), 9:369–378.

Vegis, A. 1956. Formation of the resting condition in plants. *Experientia*, 12:94–99.

Zenk, M. H., and G. Müller. 1963. In vivo destruction of exogenously applied indoleacetic acid as influenced by naturally occurring phenolic acids. *Nature*, 200:761–763.

Zucker, M., and J. F. Ahrens. 1958. Quantitative assay of chlorogenic acid and its pattern of distribution within tobacco leaves. *Plant Physiol.*, 33:246–249.

—— and C. C. Levy. 1959. Some factors which affect the synthesis of chlorogenic acid in disks of potato tuber. *Plant Physiol.*, 34:108–112.

10 | Differential growth

The multicellular organism is characterized by an organized distribution of growth and by the organization and differentiation of tissues. Some forces must exist through which cells mutually determine the location and type of growth and differentiation.

The organization of tissues has yet a prior requirement, that for polarity. Before differentiation can establish an organism with an axis, there must be a unit of direction. Sinnott (1960) states that polarity is the first step in differentiation. Nearly every multicellular organism must have a top and a bottom, or less facetiously, an axis.

Polarity

Polarity appears even in primitive plant forms, including the algae and fungi. Unicellular plants exhibit distinct polarity, developing head ends with flagellae or with an eyespot. The multicellular strands of green algae and fungal hyphae characteristically exhibit a continuous polarity over the complete set of cells, with all morphological orientation in the same direction. It appears that a polar orientation is transmitted from cell to cell, resulting in the long chains of similarly oriented cells such as *Cladophora* or the cladified colonies such as *Ulva*.

Many types of cells have no polarity until they receive some external stimulus. Egg cells or zygotes may be released into the environment without any polar orientation, and then as the cell grows and multiplies, polarity of the new organism appears. These free nonpolar cells provide excellent experimental material for the study of the initiation of polarity. Animal physiologists utilize frog eggs and sea-urchin eggs for such studies, and plant physiologists utilize the spores of algae, fungi, mosses, horsetails, and ferns.

In the plant, polarity is manifested morphologically by a preferential direction of cell division, cell enlargement, and cell dif-

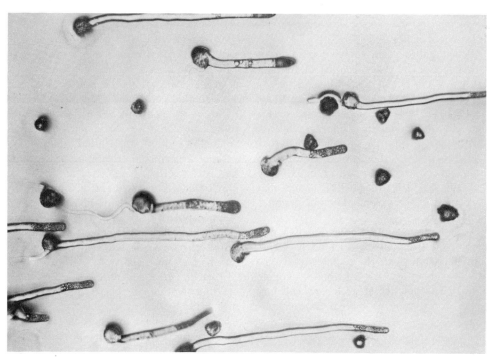

Fig. 10-1 | Light can impose a polarity on the germination of fern spores (*Pteridium aquilinum*). Light from the right side of the field has oriented the position of emergence of the protonema from the spores.

ferentiation and by the orientation of the tissues formed from these cellular activities. These preferential-direction qualities are dramatically illustrated by experiments on the induction of polarity and by regeneration and grafting characteristics.

Induction of polarity. In the lower plants polarity may be initially absent in the new spore and can be established by environmental factors. As spores are shed, the side settling on the ground ordinarily becomes the root end. Light is clearly involved in polar induction; unilateral light induces the polar establishment of the apical end in spores of ferns, horsetails, and fungi and in fern protonemata. Figure 10-1 illustrates the ability of light to orient the polarity of fern-spore germination. Haupt

(1957*a*) found that blue light is most effective in invoking polar induction. Several chemicals erase the light-polarizing effect, including chloroform (Haupt, 1957*a*), auxin, and thiamin (von Wettstein, 1953). For a brief period after initial lighting, the polarity of *Equisetum* spores can be reversed by a second light exposure from the opposite direction (Haupt, 1957).

Physical force may induce polarity. Centrifuging individual cells of filamentous algae or pieces of liverwort can sometimes alter the regeneration pattern so that new rhizoids sprout from the former apical end and new apical shoots from the former basal end. Electric fields have also altered the polarity of regeneration of fungal spores and fern prothallia, with rhizoids developing on the electrically positive side and apical shoots developing on the electrically negative side (cf. review of Bünning, 1957).

Pollen grains seem to have little or no polarity, and the determination of the side on which the pollen tube will emerge can be controlled by centrifugation (Beams and King, 1944*b*). When pollen grains germinate close to one another, there is tendency toward an orientation of emergence such that the pollen tubes are directed away from one another (Beams and King, 1944*a*). This suggests that diffusible substances may participate in the determination of germination polarity.

In most higher plants polarity of a new embryo in the ovule is oriented in a uniform direction, with the radicle developing at the end nearest the micropyle (Sinnott, 1960). The polarity of each new cell in a tissue is the same as that of its neighbor,

suggesting a possible orienting effect by contact (Bünning, 1957).

In experiments with the culture of individual cells from carrot roots, Steward et al. (1958) found that cell division occurred in a given clone while the culture solutions were rotated continuously but that differentiation proceeded only when the callus was transplanted onto a stable medium. Thus, when the culture was shifted continuously without a positional orientation, differentiation was arrested. It is not clear whether a gravitational force field was involved in the establishment of polarity in this case.

Once polarity has been established in a clone or an individual cell, it seems to be stable, and new cells added to the organism assume the same polarity.

Polarity in regeneration. Experiments on regeneration in plants produced the first basic evidences of polarity. Vöchting (1878) established that cuttings of willow stems form roots at their physiologically basal ends and buds at their apical ends regardless of their orientation during the rooting period (Fig. 10-2). He noted that ringing the bark of the cutting acted in much the same way as cutting entirely through the stem in regeneration patterns. He concluded that polarity was fixed in the plant cell and was irreversible.

Regeneration experiments with some lower plants show weaker polarity patterns. Cuttings from liverwort thalli may show only a weak polarity of rhizoid and protonema formation, and this may be modified or even reversed by environmental influences such as light or gravity (Fitting, 1938).

The polarity of regeneration of stems is the most inflexible. In root cuttings there is sometimes a less pronounced or a more readily modified polarity, and in leaf cuttings often both roots and buds form together at the basal end of the leaf piece without regard to apical position on the piece, indicating a relatively weak inherent polarity. The pattern of regeneration of root cuttings

Fig. 10-2 | Regeneration of roots in a stem cutting of willow occurs at the physiological base (*B*) of the piece, regardless of the position during regeneration (Pfeffer, 1906; after Vöchting, 1878).

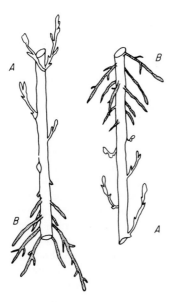

is illustrated by experiments on *Taraxacum* (Warmke and Warmke, 1950), in which any cutting from the root regenerated buds at the physiologically apical end and roots at the basal end (Fig. 10-3), regardless of the orientation of the piece during regeneration.

Polarity in graftage. Evidence of the polarity of plant cells and tissues is shown in the graftage experiments of Vöchting (1878) with kohlrabi stems and beet roots. Pieces could be readily grafted if they were in the same physiological orientation, but if a stem piece was grafted into another stem in an inverted position, the graft did not take. Instead the scion sometimes invaded the stock with roots, as if it were a soil medium. The explicit polarity for graftage is much less pronounced in fruits. Bloch (1952) found that pieces from *Lagenaria* fruits could be reinserted into the fruit in any position and the graft would be successful. As with regeneration, the polarity of grafts seems to be most pronounced in stem pieces.

Horticulturists have recognized that buds must be grafted into a stock in the proper orientation for good take. Inverted buds may sometimes knit well with cambial tissue, but the vascular connections can be made only by twisting of cells so that adjoining ones meet with the same polarity. Apparently cambial cells are somewhat more flexible in their polarity than more completely differentiated tissues (Sinnott, 1960).

Differentiation

After polarity has been established in a cell, organized patterns of cell division, enlargement, and tissue differentiation can follow. The commencement of such steps is seen in a callus tissue in culture as it develops local meristem areas with organized cell divisions, cell enlargement, and tissue differentiation (Fig. 1-4).

The meristem not only provides a source

of cells for the production of tissues but appears also to provide organizers, or stimuli of differentiation of the cells into tissues. Decapitation of a stem or root is generally followed by a period of partially suspended differentiation.

The requirements for the completion of differentiation may vary phylogenetically. Wetmore (1954) showed that cell clusters from gymnosperms cultured on a simple sugar medium will differentiate into complete new plants, but explants from angiosperm tissues will differentiate new individuals only if the culture medium contains more elaborate nutrients, including auxin, B vitamins, and coconut milk.

Morphogenetic substances. The ability of some tissues to impose differentiation on others is illustrated with tissue cultures of pith or callus which are maintained in contact with differentiated or meristematic pieces. Jablonski and Skoog (1954) found that pith tissue from tobacco stems cultured in contact with another piece containing vascular strands would undergo cell divisions. They suspected the nurse piece provided substances which evoked the cell-division response, and they obtained preliminary evidence that extracts from vascular tissue could stimulate cell divisions. Substitution of other substances such as coconut-meat extracts could cause cell divi-

Fig. 10-3 | Regeneration of roots and buds on root cuttings of *Taraxacum* shows orientation of roots to the base (*B*) and buds to the apex (*A*), regardless of the position during regeneration (Warmke and Warmke, 1950).

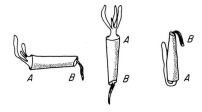

Fig. 10-4 | The differentiation of xylem can be stimulated in lilac-pith-tissue cultures by implantation of an apical meristem on one side of the cultured piece. This 10-mm³ piece of callus (cutaway representation) was implanted with a lilac meristem, and the xylem cells (shaded) were recorded after 54 days (Wetmore and Sorokin, 1955).

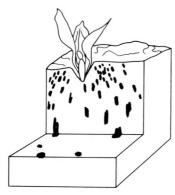

Fig. 10-5 | The differentiation of new xylem cells in the expanding *Coleus* petiole is correlated with the amount of diffusible auxin obtainable from the base of the petiole. Auxin assayed by *Avena* curvature test (Jacobs and Morrow, 1957).

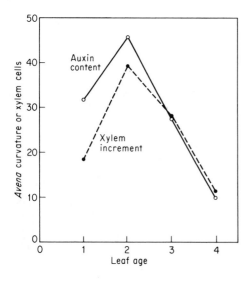

sion, differentiation of vascular tissues, and formation of buds on the pith piece.

In another example of a nurse-tissue experiment, Wetmore and Sorokin (1955) induced the differentiation of vascular tissue in a block of callus tissue. Simulating the situation in an intact stem, they inserted a small piece of stem tip into lilac-callus tissue in sterile culture. Below the point of contact, scattered rows of xylem tracheids differentiated in the callus (Fig. 10-4). They also found that some xylem differentiation in the callus could be induced by supplying a mixture of auxin and coconut-milk extract in the notch where the meristem would otherwise be introduced. These experiments suggest the exciting idea of substances in the meristem which act as the organizers of morphogenesis in adjoining cell regions. It is not surprising that the auxins and kinins should be involved in these activities.

The role of auxin in xylem differentiation is suggested by experiments on the regeneration of xylem strands around a cut in the stem of *Coleus*. A cut through a vascular strand resulted in the formation of a new chain of xylem tracheids to rejoin the strand, and the new cells were differentiated principally in a basipetal direction (Sinnott and Bloch, 1944). Jacobs (1952) found that removal of leaves above the cut reduced the xylem differentiation and that addition of auxin paste to the cut petioles restored the differentiation. Later he correlated the rate of xylem formation in expanding leaves with the diffusible auxin content, as shown in Fig. 10-5 (Jacobs and Morrow, 1957).

If auxin does stimulate xylem formation, why is xylem not randomly differentiated in tissues grown on a medium containing auxin? Clutter (1960) inserted a vial of auxin solution into the top of a callus piece in culture and obtained a localized formation of xylem near the solution application. This experiment and that of Wetmore and Sorokin (1955) imply that a localized or oriented occurrence of auxin is critical in the differentiation of xylem.

Experiments with roots have added some interesting facts. To study the question of whether the root apex imposes the pattern of differentiation on the root, Torrey (1955) excised and decapitated root-tip pieces. During regeneration of the tips he found an initial variance of the stelar configuration from the typical triarch to the hexarch stelar pattern, but after some time the triarch stele was formed. Torrey observed that thicker root tips were more liable to show increases in stelar rays. Later (Torrey, 1957), he added auxins to the nutritive medium on which the tips were regenerating, and the resulting thickening of the excised apices was associated with marked increases in the stelar rays. The apices started to form a hexarch stele in the presence of indoleacetic acid, and when the root tips were removed to an auxin-free medium, they gradually reverted to the usual triarch stele. In each instance, the stelar pattern, especially with respect to size, appears to have been established by the characteristics of the meristem.

Besides the information on morphogenetic substances from the apical meristem influencing xylem formation, there is little evidence about other transmitted influences. However, there may be some influences from the proximal parts. For example, phloem differentiation seems to be an invasive action from the older parts of the stem and leaf, maintaining its terminal limits essentially at a constant position with respect to the distance from the developing stem or leaf tip (Jacobs and Morrow, 1958). Wetmore (1959) states that high sugar concentrations in a culture medium encourage the differentiation of phloem cells, and perhaps the sugar availability regulates the projection of the phloem strands.

Tumorous or callus-type growths may be regarded as cells in which the capacity for polar orientation or for differentiation is impaired. Numerous chemical materials can induce tumorous types of growth, and among these are the synthetic auxins. De

Ropp (1947) induced tumors on leaves by application of *p*-chlorophenoxyacetic acid plus a yeast extract. This auxin and others of the phenoxyacetic series were effective tumor formers, but indoleacetic acid and naphthaleneacetic acid were not. This is suggestive in that the auxins which did induce the tumor are those which are not effectively transported in the polar transport system. Callus swellings on plants often develop following the application of auxins which are nontranslocatable either because the auxin is a misfit in the transport system or because the plant is unable to translocate it from the locus of application.

Organ formation. Organ formation may be regulated by specific substances in the plant. Root formation can be controlled by auxin in the plant (Thimann and Went, 1934). The differentiation of buds can be brought about by the supply of purines such as adenine in the culture medium for tobacco callus, as was shown by Skoog and Tsui (1948). One of the most dramatic results of their experiments was the demonstration of a mutual balance between adenine and auxin in morphological determination. Large proportions of adenine favored bud formation, and large proportions of auxin favored root formation (Fig. 10-6). Optimal differentiation of the complete new organism was obtained with an intermediate ratio of both substances. Skoog and Tsui suggested that the organ differentiation was controlled in part by a balance between the purine and the auxin.

The concept of differentiation being controlled by balances between common substances in the plant is especially interesting, for without such an idea it might be necessary to assume that specific substances in the plant control the differentiation of each tissue and each organ. This could become absurd, with bud- and root-controlling substances, flower-controlling substances, and then perhaps stamen-, pistil-, petal-, and sepal-inducing substances. The concept of controls of differentiation by balances of common regulating substances in the plant seems much more logical.

An illustration of the morphogenetic substances moving about in the plant can be the girdled tree stem. Ringing a stem results in a swelling of the bark in the region above the ring, with the formation first of a callus and then of adventitious roots. This would be the expected location of accumulation of the polar-transported growth hormone, which would favor the differentiation of the roots. Below the ring there would be a tendency to form adventitious buds. Here would be expected a dearth of accumulating auxins and a large accumulation of the organic nitrogenous materials synthesized by the root system. The apical ends of cuttings are found to be high in kinins and low in auxin content (Vardjan and Nitsch, 1961).

Reaction-wood formation. Another illustration of the differentiation of tissues under the control of apparent morphogenetic substances is reaction-wood formation. Woody stems which are oriented other than vertically tend to form reaction wood, a xylem tissue on one side of the stem consisting of short tracheids, rounder than usual, with intercellular spaces, an altered pattern of wall thickening, and a darker coloration in conifers. This wood is undesirable from a lumberman's point of view because of the irregular cell arrangements and consequent poor structural qualities. In the plant this wood may aid in righting the stem, or it may support side branches in a lateral position.

Several facts have been elucidated concerning reaction-wood formation. First, it is a georesponse by the plant. Bending a stem or placing it under tension does not lead to the tissue response, and Sinnott (1952) demonstrated that a white pine stem twisted into a complete circle forms reaction wood only in those sectors of the stem which are

Fig. 10-6 | The differentiation of buds and roots on tobacco-pith-tissue cultures can be regulated by the relative amounts of auxin and adenine applied in the medium. From left to right: control culture; with 40 mg/liter adenine; with adenine plus 1 μg/liter indoleacetic acid; with adenine plus 5 μg/liter indoleacetic acid. (Skoog and Tsui, 1951).

oriented other than vertically (Fig. 10-7). Next, Wershing and Bailey (1942) showed that in conifers, reaction wood can be induced by the application of auxin to one side of an upright stem. This may not be true in broad-leaved species; no reports of the formation of reaction wood by auxin application have appeared for such plants. Third, the stimulus for the production of reaction wood is dependent on some signal originating in the apex; removal of the growing point will essentially prevent the formation of reaction wood with subsequent geostimulation. Wardrop (1956) measured the rate of movement of the signal from the growing apex of *Eucalyptus* and arrived at the value of about 9 mm/hr for down-the-stem movement. This is comparable to the usual rates of movement of the growth hormone recorded by various experimenters.

The formation of reaction wood dramatically illustrates the existence of substantive influences of tissue differentiation in the plant—morphogenetic substances which can move in the plant and carry the signal for differentiation from one part to another. It illustrates an apparent substantive influence on differentiation, an involvement of polarity in the control, and a so-called correlation effect—an influence of one part of the plant over another.

Sato (1956) found that herbaceous stems too can form reaction wood when held in a horizontal position. Auxin applications altered the pattern of the morphological response.

Correlation effects

The abilities of one part of the plant to direct growth or development in another have been called *correlation effects*. These represent some of the most intricate involvements of chemical messengers in multicellular plants. The most common correlation effects include the controls of tissue differentiation (xylem, cambium, reaction wood), organ differentiation (buds, roots), and the phenomena of apical dominance, tropisms, and abscission, each of which is regulated in part by influences stemming from the apices or leaves.

Correlative differentiation. Differentiation of xylem can be induced by an influence from a nearby meristem, and this can be attributed in part to the presence of auxin (Jacobs, 1952). In fact, the polarity of the orientation of xylem differentiation can be attributed to the polarity of transport of the auxin participating in this correlation effect (Jacobs, 1954; Roberts, 1960*b*).

The cambium is another differentiated tissue which is subject to pronounced correlative influences. Jost (1891) noted that the activation of cambium frequently occurred first below leaves, and Coster (1927) described it as a downward flow of activation from leaves and apices. Snow (1932) caused cambial activity by pressing graft pieces to stems which were already activated and deduced that a transmissible substance was responsible. Later (1935) he evoked the same type of cambial activation with the application of auxin. Since that time

Fig. 10-7 | The formation of reaction wood (indicated by shaded areas) in branches of white pine modified by such treatments as tying a branch into an upright position (*b*), decapitating the main stem (*c*), and tying a branch into a circle (*d*) (redrawn from Sinnott, 1952).

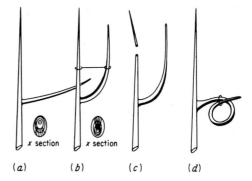

x section   *x* section

(*a*)   (*b*)   (*c*)   (*d*)

other growth substances have been implicated in this correlation effect, including gibberellins (Wareing, 1958), products of wounding (Gouwentak and Hellinga, 1935), and perhaps natural inhibitors (Wareing and Roberts, 1956).

Root differentiation occurs with a strong polarity. Stimulating effects of buds on the rooting of cuttings were noted (van der Lek, 1925, 1934) shortly before the stimulatory action of auxin on rooting was discovered by Thimann and Went (1934). The polarity of this correlation effect can be attributed to the polarity of auxin transport and the resultant accumulation of natural auxins at the base of the cutting (Warmke and Warmke, 1950). The presence of leaves, cotyledons, and flower buds on the cutting can greatly influence the rooting effectiveness, indicating that auxin is not exclusively responsible for root differentiation. The entire literature on the subject of rooting will not be reviewed here, but there are clearly nutritive involvements (Jones and Beaumont, 1937; Pearce, 1943), and these may account in large part for the promotive effects of leaves on the cutting (van Overbeek et al., 1946). Auxins may also be supplied by leaves, contributing to their promotive effects (Ruge, 1957). Regulation by growth substances other than auxin, including perhaps the kinins, appears likely (cf. Bachelard and Stowe, 1962). Several rooting cofactors have been separated in an effort to explain the loss of rooting ability with the passage from the juvenile to the mature condition (Hess, 1962).

Apical dominance. It has been known for some time that the shoot apex inhibits the growth and development of the lateral buds, and this phenomenon has been termed *apical dominance.* The inhibitory action is widespread throughout the plant kingdom, being evident in bryophytes and pteridophytes (e.g., LaRue and Narayanswami, 1957; von Maltzahn, 1959) as well as in seed plants. It is common to many different types of organs including stems and tubers

(Michener, 1942). The root apex may also inhibit branching in roots (Thimann, 1936). Apical-dominance phenomena may be grouped into three classes: inhibitions of branching, regulation of which branches or parts will grow more rapidly than others, and control of branch angles. In each of these classes of effects, the stem (or root) tip appears to contribute to the growth patterns of more or less remote parts of the plant.

The involvement of auxin has been indicated for some cases in all three classes of apical dominance. In stems, Laibach (1933b) and Thimann and Skoog (1933, 1934) showed that auxin applications could replace the stem apex in inhibiting the growth of lateral buds (Fig. 6-8). In roots, on the other hand, Thimann (1936) noted that the apex inhibited branching but that auxin application did not substitute for the apex. The regulation of the growth activities of various branches can be illustrated by the inhibition of normal elongation in the short shoots of *Ginkgo* and *Cercidiphyllum* by the apical bud, an effect which can be replaced by applied auxin (Gunckel and Thimann, 1949; Titman and Wetmore, 1955). Another illustration of the regulation of relative growth is the phenomenon of compensatory growth, in which the removal of leaves and stems can stimulate the growth of other plant parts. In this case the effect of the removed parts is not replaced by auxin applications, but evidently auxin formation by the inhibiting organs does play some role in the phenomenon (Jacobs and Bullwinkel, 1953). The third class of apical-dominance effects, the control of branching angles, also involves an auxin influence. The growing tip of a young fruit tree causes the lateral branches which grow out to assume positions away from the vertical; decapitation of the apex erases the branch-angle effect and results in vertical branches, and auxin applications will restore the effect of the removed apex (Verner, 1938; Jankiewicz, 1956). The effects of the apex both on the relative growth by laterals and on the branch angle are illustrated in Fig. 10-8 (Vardar, 1955*b*). The same type of correlation effect is sometimes imposed on leaf angles by the stem apex, and again it is replaceable with auxin (Dostal, 1962).

The inhibition of growth of lateral buds has received the most attention of the apical-dominance functions, and extensive disagreement has developed concerning the role of auxin in it. The relatively simple interpretation of Thimann and Skoog (1934) has been challenged on several grounds. Although the locus of the inhibition agrees with the locus of auxin formation and the polarity of the effects matches the polarity of auxin movement in most cases, there are quantitative uncertainties. For instance, Camus (1949) and Champagnat (1954) could not correlate the auxin content of buds with the extent of their inhibitions. Champagnat (1951, 1955) found that leaves inhibited or promoted lateral buds in a manner not obviously attributable to auxin. Jacobs et al. (1959) found that physiological concentrations of auxin applied to *Coleus* plants did not bring about lateral-bud inhibition. Gregory and Veale (1957) denied that lateral-bud inhibition was anything other than nutrient competition. There is no rational basis which can account for all instances of apical dominance as consequences of auxin controls, and in the entire plant other forces must be involved in this correlation effect. However, there is no question that auxin participates in apical dominance; in addition to the evidence that it can replace the inhibiting action of the apex, there is evidence that conditions which lower the endogenous auxin content of plants do correlate with the development of lateral buds (Leopold, 1949; Gordon, 1957). The ineffectiveness of applications of natural auxin levels in inhibiting lateral buds in *Coleus* (Jacobs et al., 1959) is not surprising since there is little natural apical dominance in that plant; the lateral buds grow out indiscriminately

even with the apical meristem intact. Similarly the nutritional involvement demonstrated by Gregory and Veale (1957) appears logical in that the flax plants used in their experiments showed almost no natural apical dominance by the terminal bud.

Two features seem to be emerging from the debates about the role of auxin in apical dominance. First, there may be factors for bud inhibition other than auxins, and second, there is an interacting force relating to mobilization phenomena. Some of the earli-

Fig. 10-8 | When an apex of *Mirabilis jalapa* is decapitated, there follows an increase in the growth of the lateral branch below it and a decline in the angle which the branch makes from vertical. Application of an auxin paste (500 mg/liter IAA) to replace the severed apex will prevent both the growth increase and the angle change (Vardar, 1955*b*).

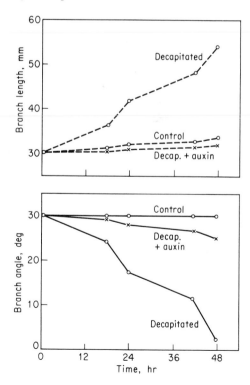

Fig. 10-9 | When sections of pea stems are placed in a dish of water, the lateral bud proceeds to grow out. Indoleacetic acid in the solution (1 mg/liter) will prevent the bud elongation, but the inclusion of kinetin (4 mg/liter) with the auxin erases the auxin inhibition (Wickson and Thimann, 1958).

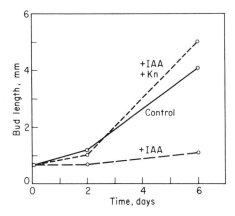

Fig. 10-9 | When sections of pea stems are placed in a dish of water, the lateral bud proceeds to grow out. Indoleacetic acid in the solution (1 mg/liter) will prevent the bud elongation, but the inclusion of kinetin (4 mg/liter) with the auxin erases the auxin inhibition (Wickson and Thimann, 1958).

Fig. 10-10 | Applying radioactive indoleacetic acid in the manner described for Fig. 10-9, the degree of inhibition of lateral-bud growth is related to the amount of radioactivity detectable in the lateral bud (Wickson and Thimann, 1960).

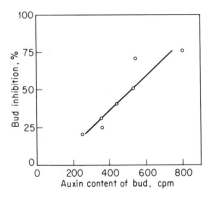

est work by Snow (1936) indicated that some factor exerted an acropetal force in bud inhibition; conversely, in roots there is a branching stimulus which moves toward the root tip (Torrey, 1956), and it is unlikely that either of these is auxin.

In contrast to auxin, kinetin has been shown to release buds from apical dominance even in the presence of indoleacetic acid (Wickson and Thimann, 1958; Fig. 10-9). Experiments on this kinetin effect showed that the amount of auxin present in lateral buds was quantitatively related to the extent of the bud inhibition (Fig. 10-10). There was an evident relationship between the amount of pea bud inhibition and the amount of exogenous auxin present as radioactivity in the bud.

In addition to the correlative effects of auxins, the role of mobilization needs clarification. In his early experiments, Went (1936) suggested that auxin may localize growth activities at the apex partly through a mobilization of nutrients into the auxin-rich tissues. A mobilizing function for auxin has seldom been indicated experimentally (Conrad, 1961), but mobilization activities themselves seem likely factors in correlative phenomena (Conrad, 1961; Mothes et al., 1961). Gregory and Veale (1957) have illustrated how nutrient levels and competition for them can alter apical dominance; Booth et al. (1962) provided some evidence that mobilization of nutrients into the stem apex may be related to the auxin levels there. Interpretation of these observations would be easier if there were some understanding of the interactions of auxin and kinetin in regulating the localization of growth activities (cf. Thimann and Laloraya, 1960).

Tropisms. The bending of plant shoots and roots in response to light or gravity is due to a differential growth on one side, resulting usually from the differential distribution of auxins. A lateral differential in auxin content occurs in shoots, coleoptiles, and roots following phototropic and geotropic stimulation (cf. review of Went and

Thimann, 1937). After extensive research on tropisms, it is not certain what the agency of perception may be (the pigment in the case of phototropism, and the particle or other locus in the case of geotropism); neither is it understood how the lateral redistribution of auxin is achieved, nor is it clear what determines the differences in sign of response between various tissues such as roots and shoots.

From the early work of Darwin (1897), it has been recognized that the apex of the stem or coleoptile is intimately involved in the tropistic responses. Removal of the apex can erase the sensitivity, as illustrated in Fig. 10-11 (Hahne, 1961). The action of the apex as a source of auxin was the apparent explanation (Went, 1928). In the phototropism of green stems, both stem and leaves are involved in the response. This is shown by the removal of leaves before unilateral illumination; phototropism is markedly lessened but is still operative (Shibaoka and Yamaki, 1959; Fig. 10-12).

The quantitative nature of the curvature induced by light is not simple, as shown in Fig. 10-13 (Briggs, 1960), a clear warning that this tropistic response is not simple. With light doses up to about 1,000 mcs, the corn coleoptile shows good reciprocity between intensity and time of light stimulation (Briggs, 1960), but at higher intensities reciprocity does not hold, suggesting that more than one mechanism is operative at the higher intensities.

The tropisms can be divided into three partial processes: the perception of the environmental stimulus, the induction of a physiological difference between the two sides of the plant organ, and the response as a differential growth rate.

Turning first to the *perception* mechanism, the action spectrum for the bending of coleoptiles to light (Fig. 20-7) should be helpful in indicating what pigment might be the perception agent for phototropism, but its close similarity to absorption curves of both β-carotene and riboflavin and its lack

Fig. 10-11 | A comparison of the geotropic bending of corn coleoptiles when held continuously in a horizontal position, horizontal for just 1 hr, or continuously horizontal but decapitated. The apex plays a critical role in the tropistic response (Hahne, 1961).

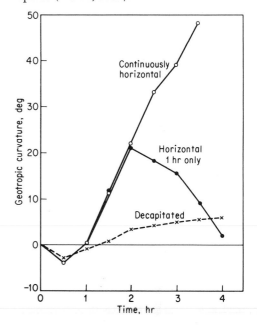

Fig. 10-12 | The phototropic curvature of green seedlings of *Helianthus* toward lateral illumination (450 ft-c) is markedly less if the leaves have been removed (Shibaoka and Yamaki, 1959).

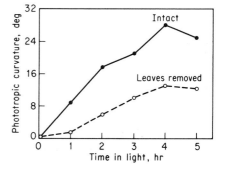

Fig. 10-13 | The phototropic curvature of etiolated corn coleoptiles increases with increasing light dosage, but not in a simple quantitative way. If light intensities are increased with dosage in order to keep all exposures within 5 min, the curve declines to near zero at about 10,000 meter-candle-seconds (*A*). If the intensities are all kept low enough to more nearly maintain reciprocity (*B*); the response curve is less erratic (Briggs, 1960).

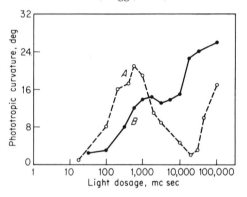

Fig. 10-14 | The induction for geotropism can be achieved in decapitated auxin-depleted sunflower seedlings. Holding them horizontal for 3 hr and then applying auxin solution to the tip (10 mg/liter) at the time of restoring the seedling to the vertical position still permits a development of tropistic curvature (Brauner and Hager, 1958).

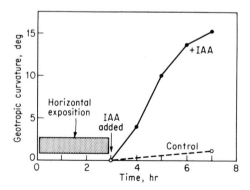

of identity with either have led to a vigorous debate over what the perception pigment might be (e.g., Wald, 1961; Galston, 1961). In addition to the blue light action, etiolated plants appear to be generally sensitized for phototropic responses by prior exposure to red light (Mohr and Peters, 1960; Asomaning and Galston, 1961). The sensitizing effect may be brought about through a phytochrome action (see Chap. 20). It is surprising that the action spectrum for phototropism of green leaves and stems is not known.

The perception of gravity in geotropism is even less well understood. The only specific suggestion that has been made is that the statoliths may move to the lower side of a horizontal cell and there induce a physiological response. These bodies, starch grains or starch-filled plastids, do move in response to gravity in a manner quantitatively suggestive of a causal relationship with geotropism (Nemec, 1900; Haberlandt, 1913).

The *induction* of a physiological difference between sides of a tropistically stimulated coleoptile does not seem to require auxin (Brauner and Hager, 1958; von Guttenberg, 1959). This was established by giving a tropistic stimulus to decapitated seedlings and then supplying auxin later to permit the curvature to develop (Fig. 10-14). The tip of the coleoptile or root seems to be the most sensitive to tropistic induction (Brauner, 1922; Dolk, 1929*b*).

By the use of decapitated auxin-depleted stems for the separation of induction from response phenomena, Brauner and Hager (1958) established that the induction of a physiological difference requires metabolic action during the perception stage. For example, holding such depleted plants in a horizontal position in a nitrogen atmosphere does not permit induction, and subsequent applications of auxin do not produce the tropistic response (Fig. 10-15). Likewise, the suppression of metabolism with cold during the tropistic stimulation prevented induction. Finally, the persistence of the induced state has been quantitatively measured by Diemer (1961) by interpolating periods of time between the tropistic stimulation of depleted stems and the applications of auxin to permit the actual growth response. She deduced that the half-life of the induced state in her plants was about 4½ hr. (Fig. 10-16).

Response of the plant to tropistic stimuli appears to be specifically dependent upon the presence of auxin. After the induction of auxin-poor coleoptiles or stems, bending responses do not develop unless some auxin is added exogenously (Fig. 10-14) or supplied naturally by the regeneration of the apex (Brauner and Hager, 1957; Hahne, 1961). In coleoptiles, the response is clearly a consequence of a lateral redistribution of auxin, both for phototropism (Went, 1928) and for geotropism (Dolk, 1929a). In roots, such a lateral redistribution is more difficult to establish since diffusion experiments there are less rewarding than in coleoptiles, but several early workers (cf. Went and Thimann, 1937) did establish a redistribution. Attempts to measure a lateral redistribution of auxin using extraction methods showed only small differences between the two sides of roots (Boysen-Jensen, 1936a). There is a notable lack of modern data to reaffirm the existence of lateral redistribution of auxins in the tropistic response of roots.

In coleoptiles, however, there are numerous precise measurements of the redistribution of auxin following tropistic stimuli; some representative data for the phototropism of corn coleoptiles are given in Fig. 10-17 (Briggs et al., 1957). These data show that although light does not alter the total amount of auxin obtained by diffusion from the coleoptiles (*a* vs. *b*), it does result in an increase on the shaded side and a corresponding decrease on the lighted side provided the coleoptile is not slit to prevent lateral movement of the auxin (*c*).

How is the lateral redistribution of auxin

Fig. 10-15 | A nitrogen atmosphere during the time of horizontal exposure of *Helianthus* seedlings (30 min) before restoring to air and the vertical position prevents geotropic induction. Time scale begins upon restoring to vertical (Brauner and Hager, 1958).

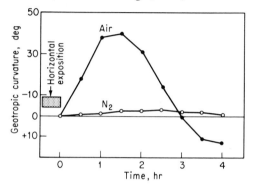

Fig. 10-16 | The induced geotropic state in laterally illuminated *Helianthus* seedlings has a half-life of about 4½ hr. This experiment, which was done with seedlings decapitated for 2 days, was made by giving lateral light (700 ft-c) for 16 hr and then waiting various times before supplying auxin (10 mg/liter IAA) to permit the development of curvature response. Curvature recorded 3 hr after auxin application (Diemer, 1961).

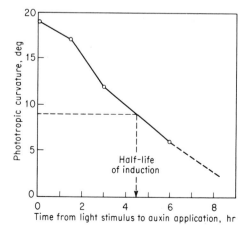

brought about? Following minimal stimuli with light or gravity, there is no decrease in total diffusible auxin present, and so a preferential destruction of auxin on one side cannot be the explanation at threshold stimulus levels. Two types of effects can apparently lead to the lateral dissymmetry: a preferential synthesis of auxin on one side and a lateral movement of auxin.

A synthesis of auxin after geostimulation of roots has been indicated in some timing experiments by Audus and Lahiri (1961). After placing broad-bean roots in a horizontal position, they found a large increase in an extractable auxin, separable by paper chromatography, and this increase occurred just before curvature began to be expressed. The increase is suggestive, but its relation to the tropistic response would seem to depend on a lateral asymmetry of synthesis,

which has not yet been shown. A synthesis of auxin in response to geostimulation has been reported for other roots (Rufelt, 1957) and stems (van Overbeek et al., 1945). In addition, an asymmetric synthesis in response to photostimulus has been reported for green stems (Schmitz, 1933; Shibaoka and Yamaki, 1959) and perhaps for flower pedicels (Zinsmeister, 1960).

The lateral transport of auxin was not actually measured until recently (Brauner and Appel, 1960; Gillespie and Thimann, 1961; Hertel, 1962). Now lateral transport of auxin with geotropism has been measured and appears to be an active transport (Hertel and Leopold, 1963). In view of the evidence that transport may be a secretion process (see Chap. 6) and that the secretion activity may shift from the base to the side of the cell upon tropistic stimulation, the induction effect of gravity might be the movement of an energy-producing particle from the base to the side. Ziegler (1953) found some organelles associated with the statoliths which are energy-producing centers, and there is a possibility, then, that statolith movement may alter the pattern of availability of metabolic energy for the secretive part of auxin transport (Hertel and Leopold, 1962). A similar possibility has been suggested for the perception of phototropism by plastids, which may move in response to light (Thimann and Curry, 1961).

Using radioactive indoleacetic acid for experiments on tropisms, many workers attempted to show a lateral movement of the auxin without success (Gordon and Eib, 1956; Bünning et al., 1956; Ching and Fang, 1958; Reisener, 1958). The explanation was later provided by Pickard and Thimann (1963), who found that the binding of auxin into a nontransported form accounted for the apparent lack of lateral redistribution following tropistic stimuli but that actual delivery of auxin at the base of a section clearly confirmed the lateral movement of transportable auxin.

Fig. 10-17 | Lateral light causes the lateral redistribution of diffusible auxin coming from corn-coleoptile tips. The amounts of auxin diffused from intact vs. split tips are compared in the dark and in lateral light. Diffusible auxin (3 hr) taken from three intact tips (*a* and *b*) or from six halved tips (*c*) for comparison in *Avena* curvature test. Note the increase in auxin on the shaded side without change in total auxin diffusible from tips (*c*) (Briggs et al., 1957).

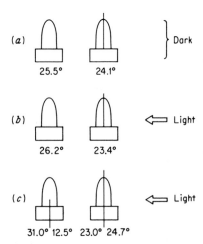

A difficult aspect of the tropism story is the question of what determines the sign of response. Why do stems show negative geotropism and roots positive? The question is complicated by the fact that the initial response of stems and coleoptiles is slightly positive, and of roots slightly negative, to gravity (Brauner and Zipperer, 1961; Rufelt, 1957). Furthermore, the sign of the response can sometimes change with age (Zinsmeister, 1960; Pilet, 1951), with nutrition (Seidel, 1957; Rufelt, 1957), or with applied chemicals (van der Laán, 1934; Huber, 1951). In addition, the sign of the tropistic response can be reversed in some cases by increasing the magnitude of the light or gravity stimulus. The most simple explanation of the difference in sign between shoots and roots is that an increase in auxin stimulates shoot growth but inhibits root growth (Figs. 6-2 and 6-3). It is odd, then, that some stem and root tropisms appear to be associated with inhibition of growth on the concave side rather than with promotion on the convex side (e.g., Went, 1928; Rufelt, 1957). Should we assume that the change of flower stems from positive to negative phototropisms (Seidel, 1957) may be due to an increasing sensitivity of the tissue to auxin with age? This basic part of the tropistic mechanism has not been clarified.

Abscission. The shedding of leaves, flowers, fruits, and stems from the parent plant is another correlation effect which is influenced by auxin. The correlative nature of the abscission control is well illustrated by leaves, in which the hormone produced by the leaf blade exerts an influence on the development of the abscission zone in the petiole.

The abscission process is clearly an active one and not merely a passive falling of the aging organs. Abscission is suppressed by a deficiency of oxygen (Carns et al., 1951) or of carbohydrate (Biggs and Leopold, 1957). It seems reasonable to consider the hormonal influences on abscission to be effects on some dynamic cell processes.

That auxin can inhibit leaf abscission was first observed by Laibach (1933a), using the auxin from orchid pollinia. LaRue (1936) found similar inhibitions for leaf diffusates, pollen extracts, and auxin pastes (Table 4). The inhibiting effect of the leaf blade on petiole abscission has been attributed to the auxin content of the blade (Mai, 1934; Myers, 1940; Wetmore and Jacobs, 1953). The advent of abscission is associated with a drop in auxin content not only in leaves but also in fruits (Luckwill, 1948) and stems (Garrison and Wetmore 1961).

Promotion of abscission by auxin was observed by Laibach (1933a) but was not generally recognized until almost 20 years later. Promotions are generally obtained experimentally under either of two conditions: when auxin is applied on the proximal side of the abscission zone (Addicott and Lynch, 1951; Fig. 10-18) or when very low concentrations are applied to either side (Biggs and Leopold, 1958; Fig. 10-19). The former instances led Addicott et al. (1955) to propose a gradient theory to account for auxin effects on abscission whereby larger amounts of auxin on the proximal side of the zone would hasten abscission, and larger amounts on the distal side would inhibit. The gradient theory is challenged by the fact that both promotive and inhibitory

Table 4 | *Abscission of debladed Coleus petioles is inhibited by leaf diffusates, by pollen, and by auxin pastes. Paired opposite leaves were given either plain lanolin or lanolin containing the tested materials (LaRue, 1936).*

Treatment	Average hours to abscission	
	Controls	Treated
Coleus-leaf diffusate	43	58
Vallota-leaf diffusate	75	123
Populus-pollen diffusate	78	124
Auxin paste (5 mg/liter) in dark	54	131
Auxin paste (5 mg/liter) in light	160	182

Fig. 10-18 | The abscission of bean-petiole explants can be either promoted or inhibited by auxin application, depending on the site of application. Indoleacetic acid (105 mg/liter) applied as solution to either end; water to the controls (Addicott and Lynch, 1951).

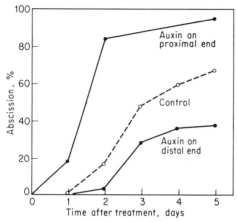

Fig. 10-19 | The concentration of auxin applied can determine whether abscission of bean explants is promoted or inhibited, the greatest promotions being commonly obtained with proximal applications. Explants of trifoliate bean-leaf petioles inserted into agar containing the auxin naphthaleneacetic acid (Biggs and Leopold, 1958).

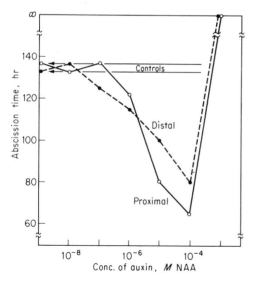

effects can be obtained with auxin applications to either side of the abscission zone and that the imposition of artificial auxin gradients across abscission zones produces only the effects predictable on the basis of the concentrations applied (Gaur and Leopold, 1955). More recent experiments with radioactive auxin (Rubinstein and Leopold, 1963) have shown a lack of relation between the proportional amounts of auxin on either side of the abscission zone and the promotive or inhibitory responses imposed.

The promotive and inhibitory effects of various auxin concentrations led Biggs and Leopold (1958) to the view that as in the growth effects, abscission has a two-phase response curve with promotions at low concentrations and inhibitions at high ones. This scheme would imply that young leaves were restrained from abscising because of the high auxin content and that old leaves were stimulated to abscise by their low auxin contents. It became apparent, however, that this concept needed revision when the sign of the auxin response was found to vary with time of application (Rubinstein and Leopold, 1963) and that older leaves are apparently neither inhibited nor stimulated to abscise by low auxin concentrations (Chatterjee and Leopold, 1964).

The development of abscission is separable into two phases by the simple technique of applying auxin treatments at different intervals after the removal of the blade (Rubinstein and Leopold, 1963). By this device (Fig. 10-20), a given concentration of auxin is found to be inhibitory only if applied during the first few hours after deblading; application after that promotes abscission, suggesting that there are two stages of the abscission process, the first of which is inhibited by auxin and the second promoted by auxin. Both the inhibitory action on the first stage and the promotive action on the second stage are shared by IAA and many synthetic auxins (Chatterjee and Leopold, 1963).

That substances other than auxins participate in the control of abscission became evident when Osborne (1955) reported that diffusates from aging leaves contained materials which stimulated abscission of petiole explants (Table 5). Since that time many workers have obtained stimulatory materials from senescing leaves (Biggs, 1957; Hall et al., 1961) and ripened fruits (van Steveninck, 1959; Liu and Carns, 1961). Experiments on the changes in sensitivity of the leaf to abscission inhibitors and promoters with age indicate that as the leaf approaches senescence, the auxin-inhibition effect is lost, and the leaf becomes increasingly responsive to the promotive effects of stimulatory factors other than auxin (Chatterjee and Leopold, 1964).

Mobilization phenomena are also related to abscission processes. Mothes (1960) described the ability of kinetin to cause mobilization of organic and perhaps some inorganic nutrients in leaves. The conditions which normally lead to abscission are generally associated with a demobilization and loss of such nutrients from leaves. Osborne and Hallaway (1960) found that auxin treatments which deterred abscission also prevented the decline of protein nitrogen in the leaf blade.

Abscission appears, then, to be a correlative effect in which the leaf blade or other organ (flower, fruit) suppresses the cellular changes which lead to separation, and this suppression involves the flow of auxin from the leaf to the abscission zone. As deterioration processes set in, however, many materials are exported from the leaf, including some which can stimulate abscission development.

Conclusion

The most apparent means by which differential growth is maintained in multicellular plants is through the transmission of chemical messengers between cells. For such messengers or hormones to have organized patterns of effects, it is necessary that there be a direction of their movement, and this is best seen in the polar transport of the plant hormone indoleacetic acid. Correlation effects which are polar in direction seem

Fig. 10-20 | The time of auxin application after leaf deblading can determine whether abscission is inhibited or promoted. It is suggested that a first stage of abscission is inhibited by auxin and that a subsequent stage is promoted. Debladed petioles of bean treated with lanolin paste of naphthaleneacetic acid (5.4×10^{-3}M) on distal side (Rubinstein and Leopold, 1963).

Table 5 | *The abscission of bean-petiole explants is hastened by diffusates from senescent leaves of several species (Osborne, 1955).*

		Average hours to abscission	
Species tested	Control	Diffusates from young leaves	Diffusates from abscised leaves
Phaseolus vulgaris	107	105	88
Ulmus glabra	102	77	48
Rhododendron sutchuense	67	77+	55

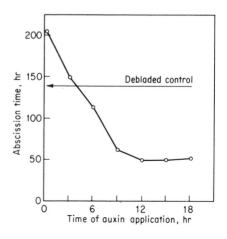

to be influenced by the auxin stemming from the more apical regions. Thus the apical influences on xylem differentiation, cambium activation, rooting, apical dominance, and tropisms seem to be accountable for on the basis of auxin. This does not mean that auxins are totally responsible for these events, but rather that they participate in the controls.

The polarity with which chemical messages organize functions between cells and tissues apparently depends on a continuity of polar orientation of the individual cells of the organism. For the polar functions which are regulated by auxin, the correlation effects rest on the polarity of auxin transport.

The substantive nature of the regulating systems over growth and development has been illustrated by the numerous types of experiments on the auxins, gibberellins, kinins, and inhibitors. There may be many more types of regulating substances in the plant. The regulating substances may be provided by the apex, as is the usual case with auxins, or they may be provided by the leaves or other organs. The evidences of substances coming from leaves and regulating such functions as flowering, dormancy, and other photoperiodic events will be discussed in Part III. A striking component of the picture of the growth and development of the multicellular plant is the intercellular communications carried by chemical regulators—regulators of plant processes by substances moving from one part to another.

GENERAL REFERENCES

Bünning, E. 1957. *Polarität, und Inaquale Teilung des Pflanzlichen Protoplasten.* Springer-Verlag, Vienna.

Champagnat, P. 1961. Differentiation, formation des racines et des bourgeons. *Handbuch Pflanzenphys.*, 14:839–869.

———. 1961. Dominance apicale, tropismes, epinastie. *Handbuch Pflanzenphys.*, 14:872–907.

Sinnott, E. W. 1960. *Plant Morphogenesis.* McGraw-Hill Book Company, New York. 550 pp.

REFERENCES CITED

Addicott, F. T., and R. S. Lynch. 1951. Acceleration and retardation of abscission by indoleacetic acid. *Science*, 114:688–689.

———, R. S. Lynch, and H. R. Carns. 1955. Auxin gradient theory of abscission regulation. *Science*, 121:644–645.

Asomaning, E. J. A., and A. W. Galston. 1961. Comparative study of phototropic response and pigment content in oat and barley coleoptiles. *Plant Physiol.*, 36:453–464.

Audus, L. J., and A. N. Lahiri. 1961. Studies on the geotropism of roots. III. Geotropism. *J. Exptl. Botany*, 12:75–84.

Bachelard, E. P., and B. B. Stowe. 1962. A possible link between root initiation and anthocyanin formation. *Nature*, 194:209–210.

Beams, H. W., and R. L. King. 1944a. The negative group effect in the pollen grains of *Vinca*. *J. Cellular Comp. Physiol.*, 23:39–46.

——— and ———. 1944b. Effect of ultra centrifuging on polarity in the pollen grains of *Vinca*. *J. Cellular Comp. Physiol.*, 24:109–116.

Biggs, R. H. 1957. Physiological basis of abscission in plants. Ph.D. Diss., Purdue Univ. 116 pp.

——— and A. C. Leopold. 1957. Factors influencing abscission. *Plant Physiol.*, 32:626–632.

——— and ———. 1958. The two phase action of auxin on abscission. *Am. J. Botany*, 45:547–551.

Bloch, R. 1952. Wound healing in higher plants. *Botan. Rev.*, 18:655–679.

Booth, A., J. Moorby, C. R. Davies, H.

Jones, and P. F. Wareing. 1962. Effects of indoleacetic acid on the movement of nutrients within plants. *Nature,* 194:204–205.

Boysen-Jensen, P. 1936a. Über die Verteilung des Wuchstoffes in Keimstengeln und Wurzeln wahrend phototropischen und geotropischen Krummung. *Kgl. Danske Videnskab. Selskab. Biol. Med.,* 13:1–31.

———. 1936b. Über ein Mikromethode zur quantitativen Bestimmung der Wuchstuffe der A Gruppe. *Planta,* 26:584–594.

———. 1936c. *Growth Hormones in Plants.* McGraw-Hill Book Company, New York.

Brauner, L. 1922. Lichtkrummung und Lichtwachstumreaktion. *Z. Botan.,* 14: 497–547.

——— and E. Appel. 1960. Zum Problem der Wuchsstoff-Querverschiebung bei der geotropischen Induktion. *Planta,* 55:226–234.

——— and A. Hager. 1957. Über die geotropische "Mneme." *Naturwissenschaften,* 15:429–430.

——— and ———. 1958. Versuche zur Analyse der geotropischen Perzeption. I. *Planta,* 51:115–147.

——— and A. Zipperer. 1961. Über die Anfangsphasen der geotropischen Krummungs-bewegung von *Avena* Koleoptilen. *Planta,* 57:503–517.

Briggs, W. R. 1960. Light dosage and phototropic responses of corn and oat coleoptiles. *Plant Physiol.,* 35:951–962.

———, R. D. Tocher, and J. F. Wilson. 1957. Phototropic auxin redistribution in corn coleoptiles. *Science,* 126:210–212.

Bünning, E. 1957. *Polarität und Inaquale Teilung des Pflanzlichen Protoplasten.* Springer-Verlag, Vienna.

———, H. J. Reisener, R. Weygand, H. Simon, and J. F. Klebe. 1956. Versuche mit radioaktiver Indolylessigsaure zur Prufung der sogenannten Ablenkung des Wuchshormonstromes durch Licht. *Z. Naturforsch.,* 11:363–364.

Camus, G. 1949. Recherches sur le role des bourgeons dans les phenomenes de morphogenese. *Rev. Cytol. Biol. Vegetales,* 11:1–199.

Carns, H. R., F. T. Addicott, and R. S. Lynch. 1951. Effects of water and oxygen on abscission *in vitro. Plant Physiol.,* 26: 629–630.

Champagnat, P. 1951. Action du cotylédon de *Bidens pilosus* L. var. *radiatus* sur son bourgeon axillaire cas d'inhibition et cas de stimulation dosages auxiniques. *Compt. Rend. Soc. Biol. (Paris),* 145: 1371–1376.

———. 1954. Recherches sur les rameaux anticipés des végétaux ligneux. *Rev. Cytol. Biol. Vegetales,* 15:1–51.

———. 1955. Les corrélations entre feuilles et bourgeons de la pousse herbacée du Lilas. *Rev. Gen. Botan.,* 62:325–372.

Chatterjee, S., and A. C. Leopold. 1963. Auxin structure and abscission activity. *Plant Physiol.,* 38:268–273.

——— and ———. 1964. Changes in abscission processes with aging. *Plant Physiol.* (in press).

Ching, R. M., and S. C. Fang. 1958. The redistribution of radioactivity in geotropically stimulated plants pretreated with radioactive indoleacetic acid. *Physiol. Plantarum,* 11:722–727.

Clutter, M. E. 1960. Hormonal induction of vascular tissue in tobacco pith *in vitro. Science,* 132:548–549.

Conrad, K. 1961. Über die Verteilung von Auxin in partiell mit Kinetin behandetten isolierten Blatt. *Flora (Jena),* 151:345–350.

Coster, C. 1927. Zur Anatomie und Physiologie der Zuwachszonen und Jahresringbildung in den Tropen. *Ann. Jard. Bot. Buitenzorg,* 37:49–160; 38:1–114.

Darwin, C. 1897. *The Power of Movement in Plants.* D. Appleton & Company, Inc., New York.

de Ropp, R. S. 1947. Studies in the physiology of leaf growth. IV. *Ann. Botany (London),* 11:439–447.

Diemer, R. 1961. Untersuchungen des phototropischen Induktionsvorganges an

Helianthus Keimlingen. *Planta,* 57:111–137.

Dolk, H. E. 1929*a*. Über die Wirkung der Schwerkraft auf Koleoptilen von *Avena sativa. Proc. Koninkl. Ned. Akad. Wetenschap.,* 32:40–47.

———. 1929*b*. Über die Wirkung der Schwerkraft auf Koleoptilen von *Avena sativa. II. Proc. Koninkl. Ned. Akad. Wetenschap.,* 32:1127–1140.

Dostal, R. 1962. Über die korrelative Erhaltung entspreiteter Blattstiele. *Biol. Plant. Acad. Sci. Bohemoslov.,* 4:191–202.

Fitting, H. 1938. V. Die Umkehrbarkeit der durch aussenfaktoren induzierten Dorsiventralität. *Jahrb. Wiss. Bot.,* 86:107–227.

Galston, A. W. 1961. *Sci. Amer.,* 202:12–13. Letter to the Editor.

Garrison, R., and R. H. Wetmore. 1961. Studies in shoot-tip abortion: *Syringa vulgaris. Am. J. Botany,* 48:789–795.

Gaur, B. K., and A. C. Leopold. 1955. The promotion of abscission by auxin. *Plant Physiol.,* 30:487–490.

Gillespie, B., and K. V. Thimann. 1961. The lateral transport of indoleacetic acid-C^{14} in geotropism. *Experientia,* 17:126–129.

Gordon, S. A. 1957. The effects of ionizing radiation on plants: biochemical and physiological aspects. *Quart. Rev. Biol.,* 32:3-14.

——— and M. Eib. 1956. Auxin transport in the phototropic response. *Plant Physiol.,* 31:xiv.

Gouwentak, C. A., and G. Hellinga. 1935. Beobachtungen über Wurzelbildung. *Mededel. Landbouwhogeschool Wageningen,* 39:1–6.

Gregory, F. G., and J. A. Veale. 1957. A reassessment of the problem of apical dominance. *Symp. Soc. Exptl. Biol.,* 11:1–20.

Gunckel, J. E., and K. V. Thimann. 1949. Studies of development in long shoots and short shoots of *Ginkgo biloba* L. III. Auxin production of short shoot. *Am. J. Botany,* 36:145–151.

Guttenberg, H. von. 1959. Über die Perzeption des phototropen Reizes. *Planta,* 53:412–433.

Haberlandt, G. 1913. Zur Physiologie der Zellteilung. *Sitz. Akad. Wiss., Physik.-Math. Cl.,* 1913:318–345.

Hahne, I. 1961. Untersuchungen zum Problem der Beteiligung des Wuchsstoffes an der geotropischen Induktion bei Koleoptilen. *Planta,* 57:557–582.

Hall, W. C., F. A. Herrero, and F. R. H. Katterman. 1961. Leaf abscission in cotton. IV. Effects of a natural promoter and amino acids on abscission in cotyledonary explants. *Botan. Gaz.,* 123:29–34.

Haupt, W. 1957. Die Induktion der Polarität bei den Spore von *Equisetum. Planta,* 49:61–90.

Hertel, R. 1962. Der Auxintransport in *Zea mais*. Ph.D. Diss., Ludwig Maximillian Univ., Munich.

——— and A. C. Leopold. 1962. Auxintransport und Schwerkraft. *Naturwissenschaften,* 49:377–378.

——— and ———. 1963. Versuche zur Analyse des Auxintransports in der Koleoptile von *Zea Mays* L. *Planta,* 59:535–562.

Hess, C. E. 1962. The physiology of root initiation in easy- and difficult-to-root cuttings. *Hormolog,* 3:3–6.

Huber, H. 1951. Über den Einfluss der Belichtung auf die Wuchsstoffempfindlichkeit der Keimstengel von *Cucumis sativus* L. *Ber. Schweiz. Botan. Ges.,* 61: 499–537.

Jablonski, J. R., and F. Skoog. 1954. Cell enlargement and cell division in excised tobacco pith tissue. *Physiol. Plantarum,* 7:16–24.

Jacobs, W. P. 1952. Role of auxin in differentiation of xylem around a wound. *Am. J. Botany,* 39:301–309.

———. 1954. Acropetal auxin transport and xylem regeneration: a quantitative study. *Am. Naturalist,* 88:327–337.

——— and B. Bullwinkel. 1953. Compensatory growth in *Coleus* shoots. *Am. J. Botany*, 40:385–392.

———, J. Danielson, V. Hurst, and P. Adams. 1959. What substance normally controls a given biological process? II. The relation of auxin to apical dominance, pp. 534–554. In *Developmental Biology*, Academic Press, Inc., New York.

——— and I. B. Morrow. 1957. A quantitative study of xylem development in the vegetative shoot apex of *Coleus*. *Am. J. Botany*, 44:823–842.

——— and ———. 1958. Quantitative relations between stage of leaf development and differentiation of sieve tubes. *Science*, 128:1084–1085.

Jankiewicz, L. 1956. The effect of auxins on crotch angles in apple trees. *Bull. Acad. Polon. Sci.*, 4:173–178.

Jones, W. W., and J. H. Beaumont. 1937. Carbohydrate accumulation in relation to vegetative propagation of the Litchi. *Science*, 86:313.

Jost, L. 1891. Über Dichenwachstum und Jahresringbildung. *Botan. Z.*, 49:485–630.

Laán, P. A. van der. 1934. Der Einfluss von Athylen auf die Wuchsstoffbildung bei *Avena* und *Vicia*. *Rec. Trav. Bot. Neerl.*, 31:691–742.

Laibach, F. 1933a. Wuchsstoffversuche mit lebenden Orchideen pollinien. *Ber. Deut. Botan. Ges.*, 51:336–340.

———. 1933b. Versuche mit Wuchsstoffpaste. *Ber. Deut. Botan. Ges.*, 51:386–392.

La Rue, C. D. 1936. Effect of auxin on abscission of petioles. *Proc. Natl. Acad. Sci. U.S.*, 22:254–259.

——— and S. Narayanswami. 1957. Auxin inhibition in the liverwort *Lunularia*. *New Phytologist*, 56:61–70.

Lek, H. A. A. van der. 1925. Over de wortelvorming van houtige stekken. Ph.D. Diss., Univ. of Utrecht (cited by Went and Thimann, 1937).

———. 1934. Over den invlaed der knappen op de wortelvorming der stekken.

Mededel. Landbouwhogeschool Wageningen, 38:1–95.

Leopold, A. C. 1949. The control of tillering in grasses by auxin. *Am. J. Botany*, 36:437–440.

Liu, W. C., and H. R. Carns. 1961. Isolation of abscisin, an abscission accelerating substance. *Science*, 134:384–385.

Luckwill, L. C. 1948. A method for the quantitative estimation of growth substances based on the response of tomato ovaries to known amounts of 2-naphthoxyacetic acid. *J. Hort. Sci.*, 24:19–31.

Mai, G. 1934. Korrelationsuntersuchungen an entspreiteten Blattstralen mit lebender Orchideen-pollinien als Wuchstoffquelle. *Jahrb. Wiss. Bot.*, 79:681–713.

Michener, H. D. 1942. Dormancy and apical dominance in potato tubers. *Am. J. Botany*, 29:558–562.

Mohr, H., and E. Peters. 1960. Der Phototropismus und das lichtabhangige Langenwachstum des Hypokotyls von *Sinapis alba* L. *Planta*, 55:646–646.

Mothes, K. 1960. Über das Altern der Blatter und die Möglichkeit ihrer Wiederverjungung. *Naturwissenschaften*, 47:337–350.

———, L. Engelbrecht, and H. R. Schutte. 1961. Über die Akkumulation von γ-Aminoisobüttersaure im Blattgewebe unter den Einfluss von Kinetin. *Physiol. Plantarum*, 14:72–75.

Myers, R. M. 1940. Effect of growth substances on the abscission layer in leaves of *Coleus*. *Botan. Gaz.*, 102:323–338.

Nemec, B. 1900. Über die Art der Wahrnehmung des Schwerereizes bei den Pflanzen. *Ber. Deut. Botan. Ges.*, 18:241–248.

Osborne, D. J. 1955. Acceleration of abscission by a factor produced in senescent leaves. *Nature*, 176:1161–1163.

———and M. Hallaway. 1960. Auxin control of protein levels in detached autumn leaves. *Nature*, 188:240–241.

Overbeek, J. van, S. A. Gordon, and L. E. Gregory. 1946. An analysis of the function of the leaf in the process of root formation in cuttings. *Am. J. Botany*, 33: 100–107.

———, D. Olivo, and E. M. S. de Vasquez. 1945. Rapid extraction method for free auxin and its application in geotropic reactions of bean and sugar cane. *Botan. Gaz.*, 106:440–451.

Pearce, H. L. 1943. The effect of nutrition and phytohormones on the rooting of *Vinca* cuttings. *Ann. Botany (London)*, 7:123–132.

Pfeffer, W. 1906. *The Physiology of Plants.* Vol. III (tr. by A. J. Ewart). Clarendon Press, Oxford.

Pickard, B. G., and K. V. Thimann. 1963. Immediate cause of phototropic curvature in the maize seedling. *Science*, 140: 384.

Pilet, P. E. 1951. Contribution à l'étude des hormones de croissance (auxines) dans la racine de *Lens culinaris*. *Mem. Soc. Vaudoise Sci. Nat.*, 10:137–244.

Reisener, H. J. 1958. Untersuchungen über den Phototropismus der Hafer-Koleoptile. *Z. Botan.*, 46:474–505.

Roberts, L. W. 1960a. Protein-bound sulfhydryl groups in *Coleus* wound meristem. *Am. J. Botany*, 47:110–114.

———. 1960b. Experiments on xylem regeneration in stem wound responses in *Coleus*. *Botan. Gaz.*, 121:201–208.

Rubinstein, B., and A. C. Leopold. 1963. Analysis of the auxin control of bean leaf abscission. *Plant Physiol.*, 38:262–267.

Rufelt, H. 1957. Influence of the composition of the nutrient solution on the geotropic reactions of wheat roots. *Physiol. Plantarum*, 10:373–396.

Ruge, U. 1957. Der Ascorbinsauregehalt von *Tradescantia*-Blattern in Abhangigkeit von der Wellenlange des Lichtes. *Naturwissenschaften*, 44:13–14.

Sato, I. 1956. Studies on the georeaction shown in the axes of some herbaceous plants. *Japan. J. Botany*, 15:249–269.

Schmitz, H. 1933. Über Wuchsstoff und Geotropismus bei Gräsern. *Planta*, 19: 614–635.

Seidel, K. 1957. Umstimmung des negativen Geotropismus. *Naturwissenchaften*, 9: 289.

Shibaoka, H., and T. Yamaki. 1959. Studies on the growth movement of sunflower plant. *Sci. Papers Coll. Gen. Educ. Tokyo*, 9:105–126.

Sinnott, E. W. 1952. Reaction wood and the regulation of tree form. *Am. J. Botany*, 39:69–78.

———. 1960. *Plant Morphogenesis.* McGraw-Hill Book Company, New York,

——— and R. Block. 1944. Visible expression of cytoplasmic pattern in the differentiation of xylem strands. *Proc. Natl. Acad. Sci. U.S.*, 30:388–392.

Skoog, F., and C. Tsui. 1948. Chemical control of growth and bud formation in tobacco stem segments and callus cultured *in vitro*. *Am. J. Botany*, 35:782–787.

——— and ———, 1951. Growth substances and the formation of buds in plant tissues, pp. 263–285. In F. Skoog (ed.), *Plant Growth Substances*, Univ. of Wisconsin Press, Madison, Wis.

Snow, R. 1932. Growth-regulators in plants. *New Phytologist*, 31:336–353.

———. 1935. Activation of cambial growth by pure hormones. *Nature*, 135:876.

———. 1936. Upward effects of auxin in coleoptiles and stems. *New Phytologist*, 35:292–304.

Steward, F. C., M. O. Mapes, and K. Mears. 1958. Growth and organized development of cultured cells. II. Organization in cultures grown from freely suspended cells. *Am. J. Botany*, 45:705–708.

Thimann, K. V. 1936. Auxins and the growth of roots. *Am. J. Botany*, 23:561–569.

——— and G. M. Curry. 1961. Phototropism, pp. 646–670. In W. D. McElroy and B. Glass (eds.), *Light and Life*. The Johns Hopkins Press, Baltimore.

——— and M. M. Laloraya. 1960. Changes in nitrogen in pea stem sections under the action of kinetin. *Physiol. Plantarum,* 13:165–178.

——— and F. Skoog. 1933. Studies on the growth hormone in plants. *Proc. Natl. Acad. Sci. U.S.,* 19:714–716.

——— and ———. 1934. Inhibition of bud development and other functions of growth substances in *Vicia faba. Proc. Roy. Soc. (London),* B,114:317–339.

——— and F. W. Went. 1934. On the chemical nature of the root forming hormone. *Proc. Koninkl. Ned. Akad. Wetenschap.,* 37:456–459.

Titman, P. W., and R. H. Wetmore. 1955. The growth of long and short shoots in *Cercidiphyllum. Am. J. Botany,* 42:364–372.

Torrey, J. G. 1955. On the determination of vascular patterns during tissue differentiation in excised pea roots. *Am. J. Botany,* 42:183–198.

———. 1956. Physiology of root elongation. *Ann. Rev. Plant Physiol.,* 7:237–266.

———. 1957. Auxin control of vascular pattern formation in regenerating pea root meristems grown *in vitro. Am. J. Botany,* 44:859–870.

van Steveninck, R. F. M. 1959. Abscission accelerators in lupine. *Nature,* 183:1246–1248.

Vardar, Y. 1955a. The change of the plagiotropic position in the peduncles with their age and its relation with IAA. *Rev. Fac. Sci. Forest. Univ. Istanbul,* 20:199–223.

———. 1955b. A study on the apical bud inhibition upon the lateral branches. *Rev. Fac. Sci. Forest. Univ. Istanbul,* 20:245–256.

Vardjan, M., and J. P. Nitsch. 1961. La regeneration chez *Cichorium:* étude des auxines et des kinines endogenes. *Bull. Soc. Botan. France,* 108:363–374.

Verner, L. 1938. Effect of a growth substance on crotch angles in apple trees. *Proc. Am. Soc. Hort. Sci.,* 36:415–422.

Vöchting, H. 1878. *Über Organbildung im Pflanzenruch.* Max Cohen u. Sohn Verlag, Bonn. 258 pp.

von Maltzahn, K. E. 1959. Interaction between kinetin and indoleacetic acid in the control of bud reactivation in *Splachnum ampullaceum* (L.) Hedw. *Nature,* 183:60–61.

Wald, G. 1961. *Sci. Am.,* 202:13. Letter to the Editor.

Wardrop, A. B. 1956. The nature of reaction wood. V. *Australian J. Botany,* 4:152–166.

Wareing, P. F. 1958. Interaction between indole-acetic acid and gibberellic acid in cambial activity. *Nature,* 181:1744–1745.

——— and D. L. Roberts. 1956. Photoperiodic control of cambial activity in *Robinia pseudoacacia* L. *New Phytologist,* 55:289–388.

Warmke, H. E., and G. L. Warmke. 1950. Role of auxin in differentiation of root and shoot of *Taraxacum* and *Cichorium. Am. J. Botany,* 37:272–280.

Went, F. W. 1928. Wuchsstoff und Wachstum. *Rec. Trav. Bot. Neerl.,* 25:1–116.

———. 1936. Allgemeine Beobachtungen über das auxin-Problem. *Biol. Zentr.,* 56:449–463.

——— and K. V. Thimann. 1937. *Phytohormones.* The Macmillan Comany, New York. 294 pp.

Wershing, H. F., and I. W. Bailey. 1942. Seedlings as experimental material in the study of redwood in conifers. *J. Forestry,* 40:411–414.

Wetmore, R. H. 1954. The use of *in vitro* cultures in the investigation of growth and differentiation in vascular plants. *Brookhaven Symp. Biol.,* 6:22–40.

———. 1959. Morphogenesis in plants: a new approach. *Am. Sci.,* 47:326–340.

——— and W. P. Jacobs. 1953. Studies on abscission: the inhibiting effect of auxin. *Am. J. Botany,* 40:272–276.

——— and S. Sorokin. 1955. On the differentiation of xylem. *J. Arnold Arboretum,* 36:305–317.

Wettstein, D. von. 1953. Beeinflussung der

Polarität und undifferenzierte Gewebe-bildung aus Moossporen. *Z. Botan.* 41: 199.

Wickson, M., and K. V. Thimann. 1958. The antagonism of auxin and kinetin in apical dominance. *Physiol. Plantarum,* 11:62–74.

———— and ————. 1960. The antagonism of auxin and kinetin in apical dominance.

II. The transport of IAA in pea stems. *Physiol. Plantarum,* 13:539–554.

Ziegler, H. 1953. Über die Bildung und Lokalisierung des Formazans in der Pflanzenzelle. *Naturwissenschaften,* 40: 144.

Zinsmeister, H. D. 1960. Das phototropische Verhatten der Blutenstiele von *Cyclamen. Planta,* 55:647–668.

Part III | DEVELOPMENT

The discussion so far has been concerned principally with characteristics of cells and tissues and their activities in assimilation and growth. The assembly of these tissues and functions into an integrated multicellular organism yields not only the characteristics of the separate parts and processes but also quite a new set of characteristics which would not have been predictable on the basis of examination of the separate parts. Went (1962) has stated that "We cannot understand an organism by studying it only on the molecular level." Nor can we understand it from exclusive study of the cellular or tissue level. One would never have been able to predict the characteristics of a bee colony on the basis of examination of individual bees.

The cliché that the whole is more than the sum of its parts becomes an elaborate theme as we observe the complicated changes which the whole plant can experience during the repeating cycle of development. This cycle may start with the germination of a seed and continue with the passage of a juvenile phase of growth and the graduation into maturity, followed by progress into a state of senescence. With maturity the organism is capable of shifting from vegetative to reproductive growth, with the initiation and development of flowers, the development of fruits, and the production again of a new generation of seed. Each of these steps in the development cycle may be controlled by more or less systemic physiological actions; and while none of these developmental steps can be adequately explained by physiological knowledge, many exciting features of the systems have been revealed—fragments of information from which we can make some mental constructs of the possible mechanisms controlling the development of whole plants.

11 | Juvenility

With germination of the seed, most plants enter a state of vigorous vegetative growth during which they cannot be readily induced to a reproductive type of growth. One can visualize ecological advantages to a plant of having a period devoted exclusively to rapid vegetative growth, achieving relatively quickly a size which would be competitively stronger in the plant community. Physiologically, the juvenile state can be described as a period when the plant is capable of exponential increases in size, when flowering processes cannot be readily induced, and when the plant develops characteristic morphological forms (of leaves, stems, thorns, etc.).

It should be emphasized that juvenility is not a period necessarily devoid of an ability to flower. Passecker (1949) noted that the morphological gradation from juvenile to mature forms of fruit trees was associated with a gradual increase in the ability of the tree to form flowers. De Muckadell (1954) emphasized that the morphological forms of trees are much better indices of juvenility than the ability or lack of ability of the tree to flower.

Some examples of the relative sensitivities of plants to flower or not as they grow older are presented in Fig. 11-1. Each of these three *Cruciferae* is induced to flower by low temperatures. *Lunaria* will not flower in response to cold treatment until it is about 7 weeks old, after which all plants will flower (Wellensiek, 1958b). Brussels sprouts likewise have a minimum age for flowering, but after that they show a gradual increasing responsiveness in numbers of plants responding to the cold (Stokes and Verkerk, 1951). Beets, on the other hand, flower in response to cold at any age, but there is a gradually increasing responsiveness as the plants grow older—a quantitative rather than a qualitative juvenility with respect to flowering (Wellensiek and Hakkaart, 1955).

These cases illustrate the point that a plant species may have a juvenile period in which the induction of flowering is completely obstructed, or it may have a juvenile period in which flowering is only quantitatively impeded.

The vegetative condition is not exclusively a property of juvenility; thus a Brussels sprout plant can pass far beyond its 11 weeks of juvenility and still not flower if it has not experienced an inductive cold condition.

Since flowering itself may not be a valid

Fig. 11-1 | Juvenility may be a period of complete inability to flower or of quantitatively poor response to flower stimuli. *Lunaria* cannot be induced by cold before 7 weeks of age (Wellensiek, 1958*b*); Brussels sprouts are not induced by cold before 11 weeks of age, after which there is a quantitatively increasing response (Stokes and Verkerk, 1951); and beets are simply increasingly responsive to cold as they pass out of juvenility (Wellensiek and Hakkaart, 1955).

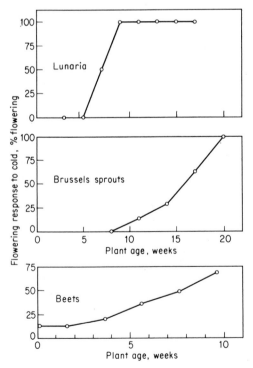

index of juvenility, perhaps the morphological expressions of juvenility may provide more meaningful information concerning the relative duration of juvenile periods in various plants. Juvenile leaf forms may occur only on the first node of the germinating seedling (as in bean) or on the first several nodes (pea, *Xanthium*). The narrow juvenile stems of Brussels sprouts persist for 11 weeks. Apple seedlings may continue the whiplike growth of the juvenile nonflowering state for 4 to 10 years. Juvenile types of stem growth, leaf form, and thorniness may persist for 10 or 15 years in *Citrus* and pecan trees, and flowering is absent or restricted during that time. A classic case of juvenility is that of the common ivy, *Hedera helix*, which retains the juvenile form of a creeping vine and palmate leaf for an indefinite time and only occasionally switches over to the mature form of an upright bush with entire leaves, after which it proceeds to flower and fruit. Some beech and oak trees may retain morphological features of juvenility for 60 years, and in fact in numerous horticultural plant materials, juvenility has become apparently fixed and permanent, as in the entire genus of *Retinospora*, which is a series of fixed juvenile forms of *Thuja* and *Chamaecyparis* (cf. Busgen et al., 1929).

As the juvenile plant grows up, its structure may reflect the gradual change from juvenile to mature types of growth. The presence of juvenile types of morphology at the base of an apple seedling and graded levels of increasing maturity up the tree were pointed out by Passecker (1949), and dramatic evidence of the presence of all the stages between juvenility and maturity in beech trees has been developed by de Muckadell (1959). Reproduced in Fig. 11-2 is Passecker's diagram of such a gradation up the tree—a gradation evident not only in the ability to flower but also in the leaf and stem forms and in the ability to transmit the physiological expression of juvenility to cuttings or graft sections taken from the various parts of the seedling. Cuttings from the base of a seedling may develop into new plants with juvenile leaf form and stem form, juvenile thorns (where present in juvenile wood), juvenile ease of rooting, and juvenile tendencies to retain leaves during the winter. In fact, then, the ontogenetic sequence of development from extreme juvenility to full maturity is preserved in a gradation from the base to the top of a mature tree. De Muckadell attributes this gradient of maturity to the progressive aging of a meristem as it grows. Thus meristems left at the base of the tree retain the stage of juvenility which existed in the apical meristem at the time the laterals were established; the meristem which has grown entirely through to the top of the tree has aged in proportion to the extent of its growth. The most mature meristems are therefore at the apex of the tree and at the ends of its longest branches.

The gradation of maturity from the base to the top of a tree is illustrated in Fig. 11-3. Juvenile oak and beech trees tend to have a delayed abscission of leaves until spring. In older trees, the juvenile characteristic of leaf retention may be very evident in lower branches, even though the upper branches are mature (de Muckadell, 1954).

Morphological expressions

One of the most readily observed morphological expressions of juvenility is that of *leaf form*. The unique leaf forms of new seedlings of conifers were pointed out by Beissner (1888) and further detailed by Busgen et al. (1929). For example, pine seedlings bear short juvenile needles in spirals instead of in fascicles of two to five elongate mature needles, and this leaf feature may persist for as long as 3 years of growth. Seedlings of *Thuja* have awl-shaped leaves for several years before changing over to the mature leaf form of appressed scales. These juvenile forms of *Thuja* and similar

ones of the genus *Chamaecyparis* have become fixed in some plants by repeated propagation during the juvenile stage, as mentioned above. Among the angiosperms, juvenile leaves may be simple, and mature leaves compound (bean, *Citrus*); or rarely the reverse may be true (koa). In the garden pea, the first juvenile leaves are reduced to scales. Increasing amounts of dissection or lobing of the leaves is often associated with increasing maturity. This has been dramatically illustrated for cotton by Ashby (1949), using a diagram of the changing extent of leaf lobing during the development of the plant, as shown in Fig. 11-4. The cotton seedling produces a simple entire leaf, and as the plant becomes mature the leaf form gradually becomes palmate (maximal extent of dissection); after the plant has started to fruit, the leaves tend to return to an entire shape. Ideally one might find an entire series from juvenile to mature and senescent leaf forms arrayed from the base to the tip of the cotton plant.

The usually simpler leaf shape and the faster growth rate of juvenile forms have led to the suggestion that the simple form

Fig. 11-2 | Diagrammatic representation of the gradient from juvenile tissues at the base of a fruit tree to mature tissues at the tip (from Passecker, 1949).

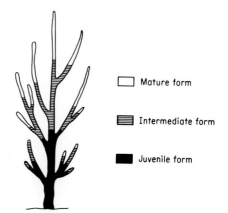

☐ Mature form

▤ Intermediate form

■ Juvenile form

may result from the more rapid growth of juvenile leaves (Sussex and Clutter, 1960). This suggestion would be conveniently compatible with the gradual transition from the formation of juvenile to more mature forms; experimental support for the idea remains to be developed.

Juvenile beech trees produce only shade leaves (Schramm, 1912), suggesting an adaptation of the seedling for growth in the shade, where beech seedlings generally become established.

In many species, the *stem* and its growing point exhibit morphological features of juvenility. Among woody plants, there is often a typical juvenile branching pattern, with long whiplike branches and a narrow branching angle (e.g., Blair et al., 1956). The presence of thorns on the stem is characteristic of juvenile seedlings of *Citrus* and juvenile parts of many locusts. As the tree matures, the new growth at the apex and the longest branches ceases to develop thorns. Again, the degree of thorniness up the tree recapitulates the ontogenetic sequence of its changes from extreme juvenility to maturity.

The stem of ivy changes from a creeping-vine habit to an erect shrub when it passes out of juvenility, as already mentioned.

A noteworthy change of stem morphology has been described for Brussels sprouts (Stokes and Verkerk, 1951). Juvenile seedlings develop a narrow pointed stem with a thin apex; upon reaching maturity (11 weeks), the stem becomes wide, and the apex broad and blunt. The rise in relative proportion of stem to leaf as Brussels sprouts reach maturity is illustrated in Fig. 11–5. Enlargement of the apical meristem with maturity may be common to many herba-

ceous species (cf. Millington and Fisk, 1956).

Physiological expressions

Juvenile wood often roots much more readily than mature wood. This was noted by horticulturists before the concept of juvenility had become generally accepted (Gardner, 1929). Illustrative data are given in Table 6. Auxins can generally stimulate the rooting of cuttings, and Pilet (1958) ob-

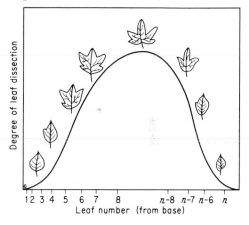

Fig. 11-4 | Diagrammatic representation of the sequential changes in leaf form in cotton, from the simple leaf at the lowest node, to the most dissected form on mature wood, to a simple form again near the flowering nodes (represented as n) (from Ashby, 1949).

Degree of leaf dissection

1 2 3 4 5 6 7   8 n-8 n-7 n-6 n
Leaf number (from base)

Table 6 | *The rooting of cuttings of* **Hedera helix** *shows a sharp decrease with maturity. This is expressed in cuttings from both dormant and growing plants (Hess, 1962).*

	Rooting of cuttings, per cent	
	Dormant	Growing
Juvenile wood	83	100
Mature wood	0	17

Fig. 11-3 | The juvenile characteristic of delayed leaf abscission is evident in beech trees in the winter, the lower branches expressing the juvenile characteristics, and the branch tips the mature characteristics, of abscission.

served more ready enzymatic oxidation of auxin in older pea tissues, suggesting that the superior rooting of juvenile cuttings might be due to a higher endogenous auxin content. Hess (1962), however, found that auxin did not restore the readiness to root in mature ivy; he proposed instead an explanation based on the decline of content of four rooting cofactors which he could extract and separate by paper chromatography.

The propagation of apples by rooting of cuttings is difficult, and English horticulturists sometimes maintain "stool beds" for propagation. Here the apple plants are repeatedly cut back to force out juvenile basal shoots, and the juvenile wood obtained in this way is used for making cuttings. Wellensiek (1952) has achieved a similar effect by continued debudding of small trees until juvenile shoots are sent out.

Propagation of woody plants by budding or cuttings provides some of the most significant evidence concerning the fixity of the juvenile morphology. Noting the gradient in degree of maturity from the base to the top of trees, de Muckadell (1954) made cuttings from graded locations up the tree

and found that propagation from the juvenile base gave new plants which retained the juvenile features of the base. Those from the mature apex gave new plants with the mature characteristics. This was true, for example, of the leaf retention in beech; propagules from the base retained their leaves through the winter. It was also true for the formation of thorns in locust; the propagules from the base developed thorns, and those from the apex were thornless.

De Muckadell (1959) has described some other physiological features of juvenility of some woody plants, including, for example, a greater tendency to develop autumnal colors and a greater shade tolerance.

Modifying juvenility

The most serious attempts to modify juvenility have been made by plant breeders, who can make crosses of fruit trees only after the juvenile period has sufficiently progressed that the development of at least a few flowers may take place. Graftage of juvenile buds onto mature stocks has frequently been employed in efforts to obtain early flowering. In some species, juvenile buds have proved to be indurate to change by graftage, most notably in the beech (de Muckadell, 1956) and Brussels sprouts (Stokes and Verkerk, 1951). In other species some modification of juvenility has been achieved through grafting; slight increases of flowering of juvenile buds grafted onto mature wood have been reported for pecan (Romberg, 1944) and *Citrus* (Furr et al., 1947). Graftage has enhanced some juvenile features in mature buds grafted onto juvenile stocks, most notably in ivy (Doorenbos, 1954) and in rubber (Muzik and Cruzado, 1958). In ivy, reversion to juvenility is most evident when only juvenile leaves are present on the graft combination and when temperatures are relatively high (Stoutemyer and Britt, 1961).

Fig. 11-5 | As Brussels sprouts pass from the juvenile to the mature form at about 11 weeks of age, the proportion of stem to leaves is markedly increased. These data are plotted as the ratio of stems to leaves in per cent (Stokes and Verkerk, 1951).

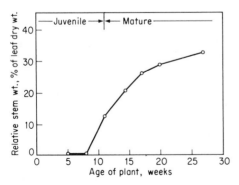

Pruning can enhance juvenility. Not only does it force lower and hence more juvenile meristems into growth, but it also appears directly to enhance the degree of juvenility expressed in growth. Many plants respond to pruning by at least temporary production of more juvenile leaf and stem forms.

Chemical treatments have modified juvenility in a few cases. Gibberellin applications to ivy enhance growth and produce a temporary reversion to juvenile stems and leaves in ivy (Robbins, 1957), especially at high temperatures (Goodin and Stoutemyer, 1961). Similar effects have been reported for *Citrus* (Cooper and Peynado, 1958). Some quantitative data for *Ipomoea* are reproduced in Fig. 11-6 (Njoku, 1958), showing the prolonged retention of juvenile leaf form after application of gibberellin. Auxin applications to juvenile Brussels sprouts have the converse effect, actually hastening the passage of juvenility (de Zeeuw and Leopold, 1955). Muzik and Cruzado (1958) reported encouragingly that extracts from juvenile rubber plants may enhance the juvenile feature of rooting, but it is not clear whether the effect is only on rooting rather than on juvenility.

Nature of the control

What may be the endogenous regulation of the juvenile condition? The description of the passage from juvenile to mature condition as a function of the overall growth of the apical meristem (de Muckadell, 1959) is interesting and helpful. It is consistent with the distribution of graded degrees of maturity up the stem, but it does not aid in understanding how pruning a plant might enhance juvenility or how the graftage of mature buds onto juvenile stocks might cause a regression to a more juvenile type of growth. The experiments on chemical modification of juvenility open the interesting possibility that growth substances may be involved in the control of these develop-mental changes and that the gradual shift from juvenile to mature growth may be due to a dilution or enrichment of a biochemical system.

Some interesting and relevant experiments on nucellar buds of *Citrus* are highly suggestive in this regard. Swingle (1928) observed that nucellar buds germinated into juvenile-type seedlings, even though they arose from strictly maternal tissue which had budded itself into the embryo sac. In a later report (Swingle, 1932), he developed the concept that the passage of an embryo-like experience in the embryo sac produced the juvenility feature, whether the new structure arose from a true embryo or from a maternal nucellar bud. Detailed experiments by Frost (1938, 1952) and Cameron and Soost (1952) showed that the juvenile features of the nucellar seedlings are stable to graftage in exactly the same manner as is the juvenility of true seedlings. The early suggestion of Swingle (1932) that the

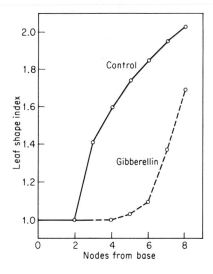

Fig. 11-6 | Application of gibberellin to *Ipomoea caerulea* causes the retention of the juvenile narrow leaf form for an additional five nodes. Leaf shape is plotted as the ratio of width to length (Njoku, 1958).

embryo-sac experience stimulates a rejuvenescence in the developing ovary appears to be a very attractive concept, with perhaps the further possibility that there may be a chemical stimulation to the juvenile condition. Thus the meristem-aging concept of de Muckadell (1959) may represent a gradual dilution of a juvenility stimulus introduced at the embryo stage of development.

The juvenile feature appears to be a quantitative expression of vigor, associated with quantitative differences in vegetative characteristics as well as quantitative limitations on flowering. The possibility that maturation may represent a dilution of an embryonic stimulus is consistent with the quantitative nature of juvenility and the occasional effectiveness of physiological and chemical treatments in modifying this developmental expression.

GENERAL REFERENCES

Busgen, M., E. Münch, and T. Thomson. 1929. *The Structure and Life of Forest Trees.* Chapman & Hall, Ltd., London.

de Muckadell, M. S. 1959. Investigations on aging of apical meristems in woody plants and its importance in silviculture. Ph.D. Diss., Royal Vet. Agr. College, Copenhagen.

REFERENCES CITED

Ashby, E. 1949. Leaf shape. *Sci. Am.,* 181: 22–24.

Beissner, L. 1888. Über Jugendformen von Pflanzen, special Coniferen. *Ber. Deut. Botan. Ges.,* 6:83.

Blair, D. S., M. MacArthur, and S. H. Nelson. 1956. Observations in the growth phases of fruit trees. *Proc. Am. Soc. Hort. Sci.,* 67:75–79.

Busgen, M., E. Münch, and T. Thomson. 1929. *The Structure and Life of Forest Trees.* Chapman & Hall, Ltd., London.

Cameron, J. W., and R. R. Soost. 1952. Size, yield and fruit characters of orchard trees of *Citrus* propagated from young nucellar seedling lines. *Proc. Am. Soc. Hort. Sci.,* 60:255–264.

Cooper, W. C., and A. Peynado. 1958. Effect of gibberellic acid on growth and dormancy in *Citrus. Proc. Am. Soc. Hort. Sci.,* 72:284–289.

de Muckadell, M. S. 1954. Juvenile stages in woody plants. *Physiol. Plantarum,* 7: 782–796.

———. 1956. Experiments on development in *Fagus silvatica* by means of herbaceous grafting. *Physiol. Plantarum,* 9:396–400.

———. 1959. Investigations on aging of apical meristems in woody plants and its importance in silviculture. Ph.D. Diss., Royal Vet. Agr. College, Copenhagen.

de Zeeuw, D., and A. C. Leopold. 1955. Altering juvenility with auxin. *Science,* 122:925–926.

Doorenbos, J. 1954. "Rejuvenation" of *Hedera helix* in graft combinations. *Proc. Koninkl. Ned. Akad. Wetenschap.,* C,57: 99–102.

Frost, H. B. 1938. Nucellar embryony and juvenile characters in clonal varieties of *Citrus. J. Heredity,* 29:423–432.

———. 1952. Characteristics in the nursery of *Citrus* budlings of young nucellar seedling lines and parental old lines. *Proc. Am. Soc. Hort. Sci.,* 60:247–254.

Furr, J. R., W. C. Cooper, and P. C. Reece. 1947. Flower formation in citrus trees. *Am. J. Botany,* 34:1–8.

Gardner, F. E. 1929. The relationship between tree age and the rooting of cuttings. *Proc. Am. Soc. Hort. Sci.,* 26:101.

Goodin, J. R., and V. T. Stoutemyer. 1961. Effect of temperature and potassium gibberellate on phases of growth of Algerian ivy. *Nature,* 192:677–678.

Hess, C. E. 1962. The physiology of rooting in easy- and difficult-to-root cuttings. *Hormalog,* 3:3–6.

Millington, W. F., and E. L. Fisk. 1956.

Shoot development in *Xanthium pensyl-vanicum*. I. The vegetative plant. *Am. J. Botany*, 43:655–665.

Muzik, T. J., and H. J. Cruzado. 1958. Transmission of juvenile rooting ability from seedlings to adults of *Hevea brasiliensis*. *Nature*, 181:1288.

Njoku, E. 1958. Effect of gibberellic acid on leaf form. *Nature*, 182:1097–1098.

Passecker, F. 1949. Zur Frage der Jugend-formen der Apfel. *Züchter*, 19:311.

Pilet, P. E. 1958. Action de l'indole sur la destruction des auxines en relation avec la senescense cellulaire. *Compt. Rend. Acad. Sci. (Paris)*, 246:1896–1898.

Robbins, J. 1957. Gibberellic acid and the reversal of adult *Hedera* to a juvenile state. *Am. J. Botany*, 44:743–746.

Romberg, L. D. 1944. Some characteristics of the juvenile and the bearing pecan tree. *Proc. Am. Soc. Hort. Sci.*, 44:255–259.

Schramm, R. 1912. Über die anatomischen Jugendformen der Blätter einheimischen Holzpflanzen. *Flora (Jena)*, 104:225–292.

Stokes, P., and K. Verkerk. 1951. Flower formation in Brussels sprouts. *Mededel. Landbouwhogeschool Wageningen*, 50:141–160.

Stoutemyer, V. T., and D. K. Britt. 1961. Effect of temperature and grafting on vegetative growth phases of Algerian ivy. *Nature*, 189:854–855.

Sussex, I. M., and M. E. Clutter. 1960. A study of the effect of externally supplied sucrose on the morphology of excised fern leaves *in vitro*. *Phytomorphology*, 10:87–96.

Swingle, W. T. 1928. Metaxenia in the date palm. *J. Heredity*, 19:257–268.

————. 1932. Recapitulation of seedling characters by nucellar buds developing in the embryo sac of *Citrus*. *Proc. Intern. Congr. Genetics*, 2:196–197.

Wellensiek, S. J. 1952. Rejuvenation of woody plants by formation of sphaero-blasts. *Proc. Koninkl. Ned. Akad. Wetenschap.*, C,55:567–573.

————. 1958a. Photoperiodical reactions of *Perilla crispa*. *Proc. Koninkl. Ned. Akad. Wetenschap.*, C,61:552–560.

————. 1958b. Vernalization and age in *Lunaria biennis*. *Proc. Koninkl. Ned. Akad. Wetenschap.*, C,61:561–571.

———— and F. A. Hakkaart. 1955. Vernalization and age. *Proc. Koninkl. Ned. Akad. Wetenschap.*, C,58:16–21.

Went, F. W. 1962. Phytotronics, pp. 149–162. In S. G. Younkin (ed.), *Plant Science Symposium on Fruit Set*. Campbell Soup Co., Camden, N.J.

12 | Senescence

The deteriorative processes which naturally terminate the functional life of an organ or an organism are collectively called *senescence*. In many respects, the development of senescence in the whole plant may be considered a continuum from juvenility to maturity, although there are some features of senescence which are distinctive and not extensions of changes originating in the earlier stages of plant development.

In contrast to senescence, aging will be used to refer to changes which occur in time without reference to the natural development of death, a distinction suggested by Medawar (1957). Thus the loss of auxin responsiveness by pieces of tissue soaked in water is properly an aging phenomenon. In contrast, the photosynthetic deterioration of leaves during the autumn before abscission is a senescence phenomenon.

It is remarkable that more attention has not been paid to the subject of senescence by plant physiologists, as this event is a basic component of the life cycle of nearly all plants. Among annuals it is extremely striking; thousands of plants of wheat or corn die in exact synchrony in the fields of the Midwestern United States in middle or late summer. In spite of the drama of the event, senescence is not even mentioned in most textbooks of plant physiology.

It may be helpful to describe the general types of senescence. In annual grains, the entire plant dies by some systemic function. In perennial herbs, the aboveground portions may die, but the root system and underground system remain viable, as indicated in Fig. 12-1 (Leopold, 1961). A somewhat less drastic development of senescence may be seen in the annual change in deciduous woody plants, in which all the leaves die, but the bulk of the stem and root system remains viable. Still less drastic is the plant in which there is only a gradual progression of death of the leaves from the base upward as the growth of the plant proceeds. These types of senescence patterns illustrate the quantitative nature of senescence phenomena in plants and point up the close relationship between the senescence of leaves and the more elaborate processes of overall plant senescence. These various types of senescence may be quantitative expressions of similar physiological signals inside the plant.

Organ senescence

The leaf is at its peak of photosynthetic effectiveness at or just before the time it completes its most rapid period of expansion. The remainder of its normal existence is a deteriorative time, with gradually lowering efficiency of photosynthesis until the leaf is shed from the plant.

The decline in photosynthetic rates starts soon after a leaf reaches full size, and the changes along with those in respiratory rates are illustrated in Fig. 12-2 (Smillie, 1962). The photosynthetic decline continues until the leaf reaches a stage of senescence as indicated by yellow color, illustrated for bean leaves in Fig. 12-3 (Das and Leopold, 1964). The latter data show that the senescing leaf cannot even photosynthesize enough to maintain its dry weight. Similar declines in photosynthesis with age have been reported for successive leaves down a single plant (Sestak and Catsky, 1962) and for synchronized *Chlorella* cultures of increasing age (Sorokin and Krauss, 1961).

As assimilative powers deteriorate, so also does the respiratory ability (Fig. 12-2). The subsiding respiratory activity of leaves with age has been described by many workers (Yemm, 1956; MacDonald and DeKock, 1958). In some species, as the leaves reach a state of senescence the respiratory rate rises again in a manner suggestive of the respiratory climacteric of some fruits (Eberhardt, 1955; Yemm, 1956).

Most experiments on the changes occurring in leaves during senescence have been done in darkness to facilitate the progress of senescence. Michael (1936) noted that the

yellowing feature of senescence developed much more rapidly in older leaves held in darkness than in younger leaves. Some of his data are plotted in Fig. 12-4. During the progressive development of the yellowing, there is a corresponding fall in the protein-nitrogen content, as shown also in the figure. This protein decline appears to be an acceleration of a decline which in some plants

Fig. 12-1 | Senescence may develop in several patterns in plants, such as overall death of the plant (left), the senescence of only the aboveground parts, the deciduous habit of leaf senescence, or the progressive senescence of leaves up the stem (right) (Leopold, 1961).

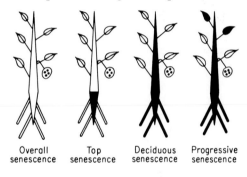

| Overall senescence | Top senescence | Deciduous senescence | Progressive senescence |

Fig. 12-2 | After pea leaves are fully expanded (at about 4 days), their photosynthesis and respiration rates start to decline. Data are for primary leaves which emerged 5 days after germination (Smillie, 1962).

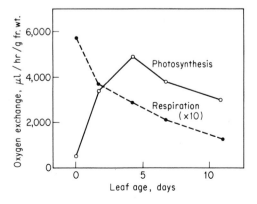

Fig. 12-3 | With increasing age, a bean leaf becomes progressively less effective as an assimilatory organ. Primary leaves were excised at various ages, and their increases in dry weight during 4 days in light were measured as an index of photosynthesis (Das and Leopold, 1964).

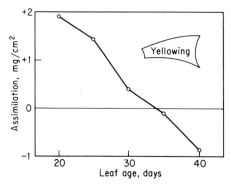

Fig. 12-4 | Yellowing of *Tropaeolum* leaves progresses in the dark more rapidly for old leaves than for young (above), and the yellowing is associated with a proportional decline in the protein-nitrogen content of the leaves (below) (data of Michael, 1936).

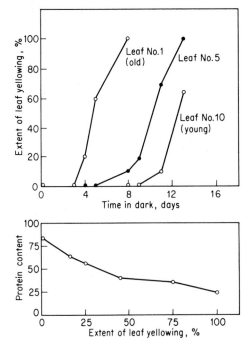

starts shortly after the leaf has expanded to full size (e.g., Plaisted, 1958).

Since the chloroplasts contain a large proportion of the protein in green leaves (Zucker and Stinson, 1962), it is possible that the degradation of chlorophyll and of protein may be structurally related.

Associated with the decline in protein nitrogen is a decline in RNA (Bottger and Wollgiehn, 1958). Some data of Smillie and Krotkov (1961) in Fig. 12-5 illustrate the change, and it is evident that the RNA subsidence likewise begins relatively early in the life of the leaves studied. Its continued progress to the time of yellowing has been described by Osborne (1962).

From these changes associated with senescence of leaves, it is clear that senescence involves a loss of assimilative powers and a catabolism of proteins and RNA. There is also a general hydrolysis of carbohydrate components and losses of organic acids (Vickery et al., 1935). The loss of these nutrients from the leaf through translocation will be mentioned in connection with entire plant senescence.

Several environmental factors can alter the rate of leaf senescence, most notably elevated temperatures, darkness, and water deficit. The action of heat in hastening senescence of tobacco leaves has been dramatically shown by Mothes and Baudisch (1958); and as senescent yellowing of the leaves was hastened with the heat treatment, so also was the deterioration of protein. The hastening of senescence by darkness was studied in detail by Vickery et al. (1937). From their detailed examination of many component changes during senescence, data showing the decline in protein nitrogen and the rise in soluble nitrogen are plotted in Fig. 12-6. The leaves in the dark became yellow and senescent in 140 hr; those held in light were still relatively vigorous at 235 hr. The experience of a rather brief period of water deficit can hasten leaf senescence (Gates, 1955*a,b*, 1957), though the effect is less dramatic than that of darkness.

The senescence of leaves is seen as an extension and magnification of deteriorative processes which begin as the leaf reaches full size. The declines of photosynthesis, respiration, and such components of the leaf as protein nitrogen and RNA appear to be natural downhill tendencies which lead to senescence. The final development of senescence with the loss of chlorophyll, the development of yellow or red pigments, and the respiratory rise (where it occurs) appears to be a consequence of the earlier trends. Hydrolysis of proteins and carbohydrates is associated with a rapid translocation of the hydrolysis products out of the senescing leaf.

Plant senescence

Just as individual leaves decline in their photosynthetic capacities with senescence, so also may the entire plant. Deterioration of the whole-plant photosynthesis begins at the time of flowering in annual species such as wheat, flax, and sugarcane (Singh and Lal, 1935). As can be seen from Fig. 12-7, when this deterioration starts, not only are the old leaves depressed in photosynthesis, but a relative depression is experienced even in the youngest leaves. The decline in productivity of overaged stands of trees (Hellmers and Bonner, 1959) appears to be related to such a senescent decline.

The period of senescence is one of depressed growth rates. In mathematical analyses of growth, Robertson (1923) has defined senescence as the period during which growth rates recede after the grand period of growth. The picture is complicated by the involvement of reproductive activities in altering the growth rates of plants. Murneek (1926) clearly showed that flowering and fruiting depressed growth rates; some of his data for the tomato plant are shown in Fig. 12-8. In this experiment, the

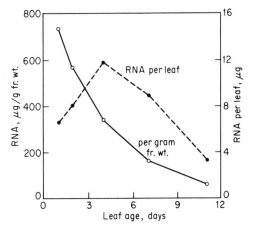

Fig. 12-5 | The RNA content of pea leaves declines from approximately the time of maximum enlargement (4 days) (Smillie and Krotkov, 1961).

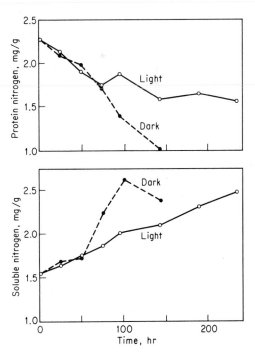

Fig. 12-6 | When tobacco leaves are excised, the protein-nitrogen content declines, and the soluble nitrogen increases. Darkened leaves show these changes more quickly and are yellow and senescent at about 100 hr (data of Vickery et al., 1937).

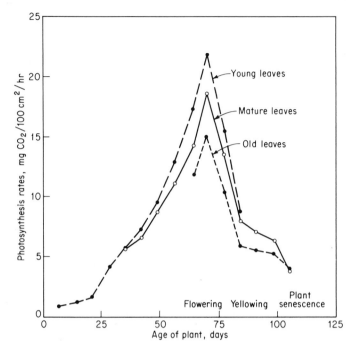

Fig. 12-7 | With increasing age of the wheat plant, individual leaves show increasing photosynthetic rates until the time of flowering, after which the rates fall off rapidly, regardless of the age of the individual leaf. Photosynthesis measured under standard conditions of light and temperature (Singh and Lal, 1935).

removal of flowers or of fruits markedly restored growth toward the maximal rates achieved by the vegetative plant. In a review of plant senescence, Sax (1962) generalized that senescence is not inevitable as long as cell growth can proceed; as an extension of this point, we might say that termination of growth sets the stage for senescence.

Molisch (1938) pointed out that reproduction is often a trigger for plant senescence; in some simple experiments he showed that removal of the flowers and fruits of several species of plants would effectively delay or even prevent plant senescence. Many perennial species such as the century plant (Molisch, 1938) and bamboo (Kennard, 1955) die promptly after they complete reproduction, and this is consistent with the fact that most annuals die at the completion of the fruiting stage. It seems reasonable to assign a causative role to reproduction in bringing about the senescence of annuals and some perennials.

The development of plant senescence can be modified by several factors. First, of course, is the deferment of senescence by removal of the flowers and fruits (Molisch, 1938). Several environmental factors which suppress normal plant growth enhance the tendencies to develop senescence, including the limitations of soil nutrients (Williams,

1936), of water (Bakhuyzen, 1926), and of heat (Pucher et al., 1948). Ionizing radiations can promote aging, a response which has been shown very clearly for seeds (Sax and Sax, 1961, 1962).

A curious phenomenon related to plant senescence is the aging of clones. The gradual deterioration of vigor in sugarcane clones (Trippi and Montaldi, 1960) has large agricultural implications. Another example of clonal senescence is the gradual decline in frond size in *Lemna minor* with aging (Wangermann and Ashby, 1950). There does not appear to be a reliable basis for assuming that these functions of plant vigor may be related to plant senescence in the sense of the deteriorative processes normally leading to plant death.

Theories of senescence

The only attempt to provide a general explanation of plant senescence was made by Molisch (1938) on the basis of his experiments in which senescence was altered by removal of the flowers and fruits. He proposed that the reproductive activities of the plant, namely, the filling of the fruits, depleted the remainder of the plant of its nutrients, thus imposing senescence. Such a death by starvation, *Erschöpfungstod*, would result from the mobilization of nutrients by the fruit. The concept found support from the studies of mobilization and retranslocation effects caused by fruiting. For example, Mothes (1931) and later Watson and Petrie (1940) followed the nitrogenous components of tobacco plants between the various plant parts during the growing season (Fig. 5-6), and they showed that the developing inflorescence caused a marked depletion of nitrogenous materials in the other plant parts, especially in the leaves. Cutting off the inflorescence largely prevented the leaf-depletion effect. The striking abilities of the reproductive organs to mobilize nutrients from other parts of

Fig. 12-8 | The growth rates of tomato plants decline after the commencement of flowering and fruiting, and they can be markedly restored by the removal of the flowers or fruits (Murneek, 1926).

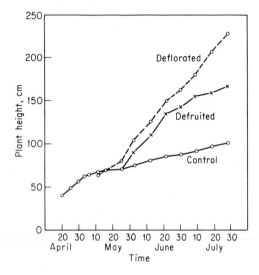

Fig. 12-9 | The time of senescence of soybean plants is deferred if the full-grown, maturing fruits are removed, but it is more extensively deferred if the young fruits are kept removed, and even more so if the flowers are removed as they open (data of Leopold et al., 1959).

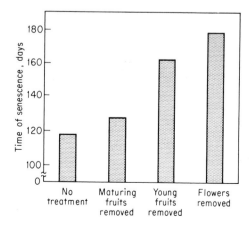

the plant have been discussed in Chap. 5. The fact that a depletion does occur following fruiting, especially in the leaves, is consistent with the concept of *Erschöpfungstod.*

Some difficulties are met with in the mobilization explanation, however. First, experiments in which the flowers and fruits are removed at increasingly later stages of development indicate that the senescence stimulus gradually increases during the entire reproductive sequence. Some data for soybean (Leopold et al., 1959; Fig. 12-9) show that the senescence-inducing effect is developing even during flower development, before any fruits are filled with nutrients, and that the effect is greatest during the period of fruit ripening—after the mobilization into the fruits is essentially completed. The development of male flowers on male

plants induces senescence fully as effectively as the development of fruits on female plants, and removal of the male structures defers senescence (Leopold et al., 1959). It is clear that flowers and fruits cause a mobilization of nutrients from the rest of the plant, but the way in which this may relate to the physiological cause of plant senescence is uncertain.

Quite a different basis for senescence may be the deterioration of structural integrity within the aging organs. Varner (1961) noted that with age there may be structural changes in tissues suggestive of losses of membrane integrity. From studies of cellular changes during abscission, Sacher (1957, 1959) also concluded that membrane deteriorations could account for cellular decline. Das and Leopold (1964) found that there are increases in the permeability of bean leaves as they approach senescence. Some of their data (Fig. 12-10) show that not only is there an increasing leakage of substance from leaves with age, but decapitation of the plant, which arrests leaf senescence, also arrests the permeability increase. The ebbing synthetic efficiencies of the leaves and of the whole plants may then be linked to declining effectiveness in maintaining structural integrity of the cells and their included organelles. Senescence may be an expression of such deteriorative changes. Whether the deteriorations during senescence may be a consequence of increasing degradative actions such as the increases in RNAase (Kessler and Monselise, 1961; Hanson and Swanson, 1962) or due to weakening of synthetic activities with respect to RNA (Monselise et al., 1962), protein (Hellebust and Bidwell, 1962), or chlorophyll (Perkins and Roberts, 1963) remains to be seen. The evident linkage of chlorophyll degradation to protein and RNA components certainly suggests that the regulation of senescence is somehow a function of RNA (Leopold, 1961).

One other aspect of the senescence mechanisms might be mentioned. Brown

Fig. 12-10 | With increasing age, the primary leaves of bean increase in permeability, as evidenced by the increases in conductivity of bathing solutions. Single leaves were bathed for 30 min, and the conductivity of the solution was measured. When plants were decapitated at 9 days to prevent leaf senescence, the leaves showed a lesser development of permeability (Das and Leopold, 1964).

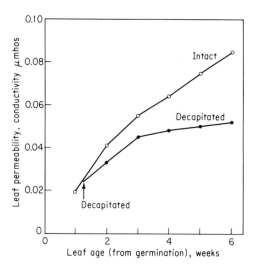

(1959) noted that root-tissue cultures experience inhibitions of growth as old root tissues accumulate in the cultures. This interesting observation suggests that there may be an actual toxifying effect of tissues with aging, and this may contribute to the senescence development.

Mobilization effects

The study of mobilization phenomena became a dynamic part of experimentation on senescence when Richmond and Lang (1957) reported that kinetin treatment deferred leaf senescence and Mothes (1959) found that this chemical could cause leaf mobilization centers in leaves. When applied to localized parts of leaves, kinetin stimulates a mobilization of carbohydrates, amino acids, and various inorganic ions from untreated zones. Treated leaves remain green, and their protein contents do not fall in the manner of the normally senescing leaves. Osborne (1962) studied the progressive changes in leaf components associated with the kinetin deferral of senescence and obtained data shown in Fig. 12-11. One can see the normal progress of senescence with the associated decline in chlorophyll, protein, and RNA, compared with the kinetin-treated leaves with their somewhat slower losses of all three of these components.

The ability of kinetin and related compounds to defer senescence is the basis for commercial treatment of some green vegetables to improve their storage life (Dedolph et al., 1961).

How can mobilization phenomena be involved in the induction of senescence? The natural ability of young tissues to act as mobilizers has been demonstrated by Oota and Osawa (1954), who showed that meristems are markedly more effective in the mobilization of phosphorus than older tissues. Oota and Takata (1959) suggested that the mobilization feature of the meristem

is related to its components of RNA; they have published evidence suggesting that RNA may migrate from older tissues into meristems, thus maintaining the mobilizing centers there.

It should be mentioned that many pathogens hasten senescence, and the mobilizing actions of rust lesions (Fig. 5-3) again imply the existence of a link between mobilization activities and the induction of leaf senescence.

Fig. 12-11 | When excised *Xanthium* leaves are held in darkness, they become senescent in about 3 days, but the application of kinetin (40 mg/liter) defers that senescence, as evidenced by the slower decline in chlorophyll content, protein content, and RNA content (Osborne, 1962).

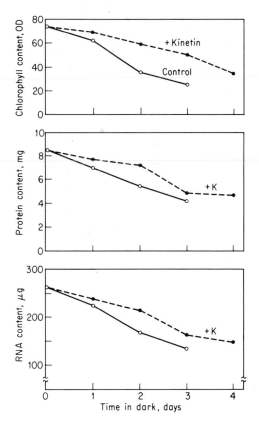

Conclusion

It seems that senescence in plants may be due to some physiological mechanism which creates a distinctive catabolic condition. This distinctive condition appears to be related to mobilizing functions between plant parts, for the presence of such strong mobilizing centers as flowers, fruits, or pathogenic lesions may bring about senescence, and the application of mobilizing stimulants such as kinetin can defer the senescence development. It does not seem likely that senescence is due to the actual depletion of nutrients and a resulting starvation of the plant or organ, but certainly the tendency of a given organ to hydrolyze and dissipate its nutrients suggests a possible direct relationship with senescence. The increasing change from anabolic to catabolic activities in any organ may be more immediately related to the senescence than to the actual depletion of nutrients. In turn, the decline in anabolic activities seems to be a natural consequence of the deterioration of the protein and RNA components as senescence advances.

In a developmental sense, senescence can have many advantages for a plant (Leopold, 1961). The senescence of the older leaves of stems permits a conservation and reutilization of organic and inorganic nutrients from these organs. The senescence of the entire plant offers a means of adaptability to limitations of the environment such as periods of greater plant competition, of temperature extremes, or of water stress. Furthermore, it appears that senescence may permit a more rapid evolutionary development through a more rapid genetic turnover.

The development of a physiological understanding of this interesting state in the plant should be both interesting and useful.

GENERAL REFERENCES

Leopold, A. C. 1961. Senescence in plant development. *Science,* 134:1727–1732.

Sax, K. 1962. Aspects of aging in plants. *Ann. Rev. Plant Physiol.,* 13:489–506.

REFERENCES CITED

Bakhuyzen, H. L. S. 1926. Physiological phenomena at the time of flowering. *Proc. Soc. Exptl. Biol. Med.,* 24:143–145.

Bottger, I., and R. Wollgiehn. 1958. Untersuchungen über den Zuzammenhang zwischen Nucleinsaure und Eiweissstoffwechsel in grünen Blättern. *Flora (Jena),* 146:302–320.

Brown, R. 1959. The growth of the isolated root in culture. *J. Exptl. Botany,* 10:169–177.

Das, T. M., and A. C. Leopold. 1964. Physiological changes with leaf senescence (in preparation).

Dedolph, R. R., S. A. Wittwer, and V. Tuli. 1961. Senescence inhibition and respiration. *Science,* 134:1075.

Eberhardt, F. 1955. Der Atmungsverlauf alternder Blätter und reifender Früchte. *Planta,* 45:57–67.

Gates, C. T. 1955a. The response of the young tomato plant to a brief period of water shortage. I. The whole plant and its principal parts. *Australian J. Biol. Sci.,* 8:196–214.

———. 1955b. The response of the young tomato plant to a brief period of water shortage. II. The individual leaves. *Australian J. Biol. Sci.,* 8:215–230.

———. 1957. The response of the young tomato plant to a brief period of water shortage. III. Drifts in nitrogen and phosphorus. *Australian J. Biol. Sci.,* 10:125–146.

Hanson, J. B., and H. R. Swanson. 1962. The role of basic proteins in the declining respiration of senescing corn scutellum.

Biochem. Biophys. Res. Commun., 9:442–446.

Hellebust, J. A., and R. G. S. Bidwell. 1962. Protein turnover in wheat and snapdragon leaves. *Can. J. Botany*, 41:969–983.

Hellmers, H., and J. Bonner. 1959. Photosynthetic limits of forest tree yields. *Proc. Soc. Am. Foresters*, 1959:32–35.

Kennard, W. C. 1955. Flowering of the bamboo *Guadua amplexifolia* in Puerto Rico. *Lloydia*, 18: 193–196.

Kessler, B., and S. P. Monselise. 1961. Ribonucleic acid content and RNAase activity of developing apple and orange leaves. *Proc. Am. Soc. Hort. Sci.*, 78:53–58.

Leopold, A. C. 1961. Senescence in plant development. *Science*, 134:1727–1732.

———, E. Niedergang-Kamien, and J. Janick. 1959. Experimental modification of plant senescence. *Plant Physiol.*, 34: 570–573.

MacDonald, I. R., and P. C. De Kock. 1958. The stimulation of leaf respiration by respiratory inhibitors. *Physiol. Plantarum*, 11:464–477.

Medawar, P. B. 1957. *The Uniqueness of the Individual.* Basic Books, Inc., Publishers, New York. 191 pp.

Michael, G. 1936. Über die Beziehungen zwischen Chlorophyll und Eiweissabbau im vergilbenden Laubblätt von *Tropaeolum. Z. Botan.*, 29:385–425.

Molisch, H. 1938. *The Longevity of Plants.* Science Press, Lancaster, Pa. 226 pp.

Monselise, S. P., A. Cohen, and B. Kessler. 1962. Changes in RNA and DNA in developing orange leaves. *Plant Physiol.*, 37:572–578.

Mothes, K. 1931. Zur Kenntnis des N-Stoffwechsels höherer Pflanzen. *Planta*, 12: 686–731.

———. 1959. Bemerkungen über die physiologischen Voraussetzungen der Eiweissynthese in isolierten Blättern. *Colloq. Ges. Physiol. Chem.*, 10:72–81.

——— and W. Baudisch. 1958. Untersuchungen über die Reversibitität der Aus-

bleichung gruner Blätter. *Flora (Jena)*, 146:521–531.

Murneek, A. E. 1926. Effects of correlation between vegetative and reproductive functions in the tomato. *Plant Physiol.*, 1:3–56.

Oota, Y., and S. Osawa. 1954. Migration of "storage DNA" from cotyledon into growing organs of bean seed embryo. *Experientia*, 10:254–256.

——— and K. Takata. 1959. Changes in microsomal ribonucleoproteins in the time course of germination. *Physiol. Plantarum*, 12:518–525.

Osborne, D. J. 1962. Effect of kinetin on protein and nucleic acid metabolism in *Xanthium* leaves during senescence. *Plant Physiol.*, 37:595–602.

Perkins, H. J., and D. W. A. Roberts. 1963. On chlorophyll turnover in monocotyledons and dicotyledons. *Can. J. Botany*, 41:221–226.

Plaisted, P. H. 1958. Some biochemical changes during development and aging of *Acer platanoides* leaves. *Contrib. Boyce Thompson Inst.*, 19:245–254.

Pucher, G. W., C. S. Leavenworth, W. D. Ginter, and H. B. Vickery. 1948. Studies in the metabolism of crassulacean plants: the effect of temperature on the culture of leaves of *Bryophyllum. Plant Physiol.*, 23:123–132.

Richmond, A. E., and A. Lang. 1957. Effect of kinetin on protein content and survival of detached *Xanthium* leaves. *Science*, 125:650–651.

Robertson, T. B. 1923. *The Chemical Basis of Growth and Senescence.* J. B. Lippincott Company, Philadelphia. 389 pp.

Sacher, J. A. 1957. Relationship between auxin and membrane-integrity in tissue senescence and abscission. *Science*, 125: 1199–1200.

———. 1959. Studies of auxin-membrane permeability relations in fruit and leaf tissues. *Plant Physiol.*, 34:365–372.

Sax, K. 1962. Aspects of aging in plants. *Ann. Rev. Plant Physiol.*, 13:489–506.

——— and H. J. Sax. 1961. Effect of age of seed on the frequency of spontaneous and gamma ray induced chromosome aberrations. *Radiation Botany*, 1:80–83.

——— and ———. 1962. Effects of x-rays on the aging of seeds. *Nature*, 194:459–460.

Sestak, Z., and J. Catsky. 1962. Intensity of photosynthesis and chlorophyll content as related to leaf age in *Nicotiana*. *Biol. Plantarum (Prague)*, 4:131–140.

Singh, B. N., and K. N. Lal. 1935. Investigations of the effect of age on assimilation of leaves. *Ann. Botany (London)*, 49:291–307.

Smillie, R. M. 1962. Photosynthetic and respiratory activities of growing pea leaves. *Plant Physiol.*, 37:716–721.

——— and G. Krotkov. 1961. Changes in dry weight, protein, nucleic acid and chlorophyll content of growing pea leaves. *Can. J. Botany*, 39:891–900.

Sorokin, C. and R. W. Krauss. 1961. Relative efficiency of photosynthesis in the course of cell development. *Biochim. Biophys. Acta*, 48:314–319.

Trippi, V., and E. Montaldi. 1960. The aging of sugar cane clones. *Phyton (Buenos Aires)*, 6:79–91.

Varner, J. E. 1961. Biochemistry of senescence. *Ann. Rev. Plant Physiol.*, 12:245–264.

Vickery, H. B., G. W. Pucher, C. S. Leavenworth, and A. J. Wakeman. 1935. Chemical investigations of the tobacco plant. V. Chemical changes during growth. *Conn. Agr. Expt. Sta. (New Haven) Bull.*, 374:557–608.

———, G. W. Pucher, A. J. Wakeman, and C. S. Leavenworth. 1937. Chemical investigations of the tobacco plant. VI. Chemical changes in light and darkness. *Conn. Agr. Expt. Sta. (New Haven) Bull.*, 399:757–828.

Wangermann, E., and E. Ashby. 1950. A discussion on morphogenesis. Morphogenesis in *Lemna minor*. *Proc. Linnean Soc. (London)*, 162:10–13.

Watson, R., and A. H. K. Petrie. 1940. Physiological ontogeny in the tobacco plant. *Australian J. Exptl. Biol. Med. Sci.*, 18:313–339.

Williams, R. F. 1936. Physiological ontogeny in plants and its relation to nutrition. *Australian J. Exptl. Biol. Med. Sci.*, 14:165–185.

Yemm, E. W. 1956. The metabolism of senescent leaves. *CIBA Found. Colloq. on Aging*, 2:207–214.

Zucker, M., and H. T. Stinson. 1962. Chloroplasts as the major protein-bearing structures in *Oenothera* leaves. *Arch. Biochem. Biophys.*, 96:637–644.

13 | Flowering

The complexity of the developmental processes involved in the formation of flowers, fruits, and seeds is a tribute to the evolutionary values of sexual reproduction. How much simpler the plant organisms would be if the vegetative processes constituted the physiological entity. And how diverse and complex are the regulatory systems and their environmental controls, developed around the ornate and even baroque structures for sexual reproduction.

The flowering process involves a complete alteration of the products of developing meristems, usually terminating the meristem's formation of leaves and internodes and imposing instead the formation of flowers and associated appendages. The physiological controls of flowering may be exerted at any of several fairly definitive stages. Flowering may be regulated by the termination of the juvenile phase of development. Environmental cues may provoke the *induction* of the reproductive state in leaves, the *initiation* of floral meristems, the morphological *development* of flowers, or *anthesis* itself.

The triggering of these reproductive developments is usually done by such environmental variables as temperature, light, and photoperiods. These are variables which change with the seasons, hence permitting a programming of reproductive activities on a seasonal basis.

A great deal of attention has been given to the environmental cues which may regulate flowering, though only a small proportion of species are completely controlled by them; many more are only quantitatively influenced by them, and a large number are not apparently sensitive to environmental signals. Furthermore, as an individual plant becomes older and larger, its innate tendencies to flower become increasingly forceful. Many species thus lose their dependence upon environmental variables to start flowering. Environmental cues serve principally to synchronize the timing of the flowering events. Since flowering is intrinsically a mechanism for outcrossing, the value of timing mechanisms which would synchronize anthesis in numerous individuals is obvious; the environmental cues regulating flowering are the means by which such synchrony is achieved.

There are also distinct ecological benefits to the plant in being able to control the timing of the reproductive processes. In addition to the synchronization of flowering between individuals, the timing of flowering permits the adaptation of reproduction to seasonal changes of climate. In addition, the existence of a strictly vegetative period permits a full application of the plant's resources to vegetative growth, with associated benefits in the competition with other plants of the community. Some perennial plants alternate vegetative with reproductive growth on an annual basis and thus are able to devote full energies to vegetative growth at some seasons and to reproductive growth at others. Some tree fruits have developed the capacity for biennial bearing; that is, they are able to bear a crop of fruit in alternate years, growing vegetatively in the intervening years. Ecologically, each of these patterns offers the plant advantages over the alternative of uncontrolled or nonsynchronized flowering.

EARLINESS

To the agronomist, the term *earliness* may often refer to the calendar date of the first flowering or fruiting of a variety, but in the physiological sense it is usually applied to the morphological state of earliness. Thus greater earliness would refer to an earlier morphological differentiation of flowers and hence to the formation of the first flower primordia at a lower node. In some plants there may be a physiological state of more rapid development of flowers without an alteration of the node of flowering, and this too may be spoken of as a greater earliness.

In either of its physiological contexts, earliness is an expression of the increasing tendency of plants to become reproductive with increasing age. In some species, the arrival at the reproductive state is apparently unalterably set, and treatments of the seed or the seedling are without effect on the earliness of flowering. The various species of bean are promiscuously flowering, and their earliness is apparently not alterable. The peanut, *Arachis,* is beyond any alteration of morphological earliness, for the first flower primordia are laid down at a standard node within the seed. Many species, however, are slower to develop their first flowers and are more amenable to environmental modification of earliness.

Developmental factors

The plant breeder is frequently concerned with the development of earlier or later varieties of horticultural species, and we may presume that in doing so he is modifying the rapidity of expression of endogenous factors for flowering. Working with peas, Barber and Paton (1952) attempted to locate such earliness factors by graftage of early and late varieties. They found that an early variety of scion grafted onto a late variety would flower at a higher node, i.e., would be later. They suggested that some factor for lateness was supplied by the root system of the late varieties.

Haupt (1955) noted that the outcome of such graftage experiments with seedlings was influenced by the cotyledons, and he attempted to simulate the inhibitory effects of the cotyledons with extracts applied to excised embryos in tissue culture. Not only did cotyledon extracts inhibit flowering, but so also did sugar solutions and numbers of other organic nutrients.

More productive were some experiments in which early and late peas were grafted together to define more precisely the location of the inhibitory effect of the stock plants. Haupt (1958) then found that a

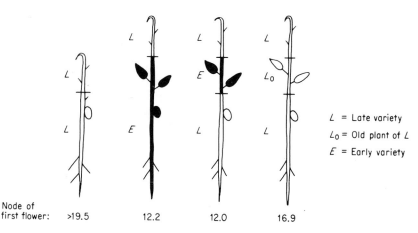

Node of
first flower: >19.5   12.2   12.0   16.9

Fig. 13-1 | The graftage of a late variety of peas (L) onto an early variety stock (E) increases earliness, as indicated by a lower node of first flower. Increased earliness is also obtained if the early variety is used as an interstock or if an older piece of the late variety is used as an interstock (adapted from Haupt, 1958).

late scion grafted onto a leafy early stock would flower early (Fig. 13-1). If the early stock was reduced to an interstock with leaves, the increase in earliness was obtained. The stock and interstock effects required the presence of leaves, indicating that there was also a promotive effect from the leaves of early varieties (Fig. 13-1).

From this and other analyses of flowering, it appears that there are both inhibitory and promotive factors of earliness. Lang and Melchers (1943) found that mature leaves of *Hyoscyamus* apparently impose the photoperiod requirement for flowering, since removal of all mature leaves permits the plants to flower in the dark. Presumably the leaves produce an inhibitory factor which is overcome by long photoperiods. Defoliation can also remove the photoperiod requirement of strawberry (Thompson and Guttridge, 1960). As a further illustration of promotive substances, Lam and Cordner (1955) succeeded in bringing about the flowering of the Jersey type of sweet potato, which is otherwise stubbornly vegetative, by graftage onto readily flowering stock plants of other species of *Ipomoea*. The flower-formation activities in the scion continued only as long as leaves remained on the stock plant, for precisely at the time of abscission of the last leaves from the stock plant all formation of new flower primordia on the scion ceased. This clearly indicates that flower-promoting substances are formed in the leaves of the stock plant.

The increasing readiness to flower with increasing age is illustrated by the experiments shown in Fig. 13-1. An interstock of an old individual increased earliness, even though it was of a late variety. The age effect is illustrated again by some data for celery published by Pawar and Thompson (1950) in Fig. 13-2. Celery seedlings of different ages were given 4 weeks at 8°C to induce flowering, and the responsiveness was markedly greater in the older seedlings in terms of the times to flower initiation and to anthesis. Using a photoperiod-requiring species, Evans (1960a) found a similar situation for *Lolium tementulum;* the older the seedlings at the time of long-day induction, the fewer the number of long days needed

Fig. 13-2 | The ability of celery plants to flower in response to a low-temperature treatment increases as the plants grow older, as evidenced by the shorter time to flower initiation and to anthesis after the completion of the cold treatment (4 weeks at 8°C) (data of Pawar and Thompson, 1950).

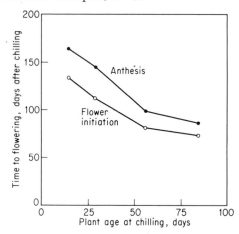

Fig. 13-3 | The long-day requirement for flower induction of *Lolium tementulum* declines as the plants increase in age. Plants dissected 2 weeks after start of long days (data of Evans, 1960a).

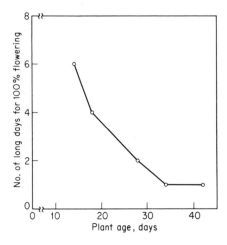

to induce all plants to flower (Fig. 13-3).

Earliness is an expression of internal factors of both promotive and inhibitory natures, acting on an increasing inherent tendency to develop flowers with increasing age of the plant. In many cases it is not so much a matter of age as it is of the size of the plant (e.g., Boswell, 1929; Longman and Wareing, 1959).

Environmental factors

Between the groups of plants which are quite predetermined in their flowering time and those which are unable to flower until they receive a fairly specific environmental cue, there are many species which are quantitatively modifiable in their earliness of flowering by environmental influences. The ability of temperature treatments to shift earliness was noted long ago by Sachs (1860), and since that time many plants have proved to be so modifiable. Low temperatures commonly increase earliness, the phenomenon of vernalization of winter grains being a well-known example. The flowering of some biennials in response to low-temperature experience is another example, though the term *earliness* applies more precisely to the changeable tendency of indeterminate plants to flower, and many biennials may specifically require a low temperature for flowering.

Some examples of environmental modifications of earliness have been seen in Figs. 13-2 and 13-3; more widely studied modifications are those of tomato and pea. The tomato ordinarily sets its first flower buds at about the twelfth to the seventeenth node, depending on the earliness of the variety. Lewis (1953) found that by holding newly emerged seedlings at a low temperature, the first flower could be brought down to a lower node. This effect is illustrated by some data of Calvert (1957) shown in Fig. 13-4, concerning exposure of seedlings to various durations of low temperature

(16 to 10°C). Three weeks of such treatment lowered the first flower almost six nodes. Seedling experiences at high temperatures (27°C) had the opposite effect, shifting the first flower to a higher node.

The earliness of peas can likewise be altered, either by temperature treatments (Leopold and Guernsey, 1953; Highkin, 1956; Moore and Bonde, 1962) or by light effects (Haupt, 1957, 1958).

The ability of light to alter earliness was most dramatically revealed by Garner and Allard (1920) with the discovery of photoperiodism. In this and subsequent research (1923), they were able actually to control flowering in some species and quantitatively to hasten or delay it in others.

When day-length treatments alter the flowering of a given species, this does not necessarily mean that the influence is photoperiodic. In numerous cases instead of the effect being due to the specific light and dark interactions, it may be due merely to the quantity of light being applied. Influences of quantity of light are best revealed by light-intensity experiments, as illustrated by some data of Haupt (1958) with peas (Fig. 13-5). Plants which had been decoty-

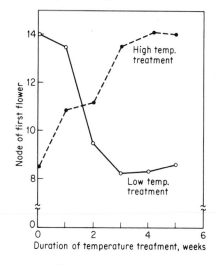

Fig. 13-4 | The earliness of Ailsa Craig tomato plants is increased by 2 to 5 weeks of low temperature (16 to 10°C) given at the cotyledon-expansion stage. The increased earliness is indicated by the lower node of first flower. Inverting the temperature treatments shows a delay in flowering by high-temperature treatment (27°C) (Calvert, 1957).

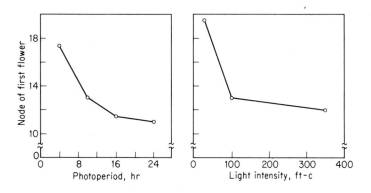

Fig. 13-5 | The flowering of pea (Kleine Rheinlanderin) is similarly increased in earliness either by increases in photoperiod or by increases in light intensity under constant photoperiod. Cotyledons were removed to increase the light sensitivity. Experiment at left was with 350 ft-c; at right, with continuous light (Haupt, 1958).

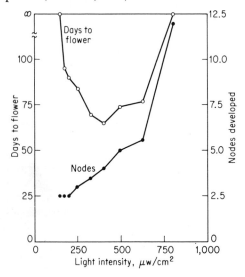

Fig. 13-6 | The earliness of *Perilla* seedlings is altered by light intensity. The greatest earliness (as days to flower) was achieved at about 400 microwatts/cm². Further lowering of the light intensity delayed flowering, as well as the development of nodes. Eighteen-hour photoperiods (de Zeeuw, 1953).

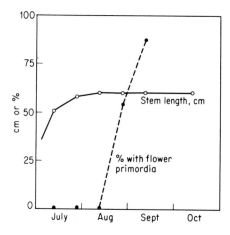

Fig. 13-7 | In black currant, stem-length increases are completed in mid-August, and the appearance of flower primordia follows in the next 4 weeks (data of Nasr and Wareing, 1961).

ledonized to increase their sensitivity to light flowered at a lower node when longer day lengths were given, and the same effect was achieved if the light intensity was increased in a constant day length of 24 hr.

A slightly different effect of light intensity on earliness is evident in some data on *Perilla* by de Zeeuw (1953). Growing seedlings under various light intensities (with constant photoperiod), he found that the plants were brought into the flowering condition markedly earlier with lower light intensities (Fig. 13-6). If the intensity was lower than about 400 ft-c, the appearance of flowers was delayed, presumably because of the almost complete cessation of growth.

Growth rate

In many species, the completion of the juvenile phase of growth may be associated with a slackening of the stem growth rate, and horticulturists have often attempted to stimulate the emergence from juvenility to maturity and flowering by applying treatments which would retard stem growth. Such treatments as ringing (cutting a complete ring of bark from around a branch or stem), tying branches into a downward-pointing direction, or pinching off the terminal buds of shoots have all been employed by horticulturists to encourage earliness in fruit trees.

In many perennials, the differentiation of flower primordia in the meristems occurs at the time when rapid stem growth has ended. A dramatic example of the occurrence of flower initiation at the time of growth termination can be seen in some data of Nasr and Wareing (1961) for black 'currant (Fig. 13-7). Such a correlation is probably common to many fruit trees.

Ringing the bark of fruit trees can often be effective in increasing earliness, usually bringing about flowering on trees of apple and citrus 1 or 2 years earlier than the 4 to 15 years needed for flowering (e.g., Harley et al., 1942; Magness et al., 1933*a*; Furr et al., 1947). The resulting wound retards the translocation of sap out of the branch so treated, resulting in both the retardation of growth and a damming of nutrients and growth substances in the branch. The Peruvian cube tree grown in California never flowers naturally, but the ringing treatment can cause flowering at will (Cooper et al., 1945). The leaves produce a positive stimulus for flowering, for removal of leaves above the ring erases the flowering tendency (Magness et al., 1933*a*; Furr and Armstrong, 1956). The bending of stems out of the vertical orientation is also effective in retarding growth and enhancing earliness in woody fruits. Such a bending occurs naturally in older branches of fruit trees as they become weighed down by fruit loads, and pruning practices take advantage of the resulting abundant flowering of the more pendant branches (Christopher, 1954). Artificially bending branches down can force numerous woody plants to flower earlier (Longman and Wareing, 1959; Longman, 1961).

An ingenious device for experimentally retarding growth to assess its effect on flowering has been utilized by Kojima and Maeda (1958). Embedding radish seedlings in gypsum plaster to restrain growth, these workers found that there was a pronounced increase in the flowering tendencies of the restrained plants. Other growth-retarding treatments enhancing flowering included the application of the growth inhibitor maleic hydrazide or of sugar solutions of high osmotic values.

After an unexpectedly strong fumigation of a greenhouse, Fisher and Loomis (1954) noted that soybean plants were forced into flowering; similar effects could be obtained with pinching or even partial leaf-removal treatments, which inhibited stem elongation. They proposed that there was an antagonism between vegetative and reproductive growth, a concept that has been seriously considered also by Wellensiek's group in the Netherlands (Wellensiek et al., 1954; cf. also Carr and Ng, 1955).

Many chemical treatments of plants can induce flowering. Most dramatic of these is the auxin induction of flowering in pineapple (Clark and Kerns, 1942). This treatment is associated with a temporary suspension of leaf growth. Auxins are also effective in encouraging the flowering of the litchi tree in Hawaii (Shigeura, 1948), and this too is associated with an overall inhibition of vegetative growth. Numbers of other growth-retarding treatments are similarly effective, including the withholding of irrigation water to suppress vegetative growth (Nakata, 1955). Naphthylphthalamic acids have been employed by Teubner and Wittner (1955) to force early and abundant flowering of tomatoes, and this treatment, which parallels the effects of cold treatment of seedlings shown in Fig. 13-4, appears to act through an inhibition of vegetative growth. De Zeeuw (1956) showed that the chemical treatment is ineffective if the young expanding leaves of the tomato are removed, and such pinching treatments cause increases in flowering similar to those obtained by the chemical application.

The increases in tomato earliness obtained by leaf removal are illustrated in Fig. 13-8 (de Zeeuw, 1954). Subsequent studies have revealed that early varieties of tomato are not made earlier by such pinching treatments, but each of the late varieties tested is made earlier (Heinze, 1959; Leopold and Lam, 1960). These observations are consistent with the possibility that lateness in tomatoes may be due to a flowering inhibition in the late varieties associated with the activities of vegetative growth.

A word of amplification should be added here. It is by no means implied in the above statements that all treatments which promote flowering inhibit vegetative growth; there are many cases in which flower-promoting treatments also promote growth, especially among the long-day plants and bolting plants in general. Nor is it implied that any treatment which would inhibit vegetative growth would necessarily promote earliness; numerous experiments have shown quite the reverse (e.g., Longman and Wareing, 1959). It can be implied only that in some plants, forces tending to encourage flowering can be released into expression through treatments which alter the growth rate. That this enhancement of flowering may be achieved with a promotion of growth rates is amply illustrated by the gibberellin induction of flowering in many species which undergo bolting or shooting just prior to initiation of flowers. These species can frequently be forced to flower with gibberellin treatments (Lang, 1957; Wittwer and Bukovac, 1957) with an associated burst of growth.

Conclusion

The gradual amplification of the flowering tendencies of plants with age can result in varying degrees of earliness between species and varieties. The evidence concerning the endogenous factors influencing earliness suggests that there are both promotive and inhibitory influences acting on the potential of the plant to flower. The ability of various environmental factors such as temperature, light, and photoperiod, or of mechanical and chemical treatments to alter the earliness of a plant can be tentatively interpreted as relating to the relative expression of these endogenous factors. The similarities of the environmental factors which can alter earliness to those which can actually induce flowering (temperature, photoperiod) strongly suggest that the same mechanisms may be involved in the earliness as in the flower-induction processes.

Fig. 13-8 | The flowering of Ailsa Craig tomato is hastened and intensified by removal of young, expanding leaves. Initiation and anthesis were achieved sooner when leaf removal was started at the seventh, fifth, or third node or if all the leaves above the cotyledons were removed. The number of flowers on the first cluster was increased (data of de Zeeuw, 1954).

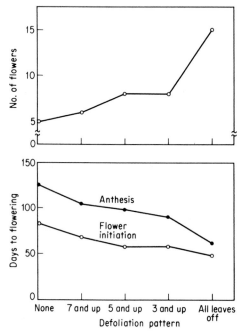

PHOTOPERIODISM AND FLOWERING

The concept that flowering might be controlled by a hormonal stimulus was first proposed by Sachs (1882), and it appears to be borne out by the more recent finding that the stimulus is mobile in the plant (Chajlakjan, 1936; Moskov, 1936). The mobility of the stimulus really became clear only after the discovery of the effects of day length on flowering by Garner and Allard (1920), day lengths being most effectively perceived by the leaves of plants. The flowering stimulus must move then from the leaves to the meristem, where the morphological change is initiated.

The fact that day lengths could control reproductive activities was touched upon by

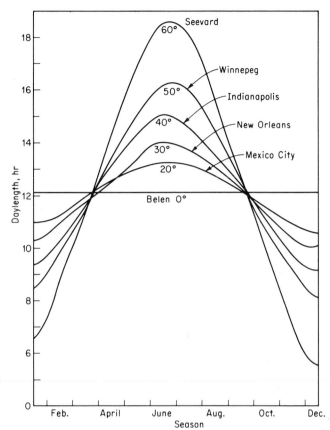

Fig. 13-9 | The annual changes in day length, showing the increases in amplitude with increasing latitude. Plotted here are the times from sunrise to sunset for six different locations.

several plant physiologists, especially Klebs (1918), who actually succeeded in causing the flowering of *Sempervivum* by illumination during the night; but it remained for Garner and Allard (1920, 1923) really to establish the concept of day length as a control of seasonal events—or photoperiodism.

The seasonal changes in photoperiods provide a precise and reliable cue of the seasons; for biological systems in the middle latitudes, day lengths oscillate between about 9 and 15 hr of light per day, the oscillation increasing in amplitude with increasing latitude, and decreasing toward the equator to almost a uniform day length

at the equator itself (Fig. 13-9). It is evident that day length is a more effective signal in the middle latitudes than in the tropics, and in fact it is probably more common as a physiological cue to plants in the middle latitudes.

An interesting means of representing the photoperiod and temperature features of different climates has been devised by Ferguson (1957). This is shown in Fig. 13-10, where the day lengths are plotted against the mean monthly temperatures. The annual climatic cycle of seasons appears as an orbit through these two environmental coordinates. Associated with the small photoperiod changes in the tropics, there is a small temperature flux. The increasing seasonality of the climate with increasing latitude is evident as the increasing range of climatic orbit. Not only is the magnitude of the seasonal cue larger in higher latitudes, but the need for seasonal changes in plant development is also greater.

Photoperiod classes

Garner and Allard (1920) recognized three classes of photoperiod responses: short-day plants (SDP), long-day plants (LDP), and

Fig. 13-10 | The annual climatic cycle can be expressed as the seasonal changes in day length and temperature. The climate for any one place is represented as an orbit of these two parameters. Sample climatic orbits are shown for five locations from 6 to 59° latitude (after Ferguson, 1957).

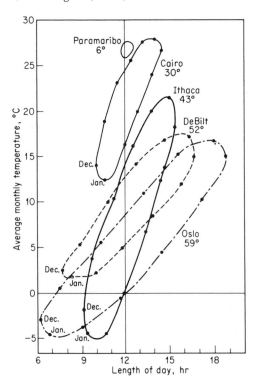

indeterminate plants. Among SDPs and LDPs, some species may be strictly controlled in flowering by photoperiods, and many others may be only quantitatively accelerated or delayed in flowering by the photoperiods. The difference is sometimes quite blurred; some plants may be strict SDPs as seedlings, becoming only quantitatively accelerated by short days as they grow older and finally becoming indeterminate with further aging.

Some common examples of strict SDPs are the fall- and winter-flowering species of tobacco, *Xanthium*, ragweed, soybeans, *Pharbitis*, and *Poinsettia*. Some common strict LDPs include *Hyoscyamus*, spinach, plantain, winter barley, and *Lolium tementulum*. The distinction between the classes lies in their responses to the length of the night period, not to any special range of day lengths. Thus, SDPs require a dark period of a greater than threshold length for flowering, whereas LDPs are prevented from flowering by dark periods of greater than threshold length. The short days of late summer provide the SDP with adequate night lengths for flowering, and the long days of early summer provide the LDP with a brief enough night to permit flowering (Fig. 13-11). The major photoperiodic influence of the night period was discovered by Hamner and Bonner (1938) and will be discussed after mentioning two other photoperiodic classes.

Some species which were originally classified as SDP were found later to be unable to flower under continuous short-day conditions (Dostal, 1950; Resende, 1952). If long days were given for a brief period and then short days again, the plants flowered. Since this finding, the multiple requirements of some species for long days followed by short days (LD-SDP) have become well recognized; among the LD-SDPs are *Bryophyllum* and other crassulaceous species, some lilies, and *Cestrum*.

The converse requirement, for short day followed by long day, is less well defined.

Resende (1952) indicated that *Campanula media* may have such a requirement, and this was clearly established later by Wellensiek (1960). Other species which may be SD-LDPs include several winter grains such as wheat and rye.

The existence of these classes of photoperiod responders provides helpful information in understanding developmental phenomena in plants, and it carries its own set of complications for our understanding. The fact that photoperiodic induction of flowering occurs in the leaf and that initiation occurs in the bud suggests clearly a transported stimulus, or hormone. However, the fact that photoperiods also control a whole spectrum of developmental events other than flowering (including photoperiodic controls of flower development, sex expression, tuber and bulb formation, growth rates, dormancy, and germination) presents a dilemma. If one assumes that the photoperiodic induction of the leaf causes the formation of a flowering hormone, one should assume either that the same environmental cue can cause the formation of separate hormones regulating the development of flowers, sex, tuber and bulb formation, dormancy, and growth rates, etc., or alternatively that the *same* hormone may control these several developmental events as it controls flowering. Neither of these is very appealing in view of present knowledge; the situation needs clarification.

Can we see any properties of the flowering stimulus which may contribute toward a clarification of the problem? The properties of the stimulus will be discussed in more detail in a later section, but there is very convincing evidence that the same kind of stimulus is common to the various types of flowering plants. Graftage of a flowering LDP to a SDP (e.g., *Hyoscyamus* to tobacco) causes the SDP to flower (Melchers and Lang, 1941). Several such cross inductions have been achieved. The converse graftage of a flowering SDP to cause flowering in a LDP has been achieved (Lang and Melchers, 1943; Zeevaart, 1957), though with more difficulty. The induction of either SDP or LDP by flowering indeterminate plants has been less difficult (Melchers, 1937). Certainly, then, the flowering stimuli between photoperiod classes have much in common or could even be identical.

Photoperiod processes

The nature of the flowering hormone or stimulus is not known, and attempts to extract such a material have not yielded definitive results. There are two principal sources of information about its characteristics, namely, the kinetics of the photoperiodic-induction processes and the separation of any partial processes which can be found in the whole milieu.

Fig. 13-11 | Some patterns of day and night periods on a 24-hr cycle that invoke short-day (left) or long-day (right) responses in photoperiodism. Above: a short day and a long day. Below: a short day with a light break near the start of the night evokes a short-day response (left), and with a light break near the middle of the night it evokes a long-day response (right).

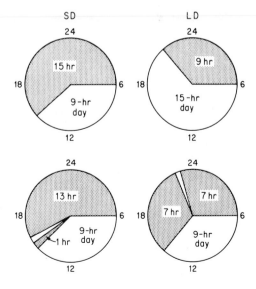

Measurement of the *kinetics* of the flowering processes can be made using such criteria as the percentage of plants flowering after an inductive treatment, the rate of development of the flowers as evidenced by the progress of meristematic change, or the number of days required for flowers to become visible. In a few species, such as *Hyoscyamus*, the number of inductive photoperiods may be reflected in a quantitative increase in the number of plants which initiate flowers, as shown in Fig. 13-12. More commonly, when a sufficient number of inductive cycles has been given, all the individuals so treated become flowering (e.g., *Xanthium pensylvanicum, Lolium tementulum*). A quantitative in-

crease in numbers of flowers can often be obtained with increases in number of photoperiods, even though the percentage of flowering is more nearly an all-or-none response (Fig. 13-13).

Neither of these parameters has been widely accepted for quantitative or kinetic measurements (Lang, 1952).

If repeated inductive photoperiods are given, one would expect that increasing amounts of the flowering stimulus would accrue in the plant and that this would be reflected in increased rates of floral development. Using meristematic stages to measure the rates of development, and presumably the amount of the flowering stimulus, Salisbury (1955) has drawn such kinetic comparisons as those shown in Fig. 13-14. This morphological measure of flowering rate has finally provided a basis for kinetic analysis and has made possible some real progress in developing an understanding of the sequence of partial processes constituting the photoperiodic phenomenon.

The light period. At least a part of the light-period influence on photoperiodism is a photosynthetic one. The minimal light intensity for an effective light period is usually about 100 ft-c, as illustrated for Biloxi soybean in Fig. 13-15; this value is in the range at which photosynthesis would pass the compensation point. In addition, it has been found that depriving the leaves of CO_2 during the light period erases its effectiveness (Parker and Borthwick, 1950), and supplying plants with sugar solutions in darkness has occasionally proved successful in bringing about flowering (Takimoto, 1960). Part of the sugar effect could be through encouragement of translocation out of the leaf (Carr, 1959).

If the light period were only a means of providing substrate, then one would expect relatively simple diurnal effects of light. Considerable question has been raised recently about such a simple interpretation of the light period. Meijer (1957) reported that dim red light during the light period

Fig. 13-12 | Expressed as the percentage of plants flowering, the photoperiodic induction of the LDP or SDP acts nearly like an all-or-none response. One inductive cycle will usually induce all *Xanthium* or *Lolium* plants to flower. Species requiring several days for induction may show a limited quantitative response, but all plants become flowering with a few inductive cycles (data from Evans, 1960*a;* Lang and Melchers, 1943; Schwabe, 1959).

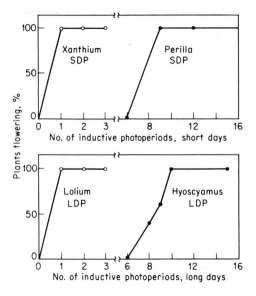

permits *Salvia* (a SDP) to flower even on long days, and several other curious light color relationships are not readily explained as photosynthetic effects. Meijer concludes that there are pigments other than chlorophyll involved in the light period. Harder et al. (1945) found that the succulent plant *Kalanchoe* could be satisfied for the light period by the application of only a few minutes of high-intensity light for a limited number of cycles, suggesting that the light experience served to entrain some cyclic or rhythmic events in the plant and not just to accumulate substrates.

The dark period. One of the most productive findings by researchers in photoperiodism was that of Hamner and Bonner (1938) that the dark period was the critical part of photoperiodic cycles under the 24-hr periodicities commonly experienced by plants. They deduced this from the simple experiment of applying a brief light period in the middle of the dark period and showing that the SDP *Xanthium* was then prevented from flowering even under SD conditions (Fig. 13-11). An interruption of the light period with darkness was essentially without effect.

The effectiveness of light exposures in disrupting the effectiveness of the dark period has opposite actions on SDP and LDPs. Placed on short days, a SDP will flower and a night interruption will prevent flowering. A LDP placed on a short day will not flower, and a night interruption will induce it to do so.

The aforementioned conclusion of Hamner and Bonner (1938) that the night period was the critical timing part of photoperiodism was substantiated indirectly by the experiments of Hamner (1940). Making measurements of the specific requirements for the day and the night periods by varying them separately, he found that the day requirement was relatively loose (Fig. 13-16), whereas the night requirement had a sharp threshold value. His experiments were done before the more precise methods of

Fig. 13-13 | Expressed as the numbers of flowering nodes per plant, the photoperiodic induction of soybean appears as a quantitative response, with increasing numbers of inductive cycles causing increased numbers of nodes with flowers. The percentage of plants flowering is still essentially an all-or-none response (Hamner, 1940).

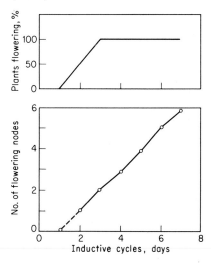

Fig. 13-14 | A quantitative expression of flowering intensity is the rate of flower-primordia development. The stage of development in *Xanthium* is seen to advance more rapidly under continuous inductive cycles than after only two short days. Floral stages range from a convex apical meristem (stage 1) to clusters of meristematic florets (stage 8) (Salisbury, 1955).

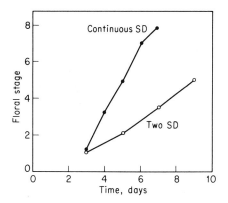

Fig. 13-15 | Comparing the flowering response to two different day lengths with various light intensities, it appears that in each case a light intensity of about 100 ft-c is minimal for the light period in Biloxi soybean (Hamner, 1940).

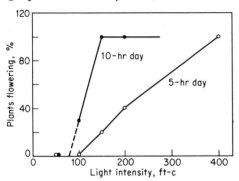

Fig. 13-16 | If the lengths of the light period and the dark period are varied independently, there appears to be a loose range of effective light periods and perhaps a more precise threshold for the night length. Biloxi soybean given seven cycles, with a 16-hr dark period (below) and a 16-hr light period (above) (data of Hamner, 1940).

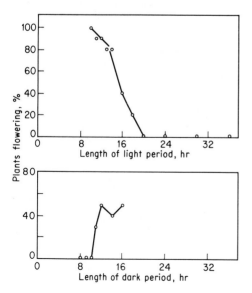

making quantitative or kinetic comparisons had been developed, but even using the less precise methods of measurement his data pointed to the night period as the critical timing part of photoperiodic induction.

Knowledge of the night-interruption effect permitted one of the major breakthroughs in the development of an understanding of the phenomenon of photoperiodism: the pursuit of the specific system which may be altered by light, thus leading to the photoperiodic control. The next step was the establishment of the action spectrum for the night-interruption effect. Applying light of various wavelengths to the leaves of SDPs in the middle of the long dark periods permitted a comparison of the relative effectiveness of the various parts of the spectrum. The results obtained are represented in Fig. 13-17 for *Xanthium,* and similar action spectra have been obtained for each of the photoperiodic plants tested (Parker et al., 1946, 1950; Hendricks and Borthwick, 1954), showing a maximal effect in disrupting the night period by red light in the region of 640 to 660 mμ. Following this came the unexpected finding that far-red light was effective in erasing the red-light action, an effect also represented in Fig. 13-17. The resolution of these two opposite light actions came with the demonstration by Hendricks et al. (1956) that light was having reversible effects on a pigment which could assume two forms, a red-absorbing and a far-red-absorbing form. This pigment was subsequently isolated by the group at Beltsville, Maryland, that had proposed its existence (Butler et al., 1959; Lane et al., 1962; Siegelman et al., 1962) and was given the name *phytochrome.* This pigment and its physiological actions are discussed in Chap. 20.

The opposite effects of the far-red and red light in modifying the night in *Xanthium* leaves are illustrated by Fig. 13-18 (Downs, 1956). In this experiment, red light was applied for various intervals during the middle of the night with a consequent inhibition of flowering, the inhibition becoming complete with sufficient exposure to red light. Note that the quantitative morphological measure is being used as shown in Fig. 13-14. If red-light-inhibited plants are then exposed to far-red light for increasing intervals of time, the inhibitory effect is removed, and the full rate of morphological development is restored. The alternate saturation of these two light reactions can be used to demonstrate the ready reversibility of the two phytochrome conditions, the last light treatment determining the flowering response.

Might it be possible to distinguish between separate reactions or partial processes going on during the dark period? This question has led to some interesting experiments since 1955, but the distinctions that have been drawn are more suggestive than definitive.

If the critical length of the dark period is due to the necessity for the completion of a sequence of two or more steps, it might be helpful to apply modifying treatments at various times during the night to look for selective changes in effectiveness of the treatment. The first factor so examined was the interruption of the night by light. When light was applied at various times to measure its comparative effectiveness, it was found to reach its maximal effectiveness approximately at, or shortly before, the critical number of hours of darkness needed for an effective night. For example, for *Kalanchoe* Harder and Bode (1943) found that a night interruption was most inhibitory of flowering when applied between the fifth and seventh hours of the night (Fig. 13-19), and Salisbury and Bonner (1956) found that for *Xanthium* it was most inhibitory at the eighth hour or shortly before (Fig. 13-19). Each of these species requires about 9 hr of darkness for the induction of flowering.

When does the phytochrome pigment participate in the dark reactions? The reversibility of the pigment between two

Fig. 13-17 | Action spectra for the effects of light on the photoperiodic night. The light interruption of the night is most effective with red light (620 to 660 mμ), and reversal of the red-light effect is most effective with far-red light (725 mμ) (data from Hendricks and Borthwick, 1954, for *Xanthium*).

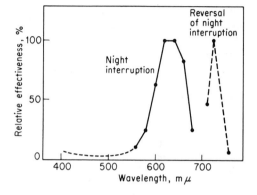

Fig. 13-18 | Quantitative experiments on the dose responses of floral development to light. Red-light interruption of the dark period (above) and far-red restoration of the dark period after 2 min of red light (below). *Xanthium* plants given three 12-hr nights with the treatments indicated; red light at 10^{-4} erg/cm^2/sec (Downs, 1956).

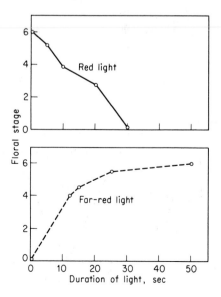

forms and the fact that red light which converts it into the far-red-absorbing form is most inhibitory of the night indicate that for the photoperiodic night to proceed, the phytochrome must be principally in the red-absorbing form. Consider, then, the possibility that the initial event in the night may be the gradual conversion of phytochrome into the red-absorbing form (which it does in darkness in vitro; Bonner, 1962) and that when it is mostly in the red-absorbing form, another set of dark reactions may proceed. Evidence supporting this attractive possibility is found in experiments by Salisbury and Bonner (1956), who compared

the relative ability of red light to inhibit after various intervals of the dark period in *Xanthium*. Their data in Fig. 13-20 indicate that the amount of red light needed to saturate the inhibition effect is approximately the same from the fourth hour of the night to the eighth hour of the night; if increasing amounts of pigment were being converted during these periods, one would expect the saturation dose to increase. Salisbury and Bonner suggest, then, that the conversion of the phytochrome to the red-absorbing form is essentially completed in the first 4 hr of the dark period. This and some other considerations (Salisbury, 1963) suggest that the pigment-conversion step is preliminary to the timing reaction of the night and is not itself the timer.

The only treatment which has been developed so far to alter fairly specifically the timing of the dark period seems to be the application of cobalt ions to the leaf. With cobalt treatment, the threshold night length of *Xanthium* leaves is markedly increased, as shown in Fig. 13-21 (Salisbury, 1959a).

The fact that the flowering stimulus does not appear to start accumulating in leaves of SDPs until a critical night length has been achieved (about 9 hr in the cases of *Xanthium* and *Pharbitis*) suggests that the actual formation of the stimulus follows after the action of the timer reaction. Until now, no experiments claim to have altered specifically the formation of the stimulus, but the most suggestive ones have been concerned with the inhibitory effects of high-temperature periods interpolated at various times through the night. Nakayama (1958) found that flower development in *Pharbitis* is inhibited by warm temperatures (e.g., 36°C) at night, and this inhibition seems to apply specifically to the later part of the night—following the completion of the critical night length (Fig. 13-22). Similar inhibitions have been reported for *Xanthium* by Salisbury (1963). These effects seem to be distinctive to the later part of the night, and it is a tempting speculation that they may

Fig. 13-19 | The effectiveness of a light break applied during the photoperiodic night measured as the delay of the time to flower in *Kalanchoe* (above) or as the inhibition of flower stage of *Xanthium* (below). In each case a standard light dose was applied at various times during the 16-hr night (Harder and Bode, 1943; Salisbury and Bonner, 1956).

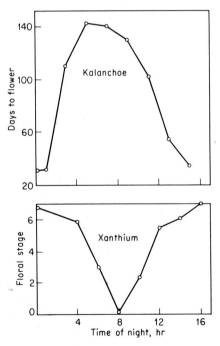

relate to the night reaction concerned with stimulus formation.

It seems reasonable to assume that the formation of the flowering stimulus is a synthetic activity involving the consumption of energy by some enzymatic acts. Kinetic analyses of photoperiodism have provided some indirect evidence for this assumption. Salisbury (1957) inhibited the photoperiodic processes with dinitrophenol and found that this uncoupling agent was most inhibitory when applied during the dark period. He interpreted its action as an interference with some synthetic activities which could require energy springing from ATP. Subsequently a number of inhibitors of the dark reactions have been found, including ethionine, fluorophenylalanine, 2,6-aminopurine, picolinic acid, and quercitin (Collins et al., 1963), but the actions of these inhibitors have not pointed to any special enzyme system that might be involved in the synthesis of the flowering stimulus.

The various experiments concerning the dark period suggest the following sequence of events: first, for the dark period to become effective there must be a conversion of phytochrome from the far-red to the red-absorbing form; then a timing reaction can proceed; and then the synthesis of some regulating principal. The phytochrome conversion can proceed in darkness, but red light will ordinarily send it back to the far-red form and stop the timer reaction. The timer reaction can be slowed with cobalt applications. The synthesis of the regulating principal can be suppressed by high temperatures in *Pharbitis*. This last step is considered by research workers using SDPs to be the synthesis of the flowering stimulus, but since the product of the long night may be either stimulatory or inhibitory of flowering depending upon the photoperiodic class of plant being used, it seems more logical to consider the product in the more neutral category of a regulatory principal rather than specifically as the flowering stimulus.

Translocation. In addition to the dark

Fig. 13-20 | A comparison of red-light-saturation curves for night interruptions applied to *Xanthium* after 4, 6, and 8 hr of the 16-hr night. The flower-inhibiting effect of the red light was apparently saturated at about the same doses for each of the three times of application (Salisbury and Bonner, 1956).

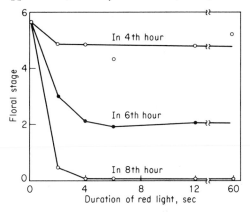

Fig. 13-21 | Application of cobalt salts to *Xanthium* leaves alters the timing mechanism of the photoperiodic night, as indicated by a change in the length of dark period needed for flower induction. $CoCl_2$ at $4 \times 10^{-3}M$ applied at start of the night (Salisbury, 1959a).

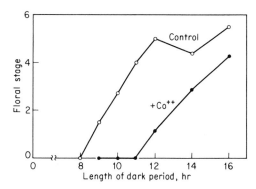

processes of a pigment conversion, a timing reaction, and a stimulus formation, there is a requirement for translocation of the stimulus out of the leaf. That the flower stimulus may move in the carbohydrate translocation system was first suggested by Stout (1945), and subsequent studies have lent much support to his idea. The beneficial effects on flowering from adding sugars to an induced leaf have been attributed to the provision of better translocation activity in the phloem (Carr, 1959).

The timing of translocation out of the leaf can be observed by the simple device of removing the induced leaves at various time intervals after completion of an inductive night (Imamura, 1953). But for actual calculations of velocities of translocation, longer distances need to be traversed. Some ingenious experiments on this question have been done by Imamura and Takimoto (1955) who used two-branched *Pharbitis* plants with a single leaf on one branch and a single bud on another, timing the arrival of the flower stimulus in terms of the node in the remaining bud at which flowering first occurred. Using several variations of this experiment, they found velocities of

Fig. 13-22 | Inhibitory effects of high temperature (36°C for 2 hr) on the photoperiodic night are restricted to the later part of the night in *Pharbitis*. This suggests that its effect is on the formation of the flower stimulus (Nakayama, 1958).

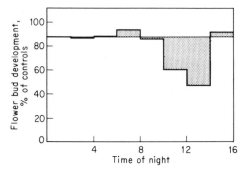

translocation of about 2 to 4 mm/hr. Defoliation experiments have indicated (Lockhart and Hamner, 1954) that about 10 hr was needed for the first stimulus to come out of the petiole of an induced *Xanthium* leaf.

This stimulus seems to flow to the same destinations as photosynthate from the leaves, for in addition to the already cited evidence that it moves with the carbohydrate stream, Chajlakjan and Butenko (1957) compared the patterns of distribution of the flower stimulus and radioactive photosynthate and found them indistinguishable.

The photoinduced state

The persistence of the reproductive condition is an interesting and instructive feature. First of all, many plants can "remember" the experience of photoperiods which induce flowering and then continue to flower for extended periods after return to a noninductive photoperiod. For example, *Xanthium* plants given several short days will continue to flower for several months. Others such as Biloxi soybean will cease to differentiate flowers as soon as they are removed from the inductive photoperiods.

If a given leaf is permanently altered by an inductive photoperiod and then forever after produces a stimulus that had not been produced before, some component of the synthetic system would presumably have been permanently altered in such a way as to continue a new synthesis; this situation might suggest an alteration of the RNA, for example, which would continue to propagate the new stimulus. Alternatively, if the leaf is altered only temporarily, as for a few days, then this situation would be more suggestive of the formation of a new enzyme which led to the stimulus production; and when the enzyme wore out, stimulus formation might stop. Looking at induced leaves, one finds that there is quite a graded series, running from plants with leaves which remain induced for only a few days (e.g., *Xanthium;* Carr, 1959) to others which remain induced for several months (e.g., *Perilla;* Lona, 1946; Zeevaart, 1957*a,b*, 1958). In *Pharbitis,* Imamura (1953) reports that a leaf given a few inductive cycles stops producing the flower stimulus in a few days, but given many cycles it continues for extended periods. Lam and Leopold (1961) suggested that even in *Perilla* the leaf gradually ceases to provide the flower stimulus with time, as indicated by the declining ability of single induced leaves to provide flower stimulus to the bud (Fig. 13-23). Zeevaart (1962) suggested that a leaf may remain induced but fail to export the flower stimulus; the loss of inductive abilities of leaves in the noninductive photoperiod could be attributed to such a multiple function.

The photoinduced state may be "remembered" either in the leaves or in the growing point. In some definitive grafting experiments, Zeevaart (1958) established that whereas the leaves of *Perilla* continue to produce flower stimulus for months after the withdrawal of the inductive short-day treatment, *Xanthium* leaves lose the ability within a few days. Instead, the growing points become a source of flower stimulus, and repeated grafting of growing points of an induced *Xanthium* from plant to plant can cause flowering. One must conclude that the flowering condition can be evoked not only by products formed in induced leaves but sometimes by products formed by buds and young leaves of the growing points.

Another feature of photoinduction is the problem of whether it involves the formation of stimulatory substances (as a hormone) or inhibitory substances. The evidence for the existence of stimulatory substances is clear in the quantitative experiments already described, but in addition there is evidence that inhibitors of flowering are also involved in photoperiodism. Moskov (1936) noted that in chrysanthemum, a

Fig. 13-23 | After 15 to 25 short days, the leaves of *Perilla* may become decreasingly effective as suppliers of the flower stimulus. In paired leaf experiments, one leaf was induced; after various intervals of time the opposing leaf was removed, and the flowering of its axillary bud was used as an indication of the flower stimulus still coming from the induced leaf. As long as it remains on the plant, the opposite leaf prevents the short-day leaf from inducing its axillary bud. With time, the induced leaf becomes less effective as a flower stimulator, indicated by longer times to flowering (above) and by fewer flowers induced (below). (Lam and Leopold, 1961).

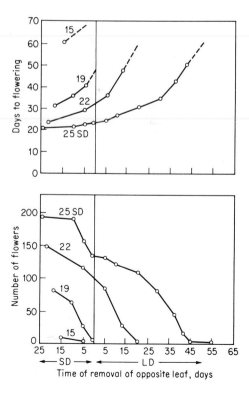

SDP, leaves which received only long days inhibited the flower initiation. While numerous photoperiodic species show such inhibitions by uninduced leaves, other species like *Xanthium* may not (Hamner and Bonner, 1938). Finding that removal of all leaves would permit flowering of the LDP *Hyoscyamus*, Lang and Melchers (1943) suggested that the photoperiodic induction specifically involved the removal of the inhibition by uninduced leaves. More recently a similar situation has been reported for the SDP strawberry (Guttridge, 1959). Lincoln et al. (1956) have even been able to define the photoperiodic requirements for the formation of a flower inhibitor of *Xanthium* leaves and Bhargova (1963) in *Salvia* leaves. To illustrate the inhibitory effects of uninduced leaves, some data of Evans (1961) are presented in Fig. 13-24, which shows that the removal of short-day leaves

caused marked promotions of flowering in the LDP *Lolium tementulum*.

Wellensiek (1958, 1959) has identified the inhibitory state with the light period in SDPs and suggests that darkness nullifies the inhibitory state formed in light. In support of this idea is the fact that some SDPs flower more readily under weak light, and in fact at lower intensities the threshold photoperiod for flowering may be considerably lengthened (Krumweide, 1960) or even removed (de Zeeuw, 1953). Furthermore, low temperatures applied during the day period can promote flowering of *Perilla* or *Pharbitis* (Wellensiek, 1959; Ogawa, 1960) or even induce flowering of *Xanthium* on long days (de Zeeuw, 1957). Perhaps low temperatures may suppress formation of flowering inhibitors during the light period. How these features might be applied to LDPs is an interesting problem yet to be developed experimentally.

Fig. 13-24 | In the LDP *Lolium tementulum,* leaves receiving short days inhibit the flowering stimulus coming from a leaf given one long day. If the short-day leaves have been removed, a promotion of flowering response is obtained. The long-day leaf was removed at the time intervals indicated on the abscissa (Evans, 1960*b*).

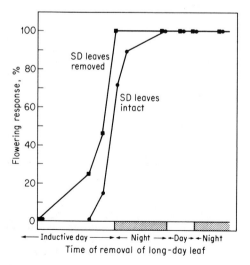

Conclusion

The photoperiodic control of flowering has provided the most important experimental tool for the development of an understanding of the physiology of flowering. In essence, cyclic experiences of light and darkness can bring about the reproductive state, and consecutive processes which require either light or darkness must proceed separately to accomplish this change.

Exploitation of photoperiodism in the analysis of flowering has developed principally along two lines: analysis of the light-sensitive changes which occur in the night period, especially with respect to the pigment involved, and analysis of partial processes through kinetic experiments with physical or chemical treatments selectively to alter some parts of the sequence of events in the photoperiodic cycle.

While the pigment involved in the dark-period regulation has been extracted and the movement of the flowering stimulus can be followed, neither the nature of the intermediate steps nor that of the stimulus has been established.

VERNALIZATION AND FLOWERING

Temperatures provide another salient climatic cue for plants, a ready signal of seasonal changes. Many species are induced or promoted to flower by low temperatures, especially many biennial and perennial plants. Less common are species which are caused to flower by high temperatures; several annuals such as spinach, rice, China aster, and *Rudbeckia* are examples.

The promotive effects of low temperatures on flowering are termed *vernalization,* a word coined by Lysenko (1928). For this discussion the term will be used to include the actual induction of flowering in species which require low temperatures (e.g., cabbage, celery, beet) as well as the hastening of flowering in species which are only quantitatively promoted by low temperatures (e.g., the winter grains, lettuce, radish). In each of these, the flowering responses to temperature can be considered as an ecological coordination of flowering times, providing the associated advantages discussed earlier (pp. 205–206).

To illustrate the quantitative and sometimes qualitative nature of the vernalization response, some data on vernalization of four species of *Lolium* are presented in Fig. 13-25 (Evans, 1960c). The flat curve for *L. tementulum* shows a lack of any apparent vernalization response, and the curves for *L. multiflorum* and its hybrid with *L. perenne* show quantitative responses to vernalization, i.e., shortening of the time required for the appearance of flowers. The hyperbolic curve for *L. perenne* illustrates an actual requirement for low temperature as well as the quantitative nature of the effects of further extensions of low-temperature experience beyond the essential minimum for flowering.

The classical case of vernalization is the hastening of flowering in winter grains, and the quantitative nature of this response is illustrated in Fig. 13-26 (Purvis and Gregory, 1937). These curves indicate that the experience of the low temperature really does advance the time of flowering whether it is plotted as time from the start of vernalization or time from planting out after completion of the vernalization treatment.

Kinetics of vernalization

The low-temperature effects may be obtained in some species when the moistened seed is chilled; in other species it may be obtained only when growing plants are chilled. Some species respond readily to chilling at either stage.

Fig. 13-25 | The relative responses of four genetic strains of *Lolium* to vernalization. *L. tementulum* shows no response; *L. multiflorum* and its hybrid with *L. perenne* show quantitative responses; and *L. perenne* shows a complete requirement for vernalization. Growth conditions: 23°C during the day; 17°C at night; long photoperiods (Evans, 1960c).

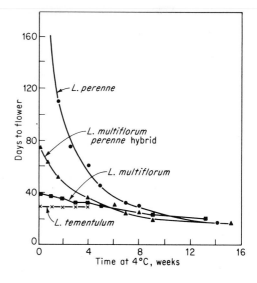

Vernalization of whole plants was discovered simultaneously for two horticultural crops: cabbage and celery (Boswell, 1929; Miller, 1929; Thompson, 1929). Each of these reports noted that as plants became older they responded more readily to the low-temperature stimulation. This is frequently so for whole-plant vernalization, and some data shown in Fig. 13-27 are representative of such a changing sensitivity (Wellensiek, 1958). In *Lunaria*, shown in this figure and in Fig. 11-1, there is a juvenile period during which low temperatures are without effect. Other species such as beet (Chroboczek, 1934; Wellensiek and Hakkaart, 1955) become increasingly sensitive with age but lack a completely insensitive juvenile period. Evans (1960) describes the temperature response as an exponential

function, the slope of which shifts with increasing plant age.

Instead of increasing vernalization responsiveness with age, in some species the best response is obtained by chilling the seeds. The vernalization of seed was perhaps first noted by Gassner (1918), who found that by moistening seeds of winter grains and keeping them in the cold before planting out, he could make them flower as spring varieties. Lysenko (1928) described vernalization of seeds as a general phenomenon, and the entanglement of this seeming alteration of genetic material with political ideology has had a curious and sad history (Huxley, 1949).

In some species, both the seed and the whole plant are capable of responding to vernalization, and these two responsive periods may be separated by a stage during which there is markedly less sensitivity. A striking example of these two stages in *Arabidopsis thaliana* has been described by Napp-Zinn (1957), and some of his data are plotted in Fig. 13-28 (Napp-Zinn, 1960). If vernalization is started within the first day or two after moistening the seed, flowering is induced very early. If the plant has several days in which to start growth before the vernalization is started, flowering is less readily induced. A gradual increasing responsiveness to vernalization then becomes evident in plants of increasing age.

The possibility that rapid growth may be antagonistic to the flowering response has occurred to many investigators, and even in the earliest reports on low-temperature induction of flowering, attempts were made to establish whether the low-temperature effect might be simply a suppression of growth (Thompson, 1929). Cholodny (1936) suggested a general explanation of vernalization based on the suppression of vegetative growth. Numerous types of evidence deny that the growth check is the essential part of the vernalization (Thompson, 1929; Gott et al., 1955), but in some special cases there is reason to believe that the growth check is

Fig. 13-26 | The quantitative response of Petkus winter rye to vernalization. The time to anthesis is decreased by vernalization, whether one measures from the start of the cold treatment (above) or from the time of planting out after the cold treatment (below) (Purvis and Gregory, 1937).

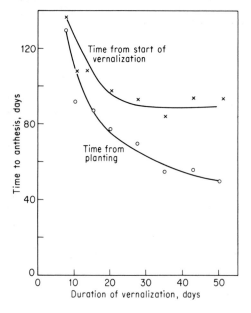

specifically involved in the response. For example, in tobacco Steinberg (1952) achieved the same increases in earliness either with low-temperature treatments or with transplanting, pruning, or other treatments which would check the growth of the plant. A similar case may be that of tomato vernalization (Lewis, 1953; and cf. Fig. 13-4). Most cases of vernalization cannot be explained in this way.

Many species which respond to vernalization are also sensitive to photoperiodic stimulations of flowering. The most common combination is that of low temperature and LDP, as, for example, in many Cruciferae and other biennials (beet and the winter grains). But some species may be LDP and induced by high temperature (spinach), SDP and induced by low temperature (chrysanthemum), or SDP and induced by high temperature (China aster). The interactions of these two environmental cues may be either supplementary or complementary. Thus low temperatures may quantitatively displace the critical photoperiod for flowering (Lang and Melchers, 1943) or increase the responsiveness to photoperiods without altering the critical day length needed (Cathey, 1957); or again low temperatures may entirely replace a photoperiod requirement (Koller and Highkin, 1960).

The actual temperature experienced greatly alters the effectiveness of any vernalization treatment, and for most species temperatures in the range of 0 to 5°C are optimal for vernalization. The temperature range for Petkus winter rye is plotted in Fig. 13-29, illustrating that in this species not only is the temperature range of 0 to 5°C effective, but there is a real effectiveness of temperatures as low as −5°C. It is curious to think what reactions in the plant might be taking place better at subfreezing temperatures than at 15°C, for example. In other species the vernalization temperatures are rather sharply limited at 0°C, as for example, the Japanese radish (Kimura, 1961; Fig. 13-30).

Fig. 13-27 | The responsiveness of *Lunaria* plants to vernalization changes with increasing age of the plant. Until they are about 8 weeks old, the plants do not respond to the cold, and after that they require decreasing amounts of vernalization with increasing age. For vernalization treatment the plants were placed in a 5°C greenhouse (Wellensiek, 1958).

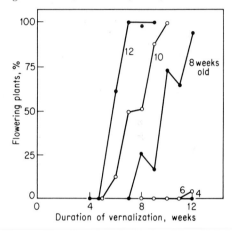

Fig. 13-28 | The effectiveness of a standard vernalization treatment of *Arabidopsis thaliana* changes with stage of growth. Vernalization applied as a seed treatment or at various ages during seedling growth reveals a period of marked responsiveness at the seed stage and then low sensitivity until the seedling has developed for a few weeks. The flowering response is plotted as the days to flower after a 38-day period at 2°C. Unvernalized plants did not flower (Napp-Zinn, 1960).

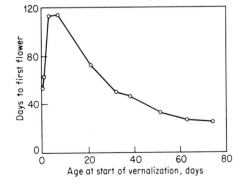

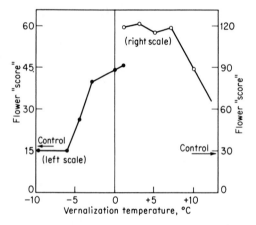

Fig. 13-29 | A comparison of the relative effectiveness of various temperatures in vernalizing seed of Petkus winter rye. Curve at right is for 42 days vernalization, dissected 133 days later (Purvis, 1948); curve at left is for 45 days vernalization, dissected 49 days later (Hänsel, 1953). Optimum temperatures seem to be between +7 and −3°C. Flower "score": meristem as a single ridge, 10; meristem as a double ridge, 20; stamens differentiated, 30; spike emergence, 40; anthesis, 50. Subsequent days each scored as 1.

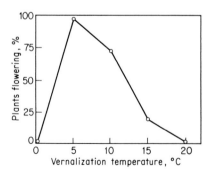

Fig. 13-30. The vernalization of Japanese radish is optimal at about 5°C, and at 0°C vernalization is not accomplished. Vernalization for 120 days (Kimura, 1961).

After the completion of vernalization, warm temperatures can have a depressing effect on flowering earliness. Purvis (1948) noted that with later planting dates of Petkus rye there was a requirement for a somewhat greater vernalization time to achieve the same degree of earliness, and she attributed that to the warmer temperatures of the soil at the time of planting (Fig. 13-31).

Devernalization

The fact that high temperatures after vernalization could nullify the effect was perhaps first noted in celery by Thompson (1929) and by various other horticulturists working with the low-temperature responses of biennials (Miller, 1929; Chroboczek, 1934). The recognition of devernalization as a physiologically significant event, however, was made by researchers at the Imperial College, London, working with the vernalization of winter grains (Purvis and Gregory, 1945). When vernalized grains were exposed to 35°C for even 1 day, the vernalization effect was erased. The plants were not damaged since devernalized plants could then be revernalized effectively by repetition of the cold treatment. The same reversible devernalization could be obtained with anaerobic conditions (Gregory and Purvis, 1937). The significance of this finding seems to be that an unstable product formed by the cold experience is probably metabolized away if high temperatures or anaerobiosis is experienced too soon for the product to establish its effect. This hypothetical product of vernalization is not known.

A horticultural application of the devernalization effect is the control of flowering of onions. This crop is properly a biennial, and the young bulb which is formed the first year may be induced to flower by vernalization during the winter (or in cold storage). For the production of large bulbs in the second year, flowering is undesirable.

After it was learned that high temperatures prevented flowering (Heath, 1943), this response was developed as a commercial devernalization treatment for onion sets after storage at low temperatures (Lachman and Upham, 1954; Fig. 22-22).

Devernalization in chrysanthemums can be achieved with low-light intensities or by decapitation and forcing out of the unvernalized basal buds (Schwabe, 1954). High temperatures are ineffective in this species.

The vernalization stimulus

Unlike the photoperiodic stimulus to flowering, the vernalization stimulus is perceived ordinarily by the apical meristem (Chroboczek, 1934). In a series of clear-cut experiments, Gregory and de Ropp (1938) and then Purvis (1940) found that the excised embryo of winter rye could be vernalized and that even a fragment of the embryo growing point could still be effectively vernalized in tissue culture.

Physiologists were satisfied that the apical meristem is in fact the locus of vernalization, but later Wellensiek (1961) reported that the young expanding leaves of *Lunaria* could be vernalized, and he further established (1962) through some ingenious experiments that leaves could receive the vernalization stimulus only if they were experiencing active cell division. Thus the more specific generalization seems to be that dividing cells are the site of vernalization, and the meristems are well qualified in this regard.

Once a meristem has been vernalized, all growth that develops from that source acts as vernalized growth (Schwabe, 1954*a*). This suggests a metastable modification of a self-replicating component in the meristematic cells. There is no experimental evidence in the literature of a declining effectiveness of vernalized meristems, though in vernalizable perennial species where growth ceases each year following

reproduction, reversion can occur through the regrowth of new buds which are nonvernalized (Schwabe, 1954*b*).

Unlike the photoperiod stimulus, the product of vernalization seems to be quite immobile. Active meristems may be vernalized, and inactive meristems on the same plant may remain nonvernalized. Graftage experiments have not shown a translocation of the product of vernalization.

Morphologically, two rather suggestive changes with seed vernalization can be detected. One is the more extensive development of vascular tissues leading to the growing points (Chakravarti, 1950), which suggests that the meristems may have a more ready supply of some translocated substances after vernalization (Chakravarti, 1954). Another morphological change described by Stokes (1952*a,b*) is the extensive reorganization of embryo and endosperm during the vernalization of *Heracleum* seeds;

Fig. 13-31 | A comparison of vernalization treatments of Petkus winter rye with various dates of transplanting into the field. With later planting dates there is a lowered effectiveness of vernalization, presumably by a devernalization effect of the warm soil. Scores as in Fig. 13-29 (Purvis, 1948).

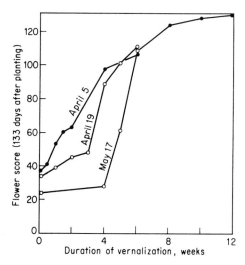

as shown in Fig. 13-32, the embryo becomes much enlarged at the expense of the endosperm, suggesting again that mobilization or the availability of substances in the meristem has been altered. The facts that gibberellins can bring about at least part of the vernalization response (Lona and Bocchi, 1956) and that gibberellins can alter mobilization events in seeds (Paleg, 1960) are consistent with this observation.

The quantitative nature of the vernalization response suggests the possibility that there is involved the accumulation of some substance stimulative of flowering. Also, the devernalization effects obtainable within a short period after vernalization suggest the involvement of some labile substance. On the other hand, the nontranslocatability of the stimulus seems to deny that the final state is imposed by a substance. Attempts to simulate or modify vernalization with various growth substances and metabolic modifiers have not been very helpful, as, for example, the apparent simulations of vernalization with auxins by Cholodny (1936) and others. With the discovery of gibberellins, a new hope that a substance

might be involved sprang up again. Several laboratories reported that at least some of the vernalization effects could be obtained with gibberellin applications to seeds (Lona and Bocchi, 1956; Purvis, 1960; Weibel, 1960), and in many biennial species a complete replacement of the vernalization effect could be obtained by gibberellin application to the plants (Lang, 1957). This complexity of responses suggests two things: At least some of the vernalization effects may be related to the natural gibberellin substances in the plants, and not all the vernalization responses are a result of the same physiological mechanism, for then a substance which could replace the cold for one species would ostensibly be expected to replace it for all species.

The salient features of the vernalization effects on flowering seem to be that dividing cells can perceive a low-temperature stimulus and that this alters the morphological expression of growth for a protracted period of time. The ability of tissues to "remember" a temperature experience and to remain altered in a metastable manner presents a prime example of one of the most remarkable problems in developmental physiology. That the change in metastable state should be provoked by temperatures near or even below freezing does not seem to imply that the perception of the temperature experience involves a synthesis of a new substantive material, but rather that some physical change occurring during the cold experience may then alter the production of regulating substances.

Fig. 13-32 | As the vernalization of *Heracleum* seeds progresses, there is a mobilization of materials out of the endosperm into the embryo (Stokes, 1952*a*).

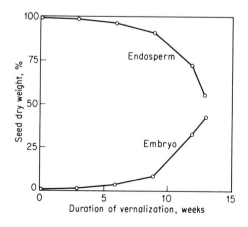

SUBSTANCES REGULATING FLOWERING

The study of developmental processes is directed toward the explanation of physiological events on a biochemical basis. The studies of earliness, photoperiodism and vernalization all hold some promise of a more complete biochemical understanding of the flowering processes. The existence of natural growth substances which regulate the quantity and quality of growth offers interesting possibilities for explaining or at least partially explaining developmental events such as flowering.

Growth substances have already been found to play important roles in the endogenous control of flowering. Historically, each of the major explanations of flowering has been founded on the particular aspect of plant physiology which is under most rapid development at the time. Thus, the first attempt at a general explanation of flowering was on the basis of the carbohydrate-nitrogen ratio (Kraus and Kraybill, 1918), at a time when nutrition was the main concern of plant physiology. Later the auxins came to the forefront, and it was soon proposed that they were the controlling entities in flowering processes (Bonner and Bandurski, 1952; Liverman, 1955). With the establishment of the gibberellins as natural growth regulators in plants, they too were invoked as endogenous controls of flowering—and with the most substantial experimental basis (Lang, 1956, 1957; Lang and Reinhard, 1961). There is a growing conservatism among plant physiologists, however, about attempting to explain developmental processes on the basis of any single endogenous factor, and, happily, the claims for gibberellin involvement in flowering have been conservative.

Gibberellin

The ability of gibberellin applications to cause rosette plants to elongate in a manner suggestive of bolting led quickly to investigations of the possibility that gibberellins could cause flowering in rosette plants. In fact, it was found to be widely effective (Lang, 1956, 1957). The effects are dramatic (Fig. 13–33) and widespread among many species of plants (Wittwer and Bukovac, 1957; Lang and Reinhard, 1961). The stimulations of flowering with gibberellins can be assigned to two groups of plants: those that are caused to flower by low temperatures and the LDPs.

An extensive array of cold-requiring species is brought to flowering by gibberellin applications, including the biennial *Hyoscyamus*, the biennial cruciferous species (cabbage, beet, turnip), and other cold-requiring species (carrot, endive, parsley). Though not all cold-requiring plants have been induced to flower with gibberellin, the list is becoming impressive.

The relation to photoperiod requirements is more complicated. Numerous LDPs have been induced to flower with gibberellins, though it may be more accurate to say that gibberellin may increase the tendency of LDPs to flower rather than entirely replace the LD requirement (Chajlakjan, 1958; Chouard, 1960). Among the LDPs gibberellin has been shown to cause or promote flowering in spinach, dill, lettuce, stock, radish, *Rudbeckia*, *Hyoscyamus*, and others. But in each case where it is effective, the species is a rosette plant which shoots or bolts before flowering; species which are LDPs and not rosette in form do not flower in response to gibberellin (Lona, 1956; Burk and Tso, 1958). If a partial photoperiodic induction is given, many LDPs which were otherwise unresponsive will then respond (Chouard, 1960). In this connection, gibberellin will replace the long-day requirement of the LD–SDP *Bryophyllum* (Harder and Bünsow, 1956) and will inhibit flowering of the SDP *Kalanchoe* in a manner suggestive of long-day-treated leaves (Harder and Bünsow, 1957).

If endogenous gibberellins participate in the control of flowering, the cold-requiring plants would be likely objects in which to find changes in gibberellin content. Measurements of the natural gibberellin contents extractable from leaves have provided some preliminary evidence that the content may in fact increase after low-temperature induction of biennial *Hyoscyamus* (Lang, 1960), though the differences are not large

Fig. 13-33 | *Silene armeria* which ordinarily requires long days for flowering is induced to flower in short-day conditions (9 hr) with applications of gibberellin. From left to right, plants were given 0, 2, 5, 10, 20, or 50 µg/plant each day (Lang, 1957).

(Fig. 13-34). Radley (1963) found that in the LDP spinach there was a brief detectable rise in extractable gibberellin during the first days of long-day treatment but that at later stages the content fell off. She suggested that the commencement of bolting might cause a more rapid turnover of the natural gibberellin, accounting for the decline.

It is attractive to believe that gibberellin is critically involved in the initiation of flowering in some species, especially those requiring cold or long photoperiods. It might be considered a component of the flowering hormone (Chajlakjan, 1958) or, better still, a flower promoter through its stimulation of stem growth and perhaps of some mobilization actions associated with growth (Lang, 1957, 1959).

One reason for the lack of response by some LDP or cold-requiring plants may be that the particular gibberellin applied is not effectively used by the plant. The wide range in effectiveness of nine gibberellins in stimulating flowering has been described by Wittwer and Bukovac (1962). Some representative data for lettuce are plotted in Fig. 13-35. By using diverse gibberellins, the list of species induced to flower has been further extended (Michniewicz and Lang, 1962).

Auxin

This growth substance really entered the flowering picture first, for in 1942 it was reported to effectively induce flowering in pineapple (Clark and Kerns, 1942) and has been used commercially for this purpose ever since. Auxin has had less effect on flowering of other species, and the most definitive effects are inhibitory (Thurlow and Bonner, 1947; Leopold and Thimann, 1949).

To establish the part of the photoperiodic cycle which was being inhibited by auxin, Salisbury (1955) carried out careful timing

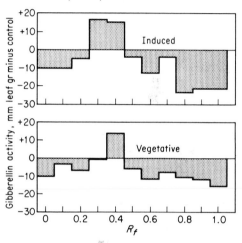

Fig. 13-34 | A comparison of the gibberellin contents of vegetative and cold-induced plants of biennial *Hyoscyamus*. 70 per cent acetone extracts chromatographed in butanol/amyl-alcohol/acetone/ammonia/water and bioassayed at each R_f by the D-3 dwarf corn test (Lang and Reinhard, 1961).

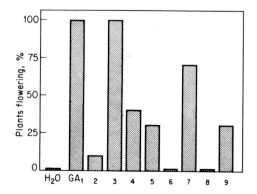

Fig. 13-35 | The relative effectiveness of nine different gibberellins inducing flowering of Great Lakes lettuce. Each plant receives $0.09\mu g$ and was scored 45 days later. Gibberellins 6 and 8 were ineffective (Wittwer and Bukovac, 1962).

Fig. 13-36 | The inhibitory effect of auxin on photoperiodic induction of flowering in a SDP is most pronounced when the auxin is applied to the leaf during the inductive night. *Xanthium* plants given one long night (16 hr) and auxin ($10^{-3}M$ naphthaleneacetic acid) applied at various times during the night or subsequent day. Flower stage determined after 14 days; two experiments (Salisbury, 1955).

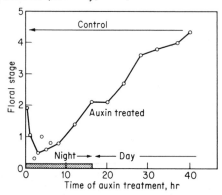

Fig. 13-37 | Auxin promotion of flowering in a LDP. Plants of *Hyoscyamus* were given a short day (8 hr) but with supplementary illumination during the night from 16 to 34 ft-c as indicated, which was close to threshold for flowering. Auxin (IAA) was applied during each night for 25 days (17 for the 34-ft-c treatment), and flowering resulted from the auxin treatments (Liverman and Lang, 1956).

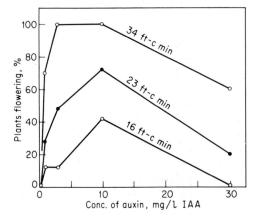

experiments in which the auxin was applied to the leaf of *Xanthium* at various times during the inductive dark period and the subsequent light period. Such experiments revealed that the inhibition was much more pronounced when application was during the dark period (Fig. 13-36). He deduced that auxin interferes with reactions occurring during the dark period (Salisbury and Bonner, 1956). There is an interesting possibility that endogenous auxin may sometimes naturally limit flowering (von Denffer, 1952), and treatments which could lower auxin levels in leaves have sometimes been successfully used to induce flowering in *Perilla* (Lona and Bocchi, 1955).

For many years the promotive effects of auxin were restricted to the effects of inducing flowering in pineapple. Promotions of the development of flowers in the LDP Wintex barley were observed by Leopold and Thimann (1949), and more dramatic effects were achieved by Liverman and Lang (1956) with the LDP *Hyoscyamus niger* (Fig. 13-37). They were actually able to induce flowering by applications of auxin made during the night in conjunction with light exposures weak enough barely to keep the plants below threshold for flowering. Again, the auxin effect is presumed to interfere with night reactions. By making the night less effective it can encourage flowering in the LDP.

If auxins play an important role in the photoperiodic induction of flowering, one would expect to find marked changes in auxin contents with photoperiodic treatments. Attempts to find such changes have given little or no support to the idea that they play such a role (Cooke, 1954; Vlitos and Meudt, 1954; Ogawa, 1962*b*).

One effect of auxins on flowering which has received continuing interest has been the modification of sex expression. Laibach and Kribben (1950) reported that the auxin applications could cause the development of female flowers instead of male flowers in some cucurbitaceous plants. This has provided a tool for some interesting experiments on sex expression in flowering (Heslop-Harrison, 1957; Galun, 1959). The auxin promotions of femaleness are in contrast to the gibberellin promotions of maleness in sex expression (Mitchell and Wittwer, 1962).

Flowering by plant extracts

Since graftage work indicated that there might be a universal flowering hormone among higher plants, many attempts have been made to separate such a material out of induced leaves and other plant parts. There were many early reports of successes, but only recently have successful experiments been repeatable.

The first convincing success with plant extracts was a report by Lang et al. (1957) that extracts of fruits of *Echinocystis* induced flowering in biennial *Hyoscyamus,* undoubtedly because of the gibberellin content of the extracts. Since that time, Harada and Nitsch (1959, 1961) have obtained extracts from cold-requiring plants and LDPs which were inductive of flowering in a manner suggestive of gibberellin, though the material in their extract did not have all the properties of gibberellin itself. Tomita (1959) has also obtained an extract which hastens flowering of small grains in a manner suggestive of a gibberellin.

Several extracts of gibberellinlike substances from SDPs are effective in inducing flowering in SDPs. Such remarkable results by Bünsow et al. (1958) and Ogawa (1960, 1962a; Ogawa and Imamura, 1958) have involved the induction of flowering in *Pharbitis* and in *Bryophyllum,* and an extract of *Xanthium* (Lincoln et al., 1961) has shown some effectiveness in inducing flowering in that species. The latter has not been tested for gibberellinlike activities.

The roles that growth substances may play in the endogenous control of flowering remain to be clarified, but the dramatic effects of gibberellin in inducing or promoting flowering suggest that this group of substances plays important functions. Many of the effective plant extracts which can induce flowering seem to do so on the basis of their gibberellin content or the content of some materials which have at least some similar biological activities. These results suggest that the flowering of cold-requiring plants may be soon clarified, but the controls in LDPs and especially SDPs remain mysterious.

The nature of the flowering stimulus

At present the major facts about the nature of the stimulus are threefold: (1) Graftage experiments and translocation experiments indicate a mobile stimulus supplied by leaves; (2) vernalization experiments indicate a nonmobile stimulus in the meristem; and (3) the various effects of growth substances and extracts suggest multiple components in the stimulus. It seems that there may be more than one stimulatory agent, and there are evidences of inhibitory influences or substances. The multiple requirement of some species for more than one photoperiod experience or for sequential photoperiod and temperature experiences adds further support to the idea of multiple factors controlling flowering.

Considering the change from vegetative growth to flowering as a shift in the phenotypic expression of genetic information, several investigators have attempted experiments which might illuminate the possible transmission of information from DNA to RNA and then to protein synthesis in the flowering processes. Salisbury and Bonner (1960) applied 5-fluorouracil to *Xanthium,* hoping that its actions as an inhibitor of DNA and RNA synthesis would interfere with the shift involved in flower initiation. Inhibitions were obtained whether the fluorouracil was applied to the leaf or to the growing point (Fig. 13-38), and the greatest sensitivity was obtained if the inhibitor was

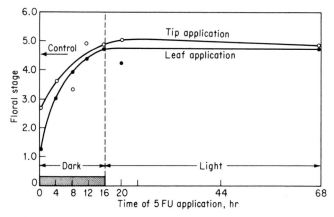

Fig. 13-38 | 5-Fluorouracil was most effective in inhibiting the flowering of *Xanthium* when applied at the beginning of the inductive dark period. Similar inhibitions were obtained whether the inhibitor was applied to the leaf or to the growing point at $2 \times 10^{-3}M$ (Salisbury and Bonner, 1960).

applied just before the inductive dark period. The inhibition was relieved by orotic acid, suggesting that the interference with the nucleic acid metabolism was responsible for the flowering inhibition. The effect seems to be an interference with RNA synthesis at the meristem (Bonner and Zeevaart, 1961) and hence more likely an interference with expression of the stimulus in meristematic growth than an interference with photoperiodic phenomena.

Several researchers have suggested that flower induction might involve an alteration of the RNA (Chajlakjan, 1960; Chajlakjan et al., 1961; Hess, 1961a,b), and although inhibitors of RNA formation or function have been found to inhibit flowering (Hess, 1961a,b; Marushige and Marushige, 1962), no measurable change in the RNA base ratios with flowering has been found (Ross, 1962).

As hormone systems so frequently involve steroids, the possibility that flower induction might involve the formation of a steroid in the induced leaf has been tested by Bonner et al. (1963). A complex fat (SKF 7997) known to inhibit steroid synthesis in animal systems was applied to leaves of *Xanthium* during short-day induction and yielded marked inhibitions of flowering. This effect was specifically located in the leaf, as shown in Fig. 13-39, applications to the stem tip being without apparent effect. The inhibitor was most effective when applied just before the inductive long night and Bonner et al. interpreted this as indicating an inhibition of dark reactions. The inhibition was not reversed by the application of steroids, but the possibility of a steroid hormone is nevertheless attractive.

The necessity for growth as a component of the flowering response is interesting as a concern in interpreting the effects of applied inhibitors on flowering and because the intimate relations of growth activities in the stem, leaf, and bud may be relevant to the flowering stimulus. Thomas (1960, 1961a,b) noted that inductive photoperiods lead to marked increases in the growth rates of leaves, implying that the achievement of the induced state may involve growth stimulations. He also noted that the photoperiodic induction of *Xanthium* was associated with marked increases in the mitotic figures in the apical meristem (Thomas, 1963; Lance, 1957).

Bünning (1952) suggested that one means by which flowering could be controlled within the plant is through a stimulation of leaf growth; this could serve to withhold inhibitors of flowering which leaves may otherwise be supplying. Thus the changes in leaf growth with photoperiodic treatments or with natural aging processes in plants could alter the availability of inhibitors of flowering stemming from the leaf.

The available evidence seems to point to the control of flowering by an array of stimuli and of inhibitors acting together in the plant. The diverse means by which plants become reproductive—through natural aging, through environmental cues, through mobile and nonmobile influences—are certainly consistent with such a concept of interacting flower-controlling agents in the plant.

GENERAL REFERENCES

Hillman, W. S. 1962. *The Physiology of Flowering.* Holt, Rinehart and Winston, Inc., New York. 164 pp.

Murneek, A. E., and R. O. Whyte. 1948. *Vernalization and Photoperiodism.* Chronica Botanica Co., Waltham, Mass. 196 pp.

Salisbury, F. B. 1961. Photoperiodism and the flowering process. *Ann. Rev. Plant Physiol.,* 12:293–326.

———. 1964. *The Flowering Process.* Pergamon Press, Ltd., Oxford. 234 pp.

Went, F. W. 1957. *The Environmental Control of Plant Growth,* especially chaps. 6 to 9. Chronica Botanica Co., Waltham, Mass.

Whyte, R. O. 1946. *Crop Production and Environment.* Faber & Faber, Ltd., London. 372 pp.

Withrow, R. B. (ed.). 1959. *Photoperiodism*

and Related Phenomena in Plants and Animals, especially sec. IV (pp. 245–328) and sec. VI (pp. 411–474). Am. Assoc. Advan. Sci., Washington, D.C. 903 pp.

Zeevaart, J. A. D. 1962. Physiology of flowering. *Science,* 137:723–731.

REFERENCES CITED

Barber, H. N., and D. M. Paton. 1952. A gene-controlled flowering inhibitor in *Pisum. Nature,* 169:592.

Bhargova, S. C. 1963. A transmissible flower bud inhibitor in the short-day plant, *Salvia occidentalis. Koninkl. Ned. Akad. Wetenschap., Proc., Ser. C,* 66:371–376.

Bonner, B. A. 1962. *In vitro* dark conversion and other properties of phytochrome. *Plant Physiol.,* 37:xxvii.

Bonner, J., and R. S. Bandurski. 1952. Studies of the physiology, pharmacology

Fig. 13-39 | An inhibitor of steroid synthesis, SKF 7997, was most effective in inhibiting the flowering of *Xanthium* when applied just before the inductive dark period. Whereas applications to the leaf were highly effective, applications to the growing point were ineffective (Bonner et al., 1963).

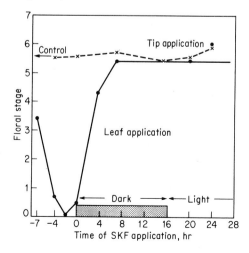

and biochemistry of auxins. *Ann. Rev. Plant. Physiol.*, 3:59–86.

———, E. Heftmann, and J. A. D. Zeevaart. 1963. Suppression of floral induction by inhibition of steroid biosynthesis. *Plant Physiol.*, 38:81–88.

——— and J. A. D. Zeevaart. 1961. Ribonucleic acid synthesis in the bud: an essential component of floral initiation in *Xanthium*. *Plant Physiol.*, 57:43–49.

Boswell, V. R. 1929. Studies of premature flower formation in wintered-over cabbage. *Maryland Agr. Expt. Sta. Bull.*, 313.

Bünning, E. 1952. Über die Ursachen der Blühreife und Blühperiodizität (mit besonderer Berücksichtigung von Beobachtungen in den Tropen). *Z. Botan.*, 40:293–306.

Bünsow, R., J. Penner, and R. Harder. 1958. Blütenbildung bei *Byrophyllum* durch Extrakt aus Bohnensamen. *Naturwissenschaften*, 45:46–47.

Butler, W. I., K. H. Norris, H. W. Siegelman, and S. B. Hendricks. 1959. Detection, assay, and preliminary purification of the pigment controlling photoresponsive development of plants. *Proc. Natl. Acad. Sci. U.S.*, 45:1703–1708.

Burk, L. G., and T. C. Tso. 1958. Effects of gibberellic acid on *Nicotiana* plants. *Nature*, 181:1672–1673.

Calvert, A. 1957. Effect of the early environment on the development of flowering in the tomato. *J. Hort. Sci.*, 32:9–17.

Carr, D. J. 1959. Translocation between leaf and meristem in the flowering response of short day plants. *Proc. Intern. Botan. Congr. 9th*, 2:60–61.

———, and E. K. Ng. 1955. Experimental induction of flower formation in kikuyu grass (*Pennisetum clandestinum* Hochst. Ex Chiov.) *Australian J. Agr. Res.*, 7:1–6.

Cathey, H. M. 1957. Chrysanthemum temperature study. F. The effect of temperature upon the critical photoperiod necessary for the initiation and development of flowers of *Chrysanthemum morifolium*. *Proc. Am. Soc. Hort. Sci.*, 69:485–491.

Chajlakjan, M. Ch. 1936. On the mechanism of the photoperiodic reaction. *Compt. Rend. Acad. URSS*, 10:89–93.

———. 1958. Hormonale Faktoren des Pflanzenbluhens. *Biol. Zentr.*, 77:641–662.

———. 1960. Effect of gibberellins and derivatives of nucleic acid metabolism on plant growth and flowering, pp. 531–542. In R. M. Klein (ed.), *Plant Growth Regulation*. Iowa State University Press, Ames, Iowa.

———, and R. Butenko. 1957. Movement of assimilates of leaves to shoots under differential photoperiodic conditions of leaves. *Compt. Rend. Acad. URSS*, 4:450–462.

———, ———, and I. I. Lyabarskaya. 1961. Effect of derivatives of nucleic acid metabolism on the growth and flowering of *Perilla*. *Fiziol. Rast.*, 8:71–80 (AIBS translation).

Chakravarti, S. C. 1950. Anatomical changes in the embryo of mustard during vernalization. *Current Sci. (India)*, 19:319–320.

———. 1954. Anatomy of roots and shoots of *Brassica campestris* L. in relation to vernalization. *Nature*, 173:407.

Cholodny, N. 1936. On the theory of yarovization. *Compt. Rend. Acad. URSS*, 3:9.

Chouard, P. 1960. Vernalization and its relations to dormancy. *Ann. Rev. Plant Physiol.*, 11:191–238.

Christopher, E. P. 1954. *The Pruning Manual*. The Macmillan Company, New York. 320 pp.

Chroboczek, E. 1934. A study of some ecological factors influencing seed-stalk development in beets. *Cornell Univ. Agr. Expt. Sta. Mem.*, 154:3–84.

Clark, H. E., and K. R. Kerns. 1942. Control of flowering with phytohormones. *Science*, 95:536–537.

Collins, W. T., F. B. Salisbury, and C. W.

Ross. 1963. Growth regulators and flowering. III. Antimetabolites. *Planta,* 60:131–144.

Cooke, A. R. 1954. Changes in free auxin content during the photoinduction of short-day plants. *Plant Physiol.,* 29:440–444.

Cooper, W. C., A. C. Burkett, and A. Hern. 1945. Flowering of Peruvian cube induced by girdling. *Am. J. Botany,* 32:655–657.

Denffer, D. von. 1952. Wuchsstoffinduzierte Hemmung der Blütenbildung durch Gallmilben und Gallinsekten. *Umschau Wiss. Tech.,* 13:1–3.

de Zeeuw, D. 1953. Flower initiation and light intensity in *Perilla. Proc. Roy. Acad. Sci.,* C,56:418–422.

————. 1954. De Invloed Van Het Blad Op De Bloei. *Mededel. Landbouwhogeschool Wageningen,* 54:1–44.

————. 1956. Leaf induced inhibition of flowering in tomato. *Proc. Koninkl. Ned. Akad. Wetenschap.* (*Amsterdam*), 59:535–540.

————. 1957. Flowering of *Xanthium* under long-day conditions. *Nature,* 180:588.

Dostal, R. 1950. Morphogenetic experiments with *Bryophyllum verticillatum. Acta Acad. Sci. Nat. Moravo-Silesiacae,* 22:57–98.

Downs, R. J. 1956. Photoreversibility of flower initiation. *Plant Physiol.,* 31:279–284.

Evans, L. T. 1960a. Inflorescence initiation in *Lolium temulentum* L. I. Effect of plant age and leaf area on sensitivity to photoperiodic induction. *Australian J. Biol. Sci.,* 13:123–131.

————. 1960b. Inflorescence initiation in *Lolium temulentum* L. II. Evidence for inhibitory and promotive photoperiodic processes involving transmissible products. *Australian J. Biol. Sci.,* 13:429–440.

————. 1960c. The influence of temperature on flowering in species of *Lolium* and in *Poa pratensis. J. Agr. Sci.,* 54:410–416.

————. 1960d. The influence of environmental conditions on inflorescence development in some long-day grasses. *New Phytol.,* 59:163–174.

————. 1961. Day-length control of inflorescence initiation in the grass *Rottboellia exaltata* L.f. *Australian J. Biol. Sci.,* 15:291–303.

Ferguson, J. H. A. 1957. Photothermographs: a tool for climate studies in relation to the ecology of vegetable varieties. *Euphytica,* 6:97–105.

Fisher, J. E., and W. E. Loomis. 1954. Auxin-florigen balance in flowering of soybean. *Science,* 119:71–73.

Furr, J. R., and W. W. Armstrong. 1956. Flower induction in marsh grapefruit in the Coachella Valley, California. *Proc. Am. Soc. Hort. Sci.,* 67:176–182.

————, W. C. Cooper, and P. C. Reece. 1947. Flower formation in citrus trees. *Am. J. Botany,* 34:1–8.

Galun, E. 1959. The role of auxins in the sex expression of the cucumber. *Physiol. Plantarum,* 12:48–61.

Garner, W. W., and H. A. Allard. 1920. Effect of length of day on plant growth. *J. Agr. Res.,* 18:553–606.

———— and ————. 1923. Further studies in photoperiodism: the response of the plant to relative length of day and night. *J. Agr. Res.,* 23:871–920.

Gassner, G. 1918. Beiträge zur physiologischer Characteristik Sommer und Winter annueller Gewächse insbesondere der Getriedepflanzen. *Z. Botan.,* 10:417–480.

Gott, M. B., F. G. Gregory, and O. N. Purvis. 1955. Studies in vernalization of cereals. XIII. Photoperiodic control of stages in flowering between initiation and ear formation in vernalized and unvernalized Petkus winter rye. *Ann. Botany* (*London*), 21:87–126.

Gregory, F. G., and R. S. de Ropp. 1938. Vernalization of excised embryos. *Nature,* 142:481–482.

———— and O. N. Purvis. 1937. Devernalization of spring rye by anaerobic conditions and revernalization by low temperatures. *Nature*, 140:547.

—— and ——. 1938. Studies in vernalization of cereals. II. Vernalization of excised mature embryos. *Ann. Botany (London)*, NS 2:237–251.

Guttridge, C. G. 1959. Evidence for a flower inhibitor and vegetative growth promoter in the strawberry. *Ann. Botany (London)*, 23:351–360.

Hamner, K. C. 1940. Interrelation of light and darkness in photoperiodic induction. *Botan. Gaz.*, 101:658–687.

—— and J. Bonner. 1938. Photoperiodism in relation to hormones as factors in floral initiation. *Botan. Gaz.*, 100:388–431.

Hänsel, H. 1953. Vernalization of winter rye by negative temperatures and the influence of vernalization upon the lamina length of the first and second leaf in winter rye, spring barley, and winter barley. *Ann. Botany (London)*, 7:418–431.

Harada, H., and J. P. Nitsch. 1959. Changes in endogenous growth substances during flowering development. *Plant Physiol.*, 34:409–415.

—— and ——. 1961. Isolement et propriétés physiologiques d'une substance de montaison. *Ann. Physiol. Vegetale*, 3:193–208.

Harder, R., and O. Bode. 1943. Wirkung von Zwischenbelichtungen wahrend der Dunkelperiode auf *Kalanchöe. Planta*, 33:469–504.

——, and R. Bünsow. 1956. Einfluss des Gibberellins auf die Blutenbildung bei *Kalanchöe blossfeldiana. Naturwissenschaften*, 23:544.

—— and ——. 1957. Zusammenwirken von Gibberellin mit photoperiodisch bedingten bluhfordernded und bluhhemmenden Vorgagen bei *Kalanchöe blossfeldiana. Naturwissenschaften*, 44:454.

——, G. Gümmer, and E. Gall. 1945.

Über die untere Zeitgrenze der blütenfördernden und blutenhemmenden Lichteinwirkungen bei *Kalanchöe blossfeldiana. Nachr. Akad. Wiss. Goettingen Math. Physik. Kl.*, 48–53.

Harley, C. P., J. R. Magness, M. P. Masure, L. A. Fletcher, and E. S. Degman. 1942. Investigations on the cause and control of biennial bearing of apple trees. *U.S. Dept. Agr. Tech. Bull.*, 792.

Haupt, W. 1955. Die stoffliche Beeinflussung der Blütenbildung bei *Pisum sativum*. II. Die Wirkung der Zuckererernährung. *Ber. Deut. Botan. Ges.*, 3:107–120.

——. 1957. Photoperiodische Reaktion bei einer als tagneutral geltenden Sorte von *Pisum sativum. Ber. Deut. Botan. Ges.*, 70:191–198.

——. 1958. Die Blütenbildung bei *Pisum sativum. Z. Botan.*, 46:242–256.

Heath, O. V. S. 1943. Studies in the physiology of the onion plant. *Ann. Appl. Biol.*, 30:208–220.

Heinze, W. 1959. Über den Einfluss des Blättes auf den Bluhtermin bei der Tomate. *Naturwissenschaften*, 21:609.

Hendricks, S. B., and H. A. Borthwick. 1954. Photoperiodism in plants. *Proc. Intern. Photobiol. Congr. 1st*, 23–35.

——, H. A. Borthwick, and R. J. Downs. 1956. Pigment conversion in the formative responses of plants to radiation. *Proc. Natl. Acad. Sci. U.S.*, 42:19–26.

Heslop-Harrison, J. 1957. The physiology of reproduction in *Dactylorchis*. I. *Botan. Notiser*, 110:28–49.

Hess, D. 1961a. Ribosenucleinsaure und Bluhinduktion. *Planta*, 56:229–232.

——. 1961b. Die Beteiligung spezifischer Ribonucleinsaure und der Bluhinduktion. *Planta*, 57:13–28.

Highkin, H. R. 1956. Vernalization in peas. *Plant Physiol.*, 31:399–403.

Huxley, J. 1949. *Soviet Genetics and World Science: Lysenko and the Meaning of Heredity*. Chatto and Windus, Ltd., London. 245 pp.

Imamura, S. 1953. Photoperiodic initiation

of flower primordia in Japanese morning glory, *Pharbitis nil* Chois. *Proc. Japan Acad.*, 29:368–373.

——— and A. Takimoto. 1955. Transmission rate of photoperiodic stimulus in *Pharbitis nil. Botan. Mag. (Tokyo)*, 68:260–266.

Kimura, K. 1961. Effect of temperature and nutrients on flower initiation of *Raphanus sativus* L. in total darkness. *Botan. Mag. (Tokyo)*, 74:361–368.

Klebs, G. 1918. Über die Blutenbildung von *Sempervivum. Flora (Jena)*, 11:128–151.

Kojima, H., and S. Maeda. 1958. Promotion of flower-initiation by restraining the vegetative growth in the Japanese radish. *Botan. Mag. (Tokyo)*, 71:841–842.

Koller, D., and H. R. Highkin. 1960. Environmental control of reproductive development in *Hordeum bulbosum*, a perennial pasture grass. *Am. J. Botany*, 47:843–847.

Kraus, E. J., and H. R. Kraybill. 1918. Vegetation and reproduction with special reference to the tomato. *Oregon State Coll. Agr. Expt. Sta. Bull.*, 149:1–90.

Krumweide, D. 1960. Über die Wirkung von Stark und Schwachlichtkombinationen auf das Bluhen von *Kalanchöe blossfeldiana. Biol. Zentr.*, 79:258–278.

Lachman, W. H., and E. L. Upham. 1954. Effect of warm storage on the bolting of onions grown from sets: a preliminary report. *Proc. Am. Soc. Hort. Sci.*, 63:342–346.

Laibach, F., and F. J. Kribben. 1950. Einfluss von Wuchsstoff auf die Blutenbildung der Gurke. *Z. Naturforsch.*, 56:160.

Lam, S., and H. B. Cordner. 1955. Flowering hormone in relation to blooming in sweet potatoes. *Science*, 121:140–141.

———, and A. C. Leopold. 1961. Reversion and reinduction of flowering in *Perilla. Am. J. Botany*, 48:306–310.

Lance, A. 1957. Récherches cytologiques sur l'évolution de quelques meristemes apicaux et sur les variations provoquées par les traitements photoperiodiques. *Ann. Sci. Nat. Botan.*, 2:91–400 (cited by Thomas, 1963).

Lane, H. C., H. W. Siegelman, W. L. Butler, and E. L. Firer. 1962. Extraction and assay of phytochrome from green plants. *Plant Physiol.*, 37:xxvii.

Lang, A. 1952. Physiology of flowering. *Ann. Rev. Plant Physiol.*, 3:265–306.

———. 1956. Gibberellin and flower formation. *Naturwissenschaften*, 23:544.

———. 1957. The effect of gibberellin upon flower formation. *Proc. Natl. Acad. Sci. U.S.*, 43:709–717.

———. 1959. The influence of gibberellin and auxin on photoperiodic induction, pp. 329–330. In R. W. Withrow (ed.), *Photoperiodism and Related Phenomena in Plants and Animals*. American Association for the Advancement of Science, Washington, D. C.

———. 1960. Gibberellin-like substances in photoinduced and vegetative *Hyoscyamus* plants. *Planta*, 54:498–504.

——— and G. Melchers. 1943. Die photoperiodische Reaktion von *Hyoscyamus niger. Planta*, 33:653–702.

——— and E. Reinhard. 1961. Gibberellins and flower formation. *Advan. Chem. Ser.*, 28:71–79.

———, J. A. Sandoval, and A. Bedri. 1957. Induction of bolting and flowering in *Hyoscyamus* and *Samolus* by a gibberellin-like material from a seed plant. *Proc. Natl. Acad. Sci. U.S.*, 43:960–964.

Leopold, A. C., and F. S. Guernsey. 1953. Flower initiation in Alaska pea. I. Evidence as to the role of auxin. *Am. J. Botany*, 40:46–50.

———, and S. L. Lam. 1960. A leaf factor influencing tomato earliness. *Proc. Am. Soc. Hort. Sci.*, 76:543–547.

———, and K. V. Thimann. 1949. The effect of auxin on flower initiation. *Am. J. Botany*, 36:342–347.

Lewis, D. 1953. Some factors affecting flower production in the tomato. *J. Hort. Sci.*, 23:207–220.

Lincoln, R. G., D. L. Mayfield, and A. Cunningham. 1961. Preparation of a floral initiating extract from *Xanthium*. *Science*, 133:756.

———, K. A. Raven, and K. C. Hamner. 1956. Factors influencing flowering in *Xanthium*. I. Translocation and inhibition. *Botan. Gaz.*, 117:193–206.

Liverman, J. L. 1955. The physiology of flowering. *Ann. Rev. Plant Physiol.*, 6: 177–210.

——— and A. Lang. 1956. Induction of flowering in long day plants by applied indoleacetic acid. *Plant Physiol.*, 31:147–150.

Lockhart, J. A., and K. C. Hamner. 1954. Partial reactions in the formation of the floral stimulus in *Xanthium*. *Plant Physiol.*, 29:509–513.

Lona, F. 1946. Sui fenomeni di induzione post-effecto e localizzazione fotoperiodica. *Nuova Giorn. Bot. Ital.*, 53:548–575.

———. 1956. Osservazioni orientative circa l'effetto dell'acido gibberellico sullo sviluppo riproduttivo di alcune longidiurne e brevidiurne. *Ateneo Parmense*, 27:867–875.

——— and A. Bocchi. 1955. Riduzione delle esigenze fotoperiodiche in *Perilla ocymoides* Lour. var. *nankinensis* Voss. per Ipoauxinizzazione da Eosina. *Beitr. Biol. Pflanz.*, 31:333–347.

——— and A. Bocchi. 1956. La distensione caulinare nella canapa incrementata dall'acido gibberellico. *Riv. Intern. Agr.*, 7:58–60.

Longman, K. A. 1961. Factors affecting flower initiation in certain conifers. *Proc. Linnean Soc. (London)*, 172:124–127.

——— and P. F. Wareing. 1959. Early induction of flowering in birch seedlings. *Nature*, 184:2037.

Lysenko, T. D. 1928. *Tr. Azerb. Op. Sta.*, 3:168 (cited in Whyte, 1946).

Magness, J. R., L. A. Fletcher, and W. W. Aldrich. 1933a. Time during which fruit-bud formation in apples may be influenced. *Proc. Am. Soc. Hort. Sci.*, 30:313–318.

Marushige, K., and Y. Marushige. 1962. Effects of 8-azaguanine, thiouracil and ethionine on floral initiation and vegetative development in seedlings of *Pharbitis nil* Chois. *Botan. Mag. (Tokyo)*, 75:270–272.

Meijer, G. 1957. The influence of light quality on the flowering response of *Salvia occidentalis. Acta Botan. Neerl.*, 6: 395–406.

Melchers, G. 1937. Die Wirkung von Genen, tiefen Temperaturen und blühenden Propfpartnern auf die Blühreife von *Hyoscyamus niger. Biol. Zentralbl.*, 57: 586–614.

——— and A. Lang. 1941. Weitere Untersuchungen zur Frage der Bluhhormone. *Biol. Zentr.*, 61:16–39.

Michniewicz, M., and A. Lang. 1962. Effect of different gibberellins on elongation and flowering in cold requiring and photoperiodic plants. *Planta*, 58:549–563.

Miller, J. C. 1929. Seedstalk development in cabbage. *Cornell Univ. Agr. Expt. Sta. Bull.*, 488.

Mitchell, W. D., and S. H. Wittwer. 1962. Chemical regulation of flower sex expression and vegetative growth in *Cucumis sativa, Science*, 136:880–881.

Moore, T. C., and E. K. Bonde. 1962. Physiology of flowering in peas. *Plant Physiol.*, 37:149–153.

Moskov, B. S. 1936. Die photoperiodische Reaktion der Blätter und die Moglichkeit einer Ausnutzung derselben bei Pfropfungen. *Bull. Appl. Bot. Gen. Plant Breed.*, 17:25–30.

Nakata, S. 1955. Floral initiation and fruit set in lychee, with special reference to the effect of sodium naphthaleneacetate. *Botan. Gaz.*, 117:126–134.

Nakayama, S. 1958. Studies on the dark process in the photoperiodic response of *Pharbitis* seedlings. *Sci. Rept. Tohoku Univ.*, 24:137–183.

Napp-Zinn, K. 1957. Die Abhangigkeit des Vernalizationeffektes bei *Arabidopsis* von der Vorquellung der Samen sowie von Alter der Pflanzen. *Z. Botan.*, 45:379–394.

———. 1960. Vernalization, Licht und Alter bei *Arabidopsis thaliana* (L.) Heynh. 1. Licht und Dunkelheit wahrend Kalte-und Warmebehandlung. *Planta*, 54: 409–444.

Nasr, T. A. A., and P. F. Wareing. 1961. Studies on flower initiation in black currant. I. *J. Hort. Sci.*, 36:1–10.

Ogawa, Y. 1960. Über die Aulösung der Blütenbildung von *Pharbitis nil* durch niedere Temperatur. *Botan. Mag.* (*Tokyo*), 73:334–335.

———. 1962a. Weitere Untersuchungen über die Wirkung von Gibberellin ahnlichen Substanzen auf die Blutenbildung von *Pharbitis nil*. *Plant Cell Physiol.* (*Tokyo*), 3:5–21.

———. 1962b. Über die photoperiodische Empfindlichkeit der Keimpflanzen von *Pharbitis nil* Chois mit besonderer Berucksichtigung auf den Wuchsstoffgehalt der Kotyledonen. *Botan. Mag.* (*Tokyo*), 75:92–101.

——— and S. Imamura. 1958. Über die ferdernde Wirkung von Samendiffusat auf die Blutenbildung von *Pharbitis nil* Chois. *Proc. Japan Acad.*, 34:631–632.

Paleg, L. G. 1960. Physiological effects of gibberellic acid. II. *Plant Physiol.*, 35: 902–906.

Parker, M. W., and H. A. Borthwick. 1950. Influence of light on plant growth. *Ann. Rev. Plant Physiol.*, 1:43–58.

———, S. B. Hendricks, and H. A. Borthwick. 1950. Action spectrum for the photoperiodic control of floral initiation of the long day plant *Hyoscyamus niger*. *Botan. Gaz.*, 111:242–252.

———, S. B. Hendricks, H. A. Borthwick, and N. J. Scully. 1946. Action spectrum for the photoperiodic control of floral initiation of short day plants. *Botan. Gaz.*, 108:1–26.

Pawar, S. S., and H. C. Thompson. 1950. The effect of age and size of plant at the time of exposure to low temperature on reproductive growth in celery. *Proc. Am. Soc. Hort. Sci.*, 55:367–371.

Purvis, O. N. 1940. Vernalization of fragments of embryo tissue. *Nature*, 145:462.

———. 1948. Studies in vernalization. XI. Effect of date of sowing and excising upon responses. *Ann. Botany* (*London*), 12:183–206.

———. 1960. Effect of gibberellin on the flower initiation and stem extension in Petkus winter rye. *Nature*, 185:479.

——— and F. G. Gregory. 1937. Studies in vernalization of cereals. I. *Ann. Botany* (*London*), 1:569–592.

——— and ———. 1945. Devernalization by high temperature. *Nature*, 155:113.

Radley, M. 1963. Gibberellin content of spinach in relation to photoperiod. *Ann. Botany* (*London*), 27:373–377.

Resende, F. 1952. "Long-short" day plants. *Acta Biol., Portugal*, 3:318–322.

Ross, C. W. 1962. Nucleotide composition of ribonucleic acid from vegetative and flowering cocklebur-shoot tips. *Biochim. Biophys. Acta*, 55:387–388.

Sachs, J. 1860. Physiologische Untersuchungen über die Abhangigkeit der Keimung von der Temperatur. *Jahrb., Wiss. Bot.* 1:49–83 (cited by Went, 1957).

———. 1882. Stoff und Form der Pflanzenorgane. *Arb. Bot. Inst. Würzburg*, 3: 452.

Salisbury, F. B. 1955. The dual role of auxin in flowering. *Plant Physiol.*, 30:327–334.

———. 1957. Growth regulators and flowering. I. Survey methods. *Plant Physiol.*, 32:600–608.

———. 1959a. Growth regulators and flowering. II. The cobaltous ion. *Plant Physiol.*, 34:598–604.

———. 1959b. Influence of certain growth regulators on flowering of the cocklebur. pp. 381–392, in R. B. Withrow (ed.),

Photoperiodism and related phenomena in plants and animals. Am. Assoc. Advan. Sci., Washington, D.C.

————. 1963. Biological timing and hormone synthesis in flowering of *Xanthium*. *Planta*, 59:518–534.

———— and J. Bonner. 1956. The reactions of the photoinductive dark period. *Plant Physiol.*, 31:141–147.

———— and ————. 1960. Inhibition of photoperiodic induction by 5-fluorouracil. *Plant Physiol.*, 35:173–177.

Schwabe, W. W. 1954a. Factors controlling flowering in the chrysanthemum. IV. The site of vernalization and translocation of the stimulus. *J. Exptl. Botany*, 5:389–400.

————. 1954b. Factors controlling flowering of the chrysanthemum. V. Devernalization in relation to high temperature and low light intensity treatments. *J. Exptl. Botany*, 6:435–450.

————. 1959. Studies of long-day inhibition in short-day plants. *J. Exptl. Botany*, 10:317–329.

Shigeura, G. 1948. *Ann. Rept. Director Hawaii Agr. Expt. Sta.*, 138.

Siegelman, H. W., E. M. Firer, W. L. Butler, and S. B. Hendricks. 1962. Phytochrome from corn and barley seedlings. *Plant Physiol.*, 37:xxvii.

Steinberg, R. A. 1952. Premature blossoming: effects of vernalization, seedling age and environment on subsequent growth and flowering of transplanted tobacco. *Plant Physiol.*, 27:745–753.

Stokes, P. 1952a. A physiological study of embryo development in *Heracleum sphondylium* L. I. *Ann. Botany (London)*, 16:442–447.

————. 1952b. A physiological study of embryo development in *Heracleum sphondylium* L. II. *Ann. Botany (London)*, 16:571–576.

Stout, M. 1945. Translocation of the reproductive stimulus in sugar beets. *Botan. Gaz.*, 107:86–95.

Takimoto, A. 1960. Effect of sucrose on flower initiation of *Pharbitis*. *Plant Cell Physiol. (Tokyo)*, 1:241–246.

Teubner, F. G., and S. H. Wittwer. 1955. Effect of n-m-tolylphthalamic acid on tomato flower formation. *Science*, 122:74–75.

Thomas, R. G. 1960. Promotion of leaf growth by short days in *Chenopodium amaranticolor*. *Nature*, 186:1109.

————. 1961a. Correlations between growth and flowering in *Chenopodium*. I. Leaf and bud primordia. *Ann. Botany (London)*, 25:138–151.

————. 1961b. The relationship between leaf growth and induction of flowering in long-day plants. *Naturwissenschaften*, 4:108.

————. 1963. Floral induction and the stimulation of cell division in *Xanthium*. *Science*, 140:54–56.

Thompson, H. C. 1929. Premature seeding of celery. *Cornell Univ. Agr. Expt. Sta. Bull.*, 480.

Thompson, P. A., and C. G. Guttridge. 1960. The role of leaves as inhibitors of flower induction in strawberry. *Ann. Botany (London)*, 24:482–490.

Thurlow, J., and J. Bonner. 1947. Inhibition of photoperiodic induction in *Xanthium*. *Am. J. Botany*, 34:603–604.

Tomita, T. 1959. The fractions of diffusate obtained from vernalized winter rye and their effect on flowering of annual meadow grass. *Tohoku J. Agr. Res.*, 10:1–6.

Vlitos, A. J., and W. Meudt. 1954. The role of auxin in plant flowering. II. Methods for the extraction and quantitative chemical determination of free indoleacetic acid and other indole compounds from plant tissues. *Contrib. Boyce Thompson Inst.*, 17:401–411.

Weibel, R. O. 1960. Effect of gibberellin on the vernalization period of winter wheat. *Agron. J.*, 52:122–123.

Wellensiek, S. J. 1958. Vernalization and age in *Lunaria*. *Proc. Koninkl. Ned. Akad. Wetenschap.*, C,61:561–571.

————. 1959. The inhibitory action of light on the floral induction of *Perilla*. *Proc. Koninkl. Ned. Akad. Wetenschap.*, C,62: 195–203.

————. 1960. Flower formation in *Campanula medium*. *Mededel. Landbouwhogeschool Wageningen*, 60:1–18.

————. 1961. Theoretical backgrounds of flowering. *Advan. Hort. Sci.*, 1:35–41.

————. 1962. The control of flowering. *Netherlands J. Agr. Sci.*, 10:390–398.

————, J. Doorenbos, and D. de Zeeuw. 1954. The mechanism of photoperiodism. *Proc. Intern. Botan. Congr. 8th*, 12:307–315.

———— and F. A. Hakkaart. 1955. Vernalization and age. *Proc. Koninkl. Ned. Akad. Wetenschap.*, 58:16–21.

Went, F. W. 1957. *Environmental Control of Plant Growth*. Chronica Botanica Co., Waltham, Mass. 343 pp.

Whyte, R. O. 1946. *Crop Production and Environment*. Faber & Faber, Ltd., London. 372 pp.

Wittwer, S. H., and M. B. Bukovac. 1957. Gibberellins: new chemicals for crop production. *Mich. State Univ. Agr. Expt. Sta. Quart. Bull.*, 39:469–494.

———— and ————. 1957. Gibberellin and higher plants. III. Induction of flowering in long-day annuals grown under short days. *Mich. State Univ. Agr. Expt. Sta. Quart. Bull.*, 39:661–672.

———— and ————. 1962. Exogenous plant growth substances effecting floral initiation and fruit set. *Proc. Plant Sci. Symp. on Fruit Set*, pp. 65–93. Campbell Soup Co., Camden, N.J.

Zeevaart, J. A. D. 1957a. Studies on flowering by means of grafting. I. Photoperiodic induction as an irreversible phenomenon in *Perilla*. *Proc. Koninkl. Ned. Akad. Wetenschap.*, 60:324–331.

————. 1957b. Studies on flowering by means of grafting. II. Photoperiodic treatment of detached *Perilla* and *Xanthium* leaves. *Proc. Koninkl. Ned. Akad. Wetenschap.*, 60:332–337.

————. 1957c. Studies on flowering by means of grafting. IV. Flowering of two long-day *Sedum* species in short day on induced *Kalanchöe* stocks. *Proc. Koninkl. Ned. Akad. Wetenschap.*, 60:630–639.

————. 1958. Flower formation as studied by grafting. *Mededel. Landbouwhogeschool Wageningen*, 58:1–88.

————. 1962. Physiology of flowering. *Science*, 137:723–731.

14 | Flower physiology

Relatively little is known about the growth and functioning of the flower per se, and any discussion of its physiology will necessarily be sketchy and incomplete.

Growth of the flower

An appurtenance to flower growth is the development of the pedicel. It is apparently dominated by stimuli produced in the developing flower bud, for the pedicel growth rate appears to reflect the production of growth substances within the bud (Katunsky, 1936). Kaldewey (1957) and Zinsmeister (1960) have plotted the growth rates of the pedicels of *Fritillaria* and *Cyclamen*, and sample data in Fig. 14-1 show a double growth peak. Most rapid growth occurs just before flower opening; there is a drop in growth during bloom and another peak just after fruit set. They found that each of the two growth peaks was associated with peaks of auxin production by the flower and that the depressed growth period in *Fritillaria* was associated with the production of an inhibitor as well. The stamens appear to be the source of the inhibitor, which has a pronounced effect on the development of a hook in the pedicel during the period of bloom.

Within the flower, there are distinctive effects of several floral parts on the growth of the whole flower. Marré (1946) observed that the removal of stamens from young, developing flowers of several genera resulted in a striking decline in the mobilization of starches into the developing flower and a cessation of mitotic activity in the developing ovary. Kaldewey's work (1957) implicated the stamens in the production of the inhibitor which was involved in the bending of the pedicel during bloom. The ovary, too, plays a critical role in flower development and is a rich source of auxin (Katunsky, 1936; Wittwer, 1943). Ovary removal during development ordinarily leads to floral abscission. Laibach and Troll

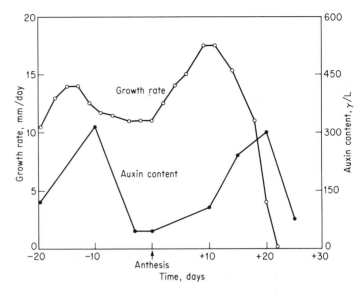

Fig. 14-1 | The growth rate of the *Fritillaria* pedicel peaks before anthesis, declines as the flower opens, and rises again when fruit growth proceeds. The diffusible auxin content also shows a two-peaked curve, but it is not entirely coincident with the growth peaks (Kaldewey, 1957).

(1955) find that in *Coleus,* this abscission-preventing action is limited to the stigma of the ovary. In their experiments removal of the stigma led to prompt flower abscission, and neither auxin nor pollen applications were effective in replacing the stigma in this prevention of abscission. More often, however, it has been found that auxin applications to flowers would retard their abscission (Fitting, 1909; Roberts and Struckmeyer, 1944).

Flower movements

Flowers are capable of several different types of movements, some turning toward the sun (e.g., *Helianthus*) and some being elevated during the day and drooping during the night or opening and closing in a diurnal fashion.

Illustrating the sun movement, Shibaoka and Yamaki (1959) have performed experiments on the east-west movements of *Helianthus* and describe this as a growth phenomenon of the stem. It appears from their experiments that the growth differential is regulated by the auxin content of the sides of the stem toward or away from the sun. There is a diurnal periodicity involved, however, for removal of the plants to continuous darkness does not terminate the east-west movements for several days.

Movement in an up-and-down direction is common to many flowers and is a function of the growth of the pedicel. In *Kalanchoe* (Bünsow, 1953*a,b*) the movement is repeated daily during the period of anthesis. Like the east-west movement, the elevation of the flower is a diurnal periodicity, for placing the plant in continuous darkness does not terminate the movement for several days (Fig. 14-2). The experiments of Kaldewey (1957) with *Fritillaria* indicate that

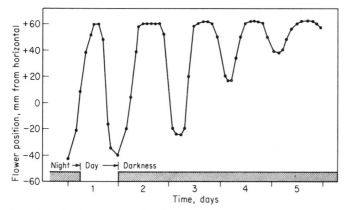

Fig. 14-2 | Flowers of *Kalanchoe* have a diurnal pattern of movement, being elevated in daytime and drooping at night. Endogenous rhythms are evidenced by the continuing diurnal movements even after the plant has been placed in continuous darkness (Bünsow, 1953*b*).

the raising of the flower is regulated by auxin and inhibitor contents of the pedicel.

Another movement of flowers is the opening and closing of the corolla. In some species this movement is repeated daily with usually an opening of the flower in the day and closure at night (Bünsow, 1953*a,b*). The night jasmine (*Cestrum nocturnum*) shows the reverse cycle of opening at night and closing during the day (Fig.

14-3) and also has a parallel diurnal cycle of fragrance emission and nectar secretion (Overland, 1960).

Flower closure commonly takes place after pollination. In *Portulaca* the closing movement occurs 4 hr after pollination, as the pollination timing experiments of Iwanami and Hoshino (1963; Fig. 14-4) show. Here the closure appears to be controlled by the stigma, for its removal causes closure

Fig. 14-3 | The diurnal cycle of flower opening and closure of *Cestrum nocturnum* may continue even when the flowers are placed in continuous darkness (Overland, 1960).

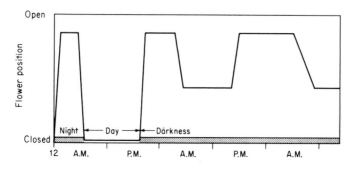

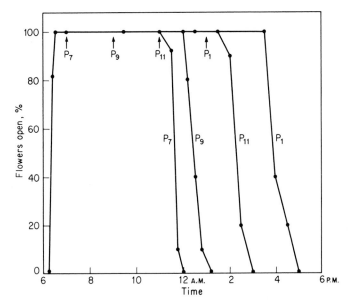

Fig. 14-4 | The closure of flowers of *Portulaca grandiflora* occurs about 4 hr after pollination. For example, pollination at 7 A.M. (P₇), just after the flower has opened, results in closure between 11 and 12 A.M. Pollination at 1 P.M. (P₁) results in closure between 4 and 5 P.M. (Iwanami and Hoshino, 1963).

at any time. Many species respond to pollination by wilting of the corolla rather than closure (e.g., Hsiang, 1951).

A curious type of movement in flowers has been reported for the stamens of *Portulaca grandiflora* (Iwanami, 1960). An insect visiting the flower causes the stamens to bend, and a reflex movement sets in bending the stamen toward the body of the insect. This thigmotropic response is completed in 5 or 10 sec (Fig. 14-5).

Growth substances in flowers

The production of relatively large amounts of auxin by the flower bud has been mentioned. In addition to large amounts of auxin produced in the ovary and in the pollen, there is evidence that a substantial amount of auxin is produced in the petals of some

flowers during the limited period of flower opening (Takeyosi and Fujii, 1961). It appears that auxin produced in flower parts may prevent abscission of the flower.

Auxin can also have a strong influence on developmental activities taking place in the flower. A dramatic stimulating effect of auxin on the development of the orchid embryo sac has been described by Heslop-Harrison (1957). He found that auxin introduced to the orchid ovary by pollination triggered the entire development of the embryo sac (Fig. 14-6). Until the flower is pollinated or supplied with an external source of auxin, the orchid embryo sac does not develop beyond the single-cell stage.

The stimulating effects of gibberellins on flower development have been described by Wittwer and Bukovac (1957) and Chajlakjan (1958). Vasil (1957) has demonstrated that auxins, gibberellins, and kinins

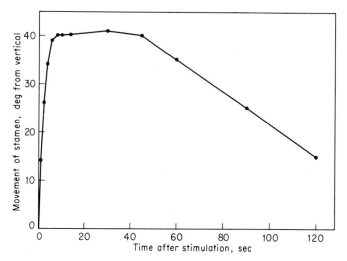

Fig. 14-5 | Stamens of *Portulaca grandiflora* flowers show a thigmotropic response to touch, serving to bend the anthers toward a visiting insect. Bending the stamen with a needle results in a tropistic bending of 40° in about 5 sec, followed by slower recovery (Iwanami, 1960).

Fig. 14-6 | In the orchid, *Dactylorchis*, the embryo sac is quite undeveloped at the time of anthesis (above), and either pollination or auxin application (5,000 parts per million NAA in lanolin) can stimulate the ontogeny of the complete structure (Heslop-Harrison, 1957).

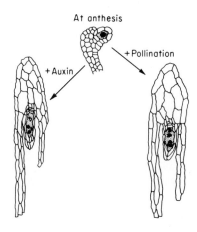

are all needed for the maturation of the anther sacs of onion flowers. Neither kinins nor gibberellins have been detected in flowers, but the effects of the exogenous substances suggest that they may be involved in normal flower development.

Pollen physiology

The understanding of the germination of pollen and the growth of the pollen tube has stemmed more from the work of geneticists than of plant physiologists. Pollen function is so often a limitation to genetic research that it is not surprising that plant breeders have made such a contribution to this aspect of physiology.

Flowers show diverse adaptations to facilitate the spread of pollen by wind, birds, or insects. With evolutionary specialization, there has been a tendency toward the development of increasingly limited means of pollen dispersal, including more limited types of insects which can successfully carry the pollen of a given species, and there are even limitations of the time of day when the flower is open and receptive to visiting insects. With increasing specialization there has evolved an increased specialization in pollen morphology and in the requirements for successful germination and growth of pollen and pollen tubes.

Two morphological types can be recognized among angiosperm pollens: a binucleate type with relatively simple requirements for germination and growth, and a trinucleate type with apparently much more complicated requirements (Brewbaker, 1959). These are represented diagrammatically in Fig. 14-7.

Binucleate pollen is characteristic of many relatively primitive orders such as the Magnoliales, Ranales, and Liliales and of the common tree families including the Juglandaceae, Betulaceae, Fagaceae, and Urticaceae. Some relatively advanced taxa have this pollen type, including the Leguminosae. These pollens experience one mitosis after the microspore stage, having then a loose vegetative nucleus which gradually degenerates and a generative nucleus surrounded by a distinct unit of cytoplasm complete with mitochondria. It is in fact a cell within a cell. This generative cell advances behind the tip of the pollen tube as the germination and growth proceed, and several hours after germination a second division takes place, at which time the nuclei are ready to fertilize the embryo sac.

Trinucleate pollen is characteristic of many of the more advanced orders and families, including the Gramineae and Juncaceae, the Compositae, and the Rubiales, Caryophyllales, and Polygonales. These pollens experience two mitoses after the microspore stage, having at the time the pollen is shed a vegetative nucleus and two generative nuclei, the latter being each complete with associated cytoplasm and mitochondria. These pollens are rarely capable of germination on artificial media and hence are difficult to study. Apparently they have some very specialized requirements for germination and growth, and little is known of their physiology. Brewbaker (1959) cites these trinucleate pollens as the ultimate in gametophytic reduction, completing the last gametic mitosis even before the pollen is shed from the parent plant.

As the pollen germinates and the tube grows out, active protoplasmic streaming is evidenced in the most terminal parts of the tube, where the growth activity occurs, and following behind is a region of the tube characterized by dense clusters of starch grains. As the pollen tube continues to grow, these starch reserves become visibly diminished (Iwanami, 1957). Growth is achieved by cell-wall formation at the tip of the pollen tube.

The nutritive requirements for binucleate types of pollen are simple (Brink, 1924). This heterotrophic organism can be readily

Fig. 14-7 | Mitosis in the microspore can produce binucleate pollen (above) which then completes its last mitosis after germination, or trinucleate pollen (below) in which the last mitosis has been completed before pollen germination. Vegetative nuclei are labeled V; generative nuclei unlabeled (adapted from Brewbaker, 1959).

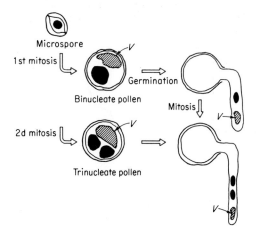

Microspore

1st mitosis

Germination

Binucleate pollen

Mitosis

2d mitosis

Trinucleate pollen

Fig. 14-8 | The beneficial effects of sucrose in the germination medium for *Cucumis melo* pollen are evident both in the improved percentage germination and in the growth of the pollen tube. Addition of borate makes the sucrose effect more extensive. Germination for 4 hr at 36°C (Vasil, 1960).

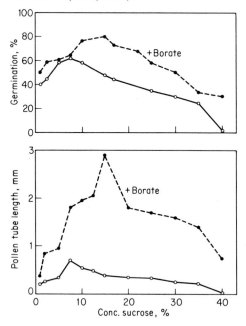

Fig. 14-9 | The beneficial effects of borate on the germination of Clapps Favorite pear pollen extend over a wide range of concentrations. Pollen on 10 per cent sucrose agar (Visser, 1955a).

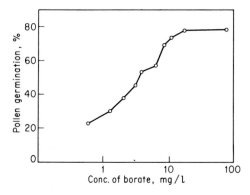

germinated and grown on agar or in water, with surprisingly high concentrations of sucrose (5 to 30 per cent). The supplied sugar maintains an osmotic equilibrium in the pollen tube, without which the cells become inflated and burst (Fig. 14-8); the sugar in many instances also serves as a nutritive substrate for the metabolism of the cell (O'Kelley, 1955; Hellmers and Machlis, 1956; but cf. Visser, 1955a). Profound benefits of added boron were first reported by Schmucker (1933), and some representative data for the growth responses of pollen tubes to boron concentrations are shown in Figs. 14-8 and 14-9 (Visser, 1955a). Boron also suppresses the bursting tendencies of pollen and pollen tubes and may influence the availability of carbohydrates for metabolism (Visser, 1955a; O'Kelley, 1955). The beneficial effects of boron are often markedly greater at elevated temperatures, as shown by Visser (1955a) in Fig. 14-10.

Like root growth, the growth of pollen tubes is highly stimulated by calcium (Mascarenhas and Machlis, 1962; Brewbaker and Kwack, 1963). The suggestion has been made by Mascarenhas and Machlis (1962) that the calcium concentrations in the ovary may provide the chemotropic stimulus to guide the growing pollen tube into the ovule.

Growth of pollen tubes is usually not materially promoted by growth substances such as auxins or gibberellins (Addicott, 1943; Vasil, 1960). This property, too, they share with roots.

There is a great deal of evidence that natural growth substances control the growth of pollen tubes. These natural growth substances include both promotive and inhibitory types. Molisch (1893) first provided experimental evidence for pollen-tube growth promoters, suggesting that such materials direct the progress of the tube to the ovule by a chemotropism. Evidence for the existence of such growth promoters has been developed by numerous workers

(Brink, 1924; Tsao, 1949; Iwanami, 1957; Rosen, 1961; Mascarenhas and Machlis, 1962), but there is considerable disagreement about the properties of such promoters. For example, there is evidence for heat-stable promoters in some cases (Iwanami, 1959; Tsao, 1949) and heat-labile ones in others (Rosen, 1961), dialyzable promoters in some (Rosen, 1961; Mascarenhas and Machlis, 1962) and nondialyzable ones in others (Tsao, 1949; Mascarenhas and Machlis, 1962), and ether-soluble promoters (Miki, 1961) and ether-insoluble promoters (Brewbaker and Majumder, 1961). Experimentally, the presence of such growth substances is shown by the tendency of pollen tubes to grow with greater or lesser rapidity on nutrient agar in the presence of style tissue or style extract. Sample evidence of a promoter and an inhibitor diffusing from slices of styles is shown in Fig. 14-11 (Iwanami, 1959). It might logically be expected that pollen-tube growth promoters may be involved in the chemotropic direction of the tube into the ovule and that growth inhibitors may be involved in incompatibility reactions between pollen and styles or stigmas.

Growth-promoting substances may be present in the pollen itself and may help to account for the common beneficial effects of abundant pollination as contrasted with pollination of a style by only a few pollen grains. This population effect was first recognized by Brink (1924) and has been quantitatively described by Brewbaker and Majumder (1961). Placing pollen at different densities on a nutritive agar, they observed increasing percentages of pollen germination with increasing densities of pollen. That this effect is due to the abundance of a germination promoter in the pollen is evident from the fact that the addition of a water extract of pollen results in maximal germination at every pollen density (Fig. 14-12).

The stigmas may provide substances of a beneficial nature, including secretions which may promote germination of the pol-

Fig. 14-10 | Temperature limitations of pollen germination are alleviated by borate, especially in the higher temperature ranges. As in Fig. 14-9, with 20 mg/liter borate (Visser, 1955*a*).

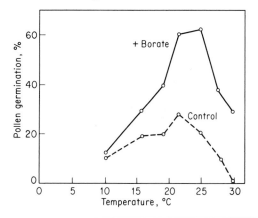

Fig. 14-11 | Diffusible substances from stigma slices can exert inhibitory (above) or promotive (below) effects on the growth of pollen tubes. Growth of *Portulaca* pollen is recorded at various distances on the sucrose agar medium from stigma slices of *Impatiens* or *Lilium* (Iwanami, 1959).

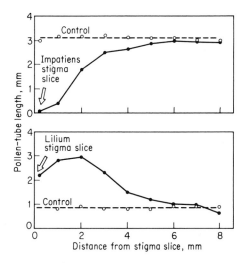

len or limit the tendency of pollen to become inflated and burst. These may be actual droplets of liquid which are secreted by the stigma upon maturation, as in the Liliaceae and Solanaceae, or when the pollen lands, as in the case of grasses (Watanabe, 1955, 1961), or which are released by rupture of a covering stigmatic film when disturbed by a visiting insect, as in the case of many legumes (Jost, 1907; Elliott, 1958).

Outcrossing mechanisms

The principal benefits provided by sexual reproduction are the opportunity for crossing of separate genomes and the consequent effects on vigor and genetic stability. For these benefits to be realized in plants, the ovary must be fertilized with pollen from other plants. The near proximity of pollen from the same flower will give self-pollination much the higher probability unless there are special mechanisms to ensure outcrossing. The mechanisms may be *positional,* as in the case of monoecious plants, which have male and female floral parts on separate plants, or as in the case of dioecious plants, which have the sexes separated into different flowers or separated by the more subtle devices of heteromorphic variabilities in relative lengths of styles and anther filaments. Another common mechanism involves a differential time of ripening of pollen and of style. Any of these positional or timing modifications can encourage the outcrossing habit. Another set of outcrossing mechanisms involves *incompatibility reactions* between the pollen or pollen tube and one of the ovary parts: stigma, style, or ovule. These incompatibility mechanisms can suppress or prevent the effectiveness of pollen in the ovaries of the same plant.

Experiments on the nature of self-incompatibility indicate that in each case the ovary imposes inhibitory actions upon the effectiveness of the pollen—through suppression of pollen germination, inhibition of pollen-tube growth, or limitation of the fertilization of the ovule itself. Lewis (1949) estimates that 40 per cent of angiosperm species have self-incompatibility mechanisms.

Self-incompatibility by the prevention of pollen germination on the stigma is most characteristic of the trinucleate pollen bearers. Some scattered instances of incompatibility due to failure of successful entry of the tube into the micropyle and fertilization of the ovule are known (e.g., Smith and Clarkson, 1956), but most attention has been given to cases of incompatibility by inhibition of pollen-tube growth in the style. This inhibition is commonly a relative slowing of the selfing pollen tubes in comparison with the crossing tubes. Emerson (1940) first described this differential slowing of the selfing tubes, and representative data are given in Fig. 14-13. A clever extension of this type of experiment

Fig. 14-12 | The germination of *Petunia* pollen is much improved by higher densities of pollen. A water extract of pollen can provide maximal pollen germination at any of the tested pollen densities. On 10 per cent sucrose agar with 100 parts per million borate (Brewbaker and Majumder, 1961).

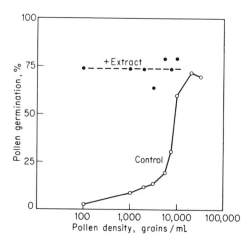

was made by Straub (1946), who pollinated excised stylar tips of *Petunia* and allowed the pollen tubes to grow through the sections and out the severed end into a nutrient agar, where they could be observed. Selfing pollen showed a markedly slower growth rate after passing through the styles, in contrast to crossing pollen.

Even moderate differences in growth rate of selfing and crossing pollen will enormously increase the probability of outcrossing. Bateman (1956) showed that a slightly slower tube growth rate by self pollen can result in over 90 per cent cross-fertilizations of the ovules when mixtures of self and crossing pollen are applied to *Cheiranthus* stigmas.

The mechanism of the retardation of pollen-tube growth may be through the formation of inhibitors of the tube growth by the ovary (Straub, 1947) or through the inhibition by immunological reactions of the tube to the stylar tissue (East, 1929; Lewis, 1952). Brewbaker and Majumder (1961) have also suggested that incompatibility may be due to the limitations of production of a factor necessary for tube growth, having shown the presence of such promotive materials in styles exposed to compatible crosses.

Genetic incompatibility in some species such as *Oenothera* and *Petunia* has been shown to be under the control of multiple alternative alleles, of which two will be present in the diploid stylar tissue and one in the haploid pollen tube. If the latter is identical with either of the stylar alleles, incompatibility will result (Emerson, 1940). Within the species of *Oenothera organensis*, 45 compatibility alleles have been identified. In that species, then, any given individual will be incompatible to itself and to only 1 of 45 other possible genetic combinations within the species (Emerson, 1940).

In the event that crossing fails, there may be real benefits to the plant in settling for self-pollination. Kerner (1895) has described numerous mechanisms by which

selfing may be achieved by flowers in which crossing has failed. Among them are devices which bring the stigma to the anther of the same flower or, conversely, the anther to the stigma. Species of *Epilobium* show continued growth of the style as the flower ages, and if crossing has not been achieved the curving growth of the style contacts the neighboring anther, and the flower is selfed. In *Digitalis* the old corolla is abscised with its attached anthers, and as it falls from the flower the anthers sweep over the stigma, and selfing results (Meeuse, 1961). In *Portulaca* the anthers grow gradually closer to the stigma as the flower ages, and if insect pollination has not been achieved by the end of the flower's life, the anthers actually touch the stigma, and selfing results (Iwanami and Hoshino, 1963). The slower growth of selfing pollen through the style (Bateman, 1956) and the increasing compatibility with selfing pollen as a flower ages (El Murabaa, 1957) offer other

Fig. 14-13 | When *Oenothera organensis* pollinations are made in incompatible crosses, the pollen-tube growth rate is relatively small, as indicated by the high frequency of short pollen tubes in the styles compared with pollen tubes in compatible styles. A summary of 2,500 measurements, 3 to 10 hr after pollination (Emerson, 1940).

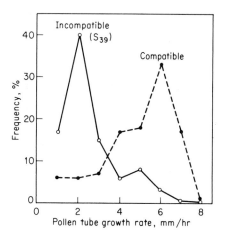

fail-safe devices for achieving self-fertilization if crossing pollen does not reach the ovule.

In some species selfing is entirely the rule; the best-known example of this "cleistogamous" type of flower is the violet, in which the pollen germinates while still in the anthers, growing through the anther wall to reach the style.

GENERAL REFERENCES

Brewbaker, J. L. 1959. Biology of the angiosperm pollen grain. *Indian J. Gen. Plant Breeding,* 19:121–133.

Johri, B. M., and I. K. Vasil. 1961. Physiology of pollen. *Botan. Rev.,* 27:325–381.

Lewis, D. 1949. Incompatibility in flowering plants. *Biol. Rev. Cambridge Phil. Soc.,* 24:472–496.

Meeuse, B. J. D. 1961. *The Story of Pollination.* The Ronald Press Company, New York. 243 pp.

REFERENCES CITED

Addicott, F. T. 1943. Pollen germination and tube growth as influenced by pure growth substances. *Plant Physiol.,* 18: 270–279.

Bateman, A. J. 1956. Cryptic self incompatibility in the wallflower, *Chieranthus. Heredity,* 10:257–261.

Brewbaker, J. L. 1959. Biology of the angiosperm pollen grain. *Indian J. Gen. Plant Breeding,* 19:121–133.

——— and B. H. Kwack. 1963. The essential role of calcium ion in pollen germination and tube growth. *Am. J. Botany,* 50: 859–865.

——— and S. K. Majumder. 1961. Cultural studies of the pollen population effect. *Am. J. Botany,* 48:457–464.

Brink, R. A. 1924. The physiology of pollen. *Am. J. Botany,* 11:417–436.

Bünsow, R. 1953a. Über tages und jahres-rhythmische Änderungen der photoperiodischen Lichtempfindlichkeit bei *Kalanchöe blossfeldiana* und ihre Beziehungen sur endogenen Tagesrhythmik. *Z. Botan.,* 41:257–276.

———. 1953b. Über den Einfluss der Lichtmenge auf die endogene Tagesrhythmik bei *Kalanchöe blossfeldiana. Biol. Zentr.,* 72:465–477.

Chajlakjan, M. Ch. 1958. Hormonale Faktoren des Pflanzenbluhens. *Biol. Zentr.,* 77:641–662.

East, E. M. 1929. Self-sterility. *Bibliog. Genetics,* 5:331.

Elliott, F. C. 1958. *Plant Breeding and Cytogenetics.* McGraw-Hill Book Company, New York. 395 pp.

El Murabaa, A. I. M. 1957. Factors affecting seed set in Brussels sprouts, radish and cyclamen. *Mededel. Landbouwhogeschool Wageningen,* 57:1–33.

Emerson, S. H. 1940. Growth of incompatible pollen tubes in *Oenothera. Botan. Gaz.,* 101:890–911.

Fitting, H. 1909. Die Beeinflussung der Orchideenbluten durch die Bestaubung und durch andere Umstande. *Z. Botan.,* 1:1–86.

Hellmers, H., and L. Machlis. 1956. Exogenous substrate utilization and fermentation by the pollen of *Pinus ponderosa. Plant Physiol.,* 31:284–289.

Heslop-Harrison, J. 1957. The physiology of reproduction in *Dactylorchis.* I. *Botan. Notiser,* 110:28–49.

Hsiang, T.T. 1951. Physiological and biochemical changes accompanying pollination in orchid flowers. I. General observations and water relations. *Plant Physiol.,* 26:441–455.

Iwanami, Y. 1957. Physiological researches of pollen. XIII. Growth inhibition of the pollen tube of *Camellia japonica. Botan. Mag. (Tokyo),* 70:144–149.

———. 1959. Physiological studies of pollen. *J. Yokohama Municipal Univ.,* 116:1–137.

———. 1960. On the movement of the

stamen of *Portulaca grandiflora. J. Yokohama Municipal Univ.*, 121:1–25.

———— and I. Hoshino. 1963. The opening and closing movement of the flower of *Portulaca. Botan. Mag. (Tokyo)*, 76:108–114.

Jost, L. 1907. Über die Selbsterilität einiger Blüten. *Bot. Zeitg.*, 65:77–117.

Kaldewey, H. 1957. Wachstumsverlauf, Wuchsstoffbildung und Nutationsbewegungen von *Fritillaria meleagris* L. im Laufe der Vegetationsperiode. *Planta*, 49:300–344.

Katunsky, V. M. 1936. On the causes of pre- and post-floral movements of peduncles and scapes. *Compt. Rend. Acad. Sci. USSR*, 12:343–456.

Kerner, A. 1895. *The Natural History of Plants* (tr. by F. W. Oliver). Henry Holt and Company, Inc., New York (cited by Meeuse, 1961).

Laibach, F., and W. Troll. 1955. Über die Ursachen des vorzeitigen Abwurfes von Blutenteilen bei *Coleus. Beitr. Biol. Pflanz.*, 31:15–26.

Lewis, D. 1949. Incompatibility in flowering plants. *Biol. Rev.*, 24:472–496.

————. 1952. Serological reactions of pollen incompatibility substance. *Proc. Roy. Soc. (London)*, B,140:127–135.

Marré, E. 1946. Histophysiological aspects of the action of the stamen on the pistil. *Boll. Soc. Ital. Biol. Sper.*, 22:1208–1209.

Mascarenhas, J. P., and L. Machlis. 1962. The pollen tube chemotropic factor from *Antirrhinum. Am. J. Botany*, 49:482–489.

Meeuse, B. J. D. 1961. *The Story of Pollination.* The Ronald Press Company, New York. 243 pp.

Miki, M. 1961. Pollen germination and pollen tube growth in the presence of pistil slices *in vitro. Mem. Coll. Sci. Univ. Kyoto. Ser. B*, 28:375–388.

Molisch, H. 1893. Zur Physiologie des Pollens mit besonderer Rücksicht auf die chemotropische Bewegungen der Pollenschläuche. *Sitzber. Wien Akad. Wiss. Math. Naturw. Kl.*, 102:423–448.

O'Kelley, J. C. 1955. External carbohydrates in growth and respiration of pollen tubes. *Am. J. Botany*, 42:322–327.

Overland, L. 1960. Endogenous rhythm in opening and odor of flowers of *Cestrum nocturnum. Am. J. Botany*, 47:378–382.

Roberts, R. H., and B. E. Struckmeyer. 1944. Use of sprays to set greenhouse tomatoes. *Proc. Am. Soc. Hort. Sci.*, 44:417–427.

Rosen, W. G. 1961. Studies on pollen tube chemotropism. *Am. J. Botany*, 48:889–895.

Schmucker, T. 1933. Zur Blutenbiologie tropischer *Nymphea arten.* II. Bor als entscheidener Faktor. *Planta*, 18:641–650.

Shibaoka, H., and T. Yamaki. 1959. Studies on the growth movement of sunflower plant. *Sci. Papers Coll. Gen. Educ. Tokyo Univ.*, 9:105–126.

Smith, F. H., and Q. D. Clarkson. 1956. Cytological studies of interspecific hybridization in *Iris. Am. J. Botany*, 43:582–588.

Straub, J. 1946. Zur Entwicklungsphysiologie der Selbsterilität von *Petunia.* Z. *Naturforsch.*, 1:287–291.

————. 1947. Zur Entwicklungsphysiologie der Selbsterilität von *Petunia.* II. Z. *Naturforsch.*, 2b:433–444.

Takeyosi, H., and M. Fujii. 1961. On the growth substance economy before and after flowering in each organ of *Portulaca grandiflora. Botan. Mag. (Tokyo)*, 74:357–360.

Tsao, T. H. 1949. A study of chemotropism of pollen tubes *in vitro. Plant Physiol.*, 24:494–503.

Vasil, I. K. 1957a. Effect of kinetin and gibberellic acid on excised anthers of *Allium cepa. Phytomorphology*, 7:138–149.

————. 1957b. Effect of kinetin and gibberellic acid on excised anthers of *Allium cepa. Science*, 126:1294–1295.

————. 1960. Studies on pollen germination of certain Cucurbitaceae. *Am. J. Botany*, 47:239–247.

Visser, T. 1955a. Germination and storage

of pollen. *Mededel. Landbouwhogeschool Wageningen*, 55:1–68.

————. 1955*b*. De Karakteristiek van Appelbleomen en-Vruchten in Verband met hun Positie in de Tros. *Mededel. Directeur Tuinbouw*, 18: 809–822.

Watanabe, K. 1955. Studies on the germination of grass pollen. I. Liquid exudation of the pollen on the stigma before germination. *Botan. Mag. (Tokyo)*, 68:40–44.

————. 1961. Studies on the germination of grass pollen. II. Germination capacity of pollen in relation to the maturity of pollen and stigma. *Botan. Mag. (Tokyo)*, 74:131–137.

Wittwer, S. H. 1943. Growth hormone production during sexual reproduction of higher plants. *Missouri Univ. Agr. Expt. Sta. Res. Bull.*, 371:1–58.

———— and M. J. Bukovac. 1957. Gibberellins: new chemicals for crop production. *Mich. State Univ. Agr. Expt. Sta. Quart. Bull.*, 39:469–494.

Zinsmeister, H. D. 1960. Das Phototropische Verhalten der Blutenstiele von *Cyclamen persicum* Hybr. *Planta*, 55:647–668.

15 | Fruit set

With the successful pollination of the flower, there occurs a burst of growth of the erstwhile ovary, and development of a fruit begins. At the same time there usually occurs a wilting and abscission of the petals and sometimes of the stamens. These changes which mark the transition of the flower into a young fruit are called *fruit set.*

The capacity of the flower to set fruit depends in many instances on the receptivity of the female parts to the pollen. The receptive condition may last for only a few hours, as in the mango, or for over a week, as in the tomato. In some species the receptive condition of the ovary is indicated by the exudation of a viscous material on the stigma which may hold the pollen and perhaps nourish it as well.

Receptivity of the ovary frequently shows the interesting feature of beginning before the flower bud is opened, and in many garden crops it has been found that the incompatibility reactions are undeveloped in the few days just before flower-bud opening—a feature which is of considerable use to the plant breeder who can effect inbreeding by dissecting flower buds and applying the pollen inside. The phenomenon of changing receptivity with time is illustrated by the experiments of El Murabaa (1957) with Brussels sprouts (Fig. 15-1). This crop is somewhat self-incompatible, and from these data it can be seen that self-pollination can be effected from 2 to 5 days before or after bud opening, whereas it is quite unsuccessful on the day the flower opens. Cross-pollination, on the other hand, can be effected over the entire 5 days before bud opening to 5 days after bloom.

Abscission of the flower frequently terminates the period of female receptivity. In the tomato flower the ovule remains viable even after abscission, for abscised flowers can be cultured on agar and successfully induced to fruit set (Leopold and Scott, 1952).

Growth relations

With successful pollination, there follows a burst of growth of the ovary. Germination of the pollen is often the catalyst of ovary growth; in many fleshy fruits the increase in ovary growth occurs before there has been sufficient time for the growth of pollen tubes into the ovules (Yasuda, 1934). The stimulus of ovary growth is illustrated by some data of Nitsch (1952) for cucumber, which show (Fig. 15-2) a perceptible ovary growth before pollination and then a marked increase in growth after pollination, whereas unpollinated flowers actually decrease in ovary size. In other species the ovary may be static in growth until pollinated.

The extent of the growth stimulus may be correlated with the pollen-population phenomenon—that is, with increasing density of pollination there may ensue a greater growth response of the ovary. In tomatoes, for example, Verkerk (1957) has described markedly faster fruit growth rates for more heavily pollinated ovaries. In the passion flower, Akamine and Girolami (1959) observed that heavier pollinations resulted in increases of fruit set (Fig. 15-3), and associated with this increase were a markedly greater seed number and an ultimately greater fruit size. In many plant-breeding programs where small amounts of pollen must be used, a carrier pollen of another species, especially of *Lycopodium,* is often utilized to partially satisfy the pollen-population effect.

Pollen is a rich source of auxin, and in fact many of the earliest studies of auxins were carried out with water extracts of pollen as an auxin supply. Fitting (1909) observed that pollen extracts applied to orchid flowers could cause wilting and abscission of the petals and swelling of the ovary in a manner suggestive of fruit set. Laibach (1932) assayed the auxin content of many species of pollen and reported quite large amounts in some species. Suspecting that the growth stimulation following fruit set could be re-

Fig. 15-1 | The successful setting of seed in Brussels sprouts is greatest for cross-pollinations at the day of flower opening; selfing, however, shows an incompatible reaction at the time of flower opening, and better set can be achieved if pollen is inserted into the bud 2 or 3 days before opening or if pollination is done 2 or 3 days after anthesis (El Murabaa, 1957).

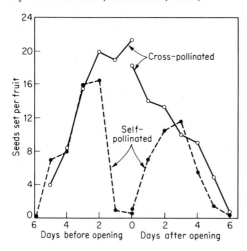

Fig. 15-2 | Growth of the ovary or fruit of *Cucumis anguria* shows a rapid rise after pollination, or an actual decline if pollination is not obtained (Nitsch, 1952).

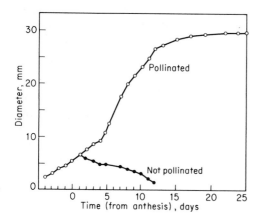

lated to auxin, Gustafson (1936) discovered that fruit set of many species could actually be induced with auxin treatments—substituting completely for the pollination requirement, particularly in the fleshy fruits of many solanaceous and cucurbitaceous species.

The auxin stimulus involved in fruit set comes not only from the pollen but also from the ovary. Pollination results in a stimulation of auxin formation in the ovary; Muir (1942) found a sudden formation of auxin in the ovary of tobacco flowers within 2 days of pollination (Fig. 15-4). In contrast, unpollinated ovaries persisted in having only small auxin contents. In later work (1951) Muir established that this ovary auxin represents a stimulated synthesis of auxin by some factor from the pollen. The synthesis of auxin does not engulf the whole ovary at once but follows a progressive pattern strikingly similar to the progress of the pollen tubes down the style. In some perceptive experiments, Lund (1956) described this correlation in tobacco. Some of his data (Fig. 15-5) show that 20 hr after pollination, auxin synthesis occurs principally at the stylar tip; at 50 hr the synthesis has moved to the base of the style, and at 90 hr, when the pollen reaches the ovule, the ovary base is the site of most auxin synthesis. Lund chromatographed his auxin extracts and identified indoleacetic acid and tryptophan as the principal forms showing the increase, though later Paleg and Muir (1959) also found an unidentified neutral auxin which increased initially after pollination.

The question which derives naturally from the fact that auxin content rises with fruit set is whether in fact endogenous auxins are responsible for fruit set. After Gustafson (1936) discovered that some species of fruits can be set with auxins, it became evident that the property is not shared by most fruits. While auxins are effective in causing set of tomato, pepper, eggplant, tobacco, holly, okra, figs, and numerous relatives of the cucumbers and melons, an estimated 80 per cent of horticultural species cannot be set with auxins. In surveying the evidence against the idea of auxins as general triggers of fruit set, Luckwill (1957) has pointed out that the postpollination increase in auxin content occurs 2 or 3 weeks after fruit set in such fruits as corn, apple, and currant. Perhaps we must look to other growth substances as possible controls of the setting of fruit.

There is some experimental basis for implicating the gibberellins and possibly the kinins in the fruit-set phenomenon. One of the first discovered sources of gibberellins

Fig. 15-3 | The density of the pollen on the stigma of passion flower has a marked influence not only on the percentage of fruit set, but also on the seed number and ultimate fruit weight achieved (Akamine and Girolami, 1959).

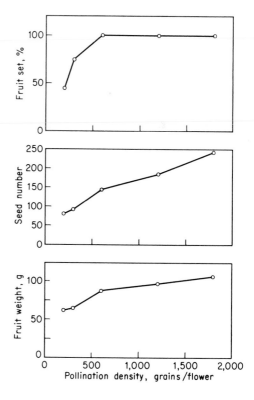

in higher plants was developing fruits (Lang et al., 1957; Mitchell et al., 1951). Soon after the rise of gibberellins into a position of popularity among physiologists, it was discovered that they would induce fruit set in tomatoes (Wittwer et al., 1957; Gustafson, 1960). But in addition, gibberellins can cause fruit set in numbers of species which are not set by the auxins, including some species of rose (Prosser and Jackson, 1959); several species of the genus *Prunus,* including cherry, almond, apricot, and peach (Crane et al., 1960); grapes (Weaver and McCune, 1958), apples and pears (Wittwer and Bukovac, 1962). The interesting possibility that gibberellins may contribute to the endogenous control of fruit set remains to be worked out. The possible involvement of kinins in fruit set is even less clear. They have been found in newly set fruits of apple (Goldacre and Bottomley, 1959; Letham and Bollard, 1961) and in parthenocarpic banana ovaries (Steward and Simmonds, 1954), but as yet there is no evidence to indicate that they may induce fruit set when added exogenously or that they may be involved endogenously.

Fig. 15-4 | Diffusible auxin obtained from the ovaries of tobacco flowers shows a striking increase after pollination. Diffusates for 3 hr assayed by *Avena* curvature test (data of Muir, 1942).

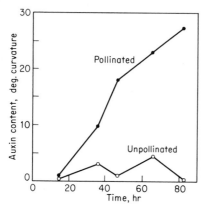

Fig. 15-5 | The increase in auxin content following pollination of tobacco ovaries is detectable first in the style tips and then later in the basal region of the style; still later it is mostly in the ovary itself. Extractable auxin, *Avena* curvature assay (Lund, 1956).

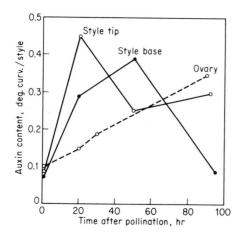

Parthenocarpy

From a general biological viewpoint, it seems surprising that some plants can experience fruit set and proceed to develop normal (though seedless) fruits without the involvement of any fertilization of the ovule. As students of natural selection we expect major developmental processes to be associated with at least some beneficial outcome for the species, but the occurrence of parthenocarpic fruit development does not seem to offer the plant any benefit whatsoever, appearing more as a biological accident.

Parthenocarpy is of widespread occurrence, especially among species which have large numbers of ovules per fruit such as bananas, pineapples, tomatoes, melons, and figs. Many seedless horticultural varieties of these fruits are exclusively parthenocarpic. On the other hand, many-seeded fruits are not necessarily capable of parthenocarpy, and even some single-seeded fruits can be parthenocarpically set (e.g., Hartmann, 1950).

Several types of parthenocarpy occur, some requiring pollination and others not. Parthenocarpy may occur as (1) fruit development without any pollination, (2) fruit development stimulated by pollination but proceeding to full development even without the pollen tube ever reaching the ovule and affecting syngamy, or (3) seedlessness as a result of the abortion of the embryo before the fruit reaches maturity. Illustrative of the first case are the occasional complete parthenocarpy of tomatoes, peppers, pumpkins, and cucumbers and the consistently seedless citrus, banana, and pineapple. Parthenocarpy stimulated by pollination without syngamy is illustrated by the orchid and the parthenogenetic species of *Poa*; fruits of triploid plants which are therefore genetically sterile also fit into this second group of parthenocarpy. The parthenocarpy which follows from embryo abortion is common in some of the cherries, peaches, and grapes. A curious type of intermediate parthenocarpy is that of the ginkgo, in which fruit development is stimulated by pollination but where the pollen tube experiences a suspended growth until the fruit is ripened and has fallen to the ground; the ripe fruit has therefore developed without syngamy, but pollen-tube growth begins again, and syngamy does occur then some months later.

Special environmental conditions are frequently associated with parthenocarpic fruit development. It often occurs following the extensive growth when normal fruit development has been prevented, as in plants which have failed to set fruit over an extended time. Osborne and Went (1953) were able to induce parthenocarpy in tomatoes with low temperatures and high light intensities—conditions under which pollination is poor. Nitsch et al. (1952) found similar induction of parthenocarpy in cucumbers at short photoperiods and with low night temperatures. In some species which are reluctant to exercise parthenocarpy, seed abortion can be induced by frost or low temperature (apples and pears) or even by fog (olives) and parthenocarpic fruits sometimes result.

After his discovery that auxins could induce parthenocarpy, Gustafson (1939) examined the ovaries of seeded and seedless species, seeking a relationship between the auxin content and the natural inclination toward seedlessness. Some of his data for the auxin contents are given in Table 7, from which it appears that among the citrus fruits and grapes the seedless varieties do have appreciably higher auxin contents than the seeded varieties. Luckwill (1957) has suggested that parthenocarpy may represent a state of auxin autotrophy in the ovaries.

The physiological basis for parthenocarpy remains obscure. It occurs most commonly among fruits which have large numbers of ovules, suggesting that the ovule might pro-

Table 7 | *Auxin contents of the ovaries of unopened flowers, comparing seeded with seedless varieties. Extractable auxin as μg/kg fr. wt.; Avena curvature assay (Gustafson, 1939).*

	Seeded varieties	Seedless varieties
Orange:		
Satsuma	. . .	4.01
Washington	. . .	0.73
Robertson	. . .	1.16
Paper rind	0.58	
Valencia	0.58	2.39
Lemon:		
Eureka	0.43	0.78
Grape:		
Thompson	. . .	2.74
Black manulka	. . .	1.30
Muskat	0.34	

vide some of the chemical constituents which stimulate fruit set and fruit growth. That the ovules are sites of auxin synthesis in some fruits seems reasonable (e.g., Nitsch, 1950), and the fact that auxin applications can bring about fruit set makes the possibility that auxins are critical in fruit set attractive. However, many fruits do not so respond to auxins, and so there must be a further component to the fruit-set stimulus in the plant. The effectiveness of the gibberellins suggests at least one further component. Luckwill (1957) has pointed out that fruits which are set with auxins achieve fruit growth principally by cell enlargement and that those which are not set with auxins commonly achieve fruit growth with some cell-division activity. The occurrence of cell-division factors in some fruits (Steward and Simmonds, 1954; Goldacre and Bottomley, 1957) holds an interesting possibility for resolving the fruit-set problem.

The chemical induction of parthenocarpy has been carried out both experimentally and commercially with auxins. Such fruit set seems to be a property of species which are naturally capable of developing parthenocarpic fruits. Again, the property is most common among the solanaceous and cucurbitaceous species, plus figs, grapes, okra, and a few other plants. There is good evidence that the fruit-set response to chemicals is a consequence of the auxin properties of the chemicals, for the molecular requirements for fruit set of tomato appear to be very much like those for the auxin stimulation of growth (Luckwill, 1948; Osborne and Wain, 1951; Luckwill and Woodcock, 1955). In some species, auxin applications can result in initial fruit set, but the subsequent development of the fruits fails without proper 'pollination, as in olive, hops, avocado, mango, and corn. Also, there are special cases in which the application of auxins improves fruit set when natural set has been poor, as in frosted flowers of apple or pear.

The auxin effect may show quantitative properties, as illustrated in Fig. 15-6, with increasing fruit set being obtained with increasing concentrations of auxin. Furthermore, with increasing amounts of applied auxin, the rate of growth of the tomato ovary is quantitatively increased (Luckwill, 1948). This latter phenomenon has been used as a quantitative auxin bioassay.

The auxin forcing of fruit set has achieved transient commercial use in the tomato industry at times when natural fruit set is poor. There has been a more extensive commercial application of auxins for fruit set in grapes.

An interesting development has occurred in the fig industry in this connection. Ordinarily the calimyrna fig orchard must have both male and female trees, and hives of the caprifying wasp must be provided for the trees in order that pollination of the female flowers can be obtained. Crane and Blondeau (1949) found that auxin treatments were completely effective in causing fruit set, with excellent development of seedless fruits. However, the calimyrna fig is used principally in the manufacture of Fig Newtons, a biscuit given a crunchy quality by the fig seeds. The chemical fruit-set treatment was not accepted because of the absence of the crunchy seeds, and although Crane (1952) developed an auxin treatment which would stimulate both fruit set and the partial development of the stony nucellar tissues, the relatively weaker effectiveness of this treatment in fruit set has not permitted its general use.

The setting of fruits with auxin commonly brings about an abortion of the developing embryos which may have already been fertilized. When auxins have been applied to tomato flowers in the field, seedless fruits commonly result even though there may have been some fertilization. The effect of auxin in causing embryo abortion has been nicely defined by some data of Luckwill (1953) in connection with studies of the manner in which auxin applications to apple fruits can cause fruit thinning. In the data of Fig. 15-7, auxin applied at the time of petal fall resulted in a striking increase in the abortion of the embryos.

On the other hand, auxin applications have sometimes been effective in actually increasing the seed yield after pollination of difficult crosses. For example, Zafar (1955) applied naphthaleneacetic acid to potato seedlings, and the flowers that were subsequently formed were markedly slower in abscission, permitting much better seed set with pollination (Table 8).

Limitations of fruit set

Fruit set may often limit the productivity of fruit crops. Three general categories of limited fruit set might be recognized: those due to limited pollination, those due to limited nutrients, and those due to the precocious abscission of flowers and newly set fruits. Some plants set fruits from only a very small proportion of flowers, perhaps only one flower in one hundred or more, as in the case of such many-flowered racemes as mango, macadamia nut, and litchi. The mango may have as many as 6,000 flowers

Table 8 | *Application of auxin (25 mg/liter naphthaleneacetic acid) as an overall spray before flowering caused a marked reduction of flower abscission in Canoga potato and large increases in fruit and seed set in both Canoga and Russet Burbank (Zafar, 1955).*

	Var. Canoga		Var. Russet Burbank	
	Controls	+NAA	Controls	+NAA
Buds formed	19.5	26	22	23
Buds abscised	16.5	1.5	22	19
Flowers pollinated	3.0	19	0	4.2
Fruits set	1.5	13	0	1.2
Seeds per fruit	46.5	90	0	38.5

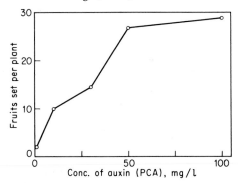

Fig. 15-6 | The effectiveness of auxin applications (*p*-chlorophenoxyacetic acid) in causing fruit set in tomatoes shows a quantitative rise over an increasing concentration range (data of Mann and Minges, 1949).

Fig. 15-7 | When apple flowers are sprayed with auxin (40 mg/liter naphthaleneacetic acid) at petal fall, there follows a dramatic increase in the frequency of seed abortion in the fruits. Under these conditions, there would result a thinning action on the fruits. Crawley Beauty apple (Luckwill, 1953).

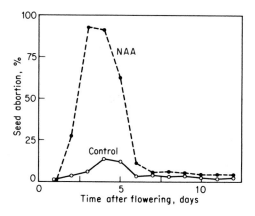

on a single panicle, of which only perhaps two to four will produce fruit (Singh, 1960).

Lack of pollination can arise from several types of situations. In tomato, which is usually a self-pollinating plant, weak light intensities or low temperatures can alter the flower structure in such a way as to prevent the dehiscence of the anthers at the time that the stigma is growing through the anther ring (Howlett, 1936). In other crops, pollination may be limited because of very short periods of female receptivity, as in the mango (Spencer and Kennard, 1955) and many legumes. Again, the pollen which does reach the stigma may be ineffective. Pollen sterility develops readily in the tomato with excessively low or high temperatures (Smith, 1932; Fig. 14-10). Rain on the flowers can cause pollen frustration, illustrated by the experiments of Akamine and Girolami (1959; Fig. 15-8). Applying a simulated rain at various intervals after pollination of passion flowers, they found that within the first hour the rain destroyed the effectiveness of the pollen by causing bursting of the pollen in the same manner as is

Fig. 15-8 | The set of passion flowers is prevented if rain falls on the style in the first hour following pollination. Data for crosspollinations of 30 to 50 flowers per time (Akamine and Girolami, 1959).

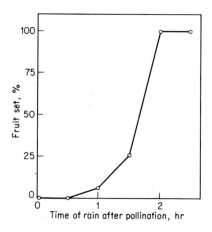

well known to occur in media of too low osmotic concentration. The use of chemical treatments to cause pollen sterility has shown marked promise in permitting chemical prevention of unwanted fruit set (Eaton, 1957; Moore, 1959; Lam et al., 1962).

Early observations of fruit set in cotton led Mason and Maskell (1928) to suggest that there might be nutritive limitations of fruit set. Eaton and Ergle (1953) later denied the idea since the foliar applications of organic nutrients did not improve cotton fruit set. While the techniques of foliar applications of nutrients generally do not improve fruit set, several lines of evidence clearly support the concept of nutritive limitations. In tomato, Leopold and Scott (1952) found that mature leaves were essential for the setting of flowers on the plant; they could substitute for the leaves by supplying various organic nutrients to excised flowers and there obtain good fruit set. Murneek (1927) established that the presence of fruits on the spider plant (*Cleome*) effectively limited further fruit set. Van Steveninck (1957) found that the deterioration of fruit set with time in yellow lupines (*Lupinus luteus*) could be averted by removal of the fruits which had already been set (Fig. 15-9). Perhaps a similar competition for nutrients is responsible for the abortion of the ovules in the stylar end of bean fruits (Gabelman and Williams, 1962), a competition effect which becomes more severe under conditions of water stress. In some species such as grape and cotton, girdling a branch can markedly improve fruit set, presumably through interference with the translocation of nutrients out of the branch.

Flower abscission frequently limits fruit set in tomato. Because the flowers are abscised in a viable condition (Leopold and Scott, 1952), any treatment which defers abscission may be effective in increasing fruit set. The data in Table 8 (Zafar, 1955) illustrate this effectiveness for auxin application to potato. In cyclamen, abscission follows promptly if the ovary ceases growth, and there the application of the auxin naphthaleneacetamide defers flower abscission and improves fruit set probably by temporarily sustaining ovary growth (El Murabaa, 1957).

Several treatments have been developed for the chemical prevention of fruit set. In addition to the pollen-abortion treatments with dichloroisobutyric acid described by Eaton (1957), the destruction of the flower can be obtained with cresols (Auchter and Roberts, 1935) or other toxic chemicals (Luckwill, 1953), though these may not be selective against pollen viability.

In conclusion, fruit set is a basic step in the life cycle of higher plants, and at present very little is known of its physiological mechanisms. While some evidence has been developed to help explain it as a function of auxins and gibberellins, it is far from clear how the dramatic abscission of the flower parts and the sudden commencement of fruit development are triggered.

GENERAL REFERENCES

Luckwill, L. C. 1957. Hormonal aspects of fruit development in higher plants. *Symp. Soc. Exptl. Biol.*, 11:63–85.

Muir, R. M. 1951. The growth hormone mechanisms in fruit development, pp. 357–364. In F. Skoog (ed.), *Plant Growth Substances.* The University of Wisconsin Press, Madison, Wis.

Wittwer, S. H. 1951. Growth substances in fruit setting, pp. 365–379. In F. Skoog (ed.), *Plant Growth Substances.* The University of Wisconsin Press, Madison, Wis.

Younkin, S. G. (ed.). 1962. *Plant Science Symposium on Fruit Set.* Campbell Soup Co., Camden, N.J. 229 pp.

REFERENCES CITED

Akamine, E. K., and G. Girolami. 1959. Pol-

lination and fruit set in the yellow passion fruit. *Hawaii Agr. Expt. Sta. Tech. Bull.*, 39:1–45.

Auchter, E. C., and J. W. Roberts. 1935. Spraying apples for the prevention of fruit-set. *Proc. Am. Soc. Hort. Sci.*, 32: 208–212.

Crane, J. C. 1952. Ovary-wall development as influenced by growth-regulators inducing parthenocarpy in the calimyrna fig. *Botan. Gaz.*, 114:102–107.

———— and R. Blondeau. 1949. Controlled growth of fig fruits by synthetic hormone application. *Proc. Am. Soc. Hort. Sci.*, 54:102–108.

————, P. Primer, and R. Campbell. 1960. Gibberellin induced parthenocarpy in *Prunus. Proc. Am. Soc. Hort. Sci.*, 75: 129–137.

Eaton, F. M. 1957. Selective gametocide opens way to hybrid cotton. *Science*, 126: 1174–1175.

Eaton, F. M., and D. R. Ergle. 1953. Relationship of seasonal trends in carbohydrate and nitrogen levels to the nutritional

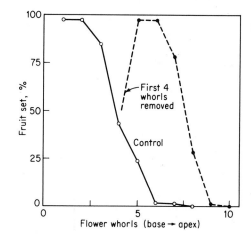

Fig. 15-9 | The presence of set fruits on yellow lupine inhibits the fruit set of subsequently opening flower whorls. If the first whorls on which set has been obtained are cut off, full fruit set is restored (van Steveninck, 1957).

interpretation of boll shedding in cotton. *Plant Physiol.*, 28:503–520.

El Murabaa, A. I. M. 1957. Factors affecting seed set in Brussels sprouts, radish and cyclamen. *Mededel. Landbouwhogeschool Wageningen*, 57:1–33.

Fitting, H. 1909. Die Beeinflussung der Orchideenbluten durch die Bestaubung und durch anderes Umstande. *Z. Botan.*, 1:1–86.

Gabelman, W. H., and D. D. F. Williams. 1962. Water relations effecting pod set of green beans, pp. 25–35. In *Plant Science Symposium on Fruit Set*. Campbell Soup Co., Camden, N.J.

Goldacre, P. L., and W. Bottomley. 1959. A kinin in apple fruitlets. *Nature*, 184: 555–556.

Gustafson, F. G. 1936. Inducement of fruit development by growth promoting chemicals. *Proc. Natl. Acad. Sci. U.S.*, 22:628–636.

———. 1939. The cause of natural parthenocarpy. *Am. J. Botany*, 26:135–138.

———. 1960. Influence of gibberellic acid on setting and development of fruits in tomato. *Plant Physiol.*, 35:521–523.

Hartmann, H. T. 1950. Tests with growth regulators for increasing fruit set in olives. *Proc. Am. Soc. Hort. Sci.*, 55:181–189.

Howlett, F. S. 1936. The effect of carbohydrate and of nitrogen deficiency upon microsporogenesis and the development of the male gametophyte in the tomato, *Lycopersicum esculentum* Mill. *Ann. Botany (London)*, 50:767–804.

Laibach, F. 1932. Pollenhormon und Wuchsstoff. *Ber. Deut. Botan. Ges.*, 50: 383–390.

Lam, S. L., A. C. Leopold, and K. W. Johnson. 1962. A chemical treatment to concentrate tomato ripening for mechanical harvest. *Proc. Am. Soc. Hort. Sci.*, 80: 530–534.

Lang, A., J. A. Sandoval, and A. Bedri. 1957. Induction of bolting and flowering in *Hyoscyamus* and *Samolus* by a gibberellin-like material from a seed plant. *Proc. Natl. Acad. Sci. U.S.*, 43:960–964.

Leopold, A. C., and F. I. Scott. 1952. Physiological factors in tomato fruit-set. *Am. J. Botany*, 39:310–317.

Letham, D. S., and E. G. Bollard. 1961. Stimulants of cell division in developing fruits. *Nature*, 191:1119–1120.

Luckwill, L. C. 1948. A method for the quantitative estimation of growth substances based on the response of tomato ovaries to known amounts of 2-naphthoxy-acetic acid. *J. Hort. Sci.*, 24:19–31.

———. 1953. Studies of fruit development in relation to plant hormones. II. The effect of naphthaleneacetic acid on fruit set and fruit development in apples. *J. Hort. Sci.*, 28:25–40.

———. 1957. Hormonal aspects of fruit development in higher plants. *Symp. Soc. Exptl. Biol.*, 11:63–85.

——— and D. Woodcock. 1955. Plant growth regulators. I. The influence of side-chain length on the activity of w-(2-naphthyloxy)-n-alkylcarboxylic acids for the induction of parthenocarpy in tomatoes. *J. Hort. Sci.*, 30:109–115.

Lund, H. A. 1956. Growth hormones in the styles and ovaries of tobacco responsible for fruit development. *Am. J. Botany*, 43: 562–568.

Mann, L. K., and P. A. Minges. 1949. Experiments on setting fruit with growth-regulating substances. *Hilgardia*, 19:309–337.

Mason, T. G., and E. J. Maskell. 1928. Studies on the transport of carbohydrates in the cotton plants. I. *Ann. Botany (London)*, 42:189–253.

Mitchell, J. W., D. P. Skaggs, and W. P. Anderson. 1951. Plant growth-stimulating hormones in immature bean seeds. *Science*, 114:159–161.

Moore, J. F. 1959. Male sterility induced in tomato by sodium dichloroisobutyrate. *Science*, 129:1738–1740.

Muir, R. M. 1942. Growth hormones as related to the setting and development of fruit in *Nictiana tabacum. Am. J. Botany*, 29:716–720.

———. 1951. The growth hormone mechanism in fruit development, pp. 357–364. In F. Skoog (ed.), *Plant Growth Substances*. The University of Wisconsin Press, Madison, Wis.

Murneek, A. E. 1927. Physiology of reproduction in horticultural plants. II. Intermittent sterility of the spider flower. *Missouri Univ. Agr. Expt. Sta. Res. Bull.*, 106.

Nitsch, J. P. 1950. Growth and morphogenesis of the strawberry as related to auxin. *Am. J. Botany*, 37:211–215.

———. 1952. Plant hormones in the development of fruits. *Quart. Rev. Biol.*, 27:33–57.

———, E. B. Kurtz, J. L. Liverman, and F. W. Went. 1952. The development of sex expression in cucurbit flowers. *Am. J. Botany*, 39:32–43.

Osborne, D. J., and R. L. Wain. 1951. Studies on plant growth regulating substances. III. Production of parthenocarpic pomaceous fruits. *J. Hort. Sci.*, 26:317–327.

——— and F. W. Went. 1953. Climatic factors influencing parthenocarpy and normal fruit set in tomatoes. *Botan. Gaz.*, 114:312–322.

Paleg, L. G., and R. M. Muir. 1959. Neutral and acidic auxins in developing tobacco fruit. *Australian J. Biol. Sci.*, 12:340–343.

Prosser, M. V., and G. A. D. Jackson. 1959. Induction of pathenocarpy in *Rosa arvenis* buds (with gibberellic acid). *Nature*, 184:180.

Singh, L. B. 1960. *The Mango*. Leonard Hill, Ltd., London. 438 pp.

Smith, O. 1932. Relation of temperature to anthesis and blossom drop of the tomato, together with histological study of the pistils. *J. Agr. Res.*, 44:183–190.

Spencer, J. L., and W. C. Kennard. 1955. Studies on mango (*Mangifera indica* L.) fruit set in Puerto Rico. *Trop. Agr. (London)*, 32:323–330.

Steward, F. C., and N. W. Simmonds. 1954. Growth-promoting substances in the ovary and immature fruit of the banana. *Nature*, 173:1083.

van Steveninck, R. F. M. 1957. Factors affecting abscission of reproductive organs of lupins. *J. Exptl. Botany*, 8:373–381.

Verkerk, K. 1957. The pollination of tomatoes. *Netherlands J. Agr. Sci.*, 5:37–54.

Weaver, R. J., and S. B. McCune. 1958. Gibberellin tested on grapes. *Calif. Agr.*, 12:6–15.

Wittwer, S. H., and M. J. Bukovac. 1962. Exogenous plant growth substances affecting floral initiation and fruit set, pp. 65–83. In S. G. Younkin (ed.), *Plant Science Symposium on Fruit Set*. Campbell Soup Co., Camden, N.J.

———, M. J. Bukovac, H. M. Sell, and L. E. Weller. 1957. Some effects of gibberellin on flowering and fruit setting. *Plant Physiol.*, 32:39–41.

Yasuda, S. 1934. Parthenocarpy caused by the stimulus of pollination in some plants of Solanaceae. *Agr. Hort. (Tokyo)*, 9: 647–656.

Zafar, M. A. 1955. Application of certain hormones to prevent flower abscission in two potato (*Solanum tuberosum*) varieties. *Am. Potato J.*, 32:283–292.

16 | Fruit growth

The growth of the fruit frequently involves an enlargement of the ovary itself, an enlargement of the receptacular tissues, or both. In the physiological literature, almost exclusive attention has been given to the growth and development of the fleshy fruits since these are of special horticultural interest; however, it should be noted that the majority of fruits are not fleshy, and there is scarcely any information on the development of such fruits.

Fruit growth phenomena are principally of a nonpolar or scarcely polar type of growth which is little understood by modern plant physiologists. There is no widely accepted test for nonpolar growth in the sense that there is for polar elongation of stem or coleoptile tissue, and the utilization of the polar types of tests in analysis of fruit growth leaves room for considerable misinterpretation of the results obtained.

Fruit growth rates

Two general types of growth centers may be recognized in the growth of fleshy fruits, namely, the enlargement of the ovarian tissues stimulated usually by pollination, and the development of the embryo and endosperm. The former type of growth may be the initial enlargement observed in fruit-set experiments, and the latter type more relevant to the later periods of fruit development.

The fertilization process in angiosperm species involves the union of one of the germinal nuclei from the pollen tube with two, three, or four of the polar nuclei of the embryo sac to form the endosperm, and the union of the other pollen nucleus with the egg nucleus to form the zygote from which the embryo will be developed. The fruit may therefore be composed of diploid tissues from the maternal parent, 3 to 5N tissue from the endosperm, and diploid tissue of the new embryo. Structurally, the fruit may be mostly parental tissue (strawberry), mostly endosperm tissue (the small grains), or mostly embryo tissue (Compositae).

Many fruits have growth patterns of the simple sigmoid type common to most cells, tissues, and organisms, starting with an exponential increase in size and then slowing in a sigmoid fashion (Fig. 16-1). This type of growth curve is common to the apple, pineapple, strawberry, pea, tomato, and many other fruits. A second group of fruits has a more complicated growth curve, involving two periods of growth increases with a period of slow or suspended growth in between, as represented also in Fig. 16-1. The double growth curve is common to probably all the stone fruits such as peach, apricot, plum, and cherry and to some non-stony fruits such as fig, grape, and currant. The growth curves do not seem to be distinctive for the different morphological types of fruits, for there are berries, pomes, and simple and accessory fruits in each type. Examination of the double growth curve impresses one with the number of physiological signals that must occur in the course of fruit development to bring about not only fruit set but all the startings and stoppings of growth plus the final signal for fruit ripening. Only the most simple beginnings have been made in developing any understanding of how these physiological signals are imposed.

The double growth curve may be expressed in overall fruit growth and in the separate growth curves for such internal parts of the fruits as the embryo, endosperm, and fleshy or stony parts of the fruits. Carr and Skene (1961) have illustrated the separate growth behaviors of the pod and seed of the bean fruit (Fig. 16-2), in which the pod develops first, and then later the embryo and seed structures. Whereas the entire fruit apparently shows a simple sigmoid type of growth curve, the seed parts develop with a double growth curve, as plotted in Fig. 16-2, with a log scale for fruit size to make the double growth curve more readily

discernible. A classic illustration of the separate periods of growth of the various parts of the fruit was the study by Tukey (1933) of the selective growth of peach fruit parts (Fig. 16-3).

The enlargement patterns of fruit growth reflect both cell-enlargement and cell-division activity. There is wide variation in the extent to which cell division participates in fruit growth, ranging from cases in which cell

Fig. 16-1 | The growth curves for fruits are commonly of two types: either sigmoid curves, as for the apple fruit, or double sigmoid curves, as for the cherry.

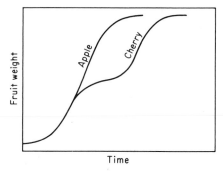

Fig. 16-2 | The double growth curve may apply to the seeds even though the entire fruit may express only a single growth curve. Data for Hawkesbury Wonder beans (Carr and Skene, 1961).

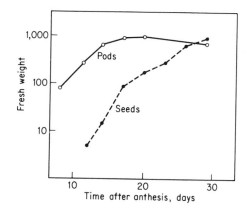

division (except in the embryo and endosperm tissues) has been completed at the time of pollination (*Ribes, Rubus*) to cases in which there is a brief period of cell division just following pollination (tomato, *Citrus,* cucurbits, apple, *Prunus*) or rather extended periods of cell division after pollination (strawberry). It is common for the early stages of fruit growth to involve not only cell enlargement but also cell division, a fact which may be related to the inability of cell-enlargement substances entirely to account for fruit set and fruit growth.

Fig. 16-3 | Comparison of the growth curves for various parts of the fruit of Elberta peach shows that the double growth curve is expressed by the pericarp tissues and that the time at which the first growth period is ended is approximately the time of completion of nucellar growth and commencement of embryo growth (Tukey, 1933).

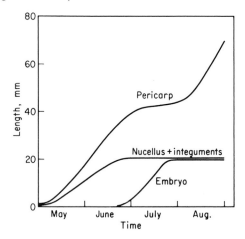

Mobilization

It is unnecessary to point out that the fruits which contain large amounts of food materials must import them from other parts of the plant. The means by which such a mobilization of substances can occur is poorly understood. Mobilization can permit fruit growth at the expense of materials in the leaves, as the data of Emmerling (1880) illustrate (Fig. 16-4). One can see changing centers of mobilization during the development of the pea fruit, with the hulls enlarging in the early stages and declining later. The successive mobilizations of materials from one part of the fruit to another are more evident in the data for the peanut shown in Fig. 16-5 (Schenk, 1961). It is evident that the growth of separate parts of a fruit can involve shifting mobilization patterns between the parts, and nutrients may be moved consecutively from part to part, following the mobilization shifts.

Mention should be made here of the interesting question of what organs supply the nutrients for fruit growth. Often the nearest leaves or other photosynthetic tissues are principal sources from which the mobilization draws, as, for example, in small grains in which even the awns of the flower head provide over 10 per cent of the fruit dry weight and the rest of the flower spike provides an additional 30 per cent (Mc-

Fig. 16-4 | Mobilization of nitrogenous materials from the leaves into the hulls and then into the seeds during fruiting of *Vicia faba* (data of Emmerling, 1880; cited by McKee et al., 1955).

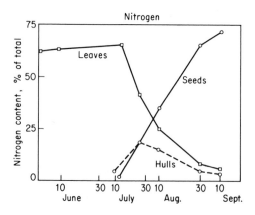

Donough and Gauch, 1959). Such determinations can be nicely made by radioactive labeling of the separate contributing plant parts.

As increasing numbers of fruits draw upon the nutrient supplies of the plant, competitive limitations on the growth rates of the fruits begin to set in. In tomato, Verkerk (1957) has shown that the fruit size achieved declines with increasing numbers of seeds developing on the plant. More simply, this may be expressed as a decrease in fruit size with increasing number of fruits developing on the plant, as shown in Fig. 16–6 (Hafen and Leopold, unpublished). The mobilizing forces existing between fruits have been mentioned in Chap. 5.

Fruit size

The ultimate fruit size achieved may be correlated with cell size in some species. For example, Tukey and Young (1939) found that in cherries the fruit size seemed to be determined by the cell sizes achieved in the fleshy parts of the fruit. In other fruits the number of cells is related to ultimate size, as Bain and Robertson (1951) have shown for the apple. The correlation obtained in the latter case is illustrated in Fig. 16-7. The apple also achieves a considerable amount of size through the development of intercellular spaces during the second half of fruit enlargement. This growth phenomenon is evident from the data of Bain and Robertson shown in Fig. 16-8, in which it is seen that during the last half of its growth fruit volume increases more rapidly than fruit weight. In the finished fruit, 25 per cent of the apple is constituted of air spaces. The white refractive quality of apple flesh is related to the resulting cell-air interfaces. In contrast to apple, the grape shows a greater increase in weight than in volume during the later periods of fruit growth (Coombe, 1960), indicating an enhancement of the deposition of solids

Fig. 16-5 | The growth of the peanut illustrates the separate growth rates for parts of the fruit. Note that an initial preferential growth of the shell yields later to a growth of skins and then later to kernel growth; also, the transfer of mobilization sites results in extensive losses from former mobilization centers (Schenk, 1961).

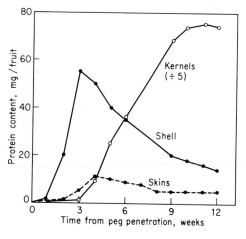

Fig. 16-6 | Competitive actions between fruits are indicated by the decreases in fruit size with increased numbers of fruits present on tomato plants (data of Hafen and Leopold unp.).

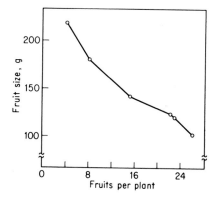

Fig. 16-7 | The correlation between fruit
weight and cell number in Granny Smith
apples from a single tree (Bain and Robertson,
1951).

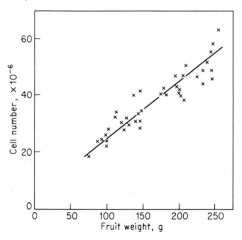

Fig. 16-8 | During the growth of the apple,
there is a greater increase in fruit volume than
in fruit weight, indicating the development of
air spaces as a part of fruit growth (Bain and
Robertson, 1951).

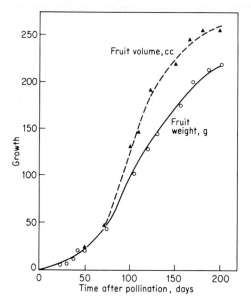

instead of the opening of air spaces. A
similar increase in relative dry weights in
the later development of sausage fruits was
earlier observed by Clements (1940).

Fruit size has been successfully altered
in many instances by the application of
auxins and gibberellins to the developing
fruits. Such increases in size can be a consequence of the extension of the duration
of the growth curve or of the foreshortening
of the period of suspended growth in the
double growth curve, as represented diagrammatically in Fig. 16-9. Not only is fruit
size altered by such treatments, but the
time of ripening of the fruits may also be
altered. For example, Clark and Kerns
(1943) prolonged the sigmoid growth curve
of the pineapple with auxin application,
obtaining a later time of ripening and a
larger fruit. Crane (1948) applied auxins
to fig fruits, eliminating the period of suspended growth, which then led to markedly
earlier ripening. In plums, auxin applications early in fruit development can increase
size and rate of maturity; later applications
hasten maturity and decrease fruit size
(Harris and Hansen, 1955). Many variations of such treatments are used by
pomologists.

From these brief comments it can be
seen that growth may be an expression of
a wide variety of events, from the development of air spaces to the loading into
the fruit of sugars without corresponding
volume increases, and from cell division to
cell enlargement (and of course the various
types of tissue differentiation); finally, there
may be preferential growth of any of several or successive morphological parts of
the fruit. The various parts of the fruit may
represent a wide range in nuclear composition, from diploid to pentaploid.

Role of seeds

The presence of viable embryos or seeds
may be critical for the normal development

of the fruit. In stone fruits, if the embryo is aborted the fruit will in many instances be abscised from the tree. In the apple if seeds are present on only one side, only that side of the fruit will fully develop, resulting in a distorted, asymmetrical fruit. Parthenocarpic fruits develop without seeds, but in many instances the presence of seeds would markedly alter the size and quality of the fruit. For example, fruits of some squash varieties are oblong when seedless and pear-shaped when seeds are present. Pears, too, are oval when parthenocarpic and develop the typical pear shape only when seeds are present.

The role of seeds in fruit development of strawberry was described by Nitsch (1950). This was a most convenient fruit to use in such a study since the seeds are all on the surface. Removal of the seeds prevented the growth of the fleshy fruit, and in fact the trimming of all the seeds from two sides prevented growth there, resulting in novel disk-shaped fruits as shown in Fig. 16-10. Nitsch provided some evidence that the seeds stimulated fruit growth by providing auxins, for an auxin paste could adequately substitute for the seeds on the fruit (Fig. 16-10). Nitsch also noted that in strawberry, the fruit size became proportional to the number of seeds developing on it.

There are many correlations between the numbers of seeds and fruit sizes. Some representative data for the apple are presented in Fig. 16-11 (Visser, 1955)—a correlation which is consistent with the concept of seeds as a source of growth-stimulating signals in the fruit.

An anomaly exists, though, in connection with the possible role of seeds in fruits showing the double growth curve. The period of suspended growth occurs at the time of maximal growth of the seeds in the fruits (see Fig. 16-3). This situation suggests a possible competition between the growth of the fruit and the growth of the seeds, and in fact in the Early Richmond cherry the feature of earliness is a conse-

quence of the abortion of the embryo at the beginning of the period of suspended growth; the cherry then shows almost no period of suspended growth and finishes off early, as shown in Fig. 16-12 (Tukey, 1934).

Seeds, then, appear to be strong influences on the growth of fleshy fruits, ranging from strongly promotive to inhibitory effects, depending upon the stage of fruit growth measured. The manner in which seedless fruits substitute for the seeds is not clear, but there is some evidence that other parts of the fruit may take over the synthesis of growth substances, and in fact the substances in control of fruit growth may be quite different in seedless fruits.

Growth substances

When Nitsch (1950) found that auxin paste would substitute for the seeds in causing

Fig. 16-9 | Stimulations of fruit growth following the applications of auxins which may either increase the duration of the single growth period (*a*) or abbreviate the period of suspended growth between the two periods of most active growth (*b*). Ripening time indicated by x.

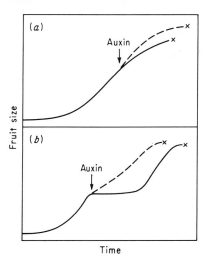

(a)   (b)   (c)   (d)

Fig. 16-10 | Removing the developing achenes on two sides of the strawberry fruit (*b*) results in a disk-shaped fruit; removing all the achenes (*c*) suppresses fruit growth; and removing all achenes but supplying the fruit with an auxin paste (*d*) can restore normal growth (Nitsch, 1950).

growth of strawberry fruits, he naturally raised the question of whether endogenous auxin was responsible for fruit growth. Analysis of the auxin content of the fruits at various stages of development encouraged him in this belief, for he found that a large production of auxin occurred in the first 2 weeks of fruit growth, at the time when

Fig. 16-11 | The correlation between the size of apple fruits and the numbers of seeds per fruit (Visser, 1955).

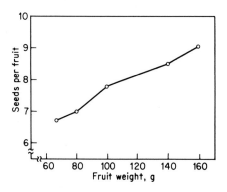

rapid growth was getting under way (Fig. 16-13). He found large increases of tryptophan in the fleshy parts of the fruit and obtained evidence that the seeds were providing factors necessary for the conversion of the tryptophan into auxin, presumably in this way stimulating the fruit growth.

The strawberry growth rate is sigmoid; what is the situation in fruits with a double sigmoid growth curve? From studies of the black currant, Wright (1956) found that by paper chromatography he could separate three auxins from the developing fruit: a neutral one which peaked with the first sigmoid growth phase; an acidic one which peaked more during the second growth phase (Fig. 16-14; cf. Fig. 6-7); and a third which was apparently more related to fruit abscission than to growth. In this case, then, the double growth curve correlated with a double peak of auxin production.

The correlation of fruit growth with endogenous auxin became clouded, however, when both grape (Nitsch et al., 1960) and fig (Crane et al., 1959) yielded evidences of an auxin increase only for the first growth period; the second period of fruit growth was not associated with a rise in auxin (Fig. 16-15). Coombe (1960) interpreted the situation in grape as evidence that the first growth period was controlled by auxin, whereas the second was not a consequence of growth substances but of an osmotic accumulation of carbohydrates. But in peaches even the first phase of growth does not have an associated rise in auxin (Stahly and Thompson, 1959); instead, the auxin content rises perceptibly only during the period of suspended growth! Three auxins were detected, and each showed the same characteristic peak at the period of least growth.

As the possibility of explaining fruit growth as an auxin effect grows dim, another growth substance enters as a possible factor in fruit growth: gibberellin. In addition to the previously mentioned observations that gibberellin treatments could stimulate fruit growth, Coombe (1960) was able to detect measurable amounts of gibberellins in the first growth stages of Seedless Emperor grape. Skene and Carr (1961) found more sustained supplies of gibberellin in the developing seeds in bean fruits. Their data, given in Fig. 16-16, show a large gibberellin content at the time of early seed growth and then a subsequent rise again during the second period of seed growth. Similar data have been reported for enlarging seeds in *Pharbitis* fruits (see Fig. 7-9). While such data are suggestive, it is not established that gibberellins participate in the growth of fruits or fruit parts.

Might kinins be involved in fruit growth? Especially for fruits with considerable amounts of cell division occurring during their growth, this might be a hopeful possibility. Aside from the few reports of kinins in young fruits of banana (Steward and Simmonds, 1954), apple (Goldacre and Bottomley, 1959; Letham and Bollard, 1961), and tomato (Nitsch and Nitsch, 1961), this remains only a prospective chance.

The auxin studies in fruits have more

Fig. 16-12 | Growth curves of two varieties of cherry, showing the rather extended period of suspended growth in the late variety, English Morello, and the almost absent period of suspended growth in Early Richmond (Tukey, 1934).

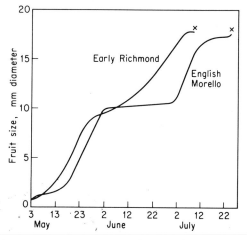

Fig. 16-13 | The growth of the strawberry fruit is associated with a burst of extractable auxin in the fruit during the first 2 weeks after pollination (Nitsch, 1950).

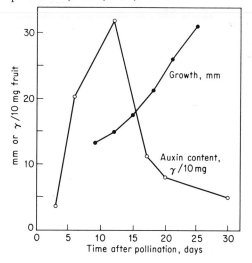

often than not led to the conclusion that the auxins which correlated with growth were not indoleacetic acid. In contrast to the situation in strawberry, the auxins in other fruits appear to be several substances (Nitsch et al., 1960; Klämbt, 1958; Wright, 1956). Remembering that the bioassays used for most growth substances are far from specific for one class of growth substance, the possibility exists that the stimulations of fruit growth might well be by substances of a more diverse nature than we have tended to believe. The fact that many fruits can be stimulated to grow with the application of auxins must not be accepted as trustworthy evidence that endogenous auxins are controlling the growth of the fruits naturally.

Fruit drop

The presence of auxins in the fruit may also be relevant to the natural control of abscission in the fruit. Fruit drop is a widespread horticultural problem, for not only does abscission occur at the time of normal fruit ripening, but in many fruits it occurs shortly after pollination and fruit set, or during the period of growth of the young embryos in the seeds. A dramatic case of fruit drop is seen in the macadamia nut (Urata, 1954; Fig. 16-17), where ordinarily more than 90 per cent of the young fruits may be shed during fruit growth; fruits resulting from self-pollinations are in this case even more susceptible to drop, and ordinarily all the selfed fruits may be lost. In apple production, two periods of precocious fruit drop are recognized: "early drop," which occurs between the period of initial swelling of the ovary and the commencement of endosperm development, and "June drop," which occurs later during the period of rapid embryo development (Luckwill, 1953).

The most simple assumptions would suggest that when the auxin content of the

Fig. 16-14 | Fruit growth in the black currant shows the two phases of most active growth, and each is associated with a peak in acid and neutral extractable auxins. Wheat-coleoptile bioassay (cf. Fig. 6-6) (Wright, 1956).

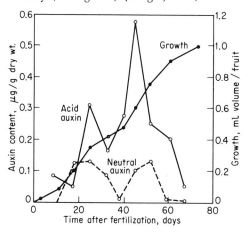

Fig. 16-15 | Growth of the Concord grape also shows two periods of growth, but extractable auxin is associated only with the first peak, and essentially no auxin is present during the second. Jerusalem artichoke bioassay (Nitsch et al., 1960).

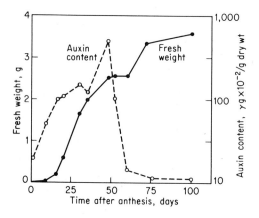

fruits became low, fruit drop would follow. Luckwill's (1953) data with apple support this scheme, for both early drop and June drop were associated with periods of lesser auxin content in the seeds. A few years later, Wright (1956) assayed for the auxins in currant fruits using both the conventional straight-growth test and also an abscission-inhibition test employing *Coleus* petioles. On his chromatograms of fruit extracts, he found one spot which was quite effective in inhibiting abscission but which did not show growth-stimulating activity common to the usual auxins. He correlated the quantities of this auxin in currants with the periods of suppressed fruit drop as shown in Fig. 16-18 and suggested that there might be some auxins in control of fruit growth and quite different ones in control of fruit drop. This situation remains unique to currant fruits up to the present, and the question of whether the retention of fruits is commonly controlled by auxin in the usual sense or by such abscission inhibitors as Wright describes remains to be ascertained.

It is relevant to this discussion to note that the applications of auxins can generally control the abscission of fruits. This effect is employed commercially in a large proportion of the apple orchards of the United States, and to a more limited extent to control fruit drop in citrus fruits, apricots, pears, and other fruits (cf. reviews of Leopold, 1955, 1958). The persistent phenoxyacetic acids are most useful for this action.

Whether the ability of exogenous auxins to control fruit drop might imply that an auxin system imposes an endogenous control of fruit abscission remains uncertain. For example, Crane and Brooks (1952) found that apricot fruits are dropped even without aborting the embryo and while containing a healthy complement of endogenous auxins, but the application of 2,4,5-trichlorophenoxyacetic acid will effectively control this fruit drop. Thus the effectiveness of

the exogenous auxin does not permit a tacit assumption that endogenous auxin controls the phenomenon naturally.

GENERAL REFERENCES

Leopold, A. C. 1958. Auxin uses in the control of flowering and fruiting. *Ann. Rev. Plant Physiol.*, 9:281–310.
———. 1962. The roles of growth substances in flowers and fruits. *Can. J. Botany*, 40:745–755.
Luckwill, L. C. 1957. Hormonal aspects of fruit development in higher plants. *Symp. Soc. Exptl. Biol.*, 11:63–85.
Nitsch, J. P. 1952. Plant hormones in the

Fig. 16-16 | The growth of seeds in bean fruits is compared with the gibberellin content. The two peaks of growth roughly correspond in time to two peaks in gibberellin level, as determined by wheat-leaf bioassay (Skene and Carr, 1961).

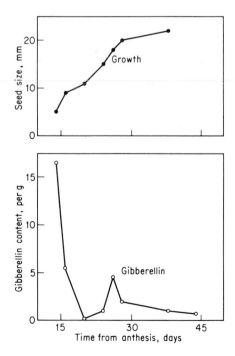

Fig. 16-17 | Fruit drop in the Macadamia nut during the period of fruit growth results in losses of a large percentage of the fruits (Urata, 1954).

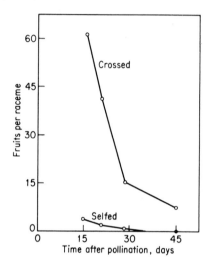

Fig. 16-18 | Fruit drop of black currant is strongly suppressed from the thirtieth to the sixtieth day of fruit growth, at which time there is a burst of extractable auxin in the fruits, effective as an inhibitor of abscission in the *Coleus* petiole bioassay (Wright, 1956).

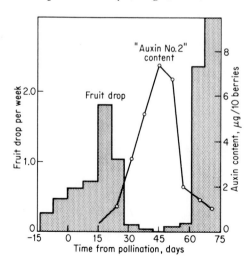

development of fruits. *Quart. Rev. Biol.*, 27:33–57.

————. 1962. Basic physiological processes affecting fruit development, pp. 5–24. In S. G. Younkin (ed.), *Plant Science Symposium on Fruit Set.* Campbell Soup Co., Camden, N.J.

REFERENCES CITED

Bain, J. M., and R. N. Robertson. 1951. Physiology of growth of apple fruits. I. Cell size, number and fruit development. *Australian J. Sci. Res.*, 4:75–91.

Carr, D. J., and K. G. M. Skene. 1961. Diauxic growth curves of seeds with reference to French beans. *Australian J. Biol. Sci.*, 14:1–12.

Clark, H. E., and K. R. Kerns. 1943. Effects of growth regulating substances on parthenocarpic fruit. *Botan. Gaz.*, 104:639–644.

Clements, H. F. 1940. Movement of organic solutes in the sausage tree. *Plant Physiol.*, 15:689–700.

Coombe, B. G. 1960. Relationship of growth and development to changes in sugars, auxins, and gibberellins in fruit of seeded and seedless varieties of *Vitis*. *Plant Physiol.*, 35:241–250.

Crane, J. C. 1948. Fruit growth of four fig varieties as measured by diameter and fresh weight. *Proc. Am. Soc. Hort. Sci.*, 52:237–244.

————, M. V. Bradley, and L. C. Luckwill. 1959. Auxins in parthenocarpic and non-parthenocarpic figs. *J. Hort. Sci.*, 34:142–153.

————, and R. M. Brooks. 1952. Growth of apricot fruits as influenced by 2,4,5-trichlorophenoxyacetic acid application. *Proc. Am. Soc. Hort. Sci.*, 59:218–224.

Emmerling, A. 1880. Studien über die Eiweissbildung in der Pflanze. I. *Londev. Vers. Sta.*, 24:113–160 (cited by McKee et al., 1955).

Goldacre, P. L., and W. Bottomley. 1959. A

kinin in apple fruitlets. *Nature*, 184:555–556.

Hafen, L., and A. C. Leopold. Unpublished.

Harris, R. W., and C. J. Hansen. 1955. The effects of 2,4,5-trichlorophenoxyacetic acid on the development and maturation of French prune. *Proc. Am. Soc. Hort. Sci.*, 66:73–78.

Klämbt, H. D. 1958. Untersuchungen über Entwicklung und Wuchsstoffhaushalt bei *Ribes-arten*. *Planta*, 50:526–556.

Leopold, A. C. 1955. *Auxins and Plant Growth*. University of California Press, Berkeley, Calif. 354 pp.

———. 1958. Auxin uses in the control of flowering and fruiting. *Ann. Rev. Plant Physiol.*, 9:281–310.

Letham, D. S., and E. G. Bollard. 1961. Stimulants of cell division in developing fruits. *Nature*, 191:1119–1120.

Luckwill, L. C. 1953. Studies of fruit development in relation to plant hormones. II. The effect of naphthalene acetic acid on fruit set and fruit development in apples. *J. Hort. Sci.*, 28:25–40.

McDonough, W. T., and H. G. Gauch. 1959. The contribution of the awns to the development of the kernels of bearded wheat. *Maryland Agr. Expt. Sta. Bull.*, A-103. 15 pp.

McKee, H. S., L. Nestel, and R. N. Robertson. 1955. Physiology of pea fruits. II. Soluble nitrogenous constituents in the developing fruit. *Australian J. Sci.*, 8:467–475.

Nitsch, J. P. 1950. Growth and morphogenesis of the strawberry as related to auxin. *Am. J. Botany*, 37:211–215.

——— and C. Nitsch. 1961. Growth factors in the tomato fruit, pp. 687–705. In R. M. Klein (ed.), *Plant Growth Regulation*. Iowa State University Press, Ames, Iowa.

———, C. Pratt, C. Nitsch, and N. J. Shaulis. 1960. Natural growth substances in Concord and Concord seedless grapes in relation to berry development. *Am. J. Botany*, 47:566–576.

Schenk, R. V. 1961. Development of the peanut fruit. *Georgia Agr. Expt. Sta. Tech. Bull.*, 22. 53 pp.

Skene, K. G. M., and D. J. Carr. 1961. A quantitative study of gibberellin of seeds of *Phaseolus*. *Australian J. Biol. Sci.*, 14:13–25.

Stahly, E. A., and A. H. Thompson. 1959. Auxin levels in developing Halehaven peach ovules. *Maryland Agr. Expt. Sta. Bull.*, A-104.

Steward, F. C., and N. W. Simmonds. 1954. Growth promoting substances in the ovary and immature fruit of the banana. *Nature*, 173:1083.

Tukey, H. B. 1933. Embryo abortion in early ripening varieties of *Prunus avium*. *Botan. Gaz.*, 94:433–468.

———. 1934. Growth of the embryo, seed, and pericarp of the sour cherry in relation to season of fruit ripening. *Proc. Am. Soc. Hort. Sci.*, 31:125–144.

——— and J. O. Young. 1939. Histological study of the developing fruit of the sour cherry. *Botan. Gaz.*, 100:723–749.

Urata, V. 1954. Pollination requirements of Macadamia. *Hawaii Agr. Expt. Sta. Tech. Bull.*, 22:1–40.

Verkerk, K. 1957. The pollination of tomatoes. *Netherlands J. Agr. Sci.*, 5:37–54.

Visser, T. 1955. De Karakteristiek van Appelbloemen en-Vruchten in Verband met hun Positie in de Tros. *Mededel. Directeur Tuinbouw*, 18:809–822.

Wright, S. T. C. 1956. Studies of fruit development in relation to plant hormones. III. *J. Hort. Sci.*, 31:196–211.

17 | Fruit ripening

As the fruit reaches the end of its growth period, it may undergo some characteristic qualitative changes, which are collectively referred to as *ripening*. Often this includes a softening of the fleshy fruit with associated changes in pigmentation and flavor. Numerous fruits may not apparently experience ripening, especially the nonfleshy fruits. In some cases ripening is stimulated by picking the fruit. For example, the ripening of avocados characteristically does not occur until after the fruit is picked; in many other fruits ripening is hastened by picking (e.g., banana, apple, papaya).

The ripening processes are frequently coincident with the termination of fruit growth, raising the question of whether growth-substance depletion might be responsible for both processes; however, though the auxin content of ripening fruits is very low, it appears unlikely that this condition is at all causative of ripening, for auxin applications to mature fruits frequently stimulate rather than retard ripening.

To clarify the terms, the word *maturation* refers to the processes associated with a fruit reaching full size, and *ripening* refers to the processes which qualitatively transform the mature fruit.

Changes with ripening

The general changes associated with ripening, including softening of the fruit flesh, hydrolytic conversions of storage materials in the fruit, and changes in the pigments and flavors, can be attributed to the energies provided by respiratory activities. This concept, first specifically proposed by Biale (1950), is now well documented. Especially relevant is the observation of Marks et al. (1957) that respiratory inhibitors effectively prevent ripening in tomato fruits. The correlation between ripening processes and metabolic activities makes a clear case for the essentiality of respiratory energies for ripening changes.

Softening with ripening is characteristic of fleshy fruits. This may occur as a consequence either of changes in pectic materials cementing the cell walls or of hydrolysis of starches or fats. The latter type of softening is illustrated by the squash (hydrolysis of starches) and avocado fruits (hydrolysis of fats).

Softening is ordinarily measured by the force needed to press a plunger a given distance into the fruit, and such changes during the ripening of apples are illustrated in Fig. 17-1 (Gerhardt and Smith, 1946). The softening is interpreted as the solubilization of pectic substances from the middle lamellae and hence the associated rise in soluble pectins evident in Fig. 17-1. The solubilizing of the pectic substances might be due to enzymes altering the methylations of the galacturonic acids or altering the length of the polygalacturonide acid chains or both (see Fig. 17-2). For some time it was doubtful whether there were any enzymes which could hydrolyze the pectic chains in ripening fruits (Kertesz, 1951), but more recent work has established the presence of such polygalacturonidases in fruits (Bell, 1951).

The loosening of cell cements can proceed very far. On eating a very ripe apple, one has the sensation of tastelessness, as if the flavor materials had disappeared with advanced ripening. Actually, however, the tastelessness may be due to the extreme ease of cellular separation, which results in a slippage of the cells during mastication; consequently, they are not ruptured enough to yield the flavor substances present inside.

Hydrolytic changes during ripening usually lead to the formation of sugars. Various fruits show widely different rates and extents of such hydrolytic activities; for example, the banana ripens extremely quickly, and the hydrolysis of starch is precipitous (Fig. 17-3). Apple fruits are more gradual in hydrolytic as well as in other ripening actions, and the citrus fruits such as orange and lemon are ponderously slow, sometimes progressing over a period of months. Hydrolytic activities can give rise to increases in fruit sugars, not only from starches but also from fats (Beevers, 1961). The hydrolysis of pectic substances may be involved in the softening of the tissues, with the formation of soluble pectins.

In contrast to the other food reserves, proteins are actually synthesized at increasing rates during the ripening process in apples, as shown by Hulme (1939, 1954). This important exception to the hydrolytic tendencies will be discussed below in connection with the mechanism of ripening.

Quality changes in ripening fruits include marked changes in pigmentation, production of flavor materials, and usually depletion of astringent substances. The pigment changes during ripening of three fruits are shown in Fig. 17-4 to illustrate the usual drop in chlorophyll content and the formation of carotenoids. The loss of chlorophyll from fruits may be synchronous with ripening (as in banana), or it may occur only in

Fig. 17-1 | During the ripening of apple fruits, the declining firmness is associated with a rise in the content of soluble pectins. Delicious apples in 2° storage (Gerhardt and Smith, 1946).

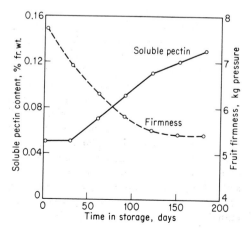

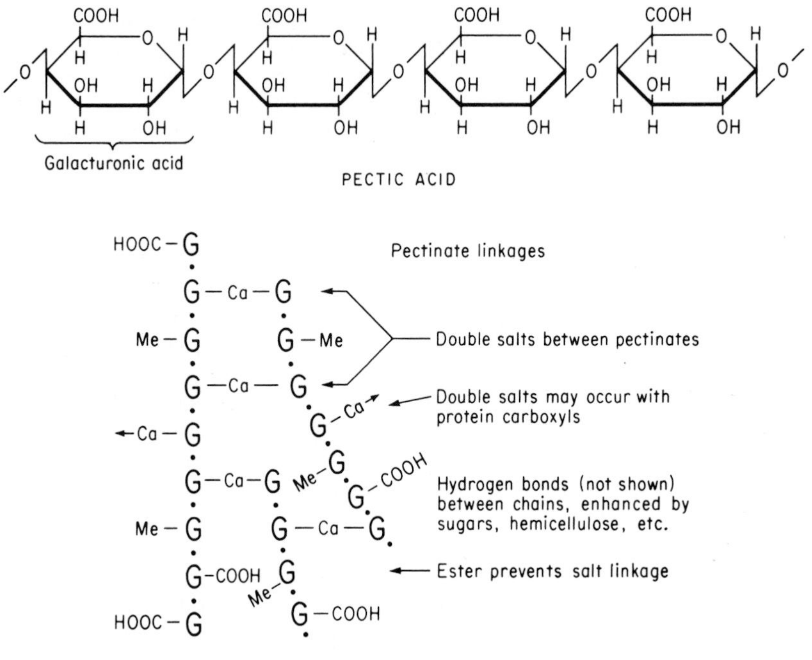

Fig. 17-2 | Unsubstituted chains of polygalacturonic acid are termed *pectic acids*, and those with varying amounts of methyl esterifications are termed *pectinic acids*. In the plant, all the pectic substances are more or less esterified. Water soluble forms are called *pectin*, and water insoluble forms *protopectin*, though the distinctions are very imprecise. Calcium can form double salt linkages between the galacturonate chains, as well as between the galacturonates and the carboxyl groups of other components such as proteins. Esters on the galacturonates hinder the formation of such salt linkages, increasing the water solubility and decreasing the cementing properties of the pectic substances.

the earliest stages of ripening (in the orange) or, rarely, after other indices of ripening have been passed (in some pears). The coloration of the ripening fruits may be a consequence of the formation of carotenoid pigments (as in the orange) or a consequence of the disappearance of chlorophyll with little or no net formation of carotenoids (as in the banana). The pigments of some fruits are limited to carotenes (papaya) and of others to anthocyanins (strawberry); in some the pigments are restricted to the shell (apple), and in others they permeate the entire fleshy parts (peach). The antho-cyanin or flavone pigments may be formed in response to sunlight (Duggar, 1913), and the action spectrum for the pigmentation of apples indicates the involvement of phytochrome (cf. Fig. 20-7). The accumulation of sugars may accentuate the tendencies to form pigments (Thimann and Edmondson, 1949; Modi and Patwa, 1960). These considerations, with the additional fact that pigmentation may be strongly altered by temperature (Denisen, 1951) in a manner distinctly different from ripening changes, indicate that color changes may not be proportional to fruit ripening.

The development of flavor substances in fruits remains for future research, and surely the advent of gas chromatography will allow rapid advances in this area soon. In apples numerous esters, aldehydes, and ketones have been identified (cf. Ulrich, 1958), plus a series of saturated and unsaturated hydrocarbons (Meigh, 1959). Siegelman and Hendricks (1958) have made the surprising observation that light inhibits the formation of some flavor substances in apples, apparently diverting the necessary substrates over to the formation of pigments instead.

The decline of astringent materials such as phenolics (Reeve, 1959) is common to pomological fruits, but little is known of the significance of the changes.

The respiratory climacteric

From studies of the ripening of apple fruits, Kidd and West (1930) discovered that ripening was associated with spectacular changes in respiratory rates, including a lowering of respiration in the mature fruit, followed by a large increase in respiration during the time of ripening. After reaching a climacteric peak, respiration falls off again

Fig. 17-3 | Fruit-ripening processes may be very rapid, as in banana; moderate, as in apple; of slow, as in orange. The most rapid ripeners are usually associated with a hydrolysis of starch or other reserve material (data from von Loesche, 1950; Smock and Neubert, 1950; and Stahl and Camp, 1936.)

Fig. 17-4 | Pigment changes during fruit ripening ordinarily involve a decline in chlorophyll, and carotenoid transformations. The banana does not change in total carotenoids; the apple carotenoids rise as the chlorophyll declines; and the orange carotenoids increase considerably later (von Loesche, 1950; Workman, 1963; Miller et al., 1940).

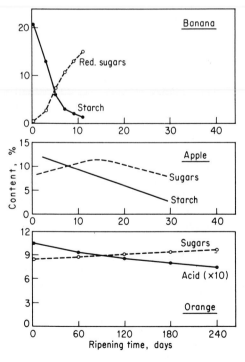

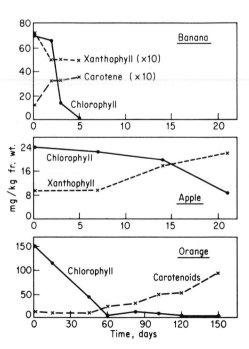

as the fruit begins to enter a senescent decline. These workers also established that .the effectiveness of refrigeration in prolonging the storage life was associated with a suppression of the *intensity* of this respiratory climacteric as well as with a prolongation of the *duration* of its progress.

In many fleshy fruits the climacteric peak occurs at the time of optimal eating quality, as in pears; in others it slightly precedes this optimum (apple, banana). In tomatoes the climacteric is reached well before the fruit is fully ripe. Biale (1950) has suggested that the climacteric is associated with the hydrolysis of food reserves in the fruit, pointing out that fruits which do not ordinarily experience a climacteric after harvest (such as orange, lemon, and fig) do not experience extensive hydrolytic activities (see Fig. 17-3).

The climacteric may occur rapidly, as in the avocado and banana; at intermediate rates, as in pear, mango, and apple; or not at all, as in orange and lemon. Some comparative climacteric curves at room temperatures are illustrated in Fig. 17-5; in each case there is a distinct respiratory decrease in the mature fruit, followed by the rise to the climacteric peak and then a drop again.

In contrast to the climacteric fruits and the fruits such as citrus that maintain a steady respiration during ripening, some fruits show only a decline in respiration during the ripening period. Examples include the pepper (Howard and Yamaguchi, 1957) and the peanut (Schenk, 1961).

An interesting fruit is the tomato, which is enclosed in a nearly gas-impermeable skin; its gas exchange must be essentially restricted to the small scar left by the abscission of the corolla at the time of fruit set (Clendenning, 1941).

Most fruits which experience the climacteric do so whether they are picked or ripen on the tree; however, some fruits, especially the avocado in California, will commence the climacteric only after being picked from the tree. As with ripening processes in general, picking will hasten the climacteric rise of many fruits. If a fruit has passed the climacteric peak before being picked, its respiratory pattern will be only a steady decline—a feature which is useful for determining the state of ripening of picked fruits (Kidd and West, 1937).

The original observations of Kidd and West (1930) that low temperature will suppress and defer the progress of the climacteric appear to apply to fruits generally. In some fruits an experience of too low a temperature will erase the ability to proceed with the climacteric (e.g., pear; Hansen and Hartman, 1937).

Knowing of the climacteric, Kidd and West (1933) were able to develop storage techniques involving the use of controlled atmospheres—low oxygen tensions, nitrogen atmospheres, or simultaneously controlled oxygen and carbon dioxide tensions. Such treatments were effective in preventing the development of the climacteric rise, especially treatments in which low oxygen levels were achieved. Such techniques for fruit storage have been rediscovered in recent times, fruits being stored in polyethylene bags which lead automatically to an elevated CO_2 and depressed O_2 atmosphere (Smock and Blanpied, 1958).

The abilities of some gases to stimulate the climacteric were the basis of an ancient Chinese custom of ripening fruits in rooms where incense was being burned. Kerosene stoves were used to improve the coloring of lemons in California in the 1920s, and Denny (1924*b*) found that unsaturated hydrocarbon gases in the fumes were responsible. Trying ethylene as a simple model, he found that this gas could strongly promote ripening activities. Gane (1937) specifically established that ethylene would stimulate the climacteric rise; fruits which had reached the climacteric peak were insensitive to the ethylene treatment. He further established that ripe bananas would stimulate the climacteric in the same manner as ethylene and that ethylene could be identified in the emanations from the ripe fruit (Gane, 1935). Quantitative measurements showed that ethylene production commonly follows a pattern similar to respiratory activity (Fig. 17-6).

As ethylene has now been identified in the emanations of many ripe fruits (cf. Biale, 1950), it is of interest to note that the effectiveness of this gas in stimulating the climacteric is sharply limited by low temperature or high and is prevented by very low oxygen tensions (Denny, 1924a).

Ethylene is so effective in stimulating respiration that even fruits such as oranges and lemons which do not naturally experience a climacteric rise can be induced to do so by ethylene treatment (Denny, 1924a).

Ripening mechanisms

Surveying the various changes in fruit constituents and emanations driven by respiratory permutations in the fruit, one is faced with the problem of how these changes are instigated. The first question one might ask is: What treatments can start or stop the ripening processes? Three treatments that trigger or stimulate ripening are readily recognized: picking fruits, exposing them to certain gases, and providing them with certain metabolites.

The ripening of avocado fruits begins immediately after picking; the ripening of many pome fruits is markedly accelerated following picking. In short, separation of the fruit from the tree can frequently promote ripening, which suggests that the signal for ripening may arise from inside the fruit or that a suppression of ripening is exerted by other plant parts (Burg, 1963).

A second ripening treatment is the application of gases. Unsaturated hydrocarbons such as ethylene can stimulate the ripening processes. Special significance is assignable to the ethylene effects, that gas being a common emanation of ripening climacteric fruits. There are some fruits

such as peaches and apricots which respond poorly to ethylene and some which can be forced into a climacteric by ethylene though they do not normally experience such a respiratory change during ripening (orange and lemon).

A third ripening treatment is the addition of distinctive respiratory substrates. Hulme and Neal (1957) made the interesting observation that the climacteric in apple tissues could be stimulated by providing the tissue with malate, suggesting that this organic acid may be intimately related to the metabolic pathways of the climacteric rise. Another report by Rakitin et al. (1957) suggests a similar ripening response to additions of methanol to persimmon fruits. These fragments of information seem to imply a chemical regulation of ripening by metabolic transformations.

Fig. 17-5 | The rate of ripening processes is reflected in the intensity of the respiratory climacteric, the fastest-ripening avocado showing the greatest climacteric peak, and banana, pear, and apple showing lesser peaks, in that order (Biale, 1950).

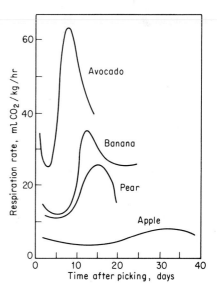

Fig. 17-6 | With the climacteric rise in respiration, pear fruits produce an associated burst of ethylene. Fruits were chilled at 0°C and then removed to room temperatures (Hansen, 1942).

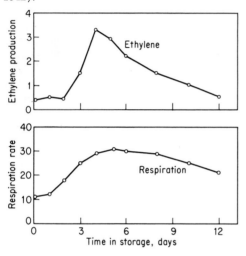

Fig. 17-7 | The respiratory climacteric in banana fruits is associated with large changes in the internal atmosphere in the fruit, including a marked depression of oxygen content and a rise in CO_2 content (Leonard and Wardlaw, 1941).

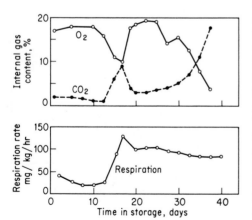

The first theory that was advanced to account for ripening was made by Kidd (1934). Following in detail the changes in constituents of apples during ripening, he observed that at the time when the climacteric rise began, fructose began to disappear from the cytoplasm of the cells, and the respiratory rise continued as long as fructose was being supplied from the vacuoles to the cytoplasm. He proposed, therefore, that the climacteric was a consequence of the metabolism of an "activated" fructose. Biale (1950) has noted the possibility that such a role could be taken by a phosphorylated fructose. In any event, the concept of substrate transformations as the mechanism for the climacteric remains a cogent one today, especially in view of the ability of some substrate additions to induce the climacteric.

A second theory was proposed at about the same time by Wardlaw and Leonard (1936) from their studies of gas-exchange experiments with several tropical fruits. They noted that with increases in size, fruits developed physical limitations to the free exchange of carbon dioxide and oxygen; and as these limitations became acute, CO_2 accumulated inside the fruit, and oxygen levels became very low. They proposed that the respiratory climacteric could be an anaerobic type of respiratory shift. Careful measurements of the internal gases revealed that in fact such accumulations of CO_2 and depletions of O_2 did occur, and as illustrated in Fig. 17-7, these changes coincided with the development of the climacteric. In further support of their idea that the climacteric rise was a type of anaerobiosis, they noted that some fruits actually ripen from the center outward (Leonard and Wardlaw, 1941) and that elevations of temperature which magnify the climacteric also enhance the state of anaerobiosis inside the fruit. While their measurements were fine for the techniques available at the time, their theory seems to be deficient in two respects: The development of anaerobiosis inside the fruit does not appear to precede the climacteric but rather accompanies it, and placing fruits in anaerobic conditions actually prevents rather than stimulates ripening (e.g., Blackman and Parija, 1928).

Twenty years passed before another theory of the climacteric was proposed. With the development of knowledge about phosphorylations as the principal means of minting the currency of metabolic energy, the possibility arose that the availability of phosphate acceptors might naturally limit metabolic rates. Pearson and Robertson (1952, 1954) first tested the possibility in ripening apples by measuring the response of fruits at different stages of ripening to additions of the uncoupling agent, dinitrophenol. This poison increases respiration by increasing the availability of phosphate acceptors at the expense of phosphate esters. They found that it evoked large respiratory increases in preclimacteric fruits but not in climacteric or postclimacteric ones. Millerd et al. (1953) further developed the idea in studies of ripening in avocado; they confirmed the dinitrophenol response in that fruit, and they found that extracts of climacteric fruits could cause respiratory uncoupling in mung bean mitochondrial preparations. They suggested specifically that the respiratory rise was a consequence of the accumulation of naturally occurring uncoupling poisons which would obstruct the effectiveness of oxidative phosphorylation. The respiratory rise would then be interpreted as a racing of the respiratory motor because of the uncoupled phosphorylation.

The uncoupling theory of ripening implies that with the climacteric rise there develops a depreciation of available energies for biosyntheses, and even before the theory was proposed, Hulme (1939, 1954) had noted that ripening in apples was associated with considerable increases in protein synthesis. The theory was further weakened by experiments of Marks et al. (1957), who noted that uncoupling poisons actually blocked ripening of tomato fruits and who deduced

that effective phosphorylation was essential to the ripening process. Indeed, Romani and Biale (1957) established that instead of the efficiency of phosphorylation decreasing with ripening, it actually rose appreciably during the ripening of avocado fruits. Some of their data are plotted in Fig. 17-8, in which it can be seen that oxidative phosphorylation improved during almost the entire climacteric rise of respiration. Similar conclusions were made by Rowan et al. (1958). Reexamining the important increase in protein synthesis during ripening of apples, Hulme (1954) noted that protein synthesis continues to increase during the entire climacteric rise, as shown in Fig. 17-9, leaving open the possibility that the constructive utilization of phosphoryl esters in this synthetic activity might help to account for the respiratory increase, as Pearson and Robertson (1954) had also suggested.

Fig. 17-8 | The respiratory climacteric in avocado fruits is reflected in an increase in oxidative phosphorylation, as indicated by the rise in the P-O ratio. Pyruvate as substrate (Romani and Biale, 1957).

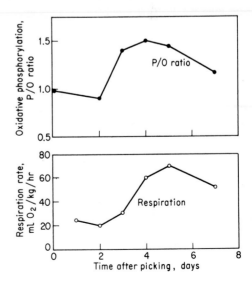

The uncoupling theory of fruit ripening has indirectly led to a new affirmation of the concept that ripening is a positive, constructive metabolic activity, requiring the expenditure of energy. The slowing of ripening by mild refrigeration of fruits can still be interpreted as a suppression of the energetic activities which drive the transformations involved in ripening.

Ethylene role

Ever since ethylene was found in fruit emanations and was known to trigger the ripening processes of fruits in general, there has been a possibility that this metabolic product could be responsible for the respiratory climacteric. Correlations of the production of ethylene with the development of the climacteric, such as that of Hansen (1942) shown in Fig. 17-6, made the possibility even more attractive. However, these and other data (Nelson, 1940) indicated that ethylene production began

after the climacteric rise had started—a feature which would be inconsistent with the argument. Using more refined chemical methods of analysis, Biale et al. (1954) measured ethylene production by several types of fruits and found no ethylene during the climacteric rise of some (mango) and ethylene production only after the respiratory rise had started in others (avocado, banana). They then deduced that ethylene was only a product of ripening, serving further to enhance the ripening progress.

With the advent of gas chromatography, tremendous increases in sensitivity of ethylene analyses became possible. Burg and Thimann (1959) made precise measurements of ethylene production in apple tissues and noted that it was prevented by temperatures near freezing or above 40°C or by very low oxygen tensions (all conditions which prevent ripening). They noted that ethylene production was consistently correlated with respiration rate in climacteric apple slices (Burg and Thimann, 1960). Reexamining the question of the relation of ethylene formation to the start of the climacteric, it was then found that ethylene was consistently produced at the onset of the climacteric (Burg and Burg, 1962a) or actually before the climacteric rise began (Burg and Burg, 1962a,b). Similar conclusions from gas-chromatography experiments were simultaneously reported by Lyons et al. (1962) for cantaloupe fruits.

Illustrating the relation of the climacteric rise to ethylene production, the data in Fig. 17-10 (Burg and Burg, 1962a) reveal that even in mango fruits there is sufficient preclimacteric formation of ethylene to cause the respiratory rise. In bananas, the quantities of ethylene produced are greater, and there ethylene formation bursts forth during the earliest part of the climacteric rise. A similar preclimacteric ethylene production was found in avocados (Burg and Burg, 1962b). The validity of the ethylene

Fig. 17-9 | After the preclimacteric dip, the rise in respiration is also associated with a rise in protein content in Bramley's Seedling apple, indicating an enhanced synthesis with the respiratory burst (Hulme, 1954).

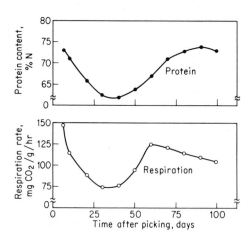

stimulus was reaffirmed in several other ways, including, for example, a correlation of the time required for mangoes to reach the climacteric peak with concentrations of ethylene applied and a similar correlation of the extent of the climacteric rise with ethylene concentrations (Fig. 17-11). Small amounts of ethylene were even found in the citrus fruits, which lack the climacteric. These authors conclude, then, that ripening in general is evoked through the formation of ethylene, and in those fruits where sufficient ethylene is produced, a respiratory climacteric results.

Ethylene treatments can induce leaves to experience a respiratory climacteric (Herrero and Hall, 1960) and to develop the pigment changes commonly associated with fruit ripening.

Accepting ethylene as the trigger of fruit ripening, the locus and manner of ethylene synthesis become of special importance. Burg and Thimann (1959) had found a close association of ethylene production with respiratory activity of apple pieces and suggested that the osmotically active cell particulates might be the site at which ethylene was produced. Spencer (1959) isolated some particulates from tomato fruits which seemed to produce ethylene. Lieberman and Craft (1961) reported the production of ethylene by the mitochondria of tomato-fruit tissue. Burg and Burg (1961) in turn denied this, producing evidence that the volatile Lieberman and Craft were following in the gas-chromatography apparatus was not identical with ethylene; the material was later identified as ethane by Meigh (1962). Chandra and Spencer (1962) rejoined the argument, however, with evidence that the volatile gas in their material was indeed ethylene and that its formation by cell fractions other than the mitochondria was due to contamination with mitochondria. The ethylene production in these preparations seems to be associated with damaged or aging mitochondria (Chandra and Spencer, 1962), and so its

relevance to the ethylene formation in pre-climacteric fruits is not assured.

It is well known that unsaturated gases other than ethylene are produced by ripening fruits (Meigh, 1959), and such gases apparently may have stimulatory properties not unlike those of ethylene (Maxie and Baker, 1954). Ethylene production in apples, however, is a thousandfold more intense than the production of other volatile unsaturated hydrocarbons, and so ethylene appears to be the dominant stimulant in this group.

Fig. 17-10 | Employing gas chromatography, the rise in respiration during ripening was found to be associated with a concomitant rise in ethylene production in mango and to be preceded by a burst of ethylene production in the banana. Fruits of Kent mango, 24°C; Gros Michel banana, 16°C (Burg and Burg, 1962*a*).

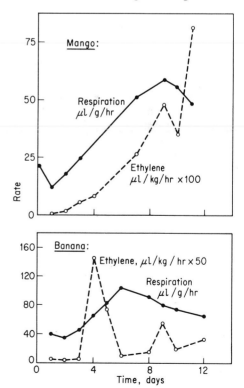

Varner (1961) pointed out that there may be a general deterioration of membrane structures associated with fruit ripening and abscission processes. Sacher (1957, 1962) has actually measured such deteriorations as increases in tissue permeability. Such membrane changes could relate to the metabolic changes associated with the ripening process, including of course the production of ethylene.

The cessation of ripening at temperature extremes or under anaerobiosis can be related to the termination of ethylene production under these conditions, but in addition there appears to be a singular inability of ethylene to cause ripening responses under these same conditions (Denny, 1924a).

In conclusion, the ripening of fleshy fruits is seen as some dramatic changes and rearrangements of the chemical components of the fruit, and these changes are driven by

large expenditures of respiratory energies. While it seems clear now that the unleashing of the respiratory actions for these chemical changes may be controlled by the metabolic production of the unsaturated hydrocarbon ethylene, the manner in which this triggering chemical might work is entirely unknown. Furthermore, though the component changes during ripening can be readily followed and cataloged, the means by which the respiratory climacteric might invoke such changes are also unknown.

GENERAL REFERENCES

Biale, J. B. 1950. Postharvest physiology and biochemistry of fruits. *Ann. Rev. Plant Physiol.*, 1:183–206.

———. 1960. The postharvest biochemistry of tropical and subtropical fruits. *Advan. Food Res.*, 10:293–354.

Burg, S. P. 1962. The physiology of ethylene formation. *Ann. Rev. Plant Physiol.*, 13:265–302.

Ulrich, R. 1952. *La Vie des Fruits.* Masson et Cie, Paris. 366 pp.

———. 1958. Postharvest physiology of fruits. *Ann. Rev. Plant Physiol.*, 9:385–416.

Fig. 17-11 | Ethylene treatments of Kent mangoes can quantitatively regulate the climacteric achieved during ripening, as shown by the shortening of the time to climacteric peak (below) and by the greater magnitude of the respiratory peak achieved (above) with increasing concentrations of ethylene applied for 2 days at 24°C (Burg and Burg, 1962a).

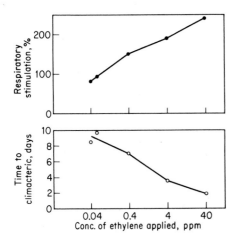

REFERENCES CITED

Beevers, H. 1961. Metabolic production of sucrose from fat. *Nature*, 191:433–436.

Bell, T. A. 1951. Pectolytic enzyme activity in various parts of the cucumber. *Botan. Gaz.*, 113:216–221.

Biale, J. B. 1950. Postharvest physiology and biochemistry of fruits. *Ann. Rev. Plant Physiol.*, 1:183–206.

———, R. E. Young, and A. Olmstead. 1954. Fruit respiration and ethylene production. *Plant Physiol.*, 29:168–174.

Blackman, F. F., and R. Parija. 1928. *Proc.*

Roy. Soc. (London), B, 103:422–445 (cited by Biale, 1950).

Burg, S. P. 1963. Studies on the formation and function of ethylene gas in plant tissues, pp. 719–725. In J. P. Nitsch (ed.), *Régulateurs Naturels de la Croissance Végétale*, CNRS, Paris.

—— and E. A. Burg. 1961. Ethylene evolution and subcellular particles. *Nature*, 191:967–969.

—— and ——. 1962*a*. Role of ethylene in fruit ripening. *Plant Physiol.*, 37:179–189.

—— and ——. 1962*b*. Postharvest ripening of avocado. *Nature*, 194:398–399.

—— and K. V. Thimann. 1959. The physiology of ethylene formation in apples. *Proc. Natl. Acad. Sci. U.S.*, 45:335–344.

—— and ——. 1960. Studies on ethylene production of apple tissue. *Plant Physiol.*, 35:24–35.

Chandra, G. R., and M. Spencer. 1962. Ethylene production by subcellular particles from tomatoes. *Nature*, 194:361–364.

Clendenning, K. A. 1941. Studies of the tomato in relation to its storage. II. *Can. J. Res.*, C, 19:500–518.

Denisen, E. L. 1951. Carotenoid content of tomato fruits. I. Effect of temperature and light. II. Effects of nutrients, storage, and variety. *Iowa State Coll. J. Sci.*, 25:549–574.

Denny, F. E. 1924*a*. Effect of ethylene upon respiration of lemons. *Botan. Gaz.*, 77:322–329.

——. 1924*b*. Hastening the coloration of lemons. *J. Agr. Res.*, 27:757–769.

Duggar, B. M. 1913. Lycopersicin, the red pigment of the tomato, and the effects of conditions upon its development. *Wash. Univ. Studies*, 1:22–45.

Gane, R. 1935. The formation of ethylene by plant tissues and its significance in the ripening of fruits. *J. Pomol. Hort. Sci.*, 13:351.

——. 1937. The respiration of bananas in presence of ethylene. *New Phytologist*, 36:170–178.

Gerhardt, F., and E. Smith. 1946. Physiology and dessert quality of delicious apples as influenced by handling, storage and simulated marketing practice. *Proc. Wash. State Hort. Assoc.*, 1945:151–172.

Hansen, E. 1942. Quantitative study of ethylene production in pears. *Botan. Gaz.*, 103:543–548.

—— and E. Hartman. 1937. Effect of ethylene and metabolic gases upon respiration and ripening of pears before and after cold storage. *Plant Physiol.*, 12:441–454.

Herrero, F. A., and W. C. Hall. 1960. General effects of ethylene on enzyme systems in the cotton leaf. *Physiol. Plantarum*, 13:736–750.

Howard, F. D., and M. Yamaguchi. 1957. Respiration and oxidative activity of particulate fractions from pepper fruits. *Plant Physiol.*, 32:418–428.

Hulme, A. C. 1939. The nitrogen metabolism of the apple fruit in relation to its growth and respiration. *Rept. Food Investigation Board*, 55.

——. 1954. Studies in the nitrogen metabolism of apple fruits. *J. Exptl. Botany*, 5:159–172.

—— and G. E. Neal. 1957. A new factor in the respiration climacteric of apple fruits. *Nature*, 179:1192–1193.

Kertesz, Z. I. 1951. *The Pectic Substances.* Interscience Publishers, Inc., New York. 628 pp.

Kidd, F. 1934. The respiration of fruits. *Proc. Roy. Inst. G. Brit.*, 1934:351–381.

—— and C. West. 1930. Physiology of fruit. I. Changes in the respiratory activity of apples during their senescence at different temperatures. *Proc. Roy. Soc. (London)*, B, 106:93–109.

—— and ——. 1933. The influence of the composition of the atmosphere upon the incidence of the climacteric in apples. *Rept. Food Investigation Board*, 51–57.

———— and ————. 1937. The keeping quality of apples in relation to their maturity when gathered. *Sci. Hort.*, 5:78.

Leonard, E. R., and C. W. Wardlaw. 1941. Studies in tropical fruits. XII. Respiration of bananas. *Ann. Botany (London)*, 5: 379–423.

Lieberman, M., and C. C. Craft. 1961. Ethylene production by cytoplasmic particles from apples and tomato fruits in the presence of thiomalic and thioglycolic acid. *Nature*, 189:243.

Loesche, H. W. von. 1950. *Bananas*. Interscience Publishers, Inc., New York. 189 pp.

Lyons, J. M., W. B. McGlasson, and H. R. Pratt. 1962. Ethylene production, respiration and internal gas concentrations in cantaloupe fruits at various stages of maturity. *Plant Physiol.*, 37:31–36.

Marks, J. D., R. Bernlohr, and J. E. Varner. 1957. Oxidative phosphorylation in ripening fruit. *Plant Physiol.*, 32:259–262.

Maxie, E. C., and C. E. Baker. 1954. Air filtration studies in a commercial type apple storage. *Proc. Am. Soc. Hort. Sci.*, 64:235–247.

Meigh, D. F. 1959. Nature of the olefins produced by apples. *Nature*, 184:1072–1073.

————. 1962. Problems of ethylene metabolism. *Nature*, 196:345–347.

————, K. H. Norris, C. C. Craft, and M. Lieberman. 1960. Ethylene production by tomato and apple fruits. *Nature*, 186: 902–903.

Miller, E. V., J. R. Winston, and H. A. Schomer. 1940. Physiological studies of plastid pigments in rinds of maturing oranges. *J. Agr. Res.*, 60:259–267.

Millerd, A., J. Bonner, and J. B. Biale. 1953. The climacteric rise in fruit respiration as controlled by phosphorylative coupling. *Plant Physiol.*, 28:521–531.

Modi, V. V., and D. K. Patwa. 1960. Enzymatic synthesis and destruction of carotenoids in mango extracts. *Experientia*, 16:352.

Nelson, R. C. 1940. Quantitative study of the production of ethylene by ripening McIntosh apples. *Plant Physiol.*, 15:149–151.

Pearson, J. A., and R. N. Robertson. 1952. The climacteric rise in respiration of fruit. *Australian J. Sci.*, 15:99–100.

———— and ————. 1954. The physiology of growth in apple fruits. VI. The control of respiration rate and synthesis. *Australian J. Biol. Sci.*, 7:1–17.

Rakitin, Y. V., A. V. Krylov, and G. A. Tsrakanova. 1957. Metabolic transformation of methyl alcohol introduced into fruits to hasten ripening. *Dokl. Bot. Sci. Sect. (English Transl.)*, 116:874.

Reeve, R. M. 1959. Histological and histochemical changes in developing and ripening peaches. I. The catechol tannins. *Am. J. Botany*, 46:210–217.

Romani, R. J., and J. B. Biale. 1957. Metabolic processes in cytoplasmic plastides of the avocado fruit. IV. *Plant Physiol.*, 32: 662–668.

Rowan, K. S., H. K. Pratt, and R. N. Robertson. 1958. Relationship of high energy phosphate, protein synthesis and the climacteric in ripening avocado and tomato. *Australian J. Biol. Sci.*, 11:329–335.

Sacher, J. A. 1957. Relationship between auxin and membrane integrity in tissue senescence and abscission. *Science*, 125: 1199–1200.

————. 1959. Studies on auxin: membrane permeability relations in fruit and leaf tissues. *Plant Physiol.*, 34:365–372.

————. 1962. Relations between changes in membrane permeability and the climacteric in banana and avocado. *Nature*, 195: 577–578.

Schenk, R. V. 1961. Development of the peanut fruit. *Georgia Agr. Expt. Sta. Tech. Bull.*, NS22. 53 pp.

Siegelman, H. W., and S. B. Hendricks. 1958. Photocontrol of alcohol, aldehyde, and anthocyanin production in apple skin. *Plant Physiol.*, 33:409–413.

Smock, R. M., and G. D. Blanpied. 1958. A comparison of controlled atmosphere storage and film liners for the storage of apples. *Proc. Am. Soc. Hort. Sci.*, 71:36–44.

———, and A. M. Neubert. 1950. *Apples and Apple Products.* Interscience Publishers, Inc., New York. 485 pp.

Spencer, M. S. 1959. Production of ethylene by mitochondria from tomatoes. *Nature*, 184:1231–1232.

Stahl, A. L., and A. F. Camp. 1936. Cold storage studies of Florida citrus fruits. I. *Florida Univ. Agr. Expt. Sta. Bull.*, 303. 67 pp.

Thimann, K. V., and Y. Edmondson. 1949. The biogenesis of the anthocyanins. I. General nutritional conditions leading to anthocyanin formation. *Arch. Biochem.*, 22:33–53.

Ulrich, R. 1958. Postharvest physiology of fruits. *Ann. Rev. Plant Physiol.*, 9:385–416.

Varner, J. E. 1961. Biochemistry of senescence. *Ann. Rev. Plant Physiol.*, 12:245–264.

Wardlaw, C. W., and E. R. Leonard. 1936. Studies in tropical fruits. I. *Ann. Botany* (*London*), 50:622–653.

Workman, M. 1963. Color and pigment changes in Golden Delicious and Grimes Golden apples. *Proc. Am. Soc. Hort. Sci.*, 83:149–161.

18 | Tuber and bulb formation

The fruit is not the only organ with mobilization properties so strong that it swells into an inflated storage structure. The swellings of stems into tubers or of leaf bases into bulbs appear to be different morphological manifestations of the same ontogenetic end. In each case a powerful set of mobilization activities builds up large stored supplies of carbohydrates or fats, and the location of this mobilized depot is an organ in which the polarity has been degraded.

The formation of tubers and bulbs has several interesting analogies to the flower and fruiting activities of plants. In addition to the powerful mobilization actions which are shared with numerous fruits, tubers and bulbs may be formed in response to an *induction* phenomenon which occurs in the leaves and is transmitted to the part which will do the swelling. There follows a morphological *differentiation* and then *growth* of the storage organ, and to continue the analogy, the tubers and bulbs, like some fruits, then experience a *ripening* phenomenon.

Morphologically, the formation of the tuber occurs as a swelling of a cluster of stem internodes, as illustrated in Fig. 18-1. The tuber retains the nodes as "eyes," with a leaf bract or scar and subtended bud; the expression of apical dominance by the terminal eye over the other eyes of the tuber is a natural carryover from the stem situation. There is an interesting loss of polarity associated with the tuber swelling. For example, Mes and Menge (1954) noted that nodes of potato stem in tissue culture developed stems without the normal upright habit, and it was from these ageotropic stems that tubers developed. Esashi (1960) noted that tuber formation in *Begonia* was preceded by a deposition of large amounts of starch in the apical meristems, which then began to show lateral enlargement—the first morphological evidence of tuber formation. Any meristem from a tuber-forming potato or *Begonia* can form tubers, whether aerial or subterranean (Scheumann and von Guttenberg, 1959; Esashi and

Nagao, 1958). Growth of the tuber is by continued cell division and enlargement.

The formation of an onion bulb is a consequence of the mobilization of carbohydrates into the bases of very young leaves. As described by Heath and Holdsworth (1948), there is a cessation of growth of the apical meristem and roots, a cessation of cell division generally, and an investment in a lateral swelling type of growth by the young leaves (Fig. 18-1). When the bulb commences to sprout, elongation activities are restored in the newest leaf primordia, which were enclosed inside the bulb scales, and the enlarged scales deteriorate as they yield their stored carbohydrates.

Relation to growth

As mentioned above, both tuber formation and bulb formation are associated with a suppression of normal elongation growth. In the onion, this suppression is apparently systemic and complete (Heath and Holdsworth, 1948), including a suppression of root growth (Sideris, 1925) and a deterioration of roots and leaves which have already expanded. The apparent antagonism of bulbing and flowering in the onion (Heath and Holdsworth, 1943) is an expression of this systemic inhibitory function. In the tuber formers, there is an inhibition of the nodes in which the tuber formation will occur (Esashi, 1960) and also a systemic inhibition of vegetative growth (Werner, 1947). The time of tuber development is associated with a retarded growth of aboveground parts, as shown in Fig. 18-2 (Wassink and Stolwijk, 1953), followed generally by a senescence of the aerial parts at the time of completion of tuber growth.

Photoperiodic effects

That photoperiods could influence the formation of storage organs was first noted by Werner (1935), who observed that potato plants more readily formed tubers under short photoperiods than long. In some potato varieties this photoperiodic effect may be a strict control (Madec and Perennec, 1962). In *Begonia*, aerial tuber formation may likewise be strictly controlled by short photoperiods (Esashi, 1960).

The research workers at Beltsville, Maryland, who discovered photoperiodism, found that onion-bulb formation was controlled

Fig. 18-1 | The morphological changes involved in tuber formation (left) include an inflation of the stem through a swelling type of growth. In the formation of a bulb (right), the inflation is not of the stem but rather of the bases of the young leaves.

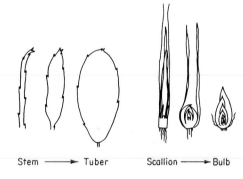

Stem ⟶ Tuber   Scallion ⟶ Bulb

Fig. 18-2 | At the time of tuber formation, the Bintje potato plant shows a suppression of growth of the aboveground parts, followed by senescence as the tubers mature (Wassink and Stolwijk, 1953).

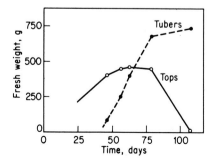

by photoperiods in a wide selection of cultivated varieties (Magruder and Allard, 1937). Bulb formation was accelerated by long days in the varieties tested, some varieties forming bulbs under day lengths as short as 12 hr and others only at longer minimum day lengths (Magruder and Allard, 1937; Fig. 18-3).

The short-day stimulation of tuber forma-

tion is shared by potato, *Begonia*, some *Dahlias*, *Helianthus tuberosus*, and *Phaseolus coccinius*. The long-day stimulation of bulb formation is shared by the onions, early garlic, the stem storage organs of Chinese radish, and some iris. Many of these photoperiod responses were noted by Allard and Garner (1940).

The photoperiod control (or influence) on tuber and bulb formation embraces all the classical features of photoperiodism as worked out for the control of flowering. The leaf is the photoperiod-perception organ; a stimulus is translocated from the leaf to the responding organ; quantitative responses are obtained in terms of the new organ formation and development; and night interruption may be effective in converting a short-day into a long-day type of stimulus. These features are illustrated in Figs. 18-4 and 18-5 (Esashi and Nagao, 1958; Esashi, 1961).

The role of leaves in the perception of day lengths for tuber formation in *Helianthus tuberosus* was noted by Hamner and Long (1939). More precise experiments on the leaf as the perceiving organ has been published for *Begonia* by Esashi (1960). He compared the relative effectiveness of leaves of different ages and areas, finding that the youngest expanded leaf is the most photoperiod-sensitive, just as it is the most sensitive to other photoperiod effects. That the photoperiodic perception for bulbing is also by leaves has been adequately demonstrated by Heath and Holdsworth (1948), who removed the leaf blades of onions and showed that the photoperiod sensitivity was lost until new blades had developed.

Fig. 18-3 | Various onion varieties show differences in the long-day requirement for bulb formation, Sweet Spanish onion forming bulbs under somewhat shorter photoperiods than Zittau Yellow (Magruder and Allard, 1937).

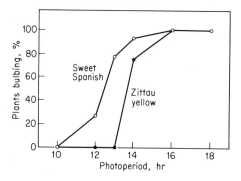

Fig. 18-4 | Tuber formation on aerial nodes of *Begonia evansiana* requires photoperiods with a night length of 11 hr or longer. The stimulus is quantitatively increased with increasing numbers of short days. The stage of tuber formation is taken to be the product of the apex height and width upon dissection (Esashi, 1961).

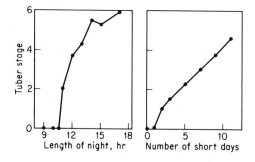

Nature of the stimulus

Studies of the tuberizing stimulus were greatly facilitated by the finding of Barker (1953) that tubers could be formed from potato meristems in tissue culture. This technique has been developed in numerous laboratories (e.g., Mes and Menge, 1954; Gregory, 1956; Chapman, 1958) with considerable benefit. Even from the initial report, it was clear that any node or meristem of potato can form tubers; the property is not distinctive to the underground stolons. But such tuber formation is characteristic of tissues taken from short-day-induced stems; pieces taken from noninduced potato plants are very slow to produce tubers in culture. Chapman (1958) noted that if a two-branched potato were given inductive short days on one branch only, cuttings from that branch readily formed tubers, and ones from the uninduced branch did not.

The stimulus to produce tubers moves characteristically down the plant, as shown not only by Chapman's (1958) experiment but also by the observation that a girdle or other interference with downward transport in the stem would lead to tuber formation just above such an obstruction (van Schreven, 1949). The tuber stimulus will move readily across a graft (Gregory, 1956) in a manner parallel to the flowering stimulus. And after photoperiodic induction, the tuber stimulus will persist in cuttings for a limited period of time (Gregory, 1956), but reversion to the noninduced state will eventually occur (Chapman, 1958; Esashi, 1960).

There is abundant evidence for the existence of a tuber-forming hormone in the same sense as in flowering—a hormone photoperiodically induced in the leaf and translocated then to a locus of morphological expression. Attempts to extract such a hormone have produced some promising results (Madec, 1961), including some evidence that the natural auxins in onion leaves may be involved in the bulbing of onion (Clark and Heath, 1959, 1962) and that both auxins and gibberellins may be involved in tuberization of potato (Booth, 1959).

Modifying factors

Before examining specifically the possible involvement of growth substances in tuber and bulb formation, it is appropriate to examine some of the more general factors which are known to alter them.

Mention has been made of the relation of tuber and bulb formation to an inhibition of growth. Many treatments which could suppress vegetative growth have been found to promote tuber formation in potato. For example, Wellensiek (1924) long ago noted that tubers could be encouraged by pinching back the vegetative growing points. Similar results have been obtained for potatoes sprouting in storage by van Schreven (1949), who pinched off the sprout tips and caused many new tubers to form peripheral to the original sprouting tuber. A suspension of growth by storage treatments of growing plants has been found to encourage new tuber formation in potato and *Ullucus* (Claver, 1956).

Lowered temperatures can promote potato-tuber formation (Werner, 1935), although they only inhibit bulbing in onions

Fig. 18-5 | Night-interruption treatments can prevent tuber formation in *Begonia* on short photoperiods (8 hr), and the light is most effective in the middle of the long dark period. Light of 45 ft-c was applied 1 hr in each of 20 nights (Esashi and Nagao, 1958).

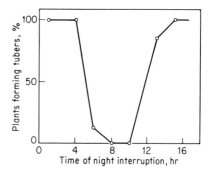

(Thompson and Smith, 1938; Heath and Holdsworth, 1948).

Noting that carbohydrate contents were very high in tuberizing plants, one might hope that the addition of sugars to a piece of stem would promote the tuber formation. Some investigators have had limited success with fairly high sugar concentrations (Mes and Menge, 1954); others have not succeeded in benefiting the response with sugar additions (Gregory, 1956; van Schreven, 1956).

The stimulation of tuber formation by the addition of auxins was first reported by Craniades (1954), using a wide array of different synthetic auxins. Van Schreven (1956) treated potatoes which were germinating in storage and obtained dozens of new little tubers on peripheral shoots from the stored tuber. Whether the extractable stimulus for tuber formation reported by Madec (1961) is an auxin is yet to be determined.

Auxins were implicated in bulb formation when Clark and Heath (1959, 1962) noted that auxin content of onion leaves under the long-day inductive conditions increased somewhat for 3 to 7 days after commencement of the long-day treatment. They further showed (1962) that the application of auxin to excised bases of onion plants could induce a swelling which was certainly suggestive of a bulbing type of growth. Unfortunately, though, the endogenous auxin content falls again before the photoperiodically induced bulbing response of leaf bases begins. The role of auxin in this developmental activity remains to be clarified. The good techniques that these authors have devised for assaying bulb-stimulating properties should enormously facilitate the further development of this subject.

Tuber and bulb growth

The progress curves for tuber growth show an exponential character (Fig. 18-6; Plaisted, 1957). Thus, the great bulk of the

Fig. 18-6 | The tuber weights of Cobbler potatoes increase in approximately an exponential manner, as shown by the plot on a log scale (Plaisted, 1957).

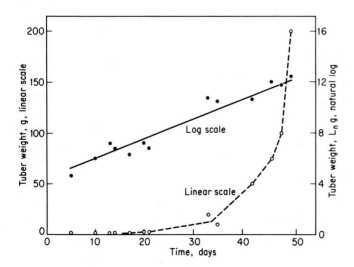

tuber-filling activity occurs very near the end of the growth season. In potato, the tuber grows by roughly equal activities of cell division and enlargement.

In the development of the bulb of onion, however, there is apparently no cell division (Heath and Holdsworth, 1943), and growth is simply by swelling of the leaf cells already there.

An interesting aspect of tuber growth is the facility with which materials can be moved from one developing tuber to another. The number of developing tubers can actually decrease during the growing season (cf. Hardenburg, 1949), and the entire contents of some tubers can be transferred into others. The translocation from a parent tuber into many peripheral tubers is illustrated by the work of van Schreven (1956). Also, it is not uncommon for potato vines to commence regrowth late in the season after a killing frost, for instance, and this regrowth is at the expense of the tuber crop.

Tuber ripening

Unlike the dramatic ripening changes common to the fleshy fruits, the ripening transformations in potato tubers are relatively subtle. In terms of tuber constituents, ripening is associated with a marked *drop* in sugar content, as shown in Fig. 18-7 (Appleman and Miller, 1926). Associated with the sugar decline is an increase in the starch content. And reminiscent of the ripening of apples and some other fruits, there is also an increase in protein content of the tuber. Respiration is apparently steady, and no evidences of a climacteric have been reported.

As the tubers ripen, the vines frequently undergo an active senescence, dying back to the ground. The ripe tuber possesses superior properties for storage, having a

markedly thicker skin and forming suberin layers over bruises more readily than an unripe tuber. Ripened tubers are also of superior quality for the production of potato chips.

The formation of tubers and bulbs appears to be another dramatic expression of mobilization phenomena in plants. Again we are confronted with the abyss of ignorance concerning how these mobilization events can transpire. The tuber and bulb formations repeat the remarkable characteristics of other photoperiodic phenomena, with the synthesis of an apparent hormonal stimulus in the leaves which transmits developmental information to the site of response. No physiologists have suggested that this photoperiodic stimulus is identical with that for the initiation of flowering or of dormancy. Can the same photoperiodic system produce a battery of different hormones, one for each of the developmental responses?

Fig. 18-7 | Tuber ripening takes place at vine senescence, at which time there is a marked increase in starch and protein contents and a drop in sugar content of the tubers. Irish Cobbler potatoes (Appleman and Miller, 1926).

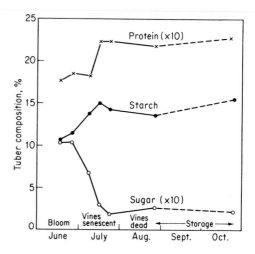

GENERAL REFERENCES

Heath, O. V. S., and M. Holdsworth. 1948. Morphogenic factors as exemplified by the onion plant. *Symp. Soc. Exptl. Biol.*, 2:326–350.

Madec, P., and P. Peremec. 1962. Les relations entre l'induction de la tuberisation et la croissance chez la plante de pomme de terre. *Ann. Physiol. Vegetale*, 4:5–84.

REFERENCES CITED

Allard, H. A., and W. W. Garner. 1940. Observations on responses to length of day. *U.S. Dept. Agr. Tech. Bull.*, 727.

Appleman, C. O., and E. V. Miller. 1926. A chemical and physiological study of maturity in potatoes. *J. Agr. Res.*, 33:569–578.

Barker, W. A. 1953. A method for *in vitro* culturing of potato tubers. *Science*, 118:384–385.

Booth, A. 1959. Some factors concerned in the growth of stolons in potato. *Proc. Linnean Soc. N.S. Wales*, 56:166–169.

Chapman, H. W. 1958. Tuberization in the potato plant. *Physiol. Plantarum*, 11:215–224.

Clark, J. E., and O. V. S. Heath. 1959. Auxin and the bulbing of onions. *Nature*, 184:345–347.

——— and ———. 1962. Studies in the physiology of the onion plant. V. Growth substance content. *J. Exptl. Botany*, 13:227–249.

Claver, F. K. 1956. La tuberizacion de brotes de papa y *Ullucus* cultivados *in vitro*. *Rev. Fac. Agron. Univ. Nac. La Plata*, 32:111–122.

Craniades, P. 1954. Tubercules aériens chez les pommes de terre. *Bull. Soc. Chim. Biol.*, 36:1671–1674.

Esashi, Y. 1960. Studies on the formation and sprouting of aerial tubers in *Begonia evansiana* Andr. IV. Cutting method and tuberizing stages. *Sci. Rept. Tohoku Univ.*, 26:239–246.

———. 1961. Studies on the formation and sprouting of aerial tubers in *Begonia evansiana* Andr. VI. Photoperiodic conditions for tuberization and sprouting in the cutting plants. *Sci. Rept. Tohoku Univ.*, 27:101–112.

——— and M. Nagao. 1958. Studies on the formation and sprouting of aerial tubers in *Begonia evansiana* Andr. I. Photoperiodic conditions for tuberization. *Sci. Rept. Tohoku Univ.*, 24:81–88.

Gregory, L. E. 1956. Some factors for tuberization in the potato plant. *Am. J. Botany*, 43:281–288.

Hamner, K. C., and E. M. Long. 1939. Localization of photoperiod perception in *Helianthus. Botan. Gaz.*, 101:81–90.

Hardenburg, E. V. 1949. *Potato Production.* Comstock Publishing Associates, a division of Cornell University Press, Ithaca, N.Y.

Heath, O. V. S., and M. Holdsworth. 1943. Bulb formation and flower production in onion. *Nature*, 152:334–335.

——— and ———. 1948. Morphogenic factors as exemplified by the onion plant. *Symp. Soc. Exptl. Biol.*, 2:326–350.

Madec, P. 1961. Sur la présence et les possibilités d'extraction de substances industrices de la tuberisation chez la pomme de terre. *Ann. Physiol. Vegetale*, 3:209–213.

——— and P. Perennec. 1962. Les relations entre l'induction de la tuberisation et la croissance chez la plante de pomme de terre. *Ann. Physiol. Vegetale*, 4:5–84.

Magruder, R., and H. A. Allard. 1937. Bulb formation in onions and length of day. *J. Agr. Res.*, 54:715–752.

Mes, M. G., and S. Menge. 1954. Potato shoot and tuber cultures *in vitro*. *Physiol. Plantarum*, 7:637–649.

Plaisted, P. H. 1957. Growth of the potato tuber. *Plant Physiol.*, 32:445–453.

Scheumann, W., and H. von Guttenberg. 1959. Studien zur Physiologie der Knollenbildung bei *Solanum demissum* Lindl. *Z. Pflanzen.*, 41:157–166.

Sideris, C. P. 1925. Observations on the development of the root system of *Allium cepa. Am. J. Botany*, 12:255–258.

Thompson, H. C., and O. Smith. 1938. Seedstalk and bulb development in onion. *Cornell Univ. Agr. Expt. Sta. Bull.*, 708.

van Schreven, D. A. 1949. Premature tuber formation in early potatoes. *Tijdschr. Plantenziekten*, 55:290–308.

———. 1956. On the physiology of tuber formation in potatoes. I and II. *Plant Soil*, 8:49–86.

Wassink, E. C., and J. A. J. Stolwijk. 1953. Effect of photoperiod on vegetative devel-opment and tuber formation in two potato varieties. *Mededel. Landbouwhogeschool Wageningen*, 53:99–112.

Wellensiek, S. J. 1924. Een orderzolk naar de factoren, die ontijdige knolvorming bij vroege aardappels bepalen. *Tijdschr. Plantenziekten*, 30:177–266 (cited by van Schreven, 1949).

Werner, H. O. 1935. The effect of tempera-ture, photoperiod and nitrogen upon tuberization in the potato. *Am. Potato J.*, 12:274–280.

———. 1947. Commerical potato produc-tion in Nebraska. *Nebraska Univ. Agr. Expt. Sta. Bull.*, 384.

19 | Dormancy

Except for a few tropical species, most plants experience periods of suspended growth. This suspension may take the form of a periodic halt of the growth rate, or it may also involve the loss of all the foliage of the plant in addition to the halt of growth rate; or in annual species, the whole plant may die and only seeds be left to pass through the period of suspended growth. In some cases the suspended growth is a consequence of only a shortage of water or some other environmental factor, but in other cases buds or seeds may be unable to grow even if the necessary moisture is supplied. The former is sometimes called *dormancy,* and the latter called *rest;* many histrionic arguments have been constructed over the distinctions between the two terms without increasing our knowledge of the biology of the matter.

For wild plants the state of dormancy is often of definite survival value. Dormancy in seeds and tubers is most characteristic in temperate and more northerly climates, where it facilitates the passage through difficult climatic seasons. However, the occurrence of dormancy does not provide any apparent benefits to cultivated species nor, for that matter, to species in mild or moist tropical climates. Yet it frequently occurs in the tropics (probably mostly as bud dormancy). One has the impression that the physiological capacity for dormancy is widespread in plants and that the occurrence of a dormant stage or stages is frequently, though not always, of positive value to the plant.

The onset of the dormant condition in buds and seeds is generally associated with the development of senescence in some or all plant parts. Thus in many woody plants, dormancy of buds is developed at the time when the leaves are senescing and falling, and in annual plants, the seeds enter dormancy at the time when the parent plant is falling into a state of senescence. The same is true of the dormancy of bulbs and tubers.

Functions of dormancy

The occurrence of dormancy may constructively limit the time at which seeds will germinate, as in the case of desert seeds, which will germinate only at the beginning of the rainy season, or the seeds of apple, which must pass through a cold period (ordinarily the winter) before germination will take place. Another constructive function is the determination of the location for germination, as in the case of the cypress seed, which normally requires standing water for germination (a desirable site for cypress-tree growth), or the spores of corn smut, which are stimulated to germinate in the proximity of corn plants (von Guttenberg and Strutz, 1952). Another function of dormancy is to adapt a species to the seasonal characteristics of the environment, either to the range or to the seasonal limits of ecological variables in the environment. As examples, one might cite the requirement of the peach buds for cold, which adapts the species to the more northerly climates of the United States; the photoperiodic imposition of bud dormancy on deciduous trees, which adapts them to the winter or the dry seasons of the year; and the requirement of weed seeds for mechanical scarification, which makes them germinate in soil which has been disturbed, thus assuring competitive conditions which will be favorable for their development.

In many instances the physiological controls of the dormancy of buds or seeds are beautifully adapted to meet the functional benefits which are provided. The cues which are utilized by the plant to terminate dormancy may match closely the environmental feature which is being functionally evaded by the interposition of dormancy. For instance, the weed seed which does best on disturbed soil requires mechanical abrasion, which is an integral part of soil disturbance. The seeds of tomato or many other fruits may achieve a type of geographic dispersal through their requirement for drying before

their dormancy is terminated; they will not germinate until they have been separated from their parental fruits. The seeds of desert annuals which must grow in the rainy season require leaching with water—another example of coordinated function and cue. The requirement for cold provides many seeds and buds with a functional limit of germination to the springtime. The photoperiodic control of dormancy of buds and seeds provides many species with a coordination of function and cue.

The development of dormancy is not always systemic; that is, the dormant condition may be restricted to some parts of the plant. In coffee plants, only the flower buds may show dormancy; in some woody plants dormancy is achieved progressively by individual buds from the base of the branch to the tip, and in some cases cutting a ring through the bark of a twig permits the buds above the ring to continue growth when the rest of the plant is dormant.

We can see dormancy as a developmental intermission which may occur in diverse parts of plants, including seeds and buds especially, and which may have many different cues or requirements for being recalled. We can anticipate, then, even before examining the internal physiology of dormancy, that there must be a wide diversity of controls possible inside the plant to match the diversity of means of breaking it.

Bud dormancy

In temperate climates woody plants show a seasonal decline of growth followed by a period of dormancy. It is difficult to draw a distinction between the termination of the growth of the stem and the dormancy of the stem tip or bud.

Early observations by Jost (1894) indicated that light can control the dormancy of some trees, and Klebs (1914) used light to break bud dormancy in trees. More recently, Wareing (1950) has quantitatively established that the day length or photoperiod can cause the onset of dormancy as well as the termination of it.

Many species of trees can be brought into a dormant condition by short photoperiods such as occur in late summer (Wareing, 1954), and many can be brought out of dormancy by long photoperiods. Woody plants which retain their foliage might be expected to respond to these photoperiods through some reactions in their leaves, but many species lose their foliage as they enter dormancy and so do not have the usual organs which we associate with photoperiodic perception. Wareing (1953) became interested in this phenomenon and found, surprisingly enough, that the buds of several species of trees are actually capable of directly perceiving photoperiodic stimuli. For example, buds of *Fagus sylvatica* are brought out of dormancy by long photoperiods, and removal of the outer bud scales considerably enhances the sensitivity of the buds to photoperiods.

Most photoperiodic phenomena are limited more by the dark periods than by the daily light periods in natural diurnal cycles, and a reliable test for this dark sensitivity can be made by applying a small amount of light in the middle of the night. Wareing (1953) found that the buds of *Fagus* were brought out of dormancy even on short photoperiods if such a night-interruption treatment was given. It is evident, then, that all the means for photoperiodic controls are present in the bud scales of some trees and that both the light and the daily dark periods are involved in the breaking of their dormancy. A similar situation exists in the buds of tubers of *Begonia*, which are brought out of dormancy by long photoperiods, and there too the buds are responsive both to long days and to short days with a night-interruption treatment (Esashi, 1961).

It is common for buds to be brought out of dormancy by low-temperature treatments. The requirement for low temperature is ordinarily satisfied during the winter or during seasonal cool spells; it has been recognized since the work by Müller-Thurgau (1880) with dormancy in potatoes and by Pfeffer (1904) with woody plants. The promotive effects of low temperature are ordinarily accumulated by the buds, and a quantitative increase in the growth of buds is obtained with increases in duration of the chilling treatment. An example with blueberries is given in Fig. 19-1 (Darrow, 1942). It is not uncommon for different types of buds to show somewhat different temperature responses, and in this case the flower buds are shown to respond over somewhat longer periods of cold than the vegetative buds. The quantitative nature of the cold requirement for apple trees was established by Chandler et al. (1937), who also showed that temperatures just above freezing were more effective in breaking dormancy than temperatures at or below freezing. This seems to imply that the cold requirement involves some metabolic action as well as a physical one.

In some instances dormancy can be broken by heat treatment instead of cold, and some species may be brought out of dormancy by either heat or chilling treatment. Molisch (1909) developed a warm-water treatment for breaking dormancy of leafless branches, using water between 30 and 40°C. An example of the heat treatment of gladiolus corms is shown in Fig. 19-2 (Loomis and Evans, 1928). Ecologically a high temperature experience may break dormancy in situations where fire or exposure to intense sunlight has elevated the temperature of the soil.

Many different chemicals have been used successfully in the breaking of bud dormancy, and an excellent review of these treatments has been written by Doorenbos (1953). Among the most generally effective are ethylene chlorohydrin and its more complex formulation as rindite.

The basis of bud dormancy

Among the chemicals which have been reported to break the dormancy of buds are several auxins such as indoleacetic acid and 2,4-D. The early reports of these effects encouraged Boysen-Jensen (1935) to propose that the state of dormancy was a consequence of the shortage of auxins necessary for the progress of growth. This idea was advanced further by the experiments of Avery et al. (1937), who measured the auxin content of apple buds as they started growth in the spring and found that there was indeed a surge in auxin formation at the commencement of growth. But if a shortage of auxin were responsible for dormancy, then auxin applications should be generally effective in relieving dormancy, and they are not.

An entirely different explanation was offered by the finding of Hemberg (1949*b*) that dormant buds of potato contained appreciable amounts of growth inhibitor and that the content of this inhibitor dropped with treatments which removed the dormancy, such as treatment with rindite or ethylene chlorohydrin. He found the same situation in dormant buds of *Fraxinus,* and his sample data are shown in Fig. 19-3. He tested for the abundance of inhibitor in his bud extracts by adding increasing amounts of the extract to agar containing auxin, which he then analyzed by the *Avena* curvature test. The added extract was powerfully inhibiting when taken from dormant buds in October and was not appreciably inhibiting when taken from nondormant buds in February, even though no growth had yet begun. In his early experiments, Hemberg (1949*b*) found that the inhibitors were acidic in nature, and in later studies (1958) he deduced that they were similar to the inhibitor β of Kefford (1955; see Chap. 9).

In numbers of studies subsequent to Hemberg's, it has been noted that as dormancy

Fig. 19-1 | The buds of blueberry emerge from dormancy in response to increasing durations of low temperatures. Plants were left outdoors during winter for varying periods and were brought indoors to test for the ability of buds to begin growth (Darrow, 1942).

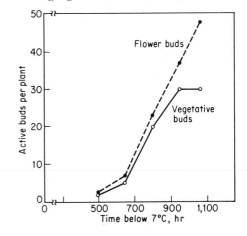

Fig. 19-2 | A high-temperature treatment can break dormancy of gladiolus corms (Loomis and Evans, 1928).

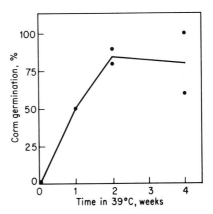

is broken, buds show a marked lowering of extractable inhibitor content. An example of such data is shown in Fig. 19-4 (Blommaert, 1955), which illustrates an experiment in which both auxin and inhibitor contents were measured for peach buds in South Africa. During the dormant period the auxin content was low and inhibitor content high, and the situation was reversed as dormancy was broken. It is curious, though, that the inhibitor content of the buds was relatively high even during the growing period of the peach. A more complete study of inhibitor content of leaves, stems, and buds of *Acer pseudoplatanus* (Phillips and Wareing, 1958) revealed that the inhibitor accumulated in both leaves and stem tips during the growing period (Fig. 19-5), reaching highest levels at roughly the time when growth was terminated. The dormant buds then showed quite high inhibitor levels, which declined as dormancy was passed in February and March.

A serious objection to the inhibitor explanation of bud dormancy has been raised by several workers, i.e., that the decline in inhibitor level sometimes occurs only after the dormant condition has been passed. For example, von Guttenberg and Leike (1958) found that while the decline was correlated with passing of dormancy in *Fraxinus*, it occurred considerably later in *Syringa* and *Acer* buds. Similar objections have been raised in connection with the inhibitor content of potato-tuber buds (e.g., Buch and Smith, 1959; Housley and Taylor, 1958). Two lines of evidence have been used to counter the criticism. Szalai (1959) has noted that as potato buds break dormancy, the inhibitor content falls to a low level and the auxin content rises in a manner similar to that shown in Fig. 19-4, but that there is a subsequent rise in inhibitor content after growth has started, suggesting that the actively growing shoot can tolerate the inhibitor. A significant drop in inhibitor content did occur at the time of breaking dormancy. Another alternative has been

Fig. 19-3 | Extracts of *Fraxinus* bud scales made in October contain large amounts of growth inhibitors, as indicated by the inhibition of the *Avena* response to auxin. In February the inhibitor content had diminished, and at that time cuttings taken indoors would proceed to grow (Hemberg, 1949*a*).

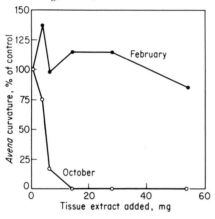

Fig. 19-4 | During the period of peach-bud dormancy (June and July in South Africa), there is a relatively high content of growth inhibitor which declines as the dormant period is passed. The auxin content is low during dormancy and rises as growth begins (Blommaert, 1955).

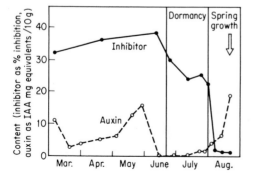

offered by invoking yet another growth substance to account for the lack of correlation. Gibberellins have been found to occur in potato buds (Okazawa, 1959), and they increase at the time of breaking dormancy (Smith and Rappaport, 1961). Such stimulative substances may either negate the effectiveness of growth inhibitors (Brian et al., 1959) or lead to the ultimate loss of inhibitors in the potato buds (Boo, 1961). While the role of growth inhibitors in explaining dormancy is very attractive, the evidence on this possibility is far from unanimous.

That growth promoters might be involved in the breaking of dormancy arises as an interesting possibility which would account perhaps for the emergence of growth even when some inhibitors are still present after dormancy. Richter and Krassnosselskaya (1945) observed that extracts of nondormant buds of *Fraxinus* and *Tilia* could force buds out of dormancy, and similar effects for extracts of other tree species were reported by Danilov (1946). While these early reports could have been effects of auxin rather than of other growth stimulants, the reports already mentioned of the presence of gibberellins in buds and their ability to break dormancy lend credence to the concept of the involvement of growth stimulants.

The dramatic effects of gibberellins in stimulating dormant peach buds into growth are illustrated in Fig. 19-6 (Donaho and Walker, 1957). Less dramatic but yet considerable responses have been obtained with kinetin applications (Kurz and Kummerow, 1957; Chvojka et al., 1962). The possibility of explaining the breaking of bud dormancy as a function of growth stimulants has considerable promise but is held back in part by the limited information about the quantitative changes in such substances as dormancy is lost, and in part by the occasional observation that gibberellin applications do not substitute for cold or photoperiod treatments in the breaking of

Fig. 19-5 | Extracts of leaves, stem apices, and buds of *Acer pseudoplantanus* inhibit the growth of coleoptile sections. The content of growth-inhibiting substances increases as dormancy is entered and then declines again as dormancy is passed. Methanol extracts chromatographed in isopropanol/ammonia/water, and the inhibitor at R_f 0.7 followed by oat-coleoptile-section assay (Phillips and Wareing, 1958).

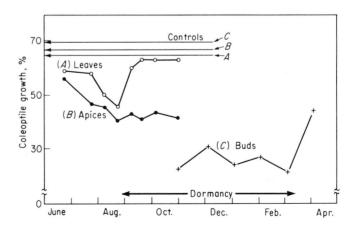

dormancy (e.g., Nagao and Mitsui, 1959).

An interesting modification of the growth-substance explanations for dormancy has been suggested by Tomaszewski (1957), who found that phenolase could cause growth inhibitions in the presence of auxin and phenols. He measured the phenolase activity of numerous fruit-tree buds and found that the onset of dormancy correlated very well with the rise in phenolase and phenol content. His theory would account for the presence of inhibitors when dormancy is broken by assuming that the force imposing dormancy on the bud was the inactivation of growth hormones by the phenolase system rather than the presence of the phenolic inhibitors per se.

A few general comments can be made about the concept of dormancy as a function of growth inhibitors. First, it is generally true that dormant buds are rich in extractable growth inhibitors, especially in the bud scales and the skins of dormant potatoes. These inhibitors usually disappear at about the time dormancy is broken or sometimes slightly later; this is true whether dormancy is broken naturally or by chemical or cold treatments. Secondly, if the inhibitor content were actually responsible for dormancy,

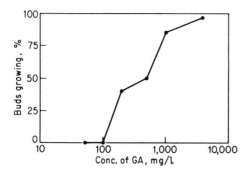

Fig. 19-6 | Application of gibberellin to buds of dormant Elberta peach can remove the dormancy. Buds treated in March after 164 hr below 8°C (Donaho and Walker, 1957).

the introduction of the inhibitor should reinstate or at least prolong dormancy. Some attempts to do this with added inhibitors have been notably unsuccessful, as in the case of the treatment of peach buds with naringenin (Dennis and Edgerton, 1961), a flavanone which has been identified as a principal inhibitor in dormant peach buds (Henderschott and Bailey, 1955; Henderschott and Walker, 1959). Some success, however, has been reported by Eagles and Wareing (1963), who added a leaf extract from short-day *Betula* to nondormant shoots and actually imposed an apparent dormancy. The dormant condition was complete with compact buds and bud scales and was relieved by the application of gibberellin.

Still another type of explanation of dormancy has been based on the respiratory requirements of the growing point. Early reports indicated that mechanical injury to buds or desiccation treatments which would cause disruption of the scale coverings would have some dormancy-breaking actions (cf. review of Doorenbos, 1953). Pollock (1953) found that the mechanical removal of maple bud scales yielded marked increases in respiration. He measured the respiratory rates of the bud scales and determined that they would strongly depress the availability of oxygen at the growing points. He found that at the time dormancy was broken, there was a strong increase in the rate of oxygen utilization by the bud, suggesting that an oxygen barrier by the bud scales had been relieved. Some of his data for the respiration of dormant and nondormant maple buds are shown in Fig. 19-7. He later suggested (Pollock, 1960) that the breaking of dormancy represented a shift in respiratory efficiency and that perhaps the aerobic type of respiration assisted in the disposal of growth inhibitors which might be contributing to the dormant condition. This will be discussed further in the section on seed dormancy. There are, however, cases in which oxygen actually inhibits the breaking of dormancy, as in the potato (Sawyer and Smith, 1955), suggesting that the oxygen explanation may not have general application.

Mention should be made of the existence of other suggestions as to possible explanations of bud dormancy as a metabolic expression, including the idea of von Guttenberg and Meinl (1954) that dormancy in potato tubers may be related to a relative impermeability of the cells to water and solutes, a situation which is aggravated by such growth inhibitors as the lactones. Water relations have been implicated in the dormancy of flower buds of coffee (Piringer and Borthwick, 1955; Mes, 1957). Another suggestion by Cotrufo and Levitt (1958) is that protein synthesis is localized in areas away from the apices in the dormant condition, depriving the apices of the synthetic requirements for growth; the breaking of dormancy may be a shifting of the centers of protein synthesis to the growing points.

step in seed dormancy in comparison with bud dormancy.

Internal seed controls. Two classes of physiological mechanisms are known to control seed dormancy, those involving structural limitations and those involving growth substances in the seed. While the two are not entirely separable, the categories may be helpful in discussing the subject.

The seed can be described as a small meristematic axis, often associated with a storage tissue and enclosed by an enveloping series of membranes and sometimes stony shells which collectively make up the seed coat. These latter structures are frequently critical to the dormancy of seeds, limiting the entry of water and oxygen, mechanically limiting the enlargement of the embryo, or sometimes altering the growth-substance relationships of the enclosed tissues. Many seeds are improved in germination by removal or rupture of the seed-coat layers. This scarification treatment will of course

Seed dormancy

Because the seed is such a convenient material for study, the experimental clarification of seed dormancy has proceeded somewhat faster than that of bud dormancy.

Since it is no longer connected to a plant with a vascular system, the seed must imbibe water as a first stage in germination; after that, the successive steps necessary for development are similar to those of buds, including, for instance, the acceleration of respiratory systems and then the growth and enlargement of cells of the meristems. The environmental controls of seed dormancy are strikingly similar to the controls of bud dormancy, including controls by temperature, light and photoperiods, growth substances, and mechanical treatments which improve the entry of moisture and oxygen through the enclosing structures. This last type of control is much more prominent in the case of seeds because of the special importance of the imbibition

Fig. 19-7 | Increases in oxygen partial pressure around buds of *Acer plantanoides* at 25°C produce only small increases in the rate of oxygen utilization in respiration (Q_{O_2}) when the buds are dormant in November and large increases when the buds are ready to grow in April (Pollock, 1953).

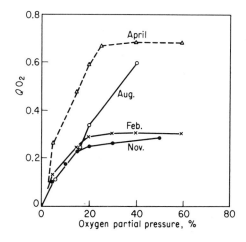

alter each of the types of limitations which the seed coats may impose on germination.

Many legumes and aquatic species develop seeds with extraordinarily thick coats which can mechanically prevent either the growth of the embryo or the imbibition of water. Scarification of these structures is widely used to encourge germination.

A most remarkable mechanism is involved in the limitation of water imbibition by these hard seeds, involving a hygroscopically activated valve in the hilum. Its structure has been examined by Hyde (1954), who described the operation of this aperture in the stony coat of some leguminous seeds (Fig. 19-8). He found that germination is not obtained even in moist conditions because of a limitation of moisture entry by closure of the hilum. Closure is brought about through the differential moisture content of internal and external seed-coat layers. If there is more moisture on the outside of the seed coat, the valve closes, and no entry of water is obtained. If there is less moisture on the outside, the valve opens, and the seed dries further. Experimental data are given in Fig. 19-9, following the moisture contents of normal hard seeds and scarified seeds as they are moved from one humidity level to another. It is evident that the hard seeds lose moisture in the low humidities but do not gain moisture in the high humidities because of the operations of the hilum valve. Hyde found that the lower the moisture level of the seed, the more pronounced the impermeability of the seed coat and thus the deeper the dormancy.

The seed coat may also limit the exchange of gases in and out of the seed. Having noted that oxygen exposures would increase the germination of many seeds, Weisner and Molisch (1890) examined the gas movement through seed coats and noted the limited permeability to oxygen and to a lesser extent to CO_2. Some precise measurements have been made by Brown (1940), who found that the membrane around cucumber seeds would pass only 4 $cm^3/cm^2/hr$ of oxygen, in comparison with 15 $cm^3/cm^2/hr$ of CO_2. This limitation of gas exchange was brought about by a living system in the seed coat, for brief exposure of the seed to extreme heat (40°C) or a strong solvent like chloroform would relieve the permeability limitation. This observation may account for the dormancy-breaking effects of high temperature and of many chemical treatments of seeds. Brown also found that the water relations of the cucumber seed coat markedly altered its gas permeability. Once the coat had dried thoroughly, the permeability was subsequently improved, probably because air spaces were introduced into the structure through which gases could diffuse. (Note that many seeds require drying before they will germinate, a feature which can prevent germination until the seeds have been removed from the fleshy fruits which bore them.) Washing the seed also markedly improved the permeability to gases, probably by washing out some impermeable constituent. (Note also that many seeds can be brought out of dormancy by washing treatments.)

Fig. 19-8 | The hard seeds of *Lupinus arboreus* have a moisture valve in the hylum operated by a counterpalisade tissue. When there is more moisture outside than inside, the counterpalisade swells and closes the hylum (Hyde, 1954).

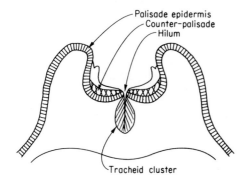

Palisade epidermis
Counter-palisade
Hilum

Tracheid cluster

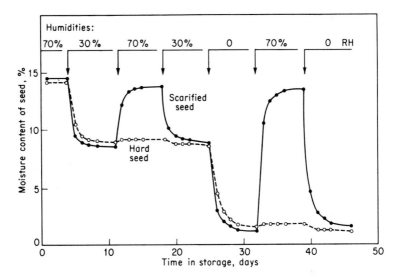

Fig. 19-9 | When hard seeds of white clover are placed in alternating high and low relative humidities, the seeds lose moisture in lowered humidities but do not gain it back in elevated humidities because of the operation of the hylum valve. Scarified seeds can gain moisture readily (Hyde, 1954).

Another limitation of germination which the seed coat may impose is through the provision of chemical materials which can prevent embryo growth. The coat may simply provide chemical species which create osmotic values unfavorable to growth (Koller, 1957); it may provide growth inhibitors which can limit growth; or it may provide more complex biochemical systems which are related to the photosensitivity of seeds. In each of these cases, the seed may be brought out of dormancy by removal of the seed coat or by washing. When seeds are planted in soil, inhibitors are less troublesome than when they are planted on moist paper, probably, at least in part, because of the adsorption of inhibitors out of the seed coat by the soil medium (cf. El-Shishiny and Thoday, 1952).

While auxins are known to be necessary for growth of the embryonic tissues, and while they do increase at the time of germination or shortly before (Hemberg, 1955;

Kawase, 1960), there is no convincing evidence that they are directly involved in dormancy mechanisms. On the other hand, growth inhibitors are of general occurrence in dormant seeds, and there is abundant evidence for their involvement in the physiological mechanisms of dormancy.

One of the most dramatic evidences for the involvement of growth inhibitors in dormancy is the fact that such materials are present in dormant seeds in many cases, and the application of such materials can readily impose dormancy on seeds. Nutile (1945) was the first to show such a dormancy imposition. He applied coumarin to lettuce seeds and then established that the seeds were dormant and required light for their germination. His observations were extended by Evenari (1952*b*) to show that the coumarin effect was enhanced by high temperature, as shown in Fig. 19-10. These lines of evidence suggest that both light-requiring dormancy and high-temperature-

imposed dormancy may be intimately related to growth-inhibitor systems in the
seed. The widespread occurrence of growth
inhibitors in seeds and in ripening fruits
has been pointed out by Evenari (1949).
More recent work by Phillips (1961) has
shown that dormancy can also be imposed
on lettuce seed by naringenin, and this can
be reversed either by light or by the application of gibberellin.

A wide variety of chemical materials may
be involved in the inhibition of seed germination, some of them as complicated as
polypeptides (Elliott and Leopold, 1952)
and some as simple as ferric chloride
(Paech, 1953).

Yet another type of growth substance
which may be involved in the dormancy
mechanisms is the gibberellin type of growth
promoter. The ability of gibberellin to break
dormancy of seeds was first observed as an
empirical treatment with a chemical material
(Kahn et al., 1957), but subsequent evi-

dence has appeared indicating that such
substances may increase as seeds emerge
from dormancy (Naylor and Simpson, 1961;
Franklin and Wareing, 1962). Kinins are
also reported to break seed dormancy in
some cases (Miller, 1958), but there is as
yet no evidence that this type of growth
regulator participates in the natural dormancy phenomena in seeds.

Some suggestive experiments by Wareing and Villiers (1961) indicate that
growth-stimulating substances may be involved in the breaking of dormancy of
Fraxinus seeds. These dormant seeds yield
inhibitors upon extraction, and the inhibitors can be separated by chromatography. Although leaching of embryos from
the dormant seeds improved their germination, there was not a detectable disappearance of the inhibitor from the seeds as
dormancy was broken naturally. Instead,
there appeared in the extracts of nondormant seeds a material which evoked the
germination of embryos even in the presence
of the endogenous inhibitors. Some sample
data of such experiments are given in Table
9. Wareing and Villiers characterized their
promoting substance by chromatography
and indicated that it was not a gibberellin
material.

In general, the dormancy of seeds ap-

Fig. 19-10 | Seeds of Grand Rapids lettuce
can be made dormant by applications of
coumarin, and the dormancy can then be
overcome with light. At higher temperatures
(30°C) the dormancy is deeper, and light is
less effective in overcoming it (Evenari,
1952*b*).

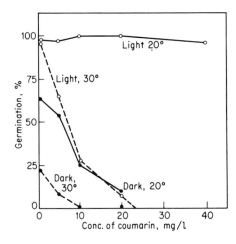

Table 9 | *Interactions of endogenous
inhibitors and stimulators of germination in
seeds of* Fraxinus excelsior (*Wareing and
Villiers, 1961*). *Aqueous extracts were
chromatographed in isopropanol ammonia
water. The inhibitor was eluted from* R_f *0.6
to 0.8, and the stimulator from* R_f *0.1 to 0.3.*

Germination medium	Percentage germination
Water only	95
Inhibitor added	30
Inhibitor plus extract from unchilled embryos (R_f 0.1–0.3)	45
Inhibitor plus extract from chilled embryos (R_f 0.1–0.3)	100

pears to be commonly either a consequence of structural characteristics of the seed coat or membranes, or a consequence of growth-regulator interactions such as inhibiting substances or promoting substances. In many cases the growth-regulator system is most pronounced in the outer layers of the seed —especially in the seed coat—and so these two types of physiological mechanisms are sometimes closely interrelated.

Environmental controls. Treatments which break seed dormancy can be roughly separated into four categories: mechanical, light, temperature, and chemical.

Mention has already been made of the effectiveness of the mechanical removal or scarification of the seed coat in breaking some types of dormancy. This treatment is useful in obtaining the germination of seeds with hard coats or of seeds with coats which limit the passage of gases as well as of some seeds limited by growth inhibitors in the seed coat.

The requirement of some seeds for low temperature has been known and utilized for centuries. In some cases only a brief exposure to temperatures near freezing is needed to break dormancy; in others an extended period is needed; and in yet others dormancy is not actually broken until two winters have been passed in the ground (cf. Crocker and Barton, 1957). Temperatures near freezing are usually the most effective, though often 10°C is low enough for breaking dormancy. The agricultural practice of chilling seeds has been given the inappropriate and unphysiological name *seed stratification.*

The quantitative nature of the low-temperature effect is illustrated by some data for peach-seed germination shown in Fig. 19-11 (Carlson and Tukey, 1945), in which germination is seen to increase with the duration of the cold treatment from 4 to about 10 weeks. During a cold treatment there may be extensive changes in the distribution of food materials in the seed, as, for example, in *Heracleum* seeds, which

translocate the bulk of their dry weight from the endosperm to the embryo during the stratification period (Stokes, 1952; see Fig. 13-32). Peony seeds have very low amino acid levels in the embryos of dormant seeds, but during the cold stratification they accumulate large amounts from the endosperm (Fine and Barton, 1958). In this latter case, gibberellin treatment which breaks the seed dormancy also brings about the rise in amino acids in the embryo.

The low-temperature treatment can depress the growth-inhibitor content of the dormant seeds. Following the evidence of Hemberg (1949a) that inhibitors were involved in bud dormancy, Luckwill (1952) found that apple seeds are greatly lowered in inhibitor content during cold stratification, as shown in Fig. 19-12. In this figure, the loss of dormancy during cold is shown by the increasing germination percentage, and the bioassay of the various seed parts indicates that a large amount of growth inhibitor initially present in the testa and endosperm disappears during the cold treatment. In the embryo there is some evidence for the actual accumulation of growth-*promoting* substances after about 60 days of chilling. Luckwill concluded that the removal of dormancy by cold was associated with a de-

Fig. 19-11 | Low temperatures can overcome dormancy in seeds of peach, the Ward Late variety being more responsive than the Lovell variety (Carlson and Tukey, 1945).

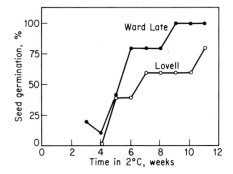

crease in inhibitor content, but he was hesitant to explain the change in dormancy entirely as a change in inhibitor content, pointing out that growth-promoting substances could also be involved and that excised embryos did not grow in inverse proportion to the inhibitor content measured.

Olney and Pollock (1960) suggested that the cold treatment may break dormancy of cherry seeds through an unblocking of phosphorus metabolism in the embryo.

A remarkable variation of the low-temperature effect is the requirement of some seeds for an alternating temperature experience. Morinaga (1926) first observed this and suggested that two temperatures were

required for the mechanical modification of some limiting feature of the seed or seed coat. Increased percentage of germination or more uniform germination can often be obtained with alternating temperatures better than with any single temperature treatment (Crocker and Barton, 1957). In some species an elevation of temperature is stimulatory to germination, and a representative example is shown in Table 10 for *Lepidium* seeds (Toole et al., 1955). The data show that saturation of the light stimulus alone can bring about only some 30 per cent germination, whereas alternating the temperature once between 15 and 25°C boosts the germination to almost 90 per cent. KNO_3 can bring about the same result as the temperature alternation and is not additive in its effect with the temperature alternation. Toole et al. proposed that the temperature and nitrate effects were a quantitative alteration of some regulating substance. Cohen (1958) has done some exacting experiments on the temperature-shift stimulation and denies the substance-regulation idea. He has deduced that the elevation of temperature brings about some structural change which is promotive of germination. Recall that the earlier experiments of Brown (1940) had shown that more extreme elevations of temperature greatly increased the permeability of seed membranes to gases. Tager and Clark

Fig. 19-12 | During cold treatment to break dormancy of apple seeds, there is a decline in content of growth inhibitors, especially in the endosperm and testa. Ether extracts were tested for growth inhibition with oat-coleoptile sections, and germination percentages were determined using excised embryos (Luckwill, 1952).

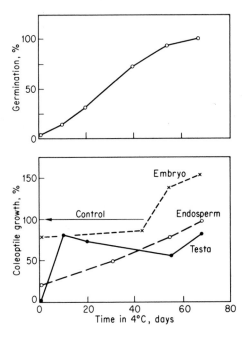

Table 10 | *Germination of Lepidium virginicum seeds as affected by light, temperature, and nitrate (Toole et al., 1955). Seeds imbibed water for 24 hr and were then given red light for 1 hr, with constant temperature or with one shift from 15 to 25°C.*

Solution	Temp., °C	Light	% germination
H_2O	20	. . .	0
H_2O	20	Red	31
H_2O	15–25	Red	88
KNO_3	20	Red	93
KNO_3	15–25	Red	90

(1961) have found that an alternating temperature plus scarification was required for the germination of *Asclepias fruticosa* seeds and that gibberellin treatment would replace the temperature requirement but not the requirement for scarification of the seed.

High temperatures ordinarily increase the dormancy of seeds rather than improve the germination. Lettuce seed, for example, which is promoted in germination by moderately low temperatures, is made dormant by temperatures of 30 or 35°C, as illustrated in Fig. 19-13 (Toole, 1959). This again is a quantitative effect, with longer periods of heating resulting in deeper dormancy. We have seen in Fig. 19-10 that the dormancy of lettuce seed imposed by high temperatures is relieved by light.

The stimulation of germination by light is ordinarily quantitative, and Fig. 19-14 is given as an illustration of a light-dosage-response curve (Toole et al., 1955). Here again emphasis is laid on the interrelation between light and temperature, the seeds which had been exposed to a high temperature after the light exposures being markedly less viable than those given high temperature before the light exposure.

The stimulation of germination of lettuce seed by light was studied in considerable detail by Flint and McAlister in 1937, who found that red light was the most effective in breaking dormancy. Some of their data are shown in Fig. 19-15. In their wavelength studies they found that blue light and more especially far-red light were very inhibitory of germination. The effects of red and far-red light on seed dormancy have since been found to be reversible (Borthwick et al., 1954), and some detailed studies have been carried out with this material to examine the nature of the reversibility and the characteristics of the pigment responsible. That the responsible pigment is phytochrome is discussed in Chap. 20.

In a few cases light has only inhibitory effects on germination (Koller et al., 1963),

and the inhibitions appear to relate to reactions which occur in the seed coat.

A most surprising development in the light studies of dormancy has been the finding that some seeds do not just require light but actually have a photoperiod requirement for germination. This was discovered simultaneously by Black and Wareing (1954) for birch seeds and by Isikawa (1954) for a wide selection of seeds, including some which have long-day requirements (e.g., *Eragrostis ferruginea*) and some with short-day requirements (e.g.,

Fig. 19-13 | Grand Rapids lettuce seed can be made dormant by exposure to 30 or 35°C. Tested for germination at 20°C (Toole, 1959).

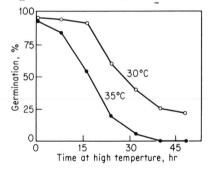

Fig. 19-14 | Light can overcome the dormancy of *Lepidium virginianum* seeds imposed by high temperature (35°C for 2 hrs) or can defer the inhibition by the same heat treatment given subsequently (Toole et al., 1955).

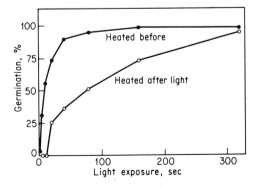

Veronica persica). Some data illustrating the photoperiodic responses of seeds are given in Fig. 19-16. These data are for *Begonia* seeds, which require a photoperiod of about 12 hr or longer for germination and three or more repeated cycles (Nagao et al., 1959). That there is a dark-period sensitivity for this photoperiod action is evident from the ability of a night interruption to depress the dark-period effect and permit germination as if in a long day (Fig. 19-17).

This brief look at the light responses of seeds may illustrate the diversity of light effects on dormancy. Some types of seeds are insensitive to light; others may be promoted or inhibited by it, depending upon the wavelength of light given; others have an absolute requirement for light; and still others are photoperiod-requiring. These effects of light are quite separate from photosynthetic effects but are closely interwoven in some manner with the temperature effects on seeds and also with the growth substances involved in imposing or relieving light requirements.

The involvement of growth inhibitors in dormancy has been illustrated by the imposition of light requirements in seeds by inhibitors such as coumarin and naringenin. The possibility that treatments which break dormancy are removing the growth inhibitors present in the dormant seed has been illustrated by Luckwill's (1952) data for apple seeds during stratification (Fig. 19-

Fig. 19-15 | Seeds of Arlington Fancy lettuce which are partly dormant can be stimulated to germinate by red light (600 to 690 mμ) or inhibited by far-red light (720 to 780 mμ) (Flint and McAlister, 1937).

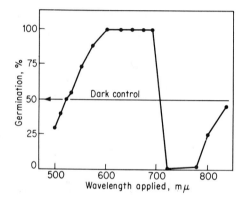

Fig. 19-16 | The germination of seeds of *Begonia evansiana* is stimulated by a photoperiodic phenomenon; it requires photoperiods of 12 hr or more, and the response is proportional to the numbers of long days given (Nagao et al., 1959).

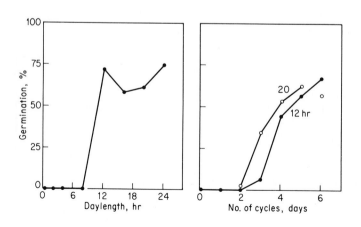

12). In many instances the dormancy of seeds while they are still associated with the fleshy fruits in which they were borne has been attributed to growth inhibitors in the fruits, where such inhibitors frequently abound (Varga, 1957).

In seeds, growth inhibitors are often most abundant in the outer seed coat. The data on the inhibitors in apple seeds (Fig. 19-12) illustrate such a condition. Consequently one may assume that many of the germination promotions obtained with seed-coat removal or seed-washing treatments may be operative at least in part through removal of a principal source of inhibitors in the seed. That the increase in germination of oat seeds was proportional to the elution of an inhibitor in a washing treatment is shown in some data of Elliott and Leopold (1953) in Fig. 19-18.

Another type of treatment to break dormancy is the exposure of seeds to elevated concentrations of oxygen. Wareing and Foda (1957) have made a detailed study of the changes in inhibitor content of the seed of *Xanthium* as dormancy is broken in this manner. They separated the inhibitors extracted from the seed coat by chromatography and then bioassayed the chromatogram for inhibitors by the *Avena* coleoptile straight-growth test as shown in Fig. 19-19. With the loss of dormancy after oxygen exposure, there was a pronounced reduction in the amounts of two inhibitors present (R_f 0.2 and 0.4). Light was also effective in removing dormancy in these seeds, and that stimulus likewise depressed the inhibitor content of the seed coat. These workers suggest that oxygen is involved in the oxidative destruction of the inhibitors of germination. Leaching *Xanthium* seed proved ineffective in breaking the dormancy, and this was attributed to an impermeability of the seed to the inhibitor, preventing its loss into the washing solution.

The promotive effects of oxygen on germination of seeds and the parallel effects of

light led Paech (1953) to suggest that dormancy was regulated by phenolic substances in the seed coat. The phenolic oxidation activities could trap oxygen, preventing its entry into the seed. The action of the phenolics could be blocked by oxygen or light through the photooxidation of the phenolics themselves. This suggestion has the merit of bringing together the actions

Fig. 19-17 | The photoperiodic sensitivity of *Begonia* seeds is shown by the ability of a night interruption to cause germination even under a short photoperiod regime; the light treatment (30 min) is most effective when applied in the middle of the 17-hr night (Nagao et al., 1959).

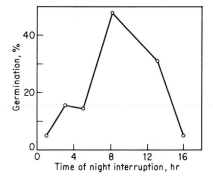

Fig. 19-18 | Washing seeds of victory oat leads to a stimulation of germination, and there is a concomitant appearance of an inhibitor of α-amylase in the eluted solutions (Elliott and Leopold, 1953).

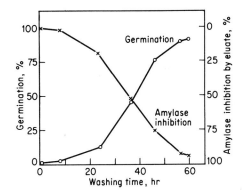

of oxygen, light, and germination inhibitors in a simple system.

Growth substances other than the inhibitors may be involved in seed dormancy. The effects of gibberellin in breaking the dormancy of many seeds suggests that this type of growth regulator could be involved if it were formed during the period in which dormancy is broken. That gibberellins are present in a wide diversity of seeds has been shown by Murakami (1959), and Naylor and Simpson (1961) have published some evidence that as seeds of *Avena fatua* emerge from dormancy, there is formed a growth-stimulating substance which is suggestive of a gibberellin. These seeds are also brought out of dormancy if they are soaked in gibberellin solutions, but there is no response to gibberellin if the seeds have

Fig. 19-19 | Treatment of *Xanthium* seeds with oxygen to break dormancy leads to a decline in extractable inhibitor content. Ether extracts chromatographed in isopropanol/ammonia/water, and the paper assayed by oat-coleoptile growth test (Wareing and Foda, 1957).

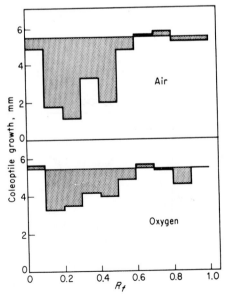

been previously brought out of dormancy by afterripening. They suggest that this case of dormancy is related to an inhibitor in the seed, which can be overcome either by leaching or by the presence of gibberellin. Kahn (1960) reported that gibberellin could overcome the dormancy of lettuce seed whether it was imposed by high temperature, by far-red light, or by osmotic solutions.

Another growth promoter which can sometimes alleviate dormancy is kinetin, along with related purines. Miller (1958) has carefully examined the kinetin stimulation and deduces that it enhances the effects of red light in breaking dormancy but that it is not able to replace it entirely. Mayer and Poljakoff-Mayber (1957) also deduced that the kinetin effect is not identical with the red-light effect.

That inhibitors are intimately involved with dormancy appears to be well established, and while the intricate interactions of inhibitors with dormancy are sometimes less than simple, there seems to be reasonable evidence that inhibitors really are responsible for many types of dormancy. The loss of dormancy, then, can occur either when the inhibitor is eluted, metabolized, or otherwise removed or through the intervention of growth-stimulating substances of the gibberellin type particularly.

Probably the strongest chemical agent for breaking dormancy is ethylene, and though it is a natural product of plant metabolism, little attention has been given to the possibility that it may play a part in the natural emergence from dormancy.

Many chemicals other than the ones mentioned already break dormancy of seeds. Thiourea is one of the most effective and commonly employed chemicals. Its action may be through the light-sensitive phase of dormancy (Evenari et al., 1954). This subject is reviewed in detail by Crocker and Barton (1957). One chemical deserves special mention here, and that is KNO_3, which markedly increases the effectiveness of many dormancy-breaking treatments. The stimulative effect of this salt has already been seen in connection with the temperature effects on dormancy. It is also markedly synergistic with the gibberellin effects on dormancy, as shown, for example, in Fig. 19-20 (Hashimoto, 1958, 1961). It is used routinely in seed-germination tests because its effectiveness in increasing germination is so general.

Dormancy mechanisms

Among the most impressive attributes of the state of dormancy are the many different types of treatments which can alleviate or impose it and the wide variety of internal mechanisms which may be involved.

In the complex mass of experimental data one can see three general types of internal controls of dormancy: (1) limitations of permeability (especially for the imbibition of water and the permeation of oxygen into the dormant piece); (2) limitations by growth substances, including inhibitors and the counteracting promotive substances and their activation or inactivation by temperature or light; and finally (3) physical limitations on the enlargement of the embryo and its emergence.

It appears that most dormancy-breaking treatments can be roughly accounted for on the basis of these three types of controls. For example, scarification treatments will alter the first and the third types of limitations; low-temperature and high-oxygen treatments to break dormancy may principally affect the water and gas entry as well as the inhibitor content which may be present. Vegis (1956) suggests that the inhibitor accumulation may be mainly a consequence of high-temperature experience. Gibberellins, kinins, and nitrate treatments may also modify the effective inhibitor levels in various ways, and the other chemicals which break dormancy may act both on the effective inhibitor level and on the water-

or gas-entry step through physical alterations of the seed coat and metabolic alterations of the tissues inside.

It seems dangerous to assign the general controls of dormancy to any one of these categories, for in some species dormancy may be controlled by one limitation, and in others there may be involvements of several limitations, some of which no doubt remain to be discovered.

GENERAL REFERENCES

Chouard, P. 1960. Vernalization and its relations to dormancy. *Ann. Rev. Plant Physiol.*, 11:191–238.

Crocker, W., and L. V. Barton. 1957. *Physiology of Seeds.* Chronica Botanica Co., Waltham, Mass. 267 pp.

Doorenbos, J. 1953. Review of the literature on dormancy in buds of woody plants. *Mededel. Landbouwhogeschool Wageningen*, 53:1–24.

Fig. 19-20 | The treatment of tobacco seeds with gibberellin to break their light-requiring dormancy shows a synergistic increase in effectiveness with KNO_3 (0.04 or 0.08M) (Hashimoto, 1958).

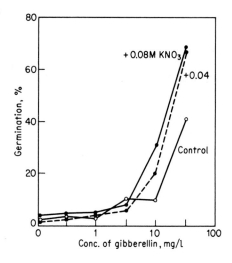

Mayer, A. M., and A. Poljakoff-Mayber. 1964. *The Germination of Seeds.* Pergamon Press Ltd., Oxford. 236 pp.

Samish, R. M. 1954. Dormancy in woody plants. *Ann. Rev. Plant Physiol.,* 5:183–204.

REFERENCES CITED

Avery, G. S., Jr., P. R. Burkholder, and H. B. Creighton. 1937. Production and distribution of growth hormone in shoots of *Aesculus* and *Malus,* and its probable role in stimulating cambial activity. *Am. J. Botany,* 24:51–58.

Black, M., and P. F. Wareing. 1954. Photoperiodic control of germination in seed of birch (*Betula pubescens Ehrh.*). *Nature,* 174:705.

Blommaert, K. L. J. 1955. The significance of auxins and growth inhibiting substances in relation to winter dormancy of the peach tree. *Union S. Africa Dept. Agr. Sci. Bull.,* 368:1–23.

Boo, L. 1961. The effect of gibberellic acid on inhibitor β complex in resting potato. *Physiol. Plantarum,* 14:676–681.

Borthwick, H. A., S. B. Hendricks, E. H. Toole, and V. K. Toole. 1954. Action of light on lettuce seed germination. *Botan. Gaz.,* 115:205–225.

Boysen-Jensen, P. 1935. *Die Wuchsstofftheorie.* Jena.

Brian, P. W., J. H. Petty, and P. T. Richmond. 1959. Extended dormancy of deciduous woody plants treated in autumn with gibberellic acid. *Nature,* 184:69.

Brown, R. 1940. An experimental study of permeability to gases of the seed coat membranes of *Cucurbita. Ann. Botany (London),* 4:379–395.

Buch, M. L., and O. Smith. 1959. The acidic growth inhibitor of potato tubers in relation to their dormancy. *Physiol. Plantarum,* 12:706–715.

Carlson, R. F., and H. B. Tukey. 1945. Differences in after-ripening requirements of several sources of peach seeds.

Proc. Am. Soc. Hort. Sci., 46:199–202.

Chandler, W. H., M. H. Kimball, G. L. Philip, W. P. Tufts, and G. B. Weldon. 1937. Chilling requirements for opening of buds on deciduous orchard trees. *Calif. Univ. Agr. Expt. Sta. Bull.,* 611.

Chvojka, L., M. Travnicek, and M. Zakourilova. 1962. The influence of stimulating doses of benzylaminopurine on awakening apple buds. *Biol. Plant. (Prague),* 4:203–206.

Cohen, D. 1958. The mechanism of germination stimulation by alternating temperatures. *Bull. Res. Council Israel Bot. Sect. D,* 6:111–117.

Cotrufo, C., and J. Levitt. 1958. Investigations of the cytoplasmic particulates and proteins of potato tubers. VI. *Physiol. Plantarum,* 11:240–248.

Crocker, W., and L. V. Barton. 1957. *Physiology of Seeds.* Chronica Botanica Co., Waltham, Mass.

Danilov, M. D. 1946. On the breaking of winter rest by buds of woody plants. *Compt. Rend. Acad. Sci. URSS,* 53:267–269.

Darrow, G. M. 1942. Rest period requirement for blueberries. *Proc. Am. Soc. Hort. Sci.,* 41:189–194.

Dennis, F. G., and L. J. Edgerton. 1961. The relationship between an inhibitor and rest in peach flower buds. *Proc. Am. Soc. Hort. Sci.,* 77:107–116.

Donaho, C. W., and D. R. Walker. 1957. Effect of gibberellic acid on breaking of the rest period in Elberta peach. *Science,* 126:1178–1179.

Doorenbos, J. 1953. Review of the literature on dormancy in buds of woody plants. *Mededel. Landbouwhogeschool Wageningen,* 53:1–24.

Eagles, C. F., and P. F. Wareing. 1963. Dormancy regulators in woody plants. *Nature,* 199:874–875.

Elliot, B. B., and A. C. Leopold. 1952. A relationship between photoperiodism and respiration. *Plant Physiol.,* 27:787–793.

Elliott, B. B., and A. C. Leopold. 1953. An inhibitor of germination and of amylase activity in oat seeds. *Plant Physiol.*, 6: 66–78.

El-Shishiny, E. D. H., and D. Thoday. 1952. Inhibition of germination in *Kochia indica*. *J. Exptl. Botany*, 4:10–22.

Esashi, Y. 1961. Studies on the formation and sprouting of aerial tubers in *Begonia evansiana* Andr. VI. Photoperiodic conditions for tuberization and sprouting in the cutting plants. *Sci. Rept. Tohoku Univ.*, 27:101–112.

Evenari, M. 1949. Germination inhibitors. *Botan. Rev.*, 15:153.

———. 1952a. The water balance of plants in desert conditions. *Desert Res.*, 2:1–9.

———. 1952b. The germination of lettuce seeds. *Palestine J. Botany*, 5:138–160.

———, G. Stein, and G. Neumann. 1954. The action of light in conjunction with thiourea on germination. *Proc. Intern. Photobiol. Congr. 1st*, 82–86.

Fine, J. M., and L. Barton. 1958. Biochemical studies of dormancy and after-ripening in seeds. I. Changes in free amino acid content. *Contrib. Boyce Thompson Inst.*, 19:483–500.

Flint, L. H., and E. D. McAlister. 1937. Wave lengths of radiation in the visible spectrum promoting the germination of light-sensitive lettuce seed. *Smithsonian Inst. Misc. Collections*, 96:1–8.

Franklin, B., and P. F. Wareing. 1962. Changes in endogenous gibberellins in relation to chilling of dormant seeds. *Nature*, 194:313–314.

Guttenberg, H. von, and H. Leike. 1958. Untersuchungen über den Wuchs und Hemmstoffgehalt ruhender und triebender Knospen von *Syringa vulgaris*. *Planta*, 52:96–120.

——— and G. Meinl. 1954. Über die Veränderung der Wasserpermeabilität von Kartoffelknollen während der Lagerzeit und durch Cumarin. *Planta*, 43:571–575.

——— and I. Strutz. 1952. Zur Keimungsphysiologie von *Ustilago zeae*. *Arch.*

Mikrobiol., 14:189–198.

Hashimoto, T. 1958. Increase in percentage of gibberellin-induced dark germination of tobacco seeds by N-compounds. *Botan. Mag. (Tokyo)*, 71:845–846.

———. 1961. Influence of inorganic nitrogenous compounds on tobacco seed germination. *Plant Cell Physiol. (Tokyo)*, 2: 463–470.

Hemberg, T. 1949a. Growth inhibiting substances in buds of *Fraxinus*. *Physiol. Plantarum*, 2:37–44.

———. 1949b. Significance of growth inhibiting substances and auxins for rest period of potato. *Physiol. Plantarum*, 2: 24–36.

———. 1955. Studies on the balance between free and bound auxin in germinating maize. *Physiol. Plantarum*, 8:418–432.

———. 1958. The significance of the inhibitor beta complex in the rest period of the potato tuber. *Physiol. Plantarum*, 11:615–626.

Henderschott, C. H., and L. F. Bailey. 1955. Growth inhibiting substances in extracts of dormant flower buds of peach. *Proc. Am. Soc. Hort. Sci.*, 65:85–92.

——— and D. R. Walker. 1959. Identification of a growth inhibitor from extracts of dormant peach flower buds. *Science*, 130:798–799.

Housley, S., and W. C. Taylor. 1958. Studies on plant growth hormones. IV. The nature of inhibitor β in potato. *Exptl. Botany*, 9:458–471.

Hyde, E. O. C. 1954. The function of the hilum in some *Papilionaceae* in relation to the ripening of the seed and permeability of the testa. *Ann. Botany (London)*, 18:241–256.

Isikawa, S. 1954. Light-sensitivity against the germination. I. "Photoperiodism" of seeds. *Botan. Mag. (Tokyo)*, 67:789–790.

Jost, L. 1894. Über den Einfluss der Licht auf das Knospentrieben der Rothbuche. *Ber. Deut. Botan. Ges.*, 12:188–197.

Kahn, A. 1960. Promotion of lettuce seed germination by gibberellin. *Plant Physiol.*, 35:333–339.

————, A. Gass, and D. E. Smith. 1957. Effect of gibberellin on germination of lettuce seed. *Science,* 125:645–646.

Kawase, M. 1960. Endogenous growth substances and the photoperiodic control of growth in *Betula.* Ph.D. Diss., Cornell Univ.

Kefford, N. P. 1955. The growth substances separated from plant extracts by chromatography. II. *J. Exptl. Botany,* 6:245–255.

Klebs, G. 1914. Über das Treiben der einheimuchen Baume speziell der Buche Abhand. *Heidelberg Akad. Wiss.,* 3:116.

Koller, D. 1957. Germination-regulating mechanisms in some desert seeds. IV. *Atriplex dimorphostegia* Kar. et Kir. *Ecology,* 38:1–13.

————, A. Poljakoff-Mayber, A. Berg, and T. Diskin. 1963. Germination regulating mechanisms in *Citrullus colocynthis. Am. J. Botany,* 50:597–603.

Kurz, L., and J. Kummerow. 1957. Brechung der Ruheperiode von *Hydrocharis* durch Kinetin. *Naturwissenschaften,* 44:121.

Loomis, W. E., and M. M. Evans. 1928. Experiments in breaking the rest period of corms and bulbs. *Proc. Am. Soc. Hort. Sci.,* 25:73–79.

Luckwill, L. C. 1952. Growth-inhibiting and growth promoting substances in relation to the dormancy of apple seeds. *J. Hort. Sci.,* 27:53–67.

Mayer, A. M., and A. Poljakoff-Mayber. 1957. The influence of gibberellic acid and kinetin on germination and seedling growth of lettuce. *Bull. Res. Council Israel Sect.* 6D:65–72.

Mes, M. G. 1957. Studies on the flowering of *Coffea arabica* L. III. Various phenomena associated with the dormancy of coffee flower buds. *Port. Acta Biol.,* 5:25–44.

Miller, C. O. 1958. The relationship of the kinetin and red-light promotions of lettuce seed germination. *Plant Physiol.,* 33:115–117.

Miller, E. C. 1938. *Plant Physiology.* McGraw-Hill Book Company, New York. 1201 pp.

Molisch, H. 1909. Warmbad und Pflanzentrieberie. *Oesterr. Gartenzeit,* 4:17–23.

Morinaga, T. 1926. Effect of alternating temperatures upon the germination of seed. *Am. J. Botany,* 13:141–159.

Müller-Thurgau, H. 1880. Über das Gefrieren und Erfrieren der Pflanzen. *Landw. Jahrb.,* 9:133–189 (cited by Miller, 1938).

Murakami, Y. 1959. The occurrence of gibberellins in mature dry seeds. *Botan. Mag. (Tokyo),* 72:857–858.

Nagao, M., Y. Esashi, T. Tanaka, T. Kumagai, and S. Fukumoto. 1959. Effects of photoperiod and gibberellin on germination of seeds of *Begonia. Plant Cell Physiol. (Tokyo),* 1:39–48.

————, and E. Mitsui. 1959. Studies on the formation and sprouting of aerial tubers in *Begonia evansiana* Andr. III. Effect of gibberellin on the dormancy of aerial tubers. *Sci. Rept. Tohoku Univ.,* 25:199–205.

Naylor, J. M., and G. M. Simpson. 1961. Dormancy studies on seed of *Avena fatua.* II. A gibberellin sensitive inhibitory mechanism in the embryo. *Can. J. Botany,* 39:281–295.

Nutile, G. E. 1945. Inducing dormancy in lettuce seed with coumarin. *Plant Physiol.,* 20:422–433.

Okazawa, Y. 1959. Studies on the occurrence of natural gibberellin and its effects on the tuber formation of potato plants. *Proc. Crop Sci. Soc. Japan,* 28:129–133.

Olney, H. O., and B. M. Pollock. 1960. Studies of rest period. II. Nitrogen and phosphorus changes in embryonic organs of after-ripening cherry seed. *Plant Physiol.,* 35:970–975.

Paech, K. 1953. Über die Lichtkeimung von *Lythrum salicaria. Planta,* 41:525–566.

Pfeffer, W. 1904. *Pflanzenphysiologie II,* pp. 247–278. Kraftwechsel 2. Aufl. Leipzig.

Phillips, I. D. J. 1961. Induction of light

requirement for germination of lettuce seed by naringenin and its removal by gibberellic acid. *Nature,* 192:240–241.

——— and P. F. Wareing. 1958. Effect of photoperiodic conditions on the level of growth inhibitors in *Acer pseudoplatanus. Naturwissenschaften,* 45:317.

Piringer, A. A., and H. A. Borthwick. 1955. Photoperiodic responses of coffee. *Turrialba,* 5:72–77.

Pollock, B. M. 1953. The respiration of *Acer* buds in relation to the inception and termination of winter rest. *Physiol. Plantarum,* 6:47–64.

———. 1960. Studies of rest period. III. Respiratory changes in leaf primordia of maple buds during chilling. *Plant Physiol.,* 35:975–977.

Richter, A. A., and T. A. Krassnosselskaya. 1945. A contribution to the knowledge of the breaking of winter dormancy in buds of woody plants. *Compt. Rend. Acad. URSS,* 47:218–219.

Sawyer, R. L., and O. Smith. 1955. A study of the oxygen-periderm relationship in potato tubers and the effect of oxygen on the normal breaking of the rest period. *Am. Potato J.,* 32:15–22.

Smith, O. E., and L. Rappaport. 1961. Endogenous gibberellins in resting and sprouting potato tubers. *Advan. Chem. Ser.,* 28:42–48.

Stokes, P. 1952. A physiological study of embryo development in *Heracleum sphondylium,* L. I. *Ann. Botany (London),* 16:442–447.

Szalai, I. 1959. Quantitative changes of growth-promoting and inhibiting substances in the potato tubers treated with rindite. *Physiol. Plantarum,* 12:237–244.

Tager, J. M., and B. Clark. 1961. Replacement of an alternating temperature requirement for germination by gibberellic acid. *Nature,* 192:83–84.

Tomaszewski, M. 1957. Phenolase complex and auxin inactivation in the leaves of some trees of the family Rosaceae at the period preceding winter dormancy. *Arboretum Kornickie,* 3:257–271.

Toole, E. H. 1959. Effect of light on the germination of seeds, pp. 89–99. In R. B. Withrow (ed.), *Photoperiodism.* American Association for the Advancement of Science, Washington, D.C.

Toole, E. H., V. K. Toole, H. A. Borthwick, and S. B. Hendricks. 1955. Photocontrol of *Lepidium* seed germination. *Plant Physiol.,* 30:15–21.

Varga, M. 1957. Examination of growth-inhibiting substances separated by paper chromatography in fleshy fruits. IV. Paper chromatography of lemon juice containing germinating seeds. *Acta Biol. Szeged.,* 3:233–237.

Vegis, A. 1956. Formation of the resting condition in plants. *Experientia,* 12:94–99.

Wareing, P. F. 1950. Growth studies in woody species. I. Photoperiodism in first year seedlings of *Pinus silvestris. Physiol. Plantarum,* 3:258–276.

———. 1953. Growth studies in woody species. V. Photoperiodism in dormant buds of *Fagus sylvatica. Physiol. Plantarum,* 6:692–706.

———. 1954. Growth studies in woody species. VI. The locus of photoperiodic perception in relation to dormancy. *Physiol. Plantarum,* 7:261–277.

——— and H. A. Foda. 1957. Growth inhibitors and dormancy in *Xanthium* seed. *Physiol. Plantarum,* 10:266–280.

——— and T. A. Villiers. 1961. Growth substance and inhibitor changes in buds and seeds in response to chilling, pp. 95–107. In R. M. Klein (ed.), *Plant Growth Regulation.* Iowa State University Press, Ames, Iowa.

Weisner, W., and H. Molisch. 1890. Untersuchungen über die Gasbewegung in der Pflanze. *Sitzber. Akad. Wien,* 98:534.

Part IV | ENVIRONMENTAL PHYSIOLOGY

One of the most impressive things about the response of the plant to its environment is that it involves not merely the direct modification of the organism by an environmental variable, or the establishment of limits to the range of habitation, or even the incorporation of environmental forces in the synthesis of foodstuffs, but that it provides a synchronizing force for actions by the plant—a regulation of the sequential steps in the plant life cycle. The feature of these synchronizing and regulating actions that is especially startling is that the plant "remembers" environmental experiences, that is, that its manner of growth or development may be altered for more or less extensive periods of time after the environmental experience has been terminated.

The relative persistence of changes imposed on plants by environmental experiences may vary widely. Some effects may be experienced only during the environmental event, such as the short-term effects of light on pigment formation or on the morphological development of leaves. Other effects may be slightly persistent, such as the geotropic induction of curvature in grass coleoptiles, which has a half-life of about 4½ hr, or the hardening of plants to high- or low-temperature experiences, which may last for a week after the environmental stimulus has been withdrawn. Still other effects may be metastable; that is, they may persist for extended periods of time or even indefinitely until the plant receives a contrary or nullifying experience to terminate them. Examples of the metastable effects include many of the photoperiodic effects on flowering, dormancy, and tuber and bulb formation and the vernalizing effects of cold on the readiness of some species to flower or on the dwarfing or nondwarfing growth habit.

The range of persistence of environmental responses is not just from short-term to slightly persistent to metastable effects. There are also the repeating effects, such as the rhythmic diurnal events, and the switching or on-off effects such as the onset and termination of dormancy. In the former case, the diurnal rhythms are imposed on the plant usually by light experiences, and can repeat themselves even when the repetition of the environmental experiences has been stopped. In the latter case, a brief environmental experience may relieve a stoppage of growth and the altered state may continue indefinitely without requiring any repetition of the environmental cue.

Plants utilize environmental cues to synchronize the season of flowering or fruiting, the time and place of seed germination, the time of day when a flower opens or when a leaf assumes a new position which is superior for interception of light. The mechanisms which plants have evolved for utilizing environmental cues to regulate the timing of growth and development present some of the most exciting problems in physiology.

20 | Light

By a current of light, the sun provides the warmth, nurture, and nutriment for life on this planet. It provides a pulsing subsidy of energy, from which the entire endowment of biological activity accumulates. In addition to supplying the capital on which life subsists, it imposes the major dynamic physical features of the environment in which life has developed, including the temperatures of the earth and the energy for rain, for winds, and for the currents of the oceans.

The extent of the light energy supplied from the sun staggers the imagination. It becomes exceedingly difficult to conceive of 10^{21} kcal of energy being invested in 1 acre of the earth's surface per year—an equivalent in electric energy of 3.5 million kw hours for each acre.

The light energy emitted by the sun is a product of nuclear reactions within the sun's body similar to the reactions of the hydrogen bomb. Through the conversion of hydrogen to helium, there is a considerable loss of mass and the release of light energy. As the energy passes through the outer gaseous layer of the sun (a layer deeper than the entire diameter of the earth), it is successively absorbed and reemitted by mixtures of carbon, metals, and other lighter components of the sun's atmosphere. From the luminous properties of these solar layers the escaping light energy is principally concentrated in the wavelengths between about 300 and 2,000 mμ. Additional small amounts are radiated in the longer radio waves or the shorter x-rays, gamma rays, and cosmic rays. The greatest amount of light energy, however, reaches the outer atmosphere of the earth in a concentrated range, as shown in Fig. 20–1.

As the sunlight passes through the atmosphere of the earth, it undergoes some changes, for the water in the atmosphere removes a large proportion of the infrared wavelengths between 850 and 1,300 mμ. Further filtering effects are brought about by the ozone and the carbon dioxide in the atmosphere. The overall effect of the atmos-

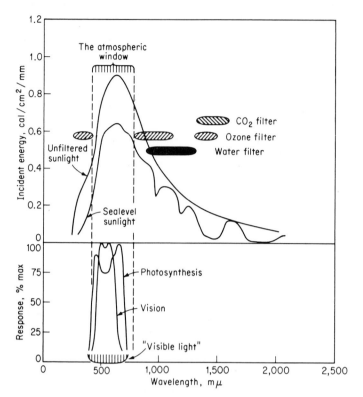

Fig. 20-1 | The incident radiation from the sun is most abundant in the same wavelengths as are used for biological reactions such as photosynthesis and vision. Sunlight is filtered by the atmosphere, narrowing the peak of radiation to the biologically utilized range.

phere is to reduce somewhat the amount of radiant energy reaching the earth's surface, preferentially lessening the amounts in the shorter wavelengths of ultraviolet and the longer wavelengths of far-red and infrared light (Fig. 20-1). Thus the atmosphere provides a window through which shine the wavelengths of highest frequency in unfiltered sunlight, the so-called "visible" wavelengths.

From the biological point of view, the qualities of the atmospheric window are particularly fortuitous, for the wavelengths of ultraviolet and infrared can be highly damaging to the biological materials. Wave-lengths below 400 mμ are absorbed with decreasing specificity by common biological constituents, and the amount of energy per quantum of light becomes increasingly large. Therefore the short wavelengths of radiation can dump relatively large units of energy onto molecules more randomly intercepted in the cell, and biological damage may be the consequence. With wavelengths longer than those of the visible region, the absorption of the light energy by cells again becomes damaging mainly because of the absorptive qualities of water to infrared light. Water is the universal cradle for biological macromolecules, and its adsorptive properties can lead to damage from excessive infrared light. Between these two relatively harmful ranges, the visible wavelengths have the fortunate quality of selective absorbability by numerous types of carbonaceous molecules, especially by some with nitrogen and metallic components through which electron resonance is enhanced. The selectivity of light absorption makes possible the selective guidance of its energy into organized chemical systems, a basic quality for light utilization.

It is probably no coincidence that the biological systems can most effectively utilize the wavelengths most abundantly supplied by the sun. The most effective wavelength band for photosynthesis straddles the same band as is best utilized for vision by animal eyes (Fig. 20-1). Within the same band lie the action spectra for the principal light-regulated systems of biology, including plant tropisms, seed germination, photoperiodism, and pigmentation responses in plants and in animals. Each of these is mediated by pigments which carry out the selective guidance of the light energy into organized chemical systems—synthetic systems, as in photosynthesis, or biochemical triggering systems, as in vision, tropisms, photoperiodism, and pigmentation responses to light. The pigments may be unsaturated carbon skeletons like the carotenoids; carbon associated with nitrogen, as in the flavins; or carbon associated with nitrogen and metals, as in chlorophyll. Through the selective absorption properties of carbonaceous biological pigments, the qualities of the light coming through the atmospheric window are most effectively utilized. The process of biochemical evolution has doubtless produced this synchrony of available and utilizable light qualities.

Light actions

The absorption of light energy by plant pigments causes a displacement of pi electrons in a resonance system through the pigment molecule. This activated state of the pigment lasts for only a fraction of a second, after which the electron falls back to its unactivated orbit, and the energy of its displacement is given up. The energy of activation can ordinarily be given up in several ways: by a reemission of light or of heat energy, by transmission of the activated state to another molecule, or by utilization of the energy in a chemical reaction. Light-activated plant pigments use all these methods to give up their energy of activation. During the process of photosynthesis, chlorophyll actually gives off measurable amounts of light as fluorescence (Wassink and Katz, 1939); pigments, such as carotenoids, which are closely associated with chlorophyll can absorb the light energy and transmit it to the chlorophyll system, and the activated chlorophyll can cause the expenditure of chemical work in photosynthetic reduction. If the pigment is separated from its chemical synthesizing components and so cannot apply its absorbed energy to chemical work there, it has only the option of reemitting the light or of oxidizing itself, both of which chlorophyll extracts will do when exposed to light in the presence of air.

Action spectra are useful in the analysis of photochemical activities. For example, Engelmann (1882) used an approximate action spectrum for photosynthesis to establish that chlorophyll was the pigment responsible for photosynthesis. He measured the relative effectiveness of light of various wavelengths and found two peaks of effectiveness, one in the region of 660 and another in the range of 440 mμ. The absorption curve for chlorophyll has similar peaks (Fig. 20-2).

Classically the action spectrum should reveal the nature of the responsible pigment, but for most light-driven plant responses the action spectra have not permitted a precise identification of the pigment. Numerous action spectra have been worked out, but positive identification of the responsible pigments has not generally been possible.

The correlation between the action spectrum and the absorption spectrum of the activating pigment may vary widely. In photosynthesis the two spectra agree rather well, except for the better effectiveness of the wavelengths between 450 and 600 mμ due to contributing actions by accessory carotenoid pigments. In the formation of chlorophyll, the action spectrum at low light intensities and the absorption spectrum for protochlorophyll match fairly well. Protochlorophyll is the absorbing pigment and is converted by the photoreaction to chlorophyll, though at higher light intensities photosynthesis may contribute to the formation of the protochlorophyll precursors, and the action spectrum is somewhat altered. In plant tropisms, the effectiveness of blue light implicates either the carotenes or the flavins in the activation of the phototropic response, and the discrepancies between the absorption spectra and the action spectra are perhaps attributable to differences in the physical associations of the pigment in vivo. The red-light responses of plants which are reversible with far-red light presumably have action spectra which are not the same as the absorption spectrum for phytochrome but which, rather, are like the difference spectra between the red- and the far-red-absorbing forms of the pigment (Fig. 20-3). Other red-light responses, especially anthocyanin formation, are sometimes altered in their action spectra by the presence or relative abundance of presumed secondary substances involved in the utilization of the light energy, resulting in marked variations in the shape of an action spectrum (cf. Fig. 20-7). Finally, matching the action spectra to the absorption spectra may be complicated by the phenomenon of changes in action due to dosage levels. Many light responses are markedly altered with increases in light level. For example, anthocyanin formation may be exclusively driven by red light at low intensities and by both red and blue light at higher intensities (Figs. 20-7 and 20-8).

Because of these complexities, the action spectra may be considerably more diverse than the absorption spectra for plant pigments. But in a general way there appear to be three major types of action spectra for plant responses (Fig. 20-4): those driven maximally by both red and blue light (photosynthesis, some tropisms, and plant movements); those driven maximally by red light (chlorophyll formation, photoperiodism, seedling morphogenetic responses, and dormancy responses); and those driven maximally by blue light (phototropism and polarization responses). These types may often be linked so that blue-light responses can be modified by red light or far-red light, making it unclear whether the responsible pigment may absorb light

Fig. 20-2 | The action spectrum for photosynthesis shows peaks at the same wavelengths as the absorption spectrum for chlorophyll. Action spectrum for wheat as Q_{CO_2} corrected for respiration (Hoover, 1937); absorption spectrum of chlorophyll a in methanol (Tanada, 1951).

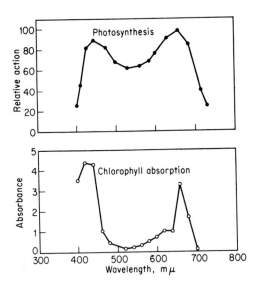

in both blue and red or whether alternatively there are two separate pigments closely interacting on the same biochemical system.

The responses driven by both red and blue light presumably are mediated by chlorophyll. Those driven mainly by red light are mediated principally by phytochrome and are usually reversible with far-red light. Those driven by blue light may be mediated by carotenoids or flavins.

Photosynthesis

This giant among all biological light actions is driven principally by chlorophyll. The ability of some carotenoids to pass absorbed light energy to chlorophyll alters the action spectrum somewhat. In some red algae the participation by other pigments becomes so great that there may be a superior effectiveness of the red pigments (Haxo and Blinks, 1950). This suggests either that these pigments can directly energize the photosynthetic system or that there may be some leakage effect of the absorbed light energy to the chlorophyll (Rabinowitch, 1951).

Fig. 20-4 | Three principal types of light responses by plants: (a) the action spectra which peak in both red and blue (photosynthesis), (b) those which peak in the red and may be reversible with far-red (such as photoperiodism and dormancy), and (c) those which peak in the blue region (such as phototropism and auxin destruction). Diagrammatically taken from Hoover, 1937; Hendricks and Borthwick, 1954; and Johnston, 1934. The red-light response may be reversed by far-red light (dashed line).

Fig. 20-3 | Responses to red light which are reversed by far-red light may be related to a difference spectrum. Absorbance of a phytochrome extract from corn shoots is shown after red and after far-red irradiation, and the difference spectrum is represented below (Butler et al., 1959).

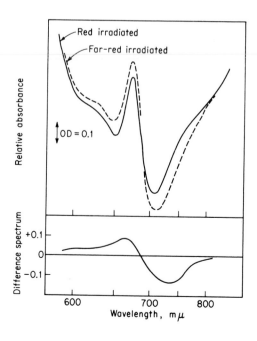

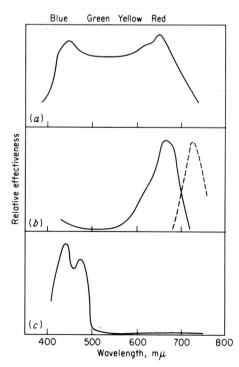

Pigmentation

As etiolated plants receive increasing amounts of light, large changes in the pigmentation of the stems and leaves result. The anthocyanin content of bean leaves increases even at very low intensities of red light, and concomitantly a dramatic conversion of protochlorophyll into chlorophyll begins (Klein et al., 1957).

The formation of chlorophyll appears to be a direct photomodification of protochlorophyll. The action spectrum for the conversion (Fig. 20-5) matches quite well the absorption spectrum for protochlorophyll (Koski et al., 1951). The greater effectiveness in the red region may be attributable to the contributions of photosynthesis through the formation of more protochlorophyll. The data of Koski (1950) show that the conversion of protochlorophyll into chlorophyll is approximately stoichiometric (Fig. 20-6).

Even in this rather simple light action, there are interactions by some other light-absorbing systems. The relatively weak action of blue light (440 mµ) in proportion to the absorption of that wavelength by protochlorophyll is presumed to be due to masking effects of carotenoid pigments. As

Fig. 20-5 | The light stimulation of chlorophyll formation in corn leaves has an action spectrum fairly similar to the absorption spectrum of protochlorophyll. The methanol solvent causes the absorption peaks to shift 10 to 20 mµ toward shorter wavelengths (Koski et al., 1951).

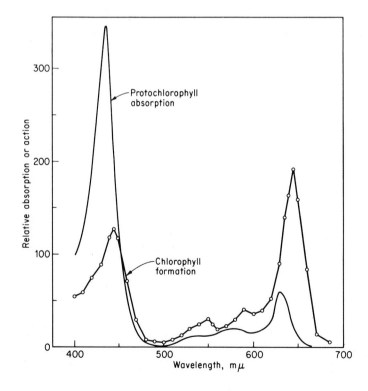

another interaction, Price and Klein (1961) established that previous experience of red light improves chlorophyll synthesis and that this potentiation effect is reversible with far-red light. The phytochrome system can apparently intervene in some way with the protochlorophyll conversion.

The stimulation of anthocyanin formation by light is more complex. A comparison of light responses by various plants (Siegelman and Hendricks, 1957) showed that not only are there quantitative differences, but there are different action spectra between species. Three types of spectra for anthocyanin formation have been described, and these are illustrated in Fig. 20-7 (Hendricks and Borthwick, 1959*b*). One type peaks in the red light (apple), another peaks in the far-red light (turnip) and another in wavelengths midway between the two (cabbage). Assuming that all are driven by the light activation of the phytochrome pigment, Hendricks and Borthwick (1959*b*) suggested that in the apple anthocyanin formation is catalyzed by driving the phytochrome to the far-red form, in the turnip by driving the pigment to the red form, and in the cabbage by the photoactivation of either form.

The light stimulation of anthocyanin formation may be activated by a different action spectrum in mustard seedlings under higher light intensities. Mohr (1957) found in *Sinapis* a peak of effectiveness with blue light and another peak with far-red light (Fig. 20-8). Far-red light does not reverse this effect, although at lower light intensities the more typical red *x* far-red reversible situation is found. This situation suggests that in *Sinapis* the phytochrome pigment system may be associated with another pigment which can activate the system more readily at higher light intensities.

Seedling morphology effects

The germination of most seeds occurs in a dark microcosm, and the growth patterns elevate the stem shoot up through the dark soil layers to the light. This action entails an exaggerated elongation type of growth of the stem (or mesocotyl in the case of grains) and essentially no enlargement of the leaves, which would interfere with the penetration through the soil. When the seedling tip emerges into the light, the etiolated growth gives way to the normal type of plant growth. The experience of light by the monocot grass-coleoptile tip signals a major transformation in the manner of growth, terminating the elongation of the mesocotyl and thus placing the bases of the stems of new plants at roughly uniform depths in the soil (Fig. 20-9). In the light the grass seedling grows by the elongation of leaves and stem instead of by mesocotyl elongation. The experience of light by the dicot seedling also causes a major change, including the loss of the hypocotyl hook (a modification of the etiolated stem tip which facilitates soil penetration without damage to the growing point), a retardation of stem growth rate, and the commencement of leaf growth. These multiple effects of light on

Fig. 20-6 | With the formation of chlorophyll by low dosages of light, there is an equivalent disappearance of protochlorophyll. Etiolated corn seedlings exposed to 150 ft-c for the times indicated (Koski, 1950).

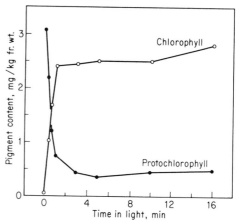

seedling growth provide some of the most dramatic light responses in plants.

The termination of mesocotyl growth in the grass seedling is triggered by red light (Weintraub and McAlister, 1942), with peak effectiveness at about 650 mμ under weak light and at somewhat shorter wavelengths for greater light intensities. The unbending of the hypocotyl hook of bean seedlings is driven by the same wavelengths of light (660 mμ), and the red-light effect is erased by subsequent exposure to far-red light (Withrow et al., 1957; Fig. 20-10). The red x far-red reversible effects imply that phytochrome is the responsible pigment.

After the stem-straightening response to light, seedling growth proceeds with a more restricted stem elongation and an enlarge-ment of the leaves. The changes in stem and leaf activities are quantitatively brought about by light, and representative data for the growth of stems and leaves of pea seedlings are shown in Fig. 20-11 (Parker et al., 1949). These two growth responses to light are also under the control of the phytochrome system, for they are most sensitive to red light at low intensities, and the red-light effects are reversible by far-red light in most cases. For instance, the action spectrum for bean-leaf enlargement is shown in Fig. 20-12, and the effectiveness of far-red light in erasing red-light effects is plotted on the same graph (Downs, 1955).

As the erstwhile etiolated seedling receives its light signal upon emergence, there are also anatomical changes invoked. Among the more dramatic of these are the stimulation of epidermis differentiation on stems and the formation of stem hairs in response to light. The former, described for peas by Borgström (1939), is essential for some growth responses of the pea seedling. A common bioassay for auxins is the curved growth of slit stems of partly etiolated peas. The response is due to differential responsivenes of the epidermis to auxin; without red light the pea stems will not produce the curvature response (Kent and Gortner, 1951) for lack of differentiation of the epidermis. The stimulation of stem hairs by light has been described by Mohr (1959a), who found that in *Sinapis* this response is best driven by red light at low light intensities (reversible by far-red light) but that at higher intensities it is best driven by light of 710 mμ and by blue light.

Another morphological response to light is the formation of palisade tissues in leaves (Watson, 1942). The cigar-shaped palisade cells, which contain the principal supply of chloroplasts, are formed in increasing numbers with increasing light intensity during leaf development. The morphological response to bright light seems to offer a

Fig. 20-7 | Action spectra for anthocyanin formation in three species of plants, showing three variants of the red x far-red action spectra. The difference spectra for phytochrome in its two forms are given below for comparison (Hendricks and Borthwick, 1959b).

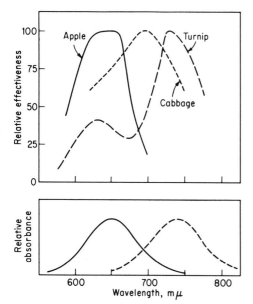

basis for the physiological adaptation of leaves to high light intensities.

Growth rates

The ability of light to alter growth rates has been recognized for some time. Sachs (1872) found that many species are inhibited in stem elongation during daylight hours, and he termed this a *light inhibition* of growth. Mason (1925) used shading experiments to study light effects and found slower growth in date palms during the day. In other species there may be greater growth rates during the day, which suggests a stimulatory effect of light (Darrow, 1929; Thut and Loomis, 1944). Much of the early work on light effects, however, was confounded by interacting effects with temperature and water (Miller, 1938).

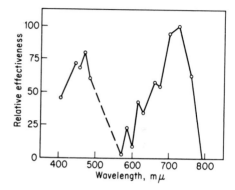

Fig. 20-8 | The action spectrum for anthocyanin formation in *Sinapis* at higher light intensities combines a red peak with an additional peak in the blue wavelengths [3,500 ergs/cm²/sec for 4 hr] (Mohr, 1957).

Fig. 20-9 | The seedling germinated in the dark penetrates the soil by etiolated growth until its tip experiences light. In grasses the etiolated growth involves elongation of the mesocotyl (the internode between seed and first node), and in dicotyledonous plants it involves the elongation of the epicotyl (pea) or hypocotyl (bean, lettuce). Light suppresses this type of elongation, removes the hypocotyl hook, and favors leaf and internode growth.

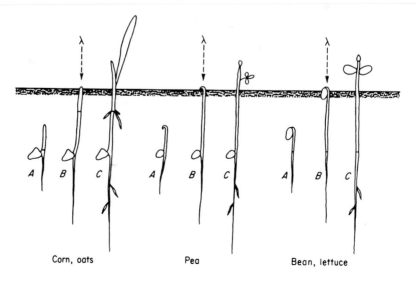

Corn, oats   Pea   Bean, lettuce

Accelerations of growth by light occur in many tissues, even in cases where the final size achieved is depressed. It is common for tissues to grow faster in light than in dark, but if the light intensity is great enough, the final size achieved is reduced. This pattern of response is shown in some data of Thomson (1950; Fig. 20-13). When smaller amounts of light were applied, the stunting of final size of *Avena* coleoptiles would sometimes be avoided. These data are for etiolated coleoptiles, but the same pattern is common for stems and leaves. The growth-stimulation effect appears to involve both cell divisions and cell enlargement (Thomson and Miller, 1963).

Inhibitions of growth by light are more commonly observed, especially with reference to stem growth. Early quantitative experiments by Withrow (1941) indicated that the seedling is most inhibited by light in the red and yellow regions of the spectrum. As equipment for establishment of an actual action spectrum became available, Parker et al. (1949) found that the inhibition effects were maximal in the red wavelengths. The action spectrum is commonly indistinguishable from the other morphological responses of seedlings (e.g., the unbending of the hypocotyl hook and the stimulation of leaf enlargement) and again implicates phytochrome. The quantitative nature of the stem inhibition is illustrated in Fig. 20-11.

Liverman and Bonner (1953) showed that the red-light effect on growth is reversed by far-red light in the usual phytochrome manner. Downs et al. (1957) demonstrated that far-red light applied during the night can actually stimulate stem elongation in the bean plant. The far-red component of daylight does not appreciably stimulate stem elongation, but weak intensities of far-red light applied at night can cause marked elongation responses.

These experiments on the red-light inhibition of stem and coleoptile growth have

Fig. 20-10 | The action spectrum for removing the hypocotyl hook from etiolated bean seedlings shows the peak effectiveness of red light; the red-light effect is removed by subsequent far-red light (Withrow et al., 1957).

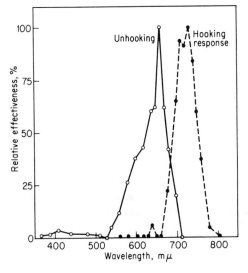

Fig. 20-11 | Light applied to etiolated pea seedlings causes an inhibition of internode growth and a stimulation of leaf enlargement (Parker et al., 1949).

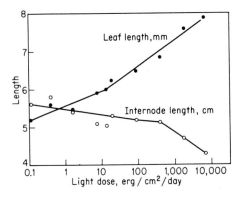

been carried out at low light intensities. Mohr (1960) expressed concern that in the natural state the light reactions which control growth responses may be driven by much higher light intensities. Mohr and Wehrung (1960) found that in higher light intensities the inhibition of stem growth in lettuce hypocotyls is maximal with wavelengths in the far-red (720 mμ) and shows another peak of effectiveness in the blue (450 mμ). Their action spectrum, shown in Fig. 20-14, is typical of a large series of action spectra, including the control of germination, the enlargement of leaves, the formation of stem hairs, and the stimulation of anthocyanin formation. The contrast between the red x far-red spectra and the far-red and blue spectra illustrates the contrasts in action spectra obtained with differing light intensities. Which type is of greater importance physiologically remains a fertile ground for discussion.

The inhibition of plant growth in the field by excessive light intensities is another order of magnitude removed from the inhibitions already discussed. In some experiments with pinto beans, Lockhart (1961a) showed that the inhibition of growth in full sunlight is removed by the application of gibberellic acid (Fig. 20-15). He interprets the gibberellin effectiveness as relieving the red-light inhibition of growth. Some species were not inhibited by high light intensities (pea), and others were even more inhibited than the beans (D_1 dwarf corn). The light-response differences may be related to the endogenous gibberellin contents.

There has been some criticism of the explanation of red-light inhibition of stem growth as a gibberellin-depressing system. Mohr and Appuhn (1961) reported that the application of gibberellin to *Sinapis* stems does not remove the sensitivity to the red x far-red light effects, and so the two responses are independent of each other. The resolution of this interesting argument should be constructive.

Fig. 20-12 | The stimulation of leaf enlargement is most effective for red light, and the red-light effect is reversed by far-red light. Etiolated bean seedlings (Downs, 1955).

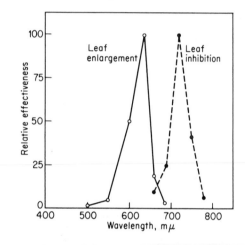

Fig. 20-13 | The growth of coleoptiles of etiolated *Avena* seedlings is accelerated by light, but the final length achieved is reduced. Light applied by a 200-watt lamp, 1 m above the plants (Thomson, 1950).

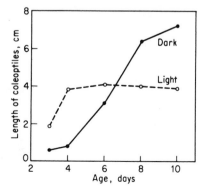

Fig. 20-14 | The inhibition of growth of etiolated lettuce seedlings is strongest with either red or blue light. As in Fig. 20-8, this action spectrum was done with relatively high light intensities [500 ergs/cm²/sec for 15 hr] (Mohr and Wehrung, 1960).

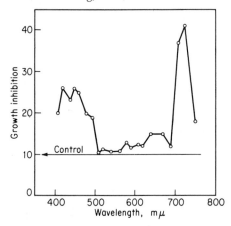

Fig. 20-15 | Pinto beans growing in the field show an inhibition of stem growth by full sunlight, but gibberellic acid application (4 μg per plant) prevents the light inhibition (Lockhart, 1961a).

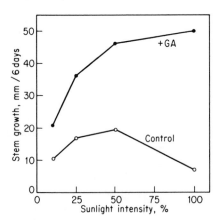

Dormancy

The effectiveness of light in breaking dormancy was the first red-light effect to be described (Flint, 1934). The red x far-red actions of light on dormancy have been shown for many seeds, and the phytochrome pigment has been assigned the responsibility for this light response; but even the very early work indicated a blue-light effect. Flint and McAlister (1937) found that either far-red or blue imposed dormancy on lettuce seeds, and Phillips (1941) showed that the same qualities of light imposed dormancy in buds of some conifers.

Photoperiodism

The most precisely measured effect of light on photoperiodism is its action in interrupting the dark period. In low light intensities the red x far-red phytochrome system appears to be commonly in control. Red light is most effective in interrupting the dark period, and its effects are erased by the subsequent application of far-red light.

As is the case with growth responses, photoperiod effects can be obtained with blue light when higher intensities are applied (Wassink et al., 1950; Stolwijk, 1954).

Quite another effect of light in photoperiodism is involved in the day response. One component of the day response is photosynthetic, and if photosynthesis is prevented, photoperiodic induction is barred (Parker and Borthwick, 1940). However, there appear to be some other functions of the day obtainable with light intensities which are too low for photosynthesis. Meijer and van der Veen (1960b) showed that blue light applied during the day at low intensities alters the effectiveness of the subsequent dark period as well as its sensitivity to night interruption with red light. Meijer (1959) asserts that the day period is dominated by a blue-light and a deep red-light action reminiscent of the actions described by Mohr (1960).

Phytochrome

The description of the red-light responses of plants has been essentially a description of phytochrome actions. The action spectra of events driven best by red light in the region of 660 mμ [such as anthocyanin formation (Fig. 20-7), the unhooking of the hypocotyl in the emerging seedling (Fig. 20-10), the light stimulation of leaf enlargement (Fig. 20-12), seed dormancy (Fig. 19-6), and photoperiodic sensitivity of the night (Fig. 13-17)] have described the major known phytochrome involvements in the regulation of development.

The concept of a pigment regulating developmental events found its antecedent in the discovery that night interruptions could destroy the effectiveness of a long night in photoperiodism (see Chap. 13 under Photoperiodism and Flowering). Hendricks and his colleagues at Beltsville, Maryland, performed the experiments which revealed the existence of such a pigment: first by establishing the action spectra for the various red-light responses (Parker et al., 1946), then by discovering that the red-light effects were generally reversible with far-red (Borthwick et al., 1952), and finally by systematically searching through plant tissues for such a pigment which would show the interconvertible forms predicted on the basis of the red and far-red reversibilities. This was a case of an accumulation of evidence for the existence of a plant pigment which nobody could see and the final resolution of the situation by the actual isolation of a pigment which had the interconvertibility characteristic deduced beforehand (Butler et al., 1959).

The discovery of phytochrome was made possible by the design of a spectrophotometer which could separately apply monochromatic light to leaves and then rapidly scan for changes in absorptive properties. Using the spectrophotometer, it was found that there was in fact a spectral shift in the absorption by etiolated plant parts following red or far-red illumination (Butler et al., 1959) and that alkaline extracts of light-sensitive plants yielded a solution which had the same spectral shift. Partial purification revealed that the pigment is a water-soluble protein (Hendricks, 1960).

The fact that the red-light effects on plants are so often reversible with far-red light and that the extracted pigment shows a spectral shift after exposure to red or far-red light establishes that there are two forms for phytochrome: a red-absorbing form and a far-red-absorbing form. Exposure to red light preferentially activates the red-absorbing form and converts it into the far-red-absorbing form. Exposure to far-red light has the reverse effect. The spectral shift is evident in Fig. 20-3. The manner in which the two forms of this pigment regulate the morphological and biosynthetic mechanisms in the plant is unknown.

In darkness many plants experience a rapid phytochrome conversion from the far-red- to the red-absorbing form, and this is presumed to be the initial step of the photoperiodic night reactions (see Chap. 13 under Photoperiodism and Flowering). In other plants the dark conversion may be very slow, resulting in the extended persistence of the condition imposed by the last light experience. The prolonged dormancy of lettuce or *Lepidium* seeds after far-red radiation is a notable example (Table 11).

In the extracted form, the phytochrome pigment of several plant species may carry out the dark conversion from the far-red- to the red-absorbing form (Bonner, 1962; Siegelman et al., 1962). The conversion occurs readily in etiolated corn shoots; an experiment on the apparent dark conversion is shown in Fig. 20-16. After exposure to red light, the leaf showed a spectral shift

Table 11 | *The effects of light on the germination of* Lepidium *seeds are determined by the last light exposure, whether it is the stimulating red or the inhibitory far-red light. If red light is given only once or after seven cycles of red followed by far-red light, the last light experience determines the response. Germination of two species is shown, one completely controlled by light and the other quantitatively influenced (Toole et al., 1955).*

Light treatments	Final light treatment	Percentage germination L. densiflorum	L. virginicum
No light	...	0	8
Red	Red	45	92
Red, far-red	Far-red	0	22
(Red, far-red)₇, red	Red	48	95
(Red, far-red)₇, red, far-red	Far-red	0	24

Fig. 20-16 | The changes in form of extracted phytochrome held in darkness at 27°C after a red-light exposure. Aliquots of etiolated corn extracts were given red (R) or far-red (FR) light at various time intervals, and the changes in absorbancy were recorded. At the time of removal of the extract to darkness, the pigment is mainly in the far-red-absorbing form (P_{FR}), and after 3 hr at 27°C almost all the pigment is in the red-absorbing form (P_R), suggesting a dark conversion (Hendricks, 1960).

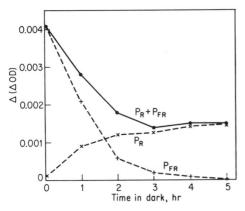

Time in dark, hr

only in response to far-red light, indicating that the pigment supply was in the far-red-absorbing form. After 2 hr of darkness more than half the far-red-absorbing form had disappeared, and after 3 hr only the red-absorbing form remained. These data were interpreted as indicating dark conversion.

Figure 20-16 also indicates that there is a lability of pigment at 27°C, and the most rapid loss seems to occur when the pigment is in the far-red-absorbing form. At temperatures near freezing the loss of pigment was essentially prevented (Hendricks, 1960).

The concentration of the pigment in plants may be as high as 1 part per million; the estimated lowest concentration capable of altering a physiological response to red light is 1 part per 10 billion (Hendricks, 1960).

From these experiments some deductions can be made about the pigment, but its nature and the manner of its regulation of developmental activities remain to be established. Certainly the effectiveness of weak light in interrupting the photoperiodic night is a function of the phytochrome system, and the length of time over which the interruption effects persist is a function of the rate of dark conversion of the phytochrome (Borthwick and Cathey, 1962). It seems unlikely that the dark conversion is responsible for the timing feature of the photoperiodic night (Salisbury, 1963). One of the more puzzling features of the phytochrome system is its ability to control some morphological or developmental phenomena without controlling other phenomena in the same plant. For example, many species show the morphological responses to red light as seedlings but lack the photoperiodic sensitivity to night interruption or the light sensitivity of seeds. Occurrence of phytochrome on various sites in the cytoplasm and organelles may account for its involvement in some light responses without regulating others (Gordon, 1960; Haupt, 1962).

Blue-light effects

One of the first action spectra made for a growth response to light was that for phototropism. In its most precise form the action spectrum (Fig. 20-17) has a three-shouldered peak of effectiveness in the blue region of 400 to 470 mμ. The interesting argument about whether the responsible pigment might be β-carotene, which has a triple absorption peak and no absorption in the near ultraviolet, or riboflavin, which has a double absorption peak and some absorption in the ultraviolet, has yet to be conclusively settled (Wald, 1960; Galston, 1960).

There may be some connection between the blue-action spectrum for phototropism and the red-action spectrum for growth. Mohr and Peters (1960) analyzed the question and deduced that the inhibitions of cell elongation by red light are quite different from the inhibitions of growth on the phototropically lighted side.

Blue light is better than red for imposing a light gradient across an etiolated stem or coleoptile because the cell contents can transmit red light relatively well. The tropistic response to blue light could be related to the gradient of light across the plant piece (Brauner, 1955). Buder (1920) studied the question of a possible directional involvement of light. By cleverly inserting a light source inside the hollow center of a corn coleoptile and illuminating one side from the center, he was able to induce phototropic curvatures toward the lighted side. He deduced that the direction of light transmission was not important in phototropism. Briggs (1963a) found that red light strongly potentiates the phototropic responsiveness of corn and oat seedlings.

An action of blue light which may be related to phototropism in some cases is the photodestruction of auxin. This has been studied both as the enzymatic destruction of indoleacetic acid and as the nonenzymatic destruction in the presence of riboflavin, and the action spectra for both are suggestive of the phototropic-action spectrum (Galston and Baker, 1949). This blue-light action is probably not involved in phototropism at low light intensities, for there is no detectable destruction of auxin at low intensities, but it could participate in the phototropism responses under high light intensities in the field. Yet Briggs (1963b) found no decrease in diffusible auxin from corn coleoptiles after phototropic stimulations over a wide range of light doses.

Another action of blue light is the effect on the polar growth of some lower plants. Mosebach (1943) observed that light could control the polar differentiation of rhizoids in the germinating spores of *Equisetum*. The application of light to one side of the spore causes that side to become the apex and the shaded side to sprout rhizoids (cf. Fig. 10-1). This effect is predominately due to blue light (Haupt, 1957). Similar polarizing effects have been observed for moss and fern spores, as well as an ability of light to convert the nonpolar fern protonema into a prothallium (Mohr, 1956).

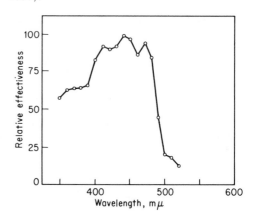

Fig. 20-17 | The action spectrum for the initial curvature of etiolated *Avena* coleoptiles toward light in phototropism (Shropshire and Withrow, 1958).

Diurnal-light effects

Many light responses of plants have become so habitual with the diurnal pulse of light that they achieve a somewhat independent diurnal periodicity in the plant. Most of these seem to be triggered by light mechanisms, but in some the light involvement is compounded with other environmental factors such as temperature and relative humidity. There is only a limited amount of information available on the nature of the light requirements for these diurnal effects, and action spectra for the diurnal periodicities are few.

Historically the first diurnal periodicity to be observed was that of growth rates. Sachs (1872) noted the more rapid growth of some plants at night and deduced that there was a light-inhibition effect on growth. However, there does appear to be a component of diurnal periodicity or endogenous rhythm in the daily growth changes. This is illustrated by some data of Ball and Dyke (1954), who observed a diurnal oscillation of growth rate of oat coleoptiles even when

kept under uniform conditions of darkness. The oscillation period was initiated at the time of removal from light into darkness.

At almost the same time, Pfeffer (1873) observed a diurnal periodicity of movements of leaves, noting that they were elevated to a horizontal position in the morning and lowered to a "sleep" position in the evening. These movements are synchronized by light; illumination during the night causes the leaves to move to the day position. If plants are placed in constant darkness, they continue for a limited number of days to move up and down, as if they were still experiencing the same daily light cycles as before. This phenomenon is illustrated by the movements of *Albizzia* leaves (Fig. 20-18). Bünning and Lorcher (1957) examined the qualitative nature of this light action and concluded that it was driven by red light and that the effect was reversible with far-red light. The situation seems to vary between species or conditions, however; Holdsworth (1959) and Fortanier (1954) have found that in some species either the red effect was not reversible with

Fig. 20-18 | The diurnal movements of *Albizzia* leaves elevate the leaves in the morning and lower them again in the evening. If they are deprived of light, the movement is repeated for a limited time and on a limited scale (Pfeffer, 1915; from Bünning, 1959*b*).

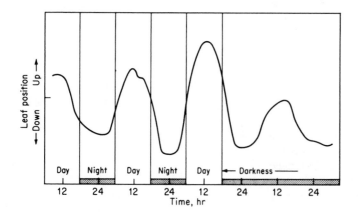

far-red light or the light response was driven by blue better than by red.

Another diurnal movement triggered by light is the daily opening of flowers. Most commonly, light causes an opening (Bünsow, 1953; Fig. 14-2), but occasionally it causes closure, resulting in night-flowering habits (Overland, 1960; Fig. 14-3).

Another type of light-driven movement is heliotropism, in which plants—for example, the sunflower—turn toward the sun and follow it across the sky in a turning action. This interesting phenomenon has been examined by Shibaoka and Yamaki (1959), who found that the movement is triggered by the light stimulus on the leaves nearest the stem tip. The shading of various leaves on sunflower seedlings revealed that the greater illumination of the leaf more distant from the sun (Fig. 20-19) resulted in a stimulation of growth on that side of the stem; hence the turning of the stem toward the sun. They found also that more auxin was diffused from the leaf receiving the more intense light, and the stem growth stimulation was therefore attributed to an auxin phenomenon. Shibaoka (1961) showed that growth inhibitors may also be involved. As in many other diurnal-light effects, if the light source is removed the plant continues for a limited time to turn daily from east to west and return, but after several days the movement ceases.

Within leaves there is frequently a daily flux in the organic acid content, with acids rising during the night and falling with the advent of light in the morning. An example of this is the variation in acid content of the pineapple leaf (Sideris et al., 1948; Fig. 20-20). Associated with the change in acid content is an inverse change in the sugar content, suggesting an interconversion between sugars and acids during the night.

Acid accumulation in leaves is generally associated with the succulent habit. Such leaves are ordinarily thick and relatively fleshy, as in the Crassulaceae. The development of the succulent type of morphology is under the control of the day length. Harder et al. (1942) showed that the succulence of *Kalanchoe* leaves increases as the length of day is shortened, with the most succulent leaves developed in a 6 hr photoperiod. In a series of experiments they established that the succulent type of leaf development is controlled by a stimulus from the newly expanded leaves which moves up to the young leaves. This

Fig. 20-19 | Heliotropic curvature of sunflower may be due to a greater amount of light falling on the young leaf farther away from the sun, as in (*a*). When bending occurs so that the two leaves receive the same amount of light (*b*), movement stops (modified from Shibaoka and Yamaki, 1959).

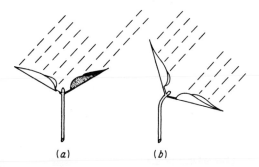

(*a*)   (*b*)

Fig. 20-20 | A diurnal flux in organic acids and sugars of pineapple leaves, showing large increases in acids during the night, followed by decreases during the day. A converse pattern is described for sugars (Sideris et al., 1948).

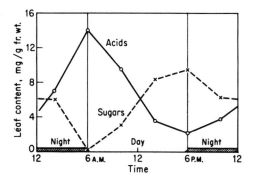

mobile stimulus is clearly separate from the photoperiodically generated flower stimulus. The light action is strongly altered by temperature.

Succulent leaves are characterized by a strong ability for dark fixation of carbon dioxide into organic acids, and one of the general sources of the CO_2 fixed is respiration. At night most stomata are closed, and so the metabolically produced CO_2 is held inside the leaf. The closure of the stomata is another light-controlled function, and except when water is limiting inside the plant, the opening of stomata is entrained by light in the morning, and the closure occurs when the light is withdrawn. A diurnal cycle of stomatal movement is illustrated in Fig. 20-21 (Campbell, 1957). If light is applied during the night, the stomata will open. Night interruption with light can depress both the succulent development of

leaves and the accumulation of organic acids (Gregory et al., 1954).

The list of diurnal functions in the plant which are regulated by light could be extended to include guttation, cell division, root growth, and ion uptake. In each of these the diurnal function is triggered by light and is regulated in its periodicity by the duration of the light. If the daily light period is removed and the plant is held in darkness, the periodicity continues to be expressed for a few days. It appears that light can *trigger* these diurnal events but that the control is compounded by some complex endogenous rhythms (Bünning, 1959*b*).

Light mechanisms

Investigations of the influence of light on the physiological processes of the plant are still in a descriptive stage. Many light responses have not been assigned to chemically known pigments, and in no case is the light action on any developmental control system understood. Metabolic phenomena will have to be invoked to carry the physiological explanation from the pigment step to the final developmental expression.

In some light responses, photosynthesis is the provider of substrates, e.g., in the light stimulation of growth of pea-stem sections (Galston and Baker, 1951) or in the light period of photoperiodism (Parker and Borthwick, 1940). In other instances, various types of growth substances are involved in the light responses, as in the auxin redistribution with phototropism, the increased auxin yield from sunflower leaves in heliotropism (Shibaoka and Yamaki, 1959), or the light inhibition of growth in etiolated pea-stem sections (Galston and Baker, 1953), where the light appears to activate an auxin oxidase system. Gibberellins may be involved in some light actions, as evidenced by the gibberellin reversal of light inhibitions (Lockhart, 1956, 1960,

Fig. 20-21 | Stomatal movements in *Xanthium* in response to light, showing the closure during the night and opening in the morning. A temporary opening is obtained when light is given for 1 min during the night (dashed line). Closure is measured as the resistance of the leaf to air movement, using the porometer method (Campbell, 1957).

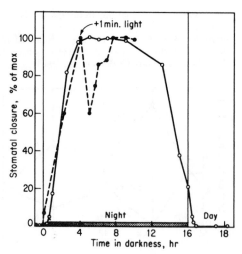

1961*a*), or by the light stimulation of formation of gibberellin-like substances (Blaauw-Jansen, 1959). Miller (1956) found that kinins were involved and that kinetin accentuated the effects of light in stimulating leaf expansion. Hillman (1957) found that kinetin accentuated the light stimulation of growth of *Lemna*. Inhibitors, too, have been implicated in light mechanisms. There is evidence for the formation of growth inhibitors in light (Blaauw-Jansen, 1954; Zucker and Ahrens, 1958; Masuda, 1962) and evidence for the removal of inhibitor action by light, as in germination and dormancy.

Metabolic activities will be intimately involved in the light controls of plant functions, but knowledge of these is just starting to develop. There is sometimes a light effect on overall respiration rates (e.g., Brown and Weis, 1959). Hendricks and Borthwick (1959*a*) deduced that the phytochrome pigment is an enzyme or is associated with some enzyme in metabolism. One appealing possibility is that phytochrome might exert a control over some central and limiting metabolic step; Hendricks and Borthwick (1959*b*) suggested that the light effects on photoperiodism and on anthocyanin formation could be related to the effects on the formation of the thiol-ester between coenzyme A and butyric acid. More specific experimental evidence supports the suggestion of Gordon and Surrey (1960) and Surrey and Gordon (1962) that the red x far-red system regulates oxidative phosphorylation activities. They found measurable effects of red and far-red light on oxidative phosphorylation by oat coleoptiles but could not find such effects with the phosphorylative activities of isolated mitochondria.

The enormous scope of light influences on plants, from the synthesis of substrates to the regulation of the quality and quantity of growth and developmental sequences, establishes light as the most powerful environmental force. The quality of light reaching the earth from the sun has been mirrored precisely in the qualities to which plant processes have become harnessed. The periodicity of light impulses imposed by the rhythmic rotation of the earth is reflected in the periodicities of plant responses, including the development of highly precise timing mechanisms for the photoperiodic adaptations to seasonal changes and the "remembered" diurnal rhythms of many growth and metabolic functions.

The major regulating actions of light fall within the general spectral types of photosynthesis, of the red phytochrome effects, or of the blue carotenoid type of actions. These principal light-response systems have become adapted to regulate an enormous array of normal growth and developmental functions, ranging from the movements of stems, leaves, and flowers to the synchronization of the complex developmental steps such as dormancy and flowering.

GENERAL REFERENCES

Bünning, E. 1956. Endogenous rhythms in plants. *Ann. Rev. Plant Physiol.*, 7:71–90.

———. 1963. *Die Physiologische Uhr.* Springer-Verlag, Berlin. 153 pp.

Hendricks, S. B. 1960. Rates of change of phytochrome as an essential factor determining photoperiodism in plants. *Cold Spring Harbor Symp. Quant. Biol.*, 25: 245–248.

——— and H. A. Borthwick. 1954. Photoperiodism in plants. *Proc. Intern. Photobiol. Congr., 1st,* 23–35.

Mohr, H. 1962. Primary effects of light on growth. *Ann. Rev. Plant Physiol.*, 13: 465–488.

Saeki, T. 1963. Light relations in plant communities, pp. 79–94. In L. T. Evans (ed.), *Environmental Control of Plant Growth.* Academic Press Inc., New York.

Withrow, R. B. (ed.). 1959. *Photoperiodism and Related Phenomena in Plants and Animals.* American Association for the

Advancement of Science, Washington, D.C. 903 pp.

REFERENCES CITED

Ball, N. G., and I. J. Dyke. 1954. An endogenous 24-hour rhythm in the growth rate of the *Avena* coleoptile. *J. Exptl. Botany,* 5:421–433.

Blaauw-Jansen, G. 1954. Chlorophyllide: the probable precursor of a growth inhibitor. *Nature,* 174:312.

———. 1959. The influence of red and far-red light on growth and phototropism of the *Avena* seedling. *Acta Botan. Neerl.,* 8:1–39.

Bonner, B. A. 1962. *In vitro* dark conversion and other properties of phytochrome. *Plant Physiol.,* 37:xxvii.

Borgström, G. 1939. *The Transverse Reactions of Plants.* C.W.K. Gleerup, Lund, Sweden. 230 pp.

Borthwick, H. A., and H. M. Cathey. 1962. Role of phytochrome in control of flowering of chrysanthemum. *Botan. Gaz.,* 123: 155–162.

———, S. B. Hendricks, M. W. Parker, E. H. Toole, and V. K. Toole. 1952. A reversible photoreaction controlling seed germination. *Proc. Natl. Acad. Sci. U.S.,* 38:662–666.

Brauner, L. 1955. Über die Funktion der Spitzenzone beim Phototropismus der *Avena*-Koleoptile. *Z. Botan.,* 43:467–498.

Briggs, W. R. 1963a. Red light auxin relationships and the phototropic responses of corn and oat coleoptiles. *Am. J. Botany,* 50:196–207.

———. 1963b. Mediation of phototropic responses of corn coleoptiles by lateral transport of auxins. *Plant Physiol.,* 38: 237–247.

Brown, A. H., and D. Weis. 1959. Relation between respiration and photosynthesis in the green alga, *Ankistrodesmus. Plant Physiol.,* 34:224–234.

Buder, J. 1920. Neue phototropische Fundamentalversuche. *Ber. Deut. Botan. Ges.,* 38:10–29.

Bünning, E. 1959a. Allgemeine Gesetze und Phänomene der pflanzlichen Bewegungsphysiologie. *Handbuch Pflanzenphys.,* 17:8–23.

———. 1959b. Tagesperiodische Bewegungen. *Handbuch Pflanzenphys.,* 17: 579–656.

——— and L. Lorcher. 1957. Regulierung und Auslosung endogentagesperiodischer Blättebewegung durch verschiedene Lichtqualitaten. *Naturwissenschaften,* 44: 472.

Bünsow, R. 1953. Über tages- und jahresrhythmische Änderungen den photoperiodischen Lichtemfindlichkeit bei *Kalanchöe blossfeldiana* und ihre Beziehungen zur endogenen Tagesrhythmik. *Z. Botan.,* 41:257–276.

Butler, W. I., K. H. Norris, H. W. Siegleman, and S. B. Hendricks. 1959. Detection, assay, and preliminary purification of the pigment controlling photoresponsive development of plants. *Proc. Natl. Acad. Sci. U.S.,* 45:1703–1708.

Campbell, C. W. 1957. Modification of light control in plant development. Ph.D. Diss., Purdue Univ.

Darrow, G. M. 1929. Effect of light, temperature and transpiration on elongation of canes of raspberry. *Proc. Am. Soc. Hort. Sci.,* 26:308–311.

Downs, R. J. 1955. Photoreversibility of leaf and hypocotyl elongation of dark grown red kidney bean seedlings. *Plant Physiol.,* 30:468–473.

———, S. B. Hendricks, and H. A. Borthwick. 1957. Photoreversible control of elongation of pinto beans and other plants under normal conditions of growth. *Botan. Gaz.,* 118:199–208.

Engelmann, T. W. 1882. Über Sauerstoffausscheidung von Pflanzenzellen im Mikrospectrum. *Botan. Z.* 40:419–433 (cited by Rabinowitch, 1951).

Flint, L. H. 1934. Light in relation to dormancy and germination in lettuce seed. *Science*, 80:38–40.

Flint, L. H., and E. D. McAlister. 1937. Wave lengths of radiation in the visible spectrum promoting the germination of light-sensitive lettuce seed. *Smithsonian Inst. Misc. Collections*, 96:1–8.

Fortanier, E. J. 1954. Some observations on the influence of spectral regions of light on stem elongation, flower bud elongation, flower bud opening and leaf movement in *Arachis hypogea* L. *Mededel. Landbouwhogeschool Wageningen*, 54: 103–114.

Galston, A. W. 1960. Letter to the Editor. *Sci. Am.*, 202:12–15.

———— and R. S. Baker. 1949. Studies on the physiology of light action. II. The photodynamic action of riboflavin. *Am. J. Botany*, 36:773–780.

———— and ————. 1951. Studies on the physiology of light action. IV. Light enhancement of auxin induced growth in green peas. *Plant Physiol.*, 26:311–317.

———— and ————. 1953. Studies on the physiology of light action. V. Photoinductive alteration of auxin metabolism. *Am. J. Botany*, 40:512–516.

Gordon, S. A. 1960. The intracellular distribution of phytochrome in corn seedlings. *Proc. Intern. Photobiol. Congr. 3rd*, 441–443.

———— and K. Surrey. 1960. Red and far-red action on oxidative phosphorylation. *Radiation Res.*, 12:325–339.

Gregory, F. J., I. Spear, and K. V. Thimann. 1954. The interrelation between CO_2 metabolism and photoperiodism in *Kalanchöe*. *Plant Physiol.*, 29:220–229.

Harder, R., O. Bode, and H. von Witsch. 1942. Über Wechselbeziehungen zwischen Blutenbildung, Brakteenverlaubung and Sukulenz der Laubblätter bei *Kalanchöe*. *Flora (Jena)*, 36:85–100.

Haupt, W. 1957. Die Induktion der Polarität bie der Spore von *Equisetum*. *Planta*, 49:61–90.

————. 1962. Über die Lokslisierung des Phytochroms in der *Mougeotia* Zelle. *Vorträgen Deut. Bot. Ges.*, 1:116–122.

Haxo, F. T., and L. R. Blinks. 1950. Photosynthetic action spectra of marine algae. *J. Gen. Physiol.*, 33:389–421.

Hendricks, S. B. 1960. Rates of change of phytochrome as an essential factor determining photoperiodism in plants. *Cold Spring Harbor Symp. Quant. Biol.*, 25: 245–248.

———— and H. A. Borthwick. 1954. Photoperiodism in plants. *Proc. Intern. Photobiol. Congr. 1st*, 23–35.

———— and ————. 1959a. Photocontrol of plant development by the simultaneous excitation of two interconvertible pigments. *Proc. Natl. Acad. Sci. U.S.*, 45: 344–349.

———— and ————. 1959b. Photocontrol of plant development by the simultaneous excitation of two interconvertible pigments. II. Theory and control of anthocyanin synthesis. *Botan. Gaz.*, 120:187–193.

Hillman, W. S. 1957. Nonphotosynthetic light requirement in *Lemna minor* and its partial satisfaction by kinetin. *Science*, 126:165–166.

Holdsworth, M. 1959. The spectral sensitivity of light-induced leaf movements. *J. Exptl. Botany*, 11:40–44.

Hoover, W. H. 1937. The dependence of carbon dioxide assimilation in a higher plant on wave length of radiation. *Smithsonian Inst. Misc. Collections*, 95:1–13.

Johnston, E. S. 1934. Phototropic sensitivity in relation to wave length. *Smithsonian Inst. Misc. Collections*, 92:1–17.

Kent, M., and W. A. Gortner. 1951. Effect of pre-illumination on response of split pea stems to growth substances. *Botan. Gaz.*, 112:307–311.

Klein, W. H., R. B. Withrow, V. Elstad, and L. Price. 1957. Photocontrol of growth and pigment synthesis in the bean seedling as related to irradiance and wavelength. *Am. J. Botany*, 44:15–19.

Koski, V. M. 1950. Chlorophyll formation

in seedlings of *Zea mays* L. *Arch. Biochem. Biophys.*, 29:339–343.

————, C. S. French, and J. H. C. Smith. 1951. The action spectrum for the transformation of photochlorophyll to chlorophyll a. *Arch. Biochem. Biophys.*, 31:1.

Liverman, J. L., and J. Bonner. 1953. The interaction of auxin and light in the growth responses of plants. *Proc. Natl. Acad. Sci. U.S.*, 39:905–916.

Lockhart, J. A. 1956. Reversal of the light inhibition of pea stem growth by the gibberellins. *Proc. Natl. Acad. Sci. U.S.*, 42:841–848.

————. 1960. Intercellular mechanism of growth inhibition by radiant energy. *Plant Physiol.*, 35:129–136.

————. 1961a. Photoinhibition of stem elongation by full solar radiation. *Am. J. Botany*, 48:387–391.

————. 1961b. Mechanism of the photoperiodic process in higher plants. *Handbuch Pflanzenphys.*, 16:390–438.

Mason, S. C. 1925. The inhibitive effect of direct sunlight on the growth of the date palm. *J. Agr. Res.*, 31:455–468.

Masuda, Y. 1962. Effect of light on a growth inhibitor in wheat roots. *Physiol. Plantarum*, 15:780–790.

Meijer, G. 1959. Photomorphogenesis in different spectral regions, pp. 101–109. In R. B. Withrow (ed.), *Photoperiodism.* American Association for the Advancement of Science, Washington, D.C.

———— and R. van der Veen. 1960a. Dual effect of nightbreak light. *Acta Botan. Neerl.*, 9:220–223.

————and ————. 1960b. Wavelength dependence on photoperiodic responses. *Acta Botan. Neerl.*, 6:429–433.

Miller, C. O. 1956. Similarity of some kinetin and red light effects. *Plant Physiol.*, 31:318–319.

Miller, E. C. 1938. *Plant Physiology.* McGraw-Hill Book Company, New York. 1201 pp.

Mohr, H. 1956. Die Abhängigkeit des Protonemawachstums und der Protonema-polarität bei Farnen von Licht. *Planta*, 47:127–158.

————. 1957. Der Einfluss monochromatischer Strahlung auf das Langenwachstum des Hypocotyls and auf die Anthocyanbildung bei Keimlingen von *Sinapis alba* L. *Planta*, 49:389–405.

————. 1959a. Der Lichteinfluss auf die Haarbildung am Hypokotyl von *Sinapis alba*. *Planta*, 53:109–124.

————. 1959b. Der Lichteinfluss auf das Wachstum der Keimblätter bei *Sinapis alba*. *Planta*, 53:219–245.

————. 1960. The effects of long visible and near infrared radiation on plants, pp. 44–49. In *Progress in Photobiology.* Elsevier Publishing Company, Amsterdam.

———— and V. Appuhn. 1961. Zur Wechselwirkung von Licht und Gibberellinsaure. *Naturwissenschaften*, 48:483.

———— and E. Peters. 1960. Der Phototropismus and das lichtabhangige Langenwachstum des Hypokotyls von *Sinapis alba* L. *Planta*, 55:637–646.

————and M. Wehrung. 1960. Die Steuerung des Hypokotylwachstums bei den Keimlingen von *Lactuca sativa* durch sichtbare Strahlung. *Planta*, 55:438–450.

Mosebach, G. 1943. Über die Polaresierung der Equisetumspore durch das Licht. *Planta*, 33:340–387.

Overland, L. 1960. Endogenous rhythm in opening and odor of flowers of *Cestrum nocturnum. Am. J. Botany*, 47:377–382.

Parker, M. W., and H. A. Borthwick. 1940. Floral initiation in Biloxi soybean as influenced by photosynthesis. *Botan. Gaz.*, 102:256–268.

————, S. B. Hendricks, H. A. Borthwick, and N. J. Scully. 1946. Action spectrum for the photoperiodic control of floral initiation of short day plants. *Botan. Gaz.*, 108:1–26.

————, S. B. Hendricks, H. A. Borthwick, and F. W. Went. 1949. Spectral sensitivities for leaf and stem growth of etiolated pea seedlings. *Am. J. Botany*, 36:194–204.

Pfeffer, W. 1873. *Physiologische Untersuch-ungen*. Leipzig (cited by Bünning, 1959).

———. 1915. Beitrage zur Kenntnis der Entstebung der Schlafbewegungen. *Ahb. Kgl. Sachs Ges. Wiss. Math Physik.*, 34: 1–154 (cited by Bünning, 1959).

Phillips, J. E. 1941. Day length and tree dormancy. *J. Forestry*, 39:55–59.

Price, L., and W. H. Klein. 1961. Red, far-red response and chlorophyll synthesis. *Plant Physiol.*, 36:733–735.

Rabinowitch, E. I. 1951. *Photosynthesis and Related Processes*. Interscience Publishers, Inc., New York. 1208 pp.

Sachs, J. 1872. Über ˙den Einfluss der Lufttemperatur und des Tageslichts auf die stundlichen und taglichen Änderungen des Langewachstums (Streckung) der Internodien. *Arb. Botan. Inst. Wurtzburg*, 1:99–192.

Salisbury, F. B. 1963. Biological timing and hormone synthesis in flowering of *Xan-thium. Planta*, 59:518–534.

Shibaoka, H. 1961. Studies on the mechan-ism of growth inhibiting effect of light. *Plant Cell Physiol. (Tokyo)*, 2:175–197.

——— and T. Yamaki. 1959. Studies on the growth movement of sunflower plant. *Sci. Papers Coll. Gen. Educ. Tokyo*, 9: 105–126.

Shropshire, W., Jr., and R. B. Withrow. 1958. Action spectrum of phototropic tip-curvature of *Avena. Plant Physiol.*, 33: 360–365.

Sideris, C. P., H. H. Young, and H. H. Q. Chun. 1948. Diurnal changes and growth rates as associated with ascorbic acid, titratable acidity, carbohydrate and nitrogenous fractions in the leaves of *Ananas comosus. Plant Physiol.*, 23:38–69.

Siegelman, H. W., E. M. Firer, W. L. Butler, and S. B. Hendricks. 1962. Phytochrome from corn and barley seedlings. *Plant Physiol.*, 37:xxvii.

——— and S. B. Hendricks. 1957. Photo-control of anthocyanin formation in turnip and red cabbage seedlings. *Plant Physiol.*, 32:393–398.

Stolwijk, J. A. J. 1954. Wave length depend-ence of photomorphogenesis in plants. *Mededel. Landbouwhogeschool Wagen-ingen*, 54:181–244.

Surrey, K., and S. A. Gordon. 1962. Influ-ence of light on phosphate metabolism in lettuce seed: spectral response red, far-red interaction. *Plant Physiol.*, 37:327–332.

Tanada, T. 1951. The photosynthetic effi-ciency of carotenoid pigments in *Navicula minima. Am. J. Botany*, 38:276–283.

Thomson, B. F. 1950. The effect of light on rate of development of *Avena* seedlings. *Am. J. Botany*, 37:284–290.

——— and P. M. Miller. 1963. The role of light in histogenesis and differentiation in the shoot of *Pisum*. III. The internode. *Am. J. Botany*, 50:219–227.

Thut, H. F., and W. E. Loomis. 1944. Rela-tion of light to growth of plants. *Plant Physiol.*, 19:117–130.

Toole, E. H., V. K. Toole, H. A. Borthwick, and S. B. Hendricks. 1955. Photocontrol of *Lepidium* seed germination. *Plant Physiol.* 30:15–21.

Wald, G. 1960. Letter to the Editor. *Sci. Am.* 202:15.

Wassink, E. C., and E. Katz. 1939. The initial changes of chlorophyll-fluorescence in *Chlorella. Enzymologia*, 6:145–172.

———, N. Krijthe, and C. van der Scheer. 1950. On the effect of light of various spectral regions on the sprouting of potato-tubers. *Proc. Koninkl. Ned. Akad. Wetenschap.*, 53:3–14.

Watson, R. W. 1942. Mechanism of elonga-tion in palisade cells. *New Phytologist*, 41: 206–221.

Weintraub, R. L., and E. D. McAlister. 1942. Developmental physiology of the grass seedling. I. Inhibition of the meso-cotyl of *Avena sativa* by continuous ex-posure to light of low intensities. *Smith-sonian Inst. Misc. Collections*, 101:1–10.

Withrow, R. B. 1941. Response of seedlings to various wavebands of low intensity irradiation. *Plant Physiol.*, 16:241–256.

———, W. H. Klein, and V. Elstad. 1957. Action spectra of photomorphogenic in-duction and its photoinactivation. *Plant Physiol.*, 32:453–462.

Zucker, M., and J. F. Ahrens. 1958. Quanti-tative assay of chlorogenic acid and its pattern of distribution within tobacco leaves. *Plant Physiol.*, 33:246–249.

21 | Radiation

Radiation provides an intermittent rain of energy units falling on the living organism. Some "droplets" of energy are deflected by the cell surfaces, and others penetrate more or less deeply into the tissues, depending upon the energy load of the droplet and the wavelength with which it hits. Each quantum of radiation absorbed by the cell unloads its energy upon the object which intercepts it. In the case of visible light, this energy can provide the intercepting molecule either with heat or with an energy of activation which involves a displacement of electrons a limited distance from the atomic nuclei. In other electromagnetic radiations of shorter wavelengths, the impact of the radiation may be great enough completely to remove electrons from the vicinity of the atomic nucleus; this is an ionizing radiation. In comparison with electromagnetic radiations, particulate radiations ordinarily carry enormous amounts of energy which can completely remove electrons and thus be ionizing radiations. Alternatively, the radiation particles may be incorporated temporarily into the atomic nucleus which has been struck and there cause a large energetic disruption before the particle or some other part of the atomic nucleus is bounced out.

This discussion will consider two classes of radiation: electromagnetic, which have mainly the characteristics of wave phenomena, and corpuscular, which have mainly the characteristics of particulate radiations. The energy of electromagnetic radiations increases with shortening wavelength, and the energy of corpuscular radiations increases roughly with the size of the radiation particle, as shown in the diagram to the left.

In this series, the radiations from x-rays to beta rays are generally ionizing, their impact commonly resulting in the ejection of an electron and the ionization of the absorbing substance.

In discussing the effects of radiation on plants, let us consider the short wavelength

Electromagnetic radiations

decreasing wavelengths

radio waves
light | infrared
visible
ultraviolet
x-rays
gamma rays

Corpuscular radiations

increasing size

cathode or electron particles
(beta rays)
protons (alpha rays)
and neutrons

ionizing radiations

electromagnetic radiations and the particulate radiations. The effects of the long wavelengths—infrared and longer—will be considered as temperature effects in Chap. 22.

Radiant absorption

In general the constituents of the plant cell are decreasingly selective with increasing energies of radiation. The absorption of visible light by plant pigments is very selective, associated with elaborate electron-resonance capacities in the pigments. Many pigments possess these electron-resonance properties through association with metal atoms in the molecules, such as magnesium in chlorophyll and iron in the cytochrome pigments. Other pigments absorb light on the basis of resonance between carbon bonds, such as carotenoid pigments of leaves and fruits and flavone and flavonole pigments of fruits and flowers. Aromatic organic compounds, nitrogenous peptides, and nucleic acids all absorb radiations in the shorter ultraviolet wavelengths. With further decreases in wavelength, the selectivity becomes even less, and absorption is exercised by all hydrocarbons. Finally, in the range of x-rays, even water absorbs the radiation. Clearly the radiations applied to a plant can strike at different cell constituents, depending in a general way upon the wavelength or radiation energy. As shorter wavelengths are applied from visible to gamma rays, the effects may become less specific and more damaging. Nucleic acids and auxins, which are not structurally adapted to transmit absorbed radiation to other compounds, are very susceptible to damage by the radiation which they directly absorb. Chlorophyll and carotenoids are adapted to transmit their absorbed energy, and in so doing they can drive photoreactions in the plant, remaining less susceptible to damage.

Linear and exponential dosage-response curves are commonly obtained from radiations. When a unitary amount of radiant energy provokes a unitary response, the dosage-response curve is linear; examples of this are common in such actions as photosynthesis (e.g., Figs. 2-11 to 2-14). The responses to ionizing radiations are usually exponential; the biological effect increases with the dosage intensity. Damage is related to the frequency of simultaneous events, such as the total ionization events in the vicinity of a chromosome locus or the total amount of peroxide formation at a given instant in a cell nucleus. Illustrating the log-dosage-response curve, Fig. 21-1 compares the x-ray effects on germination of pollen from four plant genera (Brewbaker and Emery, 1962).

Fig. 21-1 | Dosage-response curves for radiation damage may be approximately exponential. Note the increases in pollen damage with log increases in dosage. Pollen of four genera given x-irradiation before germination (Brewbaker and Emery, 1962).

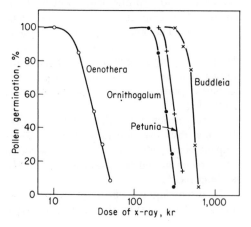

Responses to radiation

The capacities of radiations to disrupt the orderliness of normal plant growth are widely reported (cf. review by Gunckel,

Fig. 21-2 | Longitudinal sections of grape apices showing the normal structure (above) and the deterioration 33 days after 2 hr of thermal neutron radiation (below). The radiation has caused the collapse of the meristematic cells just below the tunica and the erratic enlargement of lower cells; × 360 (Pratt et al., 1959). Photograph courtesy of Brookhaven National Laboratory.

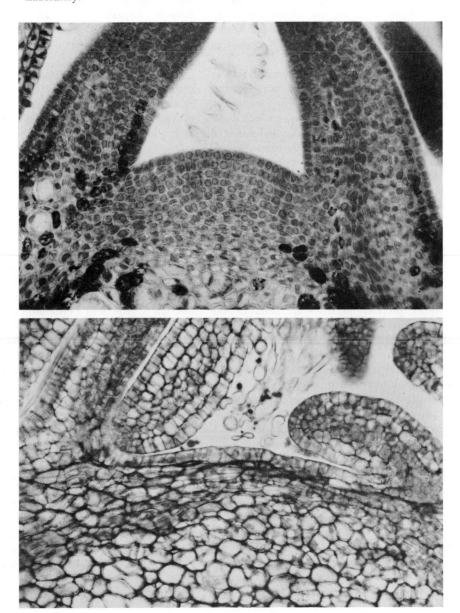

1957). One of the most common types of disorderliness after irradiation is the development of fasciations and tumors. Another is the activation of cell divisions and callus formation, resulting in local overgrowths or erratic clusters of buds in unusual locations. Frequently there are roots formed in such overgrowths. Many reports mention stimulations of flowering by irradiation (e.g., Moore and Haskins, 1932; Shull and Mitchell, 1933), but results are not consistent enough to be useful.

Disruptions of growth are common following irradiations with short wavelengths, such as ultraviolet, or with ionizing or neutron radiations. The dosages which cause such inhibitions are variable, and some of the circumstances altering the response will be mentioned. It should be pointed out that along with the inhibitions in growth there are often morphological aberrations such as clublike apices, budless shoots, and altered phyllotaxy. In cases where the cellular details of such inhibited plant parts have been examined, it is generally found that radiation damage has involved a preferential deterioration of meristematic cells. As an illustration, Fig. 21-2 (Pratt et al., 1959) shows preferential disorganization of the inner layers of the apical meristem of irradiated grape shoots.

The inhibition of plant growth has frequently been correlated with the disruption of mitotic activities in meristematic tissues. Measurements of the changes in root growth rate and mitotic frequency in mung-bean roots show that both of these functions fall off together after irradiation with 2 or 5 kr of x-rays (Quastler et al., 1952; Fig. 21-3). About 8 days after the lesser x-ray dose, the growth rate and the mitotic frequencies begin to recover.

A promising application of the inhibition of growth by radiations has appeared from research on potatoes in storage. When given a sufficiently large radiation dosage, potatoes will not sprout (Fig. 21-4), a trait useful for their commercial storage, provided that they are not to be used for seed (Sparrow and Christensen, 1954).

Occasional reports describe promotive effects of radiation on plant growth (Sax, 1955). These are generally obtained with very small doses of ionizing radiations, and usually when seeds are the irradiated material. The initial growth of seedlings may thus be increased, but there are no convincing cases of an ultimate increase in the size of mature plants or their productivity.

Radiations may either promote or inhibit respiration rates. Generally the effects are inhibitory; a typical respiratory-response curve is shown in Fig. 21-5 (Mikaelsen and Halvorsen, 1953).

Radiation tolerance

The extent of radiation responsiveness varies widely, depending on some morphological and physiological variables (cf. Fig. 21-1). To compare species differences, Sparrow and Christensen (1953) placed an assortment of plants in a cobalt-radiation field at Brookhaven National Laboratory. Using gross inhibition of growth as a criterion for comparison they found that beet, broccoli, and gladiolus were relatively resistant, being inhibited in the range of 4,000 r/day, while the plants *Tradescantia* and *Lilium* were inhibited by as little as 20 r/day. Sparrow et al. (1961) suspected that the gross responses of the plants were related to detrimental effects occurring in the nucleus. Measurement of the sizes of the nuclei of representative species over the tolerance range showed excellent correlation between tolerance and nuclear volume. Their results for 23 species are shown in Fig. 21-6. Each point on the figure represents the nuclear volume and the radiation dose required for severe growth inhibition for one species. Plants with smaller nuclear volumes tend to be more tolerant to radiation.

Increases in the ploidy of the plant also

increase the tolerance to radiation. Sparrow et al. (1961) compared nine species of *Sedum*, representing a wide range of polyploidy, as to the dose of x-irradiation which they could tolerate (Fig. 21-7). They found that larger numbers of sets of chromosomes imparted a marked degree of radiation tolerance. This is interpreted as being due to the replication of chromosomes, permitting one set to carry out a nuclear function if another one is disrupted by the radiation treatment.

Sparrow et al. (1961) suggested that increasing numbers of chromosomes in the normal diploid situation were associated with increasing radiation tolerance. With a small number of chromosomes, each destructive radiation event would delete a relatively large proportion of the genetic material in the nucleus and thus have a relatively large detrimental effect.

Thus it appears that tolerance to radiation is principally a function of (1) the nuclear volume of the plant cells and (2) the chromosome number. Increasing nuclear volumes increase the size of the radiation target, and decreasing chromosome numbers increase the unit damage when a hit occurs.

Lethal effects

Radiations can kill cells either by damage to the mitotic apparatus of the nucleus or by direct disruptive effects which may kill the cell outright regardless of its nuclear condition. About three times as much radiation is required to kill a cell outright as to incapacitate its mitotic apparatus (Lea, 1955).

For plants growing in the field, the lethal response to radiation doses is roughly a log response (Fig. 21-8). The lethality of a given dose may vary with the condition of the plant during radiation and with environmental conditions, but the shape of the curve is characteristic.

Fig. 21-3 | Irradiation of mung-bean roots with x-rays results in an inhibition of root elongation associated with a sharp decrease in mitotic activities. Note that in both types of measurement, the 2-kr treatment shows some indications of recovery (Quastler et al., 1952).

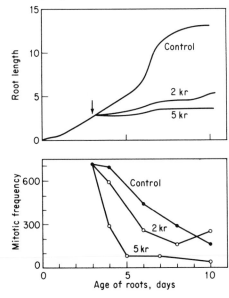

Fig. 21-4 | The inhibition of sprouting of potatoes in storage by x-irradiation. Sprout weights were taken after 8 and 18 months of storage (Sparrow and Christensen, 1954).

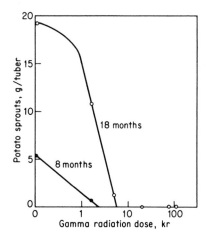

Plants which survive nearly lethal doses of radiation may subsequently recover. On the other hand, low radiation doses which are readily tolerated for a short time may become lethal if prolonged. Pine trees near the cobalt field at Brookhaven tolerated daily doses of 5 r/day for 1 year, but after 7 years of such irradiation they died.

Fig. 21-5 | X-ray treatment of barley seeds results in a depression of respiration rate. Dry seeds were irradiated, and the Q_{O_2} was measured 8 days after germination (Mikaelsen and Halvorsen, 1953).

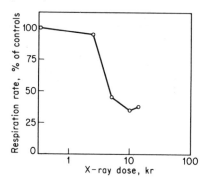

Fig. 21-6 | The dose of cobalt radiation required to severely inhibit the growth of a selection of 23 species of plants varies with the nuclear volume of the species. Each point represents the results obtained for one species. With decreasing volume of the nucleus, a higher dosage is required for inhibition (Sparrow et al., 1961).

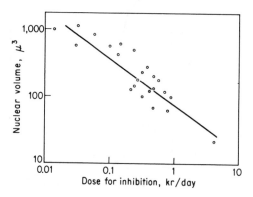

Effects of atomic explosions

The brief but violent radiation events from atomic explosions result in three types of damages to plants in the area: direct radiation effects from the explosion; effects from radioactive residues, especially in the soil medium; and blast effects.

Radiation produced by the explosion selectively removes species which are less tolerant to radiation damage. This effect is limited since the ground area which receives lethal doses of radiation is also most affected by blast.

The residual radioactive nuclides are of major importance in the effects of explosions. Ehrenberg et al. (1949) studied the amount of radioactive phosphorus which a plant can tolerate in the soil medium and found that the growth of small grains was inhibited when about 5 to 15 μC had accumulated in the plant and that the plants were killed when about 10 to 25 μC had accumulated. They also observed different sensitivities of plant parts. Seeds were more susceptible than stems, and roots somewhat less susceptible.

In soils contaminated by atomic explosions, Jacobson and Overstreet (1948) found that as little as 0.1 μC of radioactivity per g of soil produced visible damage to pea plants. The radioactive residues were mostly yttrium, cesium, zirconium, and strontium. The first three were taken up by the plant root systems but were not translocated; hence their damaging effects were localized in the roots. Strontium is preferentially translocated to the leaves (Spinks et al., 1948), and it produces more systemic damage. The accumulation of these nuclides is remarkable in that they are highly insoluble and so must enter the root by contact exchange or other nonsolution means. The accumulation of strontium in leaves may lead to levels of radioactivity which are higher than those in the soil in which the plants grow (Mills and Shields, 1961).

The details of detrimental effects of

radioactive materials from soils are not well known. Some plants appear to be quite resistant to such materials. The soil medium provides some shielding effect, but even after the uptake of relatively large amounts of radioactive materials, some plants continue to flower and fruit. Mineral prospectors found that uranium ores may cause floral and seed abnormalities in some species which may be useful in mineral-ore detection (Cannon, 1960).

The blast effects of atomic explosions may be lethal to plants either through the vaporization or physical destruction of the plants directly or through the motion induced in the soils. Shields and Wells (1962) noted that the radius of plant vaporization and burning effects was about half as great as the radius of plant destruction by soil instability. In sandy or friable soils the blast effect destroys the plants by physically breaking up the plant tissues, especially the roots.

Factors in sensitivity

The nucleus is a principal site of radiation damage in the plant. This was first demonstrated in a famous experiment by Zirkle (1932) with fern spores. Zirkle noted that the nucleus was located near one side of the spore, permitting a preferential radiation of the side containing the nucleus or the side without the nucleus. The former treatment was the most damaging, indicating in a simple manner that the nucleus was a principal site of damage.

Within the nucleus the chromosomes are the most sensitive targets. Many instances of correlation between the morphological damage from radiation and the aberration of chromosomes have been reported. The disruption of genetic material in the nucleus is one of the dominant means by which radiations alter plant growth.

Radiation sensitivity relates to the actual condition of the chromosomes at the time of radiation. Sax and Swanson (1941) were the first to observe marked changes in susceptibility of cells with changes in mitotic stages. The data in Fig. 21-9 show that *Trillium* microspores were fragmented much more frequently when irradiated in the late prophase or metaphase than when in telophase or interphase. Tissues undergoing abundant divisions are markedly more susceptible to radiation damage.

Fig. 21-7 | The dose of cobalt radiation required to inhibit the growth of nine species of *Sedum* appears to be related to the extent of polyploidy. With increasing numbers of sets of chromosomes, a higher dosage is required for damage. Each point represents the results obtained with one species (Sparrow et al., 1961).

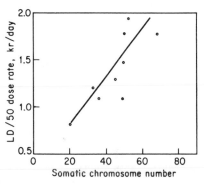

Fig. 21-8 | The lethal effects of x-rays on dormant grape cuttings appear to increase with the log of the dosage (Pratt, 1959).

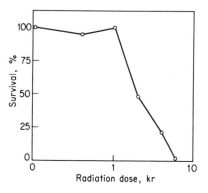

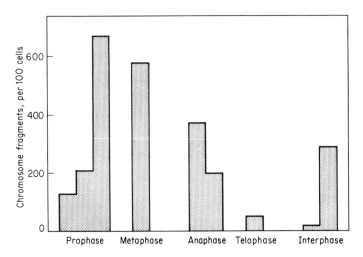

Fig. 21-9 | The sensitivity of *Trillium* anthers to x-irradiation varies markedly with mitotic stage. Cells in the early stages of mitosis at the time of radiation give rise to the greatest number of chromosome irregularities (Sparrow et al., 1952).

The frequency of chromosome aberrations with increasing dosage provides some interesting quantitative information. Sax (1938) observed that the dosage-response curves for chromosomal deletions were linear, whereas the response curves for the more complicated aberrations, such as rings and dicentric formations, more nearly approached an exponential type of response curve (Fig. 21-10). His interpretation is that deletions are the consequence of single hits by radiation events, and hence the linear response. Rings and dicentrics probably require more than one disruptive event in a given chromosome locus, and the occasions on which two radiation events would occur at once would be more nearly exponential in frequency. Such a kinetic distinction between simple, direct effects of radiation and more complicated events of multiple hits can be applied to many radiation responses.

The dosage-response curves for neutron radiations and for ultraviolet radiations are usually linear, presumably because they do not bring about ionization events.

Responses to ionizing radiations are markedly altered by the oxygen tension. This influence, first observed by Thoday and Read (1947), is illustrated by the data in Fig. 21-11 (Giles and Beatty, 1950). Higher frequencies of chromosome aberrations were observed following irradiation at higher oxygen levels. Ionizing events and free radicals in the aqueous protoplasm can bring about the formation of peroxides if oxygen is present, and it seems safe to interpret the oxygen effect as a consequence of such peroxide formation. Neutrons show little or no interaction with oxygen tension in their effectiveness (Giles, 1954).

Sax and Enzmann (1939) found that irradiations at low temperatures were markedly more damaging than at high temperatures. Some representative data on *Tradescantia* microspores are shown in Fig. 21-12 (Sax, 1957). This inverted type of temperature response is interpreted as being due to slower mitosis at lower temperatures and therefore to a longer duration of the mitotic steps during which damaging events can accumulate. The lower temperature may also retard the rate at which the chromosomes can mend breaks and may increase the effectiveness of oxygen by giving it greater solubility (Giles, 1954).

Some rather complicated alterations of radiation sensitivity can be achieved with light. Far-red light can actually increase the effectiveness of subsequent x-radiation (Swanson and Hollaender, 1946). This potentiation effect can sometimes be achieved even if the far-red light is applied after the x-radiation (Giles, 1954). There is some evidence that red light can negate the far-red potentiation (Moh and Withrow, 1957).

Another effect of light is the curious ability of visible light to reverse some radiation damage. Kelner (1951) noted that the deleterious effects of ultraviolet light on microorganisms were reversed by subsequent exposure to visible light, and Bawden and Kleczkowski (1952) reversed the ultraviolet-induced resistance of beans to virus infection by subsequent treatment with visible light. These light effects may be related to alterations of nucleotide structures; this will be discussed in the section on damage mechanisms. Light-regeneration effects are apparently obtained only for the nonionizing ultraviolet radiations. Examination of the action spectrum for the visible light reversal of the ultraviolet effects indicates maximal effectiveness for blue light in the vicinity of 420 mμ (Klein, 1963).

The water content of plant tissues alters their susceptibility to ionizing radiation. This is readily demonstrated with seeds, in which a wide range of water levels is easily obtainable. Ehrenberg (1955) observed that increased water content had a protective effect on x-irradiated grain seeds. Rather than a protective effect by water, it might be interpreted as an increased susceptibility in the absence of an adequate

Fig. 21-10 | Two kinds of dosage-response curves are obtained for *Tradescantia* anthers upon x-irradiation. Chromosome deletions appear to increase in a linear fashion with increasing dose, whereas rings and dicentric aberrations show more than a linear increase with dosage (Sax, 1957).

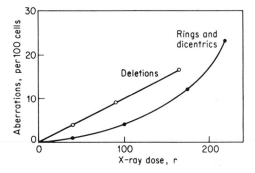

Fig. 21-11 | Chromosome damage from x-irradiation is strongly sensitive to oxygen tension. *Tradescantia* anthers given 400 r developed markedly more chromosome aberrations at higher oxygen partial pressures (Giles and Beatty, 1950).

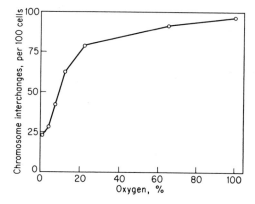

amount of water to permit metabolic activities by which the damaging effects of radiation may be repaired or outgrown. Furthermore, dry seeds continue to suffer damage from the products of irradiations for some time after exposure. As longer periods of time pass between irradiation and moistening the seeds to start germination, there is an accumulation of damage effects (Natarajan and Maric, 1961). Moisture content is apparently not a factor in neutron radiation damage.

The factors influencing radiation damage suggest that the growth rate of plant materials would be relevant to susceptibility. Plants which are growing actively at the time of irradiation are somewhat less susceptible to damage. This may be due to the ability of the growing tissue to repair radiation damage, to replace the damaged cells with new ones, and to remove the oxidative products of radiation (Merz et al., 1961).

Damage mechanisms

Radiation damage may be nuclear or cytoplasmic.

Fig. 21-12 | Less chromosome damage results from radiation at higher temperatures. *Tradescantia* anthers given 300 r at various temperatures show declining numbers of chromosome aberrations with higher temperatures (Sax, 1957).

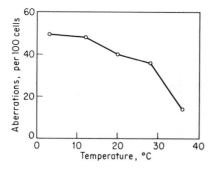

Nuclear damage appears to be a function of the deleterious effects of radiation hits on the chromosome materials—or hits on nearby molecules which then are ionized and lead to local oxidation effects on nearby nucleotides. The data of Sparrow et al. (1961; Fig. 21-6) indicate that the slope of the curve for radiation damage as a function of nuclear volume is close to -1, suggesting a uniform damage per unit of radiation per unit nuclear volume traversed. Since radiation damage increases linearly with nuclear volume (Fig. 21-6) and decreases linearly with chromosome number (Fig. 21-7), nuclear damage will be a function of the nuclear volume divided by the chromosome number. Sparrow et al. (1963) calculate that 4×10^6 electron volts per interphase chromosome represents the amount of radiation which will be lethal to a plant.

The ability of radiations to disrupt the nucleic acids was first shown by Sparrow and Rosenfeld (1946). It has since been established that radiations not only bring about a loss of DNA in the nucleus (Butler and Smith, 1950) but sometimes have a blocking effect on the new synthesis of DNA (Howard and Pelc, 1953). However, Das and Alfert (1961) found that x-irradiated onion rots increased in DNA synthesis when mitosis was inhibited.

The nucleotides are apparently also susceptible to radiation damage. Ultraviolet irradiation of solutions of DPN and ATP destroys their ability to participate in hydrogen-transfer reactions (Wells and Johnson, 1953, 1954), and the subsequent exposure to visible light has remarkable effects in restoring the metabolic abilities of the DPN (Wells, 1956).

There has been a great deal of interest in the possibility that the oxidative effects of ionizing radiations may be through the oxidation of sulfhydryl groups on proteins. This interest stems from the finding of Barron and Flood (1950) that marked protection against radiation damage to cells can be obtained with the addition of sulfhydryl-containing compounds. The sulfhydryl group is readily oxidized and is an essential part of many respiratory enzymes (hence an expected radiation effect on respiration). Sulfhydryls are essential parts of the spindle mechanism (hence an expected radiation effect on mitosis), and they are involved in the secondary structure of many proteins. Measurements of free sulfhydryls of plant tissues following x-irradiation have confirmed that there is an oxidation of these sensitive end groups (Ehrenberg, 1955). The damage to sulfhydryls is probably not limited to simple oxidations, for there is also evidence that x-rays cause a reshuffling of disulfide bonds (Eldjarn and Pihl, 1955, 1956). Such recombinations would probably have marked effects on secondary structure of proteins (Cavallini et al., 1960).

A closely related aspect of radiation damage is the formation of free radicals. The activation of many organic materials by ionizing radiation can force them to form free radicals—very reactive oxidative intermediates. The availability of oxygen greatly enhances the extent of free-radical formation, which probably accounts for the oxygen effect in sensitization to ionizing radiation. It is possible to estimate the quantity of free radicals in biological materials by microwave spectrometry. The data in Fig. 21-13 show that the amount of free-radical formation increases with x-ray dose and that the free radicals may persist for 20 hr or more (Müller and Zimmer, 1961). When irradiation is carried out under anaerobic conditions, the amount of free-radical formation is much less. The oxidative properties of free radicals must contribute to the radiation effects on sulfhydryls, as well as to other oxidizable cell components.

The synthesis of auxin is an extremely sensitive cytoplasmic function. Skoog (1935) showed that x-rays destroyed indoleacetic acid in vitro and in vivo. But Gordon and Weber (1955), reexamining the phenomenon, found that the x-ray depression of auxin levels in plants was too extensive to be accounted for by a direct oxidation of the auxin molecule by radiation. The impressive reduction of auxin levels in some representative plants is shown in Fig. 21-14. Gordon (1955) found that the depression of auxin content was felt in the plant over an extended time, often for more than a week, and if the radiation dosage was high enough, the depression was apparently permanent (Fig. 21-15). The effects on auxin were not merely the oxidation of the auxin molecules but rather a disruption of the auxin-synthesizing enzymes. In a series of perceptive experiments, Gordon established that the radiation sensitivity of the enzyme which converts indoleacetaldehyde to indoleacetic acid was the critical item in the auxin-depression effect. This enzyme is located principally in the free cytoplasm as a soluble enzyme.

The radiation sensitivity of the auxin-synthesizing system may account for several characteristics of plant responses to radiation. The inhibitory effects of very small

Fig. 21-13 | The formation of free radicals in x-irradiated barley endosperm can be measured as the amplitude of paramagnetic absorption. On the left, free radicals are seen to increase with x-ray dosage; on the right, they are seen to persist in the tissue for some time. Anaerobic conditions suppressed free-radical formation (Müller and Zimmer, 1961).

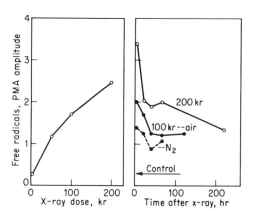

dosages (25 to 100 r) on overall plant growth reflect this sensitivity. Gordon has termed this a *multiplication effect*—an effect through which a relatively few ionizing events can bring about a relatively large growth inhibition through an interference with an enzyme. Some other plant responses which may be attributable to a lowering of the auxin system include the disruption of tropistic effects and the loss of apical dominance. The ability of indoleacetic acid either to protect against minor radiation damage (Therman and Seppala, 1959) or to reverse or overcome the inhibitions once established (Mika, 1952) reinforces this suggestion.

Gordon and Weber (1955) infer that the auxin enzyme is not depressed through a sulfhydryl oxidation, for no protection is obtained by adding free sulfhydryl compounds. They believe that there may be a close involvement of the auxin effect with the depression of DNA by radiation, and they suggest that auxin may be critical to the formation of the nucleic acids (Gordon, 1957).

Many other enzymes, including the oxidative phosphorylation system, are sensitive to radiation. Radiation also brings about increases in such disruptive enzymes as ATPase and DNAase (cf. Stocken, 1959).

Protective agents

Barron and Flood (1950) discovered that sulfhydryl compounds added to tissues could protect them against ionizing radiation damage. The protective effects of several such materials are shown in Fig. 21-16, using chromosome aberrations as the criterion of the damage sustained from Co^{60} radiation (Mikaelsen, 1954). Such protection is most effective against ionizing radiations, being less effective for alpha rays and ineffective against neutrons (Forssberg and Nybom, 1953). Cysteamine and cystamine are among the most effective protectants. These compounds have been shown to react with

Fig. 21-14 | The auxin content of three species is lowered by x-irradiation. The cocklebur and cabbage data were calculated on a microgram-per-gram basis, and the bean on a microgram-per-plant basis (Gordon, 1957).

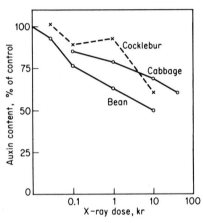

Fig. 21-15 | The auxin content of kidney beans can recover in time after x-irradiation with 25- or 100-r doses, but no recovery is evident after 5,000- or 10,000-r dosages (Gordon, 1957).

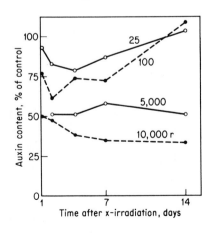

free sulfhydryl groups in plant tissues using the clever device of tagging them with radioactive sulfur (Eldjarn and Pihl, 1955, 1956). However, there is sharp disagreement among radiation experts as to whether sulfhydryl oxidations represent a critical part of radiation damage to cells.

Some protection effects against radiation have been obtained with chemicals such as hyposulfite (Mikaelsen, 1954), which lower the availability of oxygen, or with chemicals which may temporarily suspend mitotic activity (e.g., cyanide, Mikaelsen, 1954) or growth activity (e.g., boron deficiency, Skok, 1957).

Conclusion

The damaging effects from the shorter electromagnetic and the corpuscular radiations may be considered ecological handicaps from the incomplete screening of radiation from the sun by the atmosphere. Radiations of wavelengths shorter than the visible do seep through the atmosphere, and corpuscular radiations are essentially unscreened. The high energy loads carried by these radiations and the nonselectivity of their absorption by biological systems make them capable of inflicting extensive damage.

Such damage may be either nuclear, through physical disruption of large structures such as nucleic acids, or cytoplasmic, through both structural and oxidative alterations.

Because much of the cytoplasmic damage of ionizing radiations is oxidative, some protective effects can be obtained by the application of chemicals which either supply readily oxidizable end groups such as sulfhydryls or reduce the availability of oxygen. Ultraviolet damage can be protected against or even reversed through the application of visible light.

Although radiation effects are principally deleterious as environmental factors in experimental physiology, it is probable that they have exerted a powerful driving force in evolutionary development, continually provoking genetic variations from which evolution could mold its advances.

GENERAL REFERENCES

Gordon, S. A. 1957. The effects of ionizing radiation on plants: biochemical and physiological aspects. *Quart. Rev. Biol.*, 32:3–14.

Gunckel, J. E. 1957. The effects of ionizing radiations on plants: morphological effects. *Quart. Rev. Biol.*, 32:46–56.

Hollaender, A. (ed.). 1954. *Radiation Biology.* McGraw-Hill Book Company, New York. 3 vols.

Lea, D. E. 1955. *Actions of Radiations on Living Cells.* Cambridge University Press, Cambridge. 416 pp.

Sax, K. 1957. The effect of ionizing radiation on chromosomes. *Quart. Rev. Biol.*, 32:15–26.

Sparrow, A. H., L. G. Augenstine, H. Quastler, M. E. Koshland, and H. J. Curtis

Fig. 21-16 | A protection against radiation damage in *Tradescantia* cuttings can be obtained by the uptake of cysteine, glutathione (GSH), or thiourea for 1 hr. The plants were subsequently given 25 r/day for 2 days with a cobalt source, and damage was recorded as the aberration frequency in the root tips (Mikaelsen, 1954).

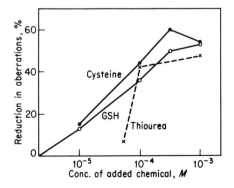

(eds.). 1961. Fundamental aspects of radiosensitivity. *Brookhaven Symp. Biol.,* 14. 308 pp.

———, J. P. Binnington, and V. Pond. 1958. Bibliography on the effects of ionizing radiations on plants. *Brookhaven Natl. Lab. Publ.,* 504. 222 pp.

REFERENCES CITED

Barron, E. S. G., and V. Flood. 1950. Studies on the mechanism of action of ionizing radiations. *J. Gen. Physiol.,* 33:229–241.

Bawden, F. C., and A. Kleczkowski. 1952. Ultra-violet injury to higher plants counteracted by visible light. *Nature,* 169:90–91.

Brewbaker, J. L. and G. C. Emery. 1962. Pollen radiobotany. *Radiation Botany,* 1:101–154.

Butler, J. A. V., and K. A. Smith. 1950. Degradation of deoxyribonucleic acid by free radicals. *Nature,* 165:847–848.

Cannon, H. L. 1960. Botanical prospecting for ore deposits. *Science,* 132:591–598.

Cavallini, D., B. Mondovi, B. Giovanella, and C. deMarco. 1960. Disulfide interchange by ionizing radiation. *Science,* 131:1441–1442.

Das, N. K., and M. Alfert. 1961. Accelerated DNA synthesis in onion root meristem during x-irradiation. *Proc. Natl. Acad. Sci. U.S.,* 47:1–6.

Ehrenberg, L. 1955. Studies on the mechanism of action of ionizing radiations in plant seeds. *Svensk Kem. Tidskr.,* 67:207–224.

———, A. Gustafsson, A. Levan, and V. von Wettstein. 1949. Radiophosphorus, seedling lethality and chromosome disturbances. *Hereditas,* 35:469–489.

Eldjarn, L., and A. Pihl. 1955. On the mechanism of chemical protection against ionizing radiation. The interaction of cysteamine and cystamine with proteins, pp. 249–259. In *Progress in Radiobiology.*

—— and ——. 1956. On the mode of action of x-ray protective agents. I. The fixation *in vivo* of cystamine and cysteamine to proteins. *J. Biol. Chem.,* 223:341–352.

Forssberg, A., and N. Nybom. 1953. Combined effects of cysteine and irradiation on growth and cytology of *Allium cepa* roots. *Physiol. Plantarum,* 6:78–95.

Giles, N. H. 1954. Radiation induced chromosome aberrations in *Tradescantia,* pp. 713–761. In A. Hollaender (ed.). *Radiation Biology.* McGraw-Hill Book Company, New York.

—— and A. V. Beatty. 1950. The effect of x-irradiation in oxygen and in hydrogen at normal and positive pressures on chromosome aberration in *Tradescantia* microspores. *Science,* 112:643–645.

Gordon, S. A. 1955. The biogenesis of natural auxins, pp. 65–75. In R. L. Wain and F. Wightman (eds.), *Chemistry and Mode of Action of Plant Growth Substances.* Butterworth Scientific Publications, London.

———. 1957. The effects of ionizing radiation on plants: biochemical and physiological aspects. *Quart. Rev. Biol.,* 32:3–14.

—— and R. P. Weber. 1955. Studies on the mechanism of phytohormone damage by ionizing radiation. I. The radio-sensitivity of indoleacetic acid. *Plant Physiol.,* 30:200–210.

Gunckel, J. E. 1957. IV. The effects of ionizing radiation on plants: morphological effects. *Quart. Rev. Biol.,* 32:46–56.

Howard, A., and S. R. Pelc. 1953. Synthesis of DNA in normal and irradiated cells. *Heredity Supp.* 6:261–273.

Jacobson, L., and R. Overstreet. 1948. Uptake by plants of plutonium and products of nuclear fission. *Soil Sci.,* 45:129–134.

Kelner, A. 1951. Action spectra for photoreactivation of ultra-violet irradiated *E. coli* and *S. griseus. J. Gen. Physiol.,* 34:835–852.

Klein, R. M. 1963. Interaction of ultraviolet and visible radiations on the growth of cell aggregates of *Ginkgo* pollen tissue. *Physiol. Plantarum*, 16:73–81.

Lea, D. E. 1955. *Actions of Radiations on Living Cells*. Cambridge University Press, Cambridge. 416 pp.

Merz, T., C. P. Swanson, and C. N. Hemalatha. 1961. Radiosensitivity and the problem of chromosome breakage and rejoining. *Brookhaven Symp. Biol.*, 14:53–61.

Mika, E. S. 1952. Effect of indoleacetic acid on root growth of x-irradiated peas. *Botan. Gaz.*, 113:285–293.

Mikaelsen, K. 1954. Cytological effect of chronic gamma irradiation and the protective property of certain chemicals against the radiation induced chromosome aberrations. *Proc. Radiobiology Symp.* (*Liége*), pp. 316–320. Butterworths Scientific Publications, London.

—— and H. Halvorsen. 1953. Experiments on the respiration of x-irradiated barley seeds. *Physiol. Plantarum*, 6:873–879.

Mills, H. L., and L. M. Shields. 1961. Root absorption of fission products by *Bromus rubens* from an underground nuclear explosion. *Radiation Botany*, 1:84–91.

Moh, C. C., and R. B. Withrow. 1957. Interaction of red and far-red radiant energy in modifying x-ray-induced chromatid aberrations in broad bean. *Plant Physiol.*, 32:xi.

Moore, C. N., and C. P. Haskins. 1932. Premature flowering in grapefruit from x-rayed seeds. *Science*, 76:167–168.

Müller, A., and K. G. Zimmer. 1961. Studies on radiation-produced free radicals in biological systems, pp. 325–335. In M. S. Blois et al. (eds.), *Free Radicals in Biological Systems*. Academic Press, Inc., New York.

Natarajan, A. T., and M. M. Maric. 1961. The time-intensity factor in dry seed irradiation. *Radiation Botany*, 1:1–9.

Pratt, C. 1959. Radiation damage in shoot apices of Concord grape. *Am. J. Botany*, 46:103–109.

——, J. Einset, and M. Zahur. 1959. Radiation damage in apple shoot apices. *Am. J. Botany*, 46:537–544.

Quastler, H., A. M. Schertiger, and W. N. Stewart. 1952. Inhibition of plant growth by irradiation. IV. Growth arrest vs. effects on mitotic activity. *J. Cellular Comp. Physiol.*, 39:357–369.

Sax, K. 1938. Induction by x-rays of chromosome aberration in *Tradescantia* microspores. *Genetics*, 23:494–516.

——. 1955. The effect of ionizing radiation on plant growth. *Am. J. Botany*, 42:360–364.

——. 1957. The effect of ionizing radiation on chromosomes. *Quart. Rev. Biol.*, 32:15–26.

—— and E. V. Enzmann. 1939. The effect of temperature on x-ray induced chromosome aberrations. *Proc. Natl. Acad. Sci. U.S.*, 25:397–405.

—— and C. P. Swanson. 1941. Differential sensitivity of cells to x-rays. *Am. J. Botany*, 28:52–59.

Shields, L. M., and P. V. Wells. 1962. Effects of nuclear testing on desert vegetation. *Science*, 135:38–40.

Shull, C. A., and J. W. Mitchell. 1933. Stimulative effects of x-rays. *Plant Physiol.*, 8:287.

Skok, J. 1957. Relationship of boron nutrition to radiosensitivity of sunflower plants. *Plant Physiol.*, 32:648–658.

Skoog, F. 1935. The effect of x-irradiation on auxin and plant growth. *J. Cellular Comp. Physiol.*, 7:227–270.

Sparrow, A. H., and E. Christensen. 1953. Tolerance of certain higher plants to chronic exposure to gamma radiation from cobalt–60. *Science*, 118:697–698.

—— and ——. 1954. Improved storage quality of potato tubers after exposure to C^{60} gammas. *Nucleonics*, 12:16–17.

——, R. L. Cuany, J. P. Miksche, and L. A. Shairer. 1961. Factors affecting responses of plants to radiation exposures. *Radiation Botany*, 1:10–34.

——, M. J. Moses, and R. J. Dubow.

1952. Relationships between ionizing radiation, chromosome breakage and certain other nuclear disturbances. *Exptl. Cell. Res. Suppl.*, 2:245–267.

—————— and F. M. Rosenfeld. 1946. X-ray induced depolymerization of thymus nucleohistone and sodium thymonucleate. *Science*, 104:245–246.

——————, L. A. Schairer, and R. C. Sparrow. 1963. Relationship between nuclear volumes, chromosome numbers, and relative radiosensitivities. *Science*, 141:163–166.

Spinks, J. W. T., E. Cumming, R. L. B. Irwin, and T. J. Aranson. 1948. Lethal effect of absorbed radioisotopes on plants. *Can. J. Res.*, 26:249–262.

Stocken, L. A. 1959. Some observations on the biochemical effects of x-radiation. *Radiation Res.*, 1:53–72.

Swanson, C. P., and A. Hollaender. 1946. The frequency of x-ray induced chromatid breaks in *Tradescantia* as modified by near infra-red radiation. *Proc. Natl. Acad. Sci. U.S.*, 32:295–302.

Therman, E., and M. Seppala. 1959. Indoleacetic acid as protective substance against x-rays. *Physiol. Plantarum*, 12:716–719.

Thoday, J. M., and J. Read. 1947. Effect of oxygen on the frequency of chromosome aberrations produced by x-rays. *Nature*, 160:608.

Wells, P. H. 1956. Photoreactivation of ultraviolet-inactivated diphosphopyridine nucleotide. *Science*, 124:31–32.

—————— and H. Johnson. 1953. Action of ultraviolet and visible light on adenosinetriphosphate. *Anat. Record*, 117:644–645.

—————— and D. C. Johnson. 1954. Photoreactivation of ultraviolet inactivated diphosphopyridine nucleotide. *Anat. Record*, 120:205.

Zirkle, R. E. 1932. Some effects of alpha radiation upon plant cells. *J. Cellular Comp. Physiol.*, 2:251–274.

22 | Temperature

At any temperature above absolute zero, molecules are in continuous motion. Such motion is accelerated in proportion to the amount of heat energy added to a population of molecules. The energetics of molecular or atomic units is an expression of heat.

With the image of motion in mind, we can conceive of heat as an energy of disordered motion. It can be generated by the physical impact of one mass onto another as when a hammer strikes an anvil, resulting in a more disordered energy. Light and the other electromagnetic waves are also energy carriers, so when light strikes a mass it likewise generates a disordered energy in the object struck—and an increase in heat.

Biologically important reactions are limited to a very small temperature range. They can operate only within close limits of disordered energy. At too low temperatures, biological reactions are stifled for inadequate energies, and at both too low and excessive temperatures the complex structures of protein substances are dismantled. Looking at the wide scale of temperatures possible (Fig. 22-1), from absolute zero to the highest temperatures at which atoms can exist intact, it can be seen that there is a range of over $10000°K$. Within this range, biological activities are essentially restricted to about $50°$, from 273 to $323°K$ (0 to $50°C$). Limited on the lower side by the freezing point of water and on the upper side by the heat of denaturation of proteins, life is squeezed into a tiny range of temperatures—about 0.5 per cent of the range over which atoms can exist.

Plant temperatures are dominated by the diurnal flow of light energy from the sun. The size of this diurnal pulse of energy varies enormously with the season of the year at most latitudes. For example, the rate of insolation in Germany is more than four times greater at midday in June than at midday in December on clear days (see Fig. 22-2). The largest value reported in this figure is slightly above 1 $cal/cm^2/min$. The rate of insolation outside the atmosphere is about double that value, illustrating the magnitude of the filter effect by the atmosphere even on a clear day.

The filtering effect of the atmosphere is also evident in the rather striking increase in insolation at higher altitudes. At 1,200 ft, insolation is roughly 50 per cent greater than it is at sea level, and at 12,000 ft it is approximately doubled. The heat-exchange problem of leaves in an alpine tundra can be very great indeed.

The heat energy absorbed by the leaf is largely taken from the visible regions of light, between 400 and 700 mμ. As shown in Fig. 22-3, most of the incident sunlight at longer wavelengths is either reflected or transmitted through the leaf. Much of the absorbed energy is utilized photosynthetically, but the remainder can create a substantial heat problem.

Russell (1961) has pointed up the extent of the heat problem from insolation, calculating that the cumulative insolation in England amounts to 76000 cal/cm^2/year. For each acre, this is the equivalent of the heat derived from burning 400 tons of coal!

Heat exchange by leaves

The temperature relations of leaves are the product of four principal vectors: heat absorption, heat loss by conduction, transpiration and reradiation.

As indicated in Fig. 22-3, absorption is principally in the visible wavelengths of light during the sunlight hours. The absorption curve displays the two absorption peaks of chlorophyll. Appreciable amounts of heat are derived from absorption in the infrared region above 1,000 mμ.

Heat absorption is markedly influenced by the position of the leaf. If a leaf is turned at a 10° angle away from perpendicular to the incoming light, the absorption is reduced about 15 per cent (Kaempfert, 1951). When a leaf is oriented more than about 70° from perpendicular to the light, the absorption of heat becomes negligible. The leaf position may be altered by leaf movements associated with water deficits and diurnal movements. The orientation of some leaves into a vertical position late in the day (Fig. 20-18) may be an adaptation lowering heat absorption. The ruffled surfaces of many leaves such as spinach are morphological adaptations which can lower heat absorption.

Shading of leaves from direct sunlight will greatly lower the heating effect. Curtis and Clark (1950) published some data showing the lowering of apple-leaf tempera-

Fig. 22-1 | The temperature range for life processes is a very narrow sector of the overall temperature range.

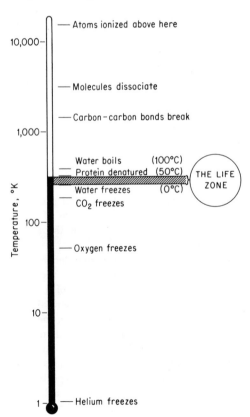

tures by shading (Fig. 22-4). They observed a 5° drop in temperature when a shade was held over the leaf. Vertically oriented leaves are much less affected.

Reflectance properties of the leaf surface can alter absorption. Nearly all leaves reflect and transmit the bulk of the light in wavelengths from about 750 to 1,000 mμ. In a comparison of mesophytic plants with ones adapted to desert or subalpine conditions, Billings and Morris (1951) found that the adapted species reflect more light in the visible region of 400 to 700 mμ. The glassy or silvery appearance of many desert leaves minimizes the absorption of insolation through an increased reflectance.

In many circumstances the most dominant vector in heat loss by leaves is *conduction.* The importance of this means of heat loss was pointed out by Brown and Wilson in 1905. The thin flat structure of most leaves is admirably adapted for conductive heat loss. Normally the leaf can lose heat to a layer of quiet air between 1 and 2 mm thick over its surface, but when air flows over the surface the conductive loss rate is arithmetically increased. This effect is illustrated in the data of Turrell et al. (1962) in Fig. 22-5, showing that the rate of conductive heat loss is more than doubled as air velocity is raised from 0 to 100 cm/sec. The conductive loss is much faster at higher temperatures than at low, in part because of the contribution of transpirational cooling at the higher temperature.

The efficiency of heat loss by conduction is illustrated by some data of Ansari and Loomis (1959) shown in Fig. 22-6. As pepper leaves were moved into the sunlight, they reached equilibration at the new elevated temperature in less than 2 min, and when shaded or exposed to an artificial wind, they were approaching equilibration at a new low temperature after about 1 min. Curtis (1936) recorded air-flow cooling of leaves by as much as 14°C.

Wolpert (1962) discussed the role of leaf hairs in improving conductive cooling.

Fig. 22-2 | The rate of insolation shows a large seasonal flux. Data for a horizontal surface at Potsdam, midday (Geiger, 1957).

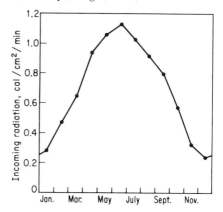

Fig. 22-3 | The leaf preferentially absorbs light energy at the wavelengths of maximal insolation (above), and on a relative basis (below) absorption is inverse to the transmission and reflection of light by the leaf. Note that infrared (800 mμ) is poorly absorbed and readily transmitted and reflected (adapted from Rabideau et al., 1946; Curtis and Clark, 1950; and Wolpert, 1962).

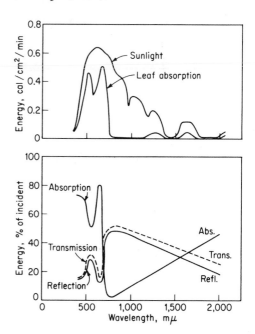

The advantages of leaf hairs in reducing transpiration are well known, but their natural efficiency as fins in improving conductive cooling has been ignored. Leaf hairs may increase enormously the leaf surface over which conduction can occur, and they also may increase the depth of air layers to which the heat can be conducted.

A second major means of heat transfer out of the leaf is by *transpiration*. The importance of this factor in the light was appreciated by Shull in 1919. Ansari and Loomis (1959) pointed out that the energy

deposited in the leaf by sunlight is enough to evaporate between 5 and 6 g of water per dm² per hr, whereas rates of 1 or 2 g of water are typically evaporated. The fact that about one-third of the heat energy is disposed of by transpiration indicates the relative importance of this means of leaf cooling in the light. At night transpiration is relatively insignificant in most leaves, and this vector is very small. At temperatures near freezing, transpiration rates drop nearly to zero, and the evaporation of water does not contribute appreciably to leaf cooling. In sunlight, however, conditions usually favor water loss, and under these circumstances transpiration may account for nearly half of the heat loss by the leaf.

Fig. 22-4 | In sunlight, a horizontal apple leaf is more than 7°C warmer than air temperature. Shading or a vertical leaf position minimizes the differences (data of Curtis and Clark, 1950).

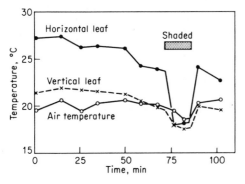

The application of a chemical which closes the stomata and hence stops the principal pathway of transpirational cooling demonstrates this means of heat transfer. Cook et al. (1964) measured the temperatures of tomato leaves in the light after treatment with sodium azide and observed temperatures about 4° higher in the treated leaves; this represented about one-third of the temperature differential between the leaf and the ambient air (Fig. 22-7).

A third means of heat transfer out of leaves is through *reradiation*. This form of heat loss was demonstrated by Curtis (1936), who showed that exposing lighted leaves to a cool black body would lower the leaf temperature by 2 or 3°C. This form of heat loss is usually a function of leaf temperatures, increasing exponentially in magnitude with the temperature difference between the radiating body and the receiving body. Thus, while the temperature depression under the conditions of Curtis's experiments was rather small, in higher leaf temperatures under desert or alpine conditions much larger cooling effects could be achieved, the sky serving as a black body to which the leaf can radiate.

In his studies of radiant loss of heat from leaves, Curtis found that shaded leaves in the field would equilibrate at temperatures

Fig. 22-5 | Wind markedly accelerates the rate of heat loss from lemon leaves. A higher leaf temperature (26°C) permits higher rates of loss at any air velocity (Turrell et al., 1962).

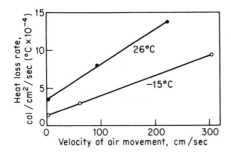

about 2 or 3°C higher than leaves which could "see" the sky. The presence of clouds acts similarly, reflecting back the radiant heat energy and essentially suppressing the radiant cooling of leaves. The role of a cloud cover in preventing frosting of leaves is well known.

Plants in the greenhouse are similarly deprived of the main part of radiant cooling. The glass reflects the energy radiated from the leaves at the infrared wavelengths.

Radiant cooling of leaves is most pronounced at night under a clear sky. When the water content of the air is low, the radiant loss is maximal, as in deserts or on clear autumn or winter nights. When the surface of the soil is cooler than the leaf, it too can serve as an acceptor of radiant energy and will have a cooling effect on leaves (Geiger, 1957).

With the increasing popularity of plant growth chambers for physiological experiments, there may be considerable modification of apparent temperature responses because of the substitution of a hot bank of electric lights for the cool sky as an acceptor of leaf reradiation.

The relative importance of these three means of leaf cooling can be compared in the calculations of Wolpert (1962), which indicate that a leaf 4 in. wide in a breeze of 10 mph loses 63 per cent of its absorbed heat by convection, 23 per cent by transpiration, and 9 per cent by reradiation. The remaining 5 per cent is presumably used for chemical work in the leaves. Wolpert points out that movement of a leaf in the wind can accentuate the transpirational cooling.

Heat exchange in the field

During the daylight hours, insolation has a large heating effect on the soil surface as well as on foliage. Bare soils become markedly heated during the day, commonly having temperatures up to 35°C higher than

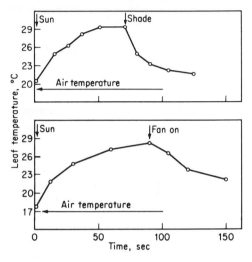

Fig. 22-6 | Leaf temperatures equilibrate very rapidly, reaching approximately steady temperature within 100 sec after sunlight is applied. Note the rapid cooling when shaded or when wind is applied (data for pepper leaves, Ansari and Loomis, 1959).

Fig. 22-7 | The magnitude of transpirational cooling of leaves can be estimated by observing leaf-temperature differences with stomata opened and stomata closed. Tomato plants placed under a 1,000-watt lamp show temperature drop after about 15 min as stomata open; leaves treated with NaN$_3$ ($10^{-3}M$) do not show such a temperature drop (Cook et al., 1964).

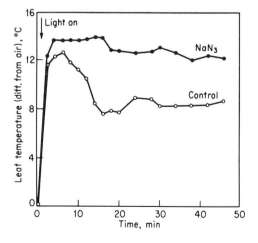

those of the surrounding air. In contrast to the situation for foliage (Fig. 22-3), soils reflect only a small proportion of insolation (7 to 10 per cent). The incident heat must be either absorbed or reflected. Reflection values are fairly high for dry soils but low for moist or for dark soil surfaces. The absorbed heat must be dissipated almost entirely by conduction since there is only a small exchange by reradiation and a very small exchange by water evaporation.

Heating of the soil surface during the day results in an elevation of the air temperature by conduction from the soil. Sample data illustrating this are shown in Fig. 22-8, where air temperatures above a fallow soil are compared with air temperatures above a sugarcane field. The air-heating effect of the bare soil resulted in a 7°C increase just above the soil surface. In contrast, the insulating effect of the vegetation resulted in surface air temperatures 7°C lower than the ambient air. Not only does vegetation suppress the heating effects from insolation during the day, but it suppresses the heat losses from the soil surface at night. Geiger (1957) describes the large changes in air-temperature patterns as vegetation grows together into a complete cover.

Burning of some crops by excessive soil temperatures may occur in cultivated fields of black muck soils, where reflection and conduction rates are small and absorption values high. Onion seedlings are sometimes burned off in the spring before the seedlings are large enough to shade the soil surface.

The greatest diurnal temperature variation is at the soil surface in fallow areas. Where there is a vegetation cover, the greatest variation is at the tips of the highest foliage. Like the bare soil surface, the tips of the vegetative cover act as a heating surface during the day and a cooling surface at night. Leaves are excellent radiators, acting as cooling centers during the night, especially when the moisture content of the air is low and the loss by radiant cooling is consequently great. As leaves cool, dew formation is encouraged, and this is of considerable importance in the water relations of many plants. Clumps of foliage are especially effective centers for dew formation, and the compact foliage in trellised grapevines or in tree crowns offers this specific advantage.

The foliage tips are most efficient for night cooling and are most susceptible to frost damage. Radiant cooling can bring an exposed leaf several degrees below air temperature, and so an exposed leaf at the top of a plant may actually freeze when air temperatures are not below 0°C.

Biochemical processes and heat

A convenient term for discussing the rate of reactions as influenced by temperature is *temperature coefficient,* or, more commonly, Q_{10}. The Q_{10} is the ratio of a reaction rate at one temperature divided into the rate at 10°C higher. It is relatively low (1.2 to 1.4) for physical reactions such as

Fig. 22-8 | Air temperatures are higher at positions nearer fallow ground and lower when there is a foliage cover. Air temperature in weather box was 29°C (Geiger, 1957).

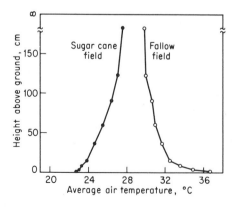

diffusion and for photo-driven reactions. For enzymatic reactions the Q_{10} values may be markedly higher, ranging from 1.3 to 5, but commonly they range around 2. As heat is applied to substances involved in a physical process, the total increase in disordered energy results in a rate increase related to the change in absolute temperature. In contrast, as heat energy is applied to reactants in an enzymatic reaction, the increased disordered energy leads to much larger increases in the frequency at which the reactants reach the energy of activation needed for enzymatic catalysis, and the reaction rate is increased more nearly exponentially. The relatively larger Q_{10} for enzymatic reactions means that as temperatures of plant materials are elevated, enzymatic activities are preferentially increased, and often physical steps such as diffusion of gases can become biologically limiting. As temperatures are lowered, physical processes are relatively less inhibited, and enzymatic steps may become more biologically limiting.

Temperature changes not only alter the rates of reactions but lead to physical changes in tissues which can alter the equilibria of enzyme reactions, in many cases altering qualitatively what reactions will take place. The solubility of two basic ingredients for metabolic activities, oxygen and CO_2, is greatly altered by temperature changes (Fig. 22-9). As the temperature is lowered, relatively large amounts of CO_2 and increased amounts of O_2 can be held in the sap of plant cells. The increased CO_2 solubility at low temperatures will be associated with a slower diffusion exchange of the gas out of the cell, and consequently there can follow some large alterations of respiratory activities in the plant cells with respect to enzymatic processes which involve the exchange of CO_2. Mass action effects will have a depressing effect on decarboxylations at low temperatures and will favor CO_2 fixation where equilibrium reactions are involved.

While low temperatures will depress these terminal aspects of metabolism, they will at the same time enhance the availability of oxygen, provided that the rate of diffusion of the oxygen into the sap does not become limiting. Therefore, low temperatures offer a beneficial situation for energy-producing aspects of metabolism but a restraint on the terminal CO_2 formation. The promotion of organic-acid type of metabolism in the dark (when CO_2 is not being diverted into photosynthesis) by low temperatures illustrates such an increased metabolic efficiency under low-temperature conditions.

Another physical effect of low temperatures will be a slight increase in acidity due to the increased CO_2 and associated bicarbonate content of the sap.

In general, then, we can visualize the effects of low temperature on cellular systems as altering the rates of enzymatic reactions and of physical activities and also as altering the physical properties of the sap. Quantitative and even qualitative changes in metabolism and in metabolic pathways will result, and there may be increases in the relative efficiency of metabolism.

Fig. 22-9 | As temperatures are lowered, the solubilities of oxygen and CO_2 increase in more than a linear fashion.

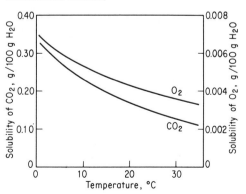

Fig. 22-10 | The growth responses of pea roots and corn coleoptiles to temperatures. Note the large Q_{10} between 12 and 22 and the relatively small Q_{10} between 20 and 30°C (data of Leitsch, 1916; and Lehenbauer, 1914).

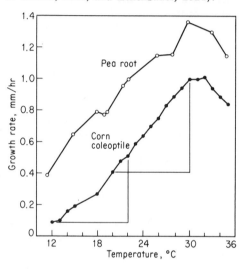

Fig. 22-11 | Though growth rates are higher at elevated temperatures, the duration of growth is commonly shorter. Data for oat coleoptile sections (Barlow and Hancock, 1959).

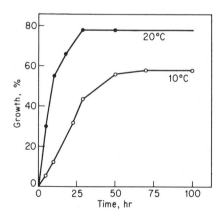

Temperatures for growth

A generalized temperature-response curve for the growth of plants would follow closely the shape of an enzyme-response curve, rising rapidly in the lower temperature ranges of 0 to 15°C and less rapidly in the intermediate range of 15 to 30°C, and then falling at higher temperatures. An illustration of such temperature curves is given in Fig. 22-10. Like enzyme activities, growth activities are more than doubled by a 10° rise in temperature, and this rate of temperature response declines with higher temperature ranges. For example, the Q_{10} for the corn growth rates given here between 12 and 22°C is 5.0, and the Q_{10} between 20 and 30°C is 2.5. The same type of temperature response is known for many plant tissues and plant-tissue responses, including the rates of photosynthesis and the growth of coleoptiles, stems, roots, leaves, and other plant parts.

Associated with the increase in growth rate at increased temperatures within the physiological range is a shortening of the duration of the growth period. Just as light often causes increases in growth rates and a shortening of the duration of growth (shown in Fig. 20-13), so frequently do elevated temperatures. An example of the shortened growth period is given in Fig. 22-11, in which oat coleoptiles are seen to have completed growth at 20°C within 30 hr, whereas at 10° growth was not completed until after 60 hr (Barlow and Hancock, 1959). In this instance the final length achieved was greater at the higher temperature, but in many cases the converse is true (e.g., Bürstrom, 1956). Similar effects of high temperatures in shortening the duration of enzymatic activities are very common (Baldwin, 1947).

The concept of temperature influences on growth has been enormously expanded by the work of F. W. Went in the Earhart Laboratories in California. His first major contribution in this area of knowledge was the finding that night temperatures were specifically important in the growth of whole plants. The ability of night temperatures to alter the growth of tomato plants is shown in Fig. 22-12. This compares the relatively low growth rates of plants in constant temperatures with those of plants experiencing a differential between day and night temperatures. It can be seen that 17°C was relatively suboptimal for plant growth when maintained continuously but was optimal when applied only during the night.

The beneficial effects of a differential day and night temperature seem to be characteristic of whole plants, and as the plant becomes larger its requirement for a differential night temperature may become successively greater. For example, in the pepper plant Dorland and Went (1947) showed that at the age of 24 days the optimum night temperature was about 26°C, whereas at 96 days the optimum night temperature declined to 12°C (Fig. 22-13).

Horticulturists have realized for some time that there are considerable advantages in lowering temperatures in greenhouses at night and that the depressed temperature is especially beneficial when the light intensities have been low during the day. Went (1945) described this interaction of light intensity during the day and optimum night temperature for the tomato with data such as those shown in Fig. 22-14. Stem growth rates are compared for plants given different light intensities and night temperatures, and it can be seen that at the highest light intensities the optimum night temperature was at least 25°C; at intermediate intensities, about 16°C; and at low intensities, about 8°C.

A lowered temperature at night may have many beneficial effects on plants other than the simple effects on stem growth. It can lead to large improvements in the quality of growth or to the earliness and intensity of flowering and fruiting processes (Went, 1957).

Lower night temperatures result in higher

Fig. 22-12 | A representation of the beneficial effect of lowered night temperatures. Growth rates of tomato plants were superior when a day temperature of 26°C was alternated diurnally with lower temperatures than when the lower temperatures were continuous (Went, 1948).

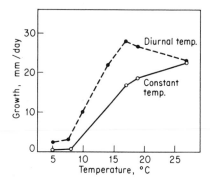

Fig. 22-13 | The optimum night temperature for growth rate of pepper plants declines with plant age, being 25°C for 24-day-old plants and 12°C for 96-day-old plants (Dorland and Went, 1947).

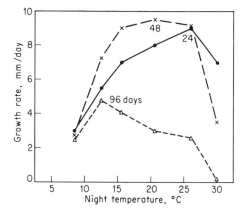

sugar contents in many plants, and Went (1948) interpreted the night-temperature phenomenon as being a result of increased sugar translocation at lower temperatures. However, the accumulated experimental evidence on this point indicates that carbohydrate translocation is best at temperatures of about 25°C (see Fig. 3-9), so another explanation is needed to account for the stimulative effects of low night temperature. One factor that encouraged Went to make this suggestion was that many plants experience an enhanced root growth when given lowered night temperatures. The stimulation of relative root growth is illustrated by data of Went (1957) comparing top-root ratios for several plants (Fig. 22-15). As root growth is favored over stem growth, the top-root ratio declines, and Went's data show that tobacco plants develop with a markedly lower top-root ratio with lower night temperature. The pea is included in the figure to illustrate a species which is essentially insensitive to night temperature with respect to the relative growth of the root system.

In root crops such as the potato it is evident that night temperatures are important in terms of yield (Went, 1959). Sugar beet illustrates this further, for lower night temperatures increase the sugar content of the beet root (Ulrich, 1952; Fig. 22-16). However, when night temperatures are depressed below about 15° under the conditions of the experiments, there is also a depression in the growth of the beet root.

Stimulatory effects of low temperature on growth can generally be accounted for as resulting from a systemic plant response, not from a direct stimulation of a given plant organ. The systemic nature is readily evident from some data of Richardson (1956) describing the growth responses of maple roots to temperatures. Applying the controlled temperatures either to the whole plants or to the aboveground parts, he observed the expected improved root growth in the lower temperatures; when he provided the temperature treatments exclusively to the roots, he found an inhibition by lower temperatures (Fig. 22-17). Went noted that intact plants show very different temperature preferences from those of each of the plant's component parts tested separately. He also demonstrated that low night temperatures were of increasing benefit to many plants as the overall plant size increased.

Fig. 22-14 | Under conditions of lower light intensities, the optimum night temperature is lower. Data for tomato at a 26.5°C day temperature (Went, 1945).

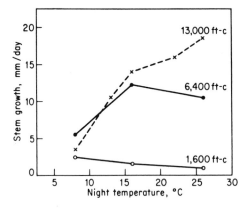

Fig. 22-15 | The top-root ratio obtained at different night temperatures illustrates the preferential growth of the roots at low night temperatures in potato and tobacco but a lack of such effect for pea plants (Went, 1957).

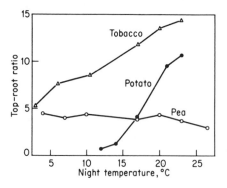

There are restraining influences on growth by environments without temperature fluctuations. This restraining effect has been illustrated by Highkin (1958) in work with peas. At a constant temperature of 10°C, growth was inhibited approximately 20 per cent in comparison with what it would have been had diurnal flux of temperature been experienced. This inhibited state was transmitted to the next generation, becoming cumulatively worse as subsequent generations of peas were grown under the constant temperature and requiring about three generations of growth under alternating temperatures to restore the full natural growth rate.

It is not certain whether the beneficial effects of lowered night temperatures are due to the absolute values of temperature experienced by the plant or whether the simple experience of some temperature flux is the beneficial item. Barney (1951) has raised this interesting question in some experiments on root growth of loblolly pine. Holding the plants at various temperatures, he obtained a root growth curve similar to that of pea roots shown in Fig. 22-10, but the growth rate increased at any temperature range if the roots were given a brief temperature change. The increase in root growth was greatest and most persistent if a brief depression of temperature was given, but some increases were obtained if the temperature was briefly elevated.

In discussing the importance of temperature fluctuations in the geographic distribution of plants, Went (1957) represented the seasonal changes in day and night temperatures in the manner of Fig. 22-18. The annual march of diurnal temperatures occurring naturally at Pasadena, California, is represented by the narrow ellipse in the figure. For example, in January, night temperatures average about 7°C and day temperatures about 14°C; during the year these parameters rise to a peak in August and then come down again to the end of the year. A species such as *Zinnia* has a range

of temperature requirements indicated by the dotted circle Z, and since the seasonal changes meet these requirements between June and September, this species grows well in Pasadena. The China aster (C) requires lower day and night temperatures, and its requirements are met in the spring and fall. *Saintpaulia* (SP), on the other hand, re-

Fig. 22-16 | Lower night temperatures lead to enhanced sugar content in sugar-beet roots and below 15°C to decreased root growth (Ulrich, 1952).

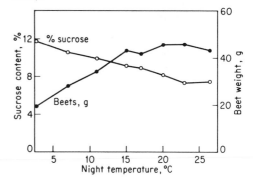

Fig. 22-17 | The beneficial effect of low night temperature on the growth of maple roots is not a direct effect on the roots themselves, for the enhanced growth is observed when the low night temperature is applied to the aboveground parts (Richardson, 1956).

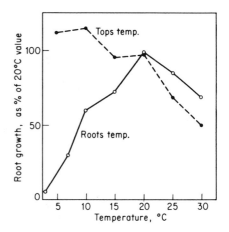

quires a high night temperature, which is not met with in Pasadena, and this species does not thrive there.

Heat units

The fact that the growth of many plants in the field is roughly proportional to the ambient temperature has been utilized to predict the time of harvest for several crops. The calculation of daily accruals of heat units was first attempted by de Candolle (1855) and has been modified in many ways since that time.

If a crop is planted at successive dates in an effort to obtain a spread of harvest times, obviously a means of predicting the time of harvest for any given planting time would be useful. The number of days to the crop maturity varies enormously, as indicated in Fig. 22-19 for the heading of wheat plantings at a single location at various dates. Using the de Candolle (1855) method of summing the mean temperature for each

Fig. 22-18 | The annual cyclical pattern of changing day and night temperatures for Pasadena intercepts the optimal temperature ranges for zinnia (Z) and China aster (C) but not for *Saintpaulia* (SP). The former species thrive at that location, but not the latter (Went, 1957).

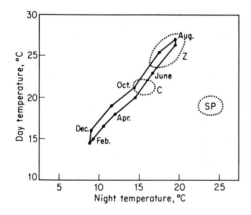

day, one can approximate more precisely the progress of the crop. This type of heat unit, "day-degrees," will lower the variability somewhat as shown in Fig. 22-19. Nuttonson (1948) suggested an additional refinement, in which day-degrees are further multiplied by the number of daylight hours. This type of calculation is shown in Fig. 22-19 as "day-length-degrees." The relative precision of these three methods is indicated by the variability around the median in each case, there being a ± 66 per cent variability in days, a ± 29 per cent variability in day-degrees, and a ± 12 per cent variability in day-length-degrees. Went (1957) pointed out that the level of precision of these heat-unit methods is better for a single geographic location than for scattered locations.

A considerable increase in precision of heat-unit prediction systems was achieved by Medcalf (1949) for pineapple. He measured the rate of growth of the pineapple plant at each temperature in the growing range and multiplied the number of hours of each day at each temperature by the relative growth rate of the plant at that temperature. Highly precise predictions of crop maturity were obtained in that way.

The heat-unit system is based on the assumption that growth is proportional to temperature; this is true only within a limited temperature range and under similar conditions of other ecological variables. The heat-unit systems are most effective for species in which development is not controlled by photoperiods. They do not take into account the sequential temperature requirements of many species for successive steps of development.

Temperatures for development

The temperature responses of individual plant organs, such as roots or stems, may be altered when integrated into the whole plant; furthermore, the integrated plant may have shifting temperature characteristics as it changes from one developmental stage to another.

In the Dutch laboratory of A. H. Blaauw, classic studies of the varying temperature requirements for different developmental stages were done. His group established that when tulips and other bulbing crops were stored in the summer and fall, they went through successive stages for which there were differing temperature requirements. Their observations were made by combining the use of simple temperature-controlled rooms with morphological criteria of the rates of development.

As an illustration of the temperature sequence for bulbs, some data for tulips are given in Fig. 22-20 (Hartsema et al., 1930). When these bulbs are lifted from the ground in the summer, they have an initial requirement for a rather high temperature, while the new flower initials are being formed. Three weeks later they require quite low temperatures, while the flower initials develop. At 16 weeks the temperature optimum begins to rise gradually as the buds and stems commence elongation, after which time the new plant has emerged.

In many instances, a plant does not proceed to the next stage of development until it has satisfied a particular temperature requirement. This is most evident among the biennial plants which require cold for the induction of flowering. For example, the flowering stock (*Mathiola*) ordinarily begins to flower after experiencing winter temperatures. Post (1935) established that this was a causative relationship, stocks being unable to flower until they had experienced a temperature below 15°C. Some of his data are presented in Fig. 22-21, and represent one of the first demonstrations of a cold requirement for flowering. It can be seen in this figure that after 2 or 3 weeks of cool temperatures, the plants went completely to the flowering condition when transferred back to a warm greenhouse.

Just as low temperatures are required for the commencement of flowering in many

Fig. 22-19 | A comparison of three methods for predicting harvest time for Marquis wheat at one location (Moro, Oregon). (*A*) Using simply the number of days; (*B*) the day-degrees above 32°F; and (*C*) the day-length-degrees—the day-degrees times the photoperiod (data from Nuttonson, 1948).

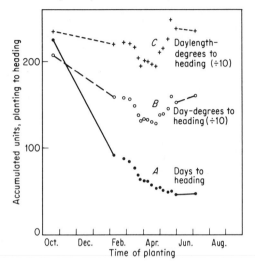

Fig. 22-20 | The optimal temperature for Copland tulip shifts with consecutive stages of development, from a conspicuous low-temperature optimum for the development of flower initials to much higher temperature optima for successive stages of elongation (Hartsema et al., 1930).

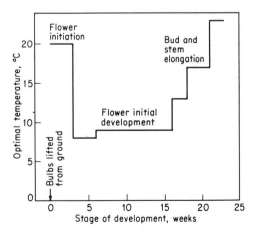

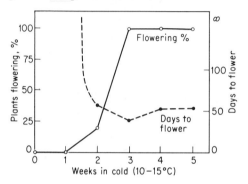

Fig. 22-21 | Placing *Mathiola* plants in a cold greenhouse for 2 or 3 weeks resulted in flowering, a clear case of low-temperature requirement for flower initiation. After the cold experience, the plants were moved to a warm greenhouse again (Post, 1935).

Fig. 22-22 | The flowering tendencies of onions can be erased by high temperatures. Onions stored at 0°C for 9 weeks are prepared to flower, but subsequent storage at 30°C for 5 or more weeks can restore the vegetative condition. Bulbs planted in the field in April or May (Lachman and Upham, 1954).

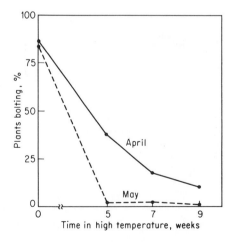

species, so can high temperatures prevent flowering. The devernalization of grains has been mentioned in Chap. 13 under Vernalization and Flowering, and this illustrates quantitatively the suppression of flowering by high temperatures; in other cases the experience of high temperature can wipe out the flowering tendencies and qualitatively maintain the vegetative condition. Sugar beets are induced to flower at low temperatures, and if they are placed in a high-temperature storage (23°C) for 3 weeks, they will subsequently remain vegetative (Stout, 1946). Similarly, onion bulbs are induced to flower by low temperature, and the subsequent removal to a high-temperature storage (30°C) can restore the plants to a completely vegetative condition (Lachman and Upham, 1954; Fig. 22-22).

Dormancy and dwarfism are two other instances of qualitative temperature regulation of developmental events. Siegel (1950) observed that seeds of *Digitalis* and *Sporobolus* could be made dormant by brief exposures to high temperature (50 to 100°C). Such an imposed dormancy was also shown for lettuce seeds by Evenari (1952*b*) and is illustrated in Fig. 19-13. In the latter case, the dormancy was completely erased by brief exposure of the lettuce seed to red light. The case of dwarfism is a novel one, first observed by Tukey and Carlson (1945) and Flemion and Waterbury (1945). Peach seeds held in warm temperatures during the first week of germination produce dwarfed plants (Fig. 22-23) which will remain so for more that 10 years (Pollock, 1962).

Temperature experiences can also have quantitative effects on developmental changes in plants. The effects of low- and high-temperature experiences in hastening the flowering of many species have been described (cf. Figs. 13-25 to 13-31). The quantitative effects of cold in improving germination of buds and seeds have been discussed in Chap. 19.

Many of the cold-requiring steps of development will be satisfied with a gibberellin treatment. Lang (1956) discovered that gibberellin applications substitute for the cold induction of flowering. The gibberellin substitution for the cold requirement of germinating peach seeds to prevent the dwarf habit was found by Flemion (1959). Gibberellin can also overcome seed dormancy (Kahn et al., 1957). Its ability to overcome the high-temperature imposition of dormancy is illustrated for lettuce seeds in Fig. 22-24 (Toole and Cathey, 1961). The seeds can be made germinable by light, made dormant again by a 35°C treatment, and made nondormant even with the high temperature if given gibberellin.

Temperature mechanisms

Since temperature is a measure of disordered energy, lowered plant temperatures will be associated with lowered molecular reactivity. There will be a depression of metabolic rates, and since the solubility of carbon dioxide increases markedly with decline in temperature, there may be a preferential depression of those sectors of metabolism which are involved in the production of CO_2. The increase in CO_2 dissolved in the cell sap will increase the acidity of the sap, and if the higher CO_2 content of the sap favors fixation into organic acids, that effect will further increase the acidity (Pucher et al., 1948).

The effects of temperature on the relative hydrolysis of starches have been measured in artichoke leaves by Wassink (1953; Fig. 22-25), who found that the usual rise in activity with increasing temperature was modified and that there was a supplementary rise in starch hydrolysis at temperatures below about 13°C. This hydrolysis at low temperatures may be related to the greater acidity of the leaves at the low temperatures or to the proportionate rates of starch synthesis and hydrolysis. It is commonly ob-

Fig. 22-23 | Peach seeds germinated in high temperature become dwarfed in growth habit. Plant height and an index of dwarfing based on internode and leaf-shape characters are compared for 5-week-old seedlings germinated at three temperatures for 1 week before transfer to a common greenhouse at 25°C (Pollock, 1962).

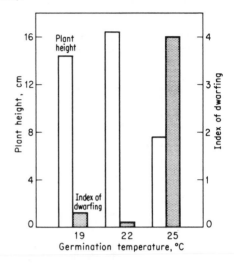

Fig. 22-24 | *Lepidium virginianum* seeds require light for germination, but after illumination they can be made dormant again by high temperature. Gibberellin treatment ($2 \times 10^{-3}M$) breaks dormancy without being temperature-reversible. Seeds at 20°C except for the period at 35°C (Toole and Cathey, 1961).

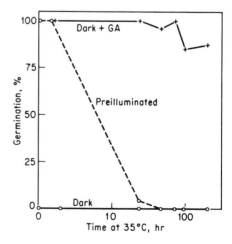

served that plant tissues show marked increases in sugars at temperatures below about 10 or 15°C. The best-known case is that of the potato tuber, which becomes undesirably sugary when stored at temperatures between 0 and 5°C (Müller-Thurgau, 1882; Arreguin-Lozano and Bonner, 1949; Fig. 22-26).

The lowering of temperatures may cause extensive changes in the amount and nature of substrates available in the plant. The increase in sugars and acids may help to account for the effects of lowered temperatures, especially the short-term effects on growth, such as the beneficial effects of low night temperatures and some cases of the alleviation of dormancy by low temperatures.

Quite a different problem exists, however, in connection with the possible mechanisms of action of lower temperature on more persistent plant functions such as flowering, vernalization, and dwarfism. There appears to be no basis for assuming that differences in availability of substrates resulting from low-temperature experience can account for the protracted effects on plant development. What alternatives are there? In view of the fact that the altered developmental state persists in all meristems derived from a vernalized meristem and that dwarfism persists in all those derived from a dwarf shoot, the most logical assumption is that the temperature experience causes a change in the metastable state of some regulating system in the cell which is self-propagated.

The fact that it is perpetuated over such extended periods of time suggests immediately that the metastable changes induced by temperature treatments may be somehow regulated by the nucleic acids. There is no evidence available on this possibility, and it remains entirely speculative.

That the control systems might involve changes in the enzymes and growth substances seems reasonable, but there is little evidence of major changes in enzyme content following a temperature experience.

Fig. 22-25 | Starch hydrolysis in *Helianthus tuberosus* leaves is greatly accelerated by temperatures above 25°C and proceeds also very well at temperatures just above 0°C. Relative values for iodine staining before and after 6½ hr at temperature indicated; plotted as differences (Wassink, 1953).

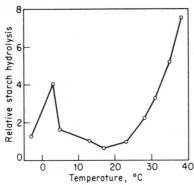

Fig. 22-26 | Low-temperature storage of potatoes results in extensive increases in content of sugars. Tubers stored for 2 weeks at temperatures indicated (Arreguin-Lozano and Bonner, 1949).

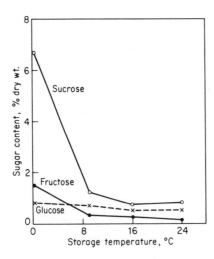

The involvement of growth substances is implied by extensive capabilities of gibberellens to substitute for temperatures in the regulation of many developmental stages. Lang and Reinhard (1961) obtained tentative evidence that the gibberellin content of *Hyoscyamus* increases with the low-temperature induction of flowering (Fig. 13-34), but the role of these growth substances in temperature responses has not been definitively established.

Almost nothing is known about how a temperature experience can alter the development of a plant for an extended time. It is tempting to suppose that physical alterations in the cell bring about structural alterations of some enzymatic or template-forming nucleic acids, which result in protracted alterations. The quantitative effects of low temperatures still lack an explanation; the interactions of physical effects, respiratory effects, and preferential alteration of metabolic systems need to be fitted together to achieve a physiological understanding of the manner in which temperatures may alter growth and development.

Thermal injury

Low-temperature injury with the formation of ice crystals in plant tissues occurs much more readily in some species than in others. Species which can become resistant to it require a hardening process. Sunflower, soybean, and *Begonia* are apparently unable to undergo hardening and are uniformly susceptible to frost. Cabbage, wheat, and many deciduous and evergreen trees can be hardened off and are then more resistant to frost.

Frost damage can occur at air temperatures scarcely in the freezing range, for leaves have a ready ability to radiate heat to the sky and so are cooled below the temperature of the air on a clear night. In an experiment with tomato leaves, Shaw (1954) recorded leaf temperatures as much

as 4° below air temperatures (Fig. 22-27). When a cloud cover moved over the location, the leaf temperatures promptly approached air temperatures. The time of formation of ice crystals is evidenced by the brief rise of leaf temperature due to the heat of ice formation.

The early explanation of frost damage was that ice crystals formed in the plants and broke the cell walls, thus killing the tissue. While there is clearly some effect of wall rupture by ice, this appears now to be a minor source of damage in comparison with the physical disruption of the cell contents by the movement of water out of the cells during freezing and into the cells again during thawing.

Levitt (1957a) recognized three times at which injury may occur with freezing. Damage is done during the freezing period, during the thawing period, and immediately after thawing. Injury during freezing is illustrated in Fig. 22-28, which compares leaf pieces which were frozen quickly with those frozen slowly. Rapid freezing is much more damaging than slow freezing, and

Fig. 22-27 | On a clear night, tomato-leaf temperatures can be markedly below air temperature. Note the temperature rise as ice formation occurs in the leaf or when a cloud cover suppresses radiant loss of heat (Shaw, 1954).

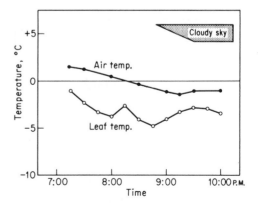

Fig. 22-28 | The lethal effects of low temperatures on cabbage leaves were markedly greater when freezing temperatures were applied rapidly than when applied slowly; hardened cabbage leaves were less damaged under either circumstance. Hardening was induced by temperatures of 2 to 5°C under continuous light (Levitt, 1957*a*).

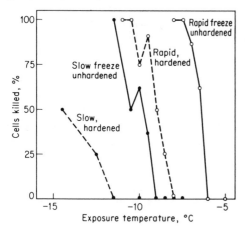

Fig. 22-29 | Low-temperature damage to hardened cabbage leaves was markedly greater when thawing was imposed rapidly by dipping the leaves in 2°C water. Slow thaw over a 30- to 60-min period at 0°C avoided damage. Leaves were slowly frozen to the temperature indicated (Levitt, 1957*a*).

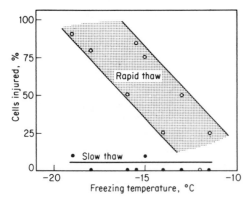

Levitt interprets this as being due to the preferential formation of ice between the cells with slow freezing and the more random formation through the tissues with rapid freezing. The formation of ice crystals between cells is often without damaging effects. Note that tissues which had previously been exposed to low temperatures were "hardened" and were markedly less susceptible to damage.

The extent to which hardening can protect tissues is sometimes dramatic. The hardened cabbage tissues shown in Fig. 22-28 withstood temperatures of nearly −15°C. By slow cooling, many tissues can be frozen without damage. In an extreme case, Sakai (1956) was able to lower hardened mulberry leaves to the temperature of liquid nitrogen (−210°C) without killing them, provided the temperature was lowered slowly for the first 30° below freezing.

Injury may occur at the time of thawing, as shown by some data of Levitt (1957*a*) in Fig. 22-29. Frozen tissues brought up to 0°C in 30 to 60 min showed a completely different degree of damage from those brought up to the same temperature within a few seconds, the slow thaw essentially avoiding injury.

Injury can occur immediately after thawing. Levitt (1957*a*) has shown that placing newly thawed tissues into solutions containing sugar or other osmotic materials can markedly lower the damaging effects. For example, cabbage leaves frozen to −7° were almost uninjured if they were slowly thawed and then placed in a sugar solution between 0.5 and 1.25 *M* (Fig. 22-30). Even with rapid thawing, damage was much less when followed by treatment with such osmotic media.

Each of these moments of injury can be interpreted (Levitt, 1957*a*) as being a time when the protoplasm is subjected to physical stress. Rapid freezing or thawing could mechanically abrade the protoplasm, disrupting its physical structure. Abrasion seems to involve the interposition of ice crystals and the simultaneous mechanical deformation of the cytoplasm as its water matrix is moved into and out of such crystals. Placing the cells in an osmotic medium after thawing would slow the reentry of water which had been removed by intercellular ice-crystal formation, and the slower reentry would cushion the stresses on the protoplasm.

Hardening against low-temperature injury may involve an increase in osmotic values of the sap which would cushion the stresses on the protoplasm by retarding the exit and reentry of water. Levitt (1957b, 1959a) increased sap osmotic value of cabbage leaves by soaking them in glycerine or in sugar solutions, and the increase in hardiness obtained was proportional to the osmotic change. The formation of ice crystals was not prevented by hardening treatments, but the injury effects were alleviated. The ice crystals probably formed and melted slowly between cells in the hardened material.

Hardening may involve not only an increase in the osmotic content of cell sap but also physical changes of the cell materials which increase the water-binding capacities. Levitt (1959b) showed that dried cells of hardened cabbage leaves contained more bound water than those of unhardened cabbage leaves.

During the hardening process there are generally some characteristic changes in the carbohydrate components. The changes observed by Siminovitch et al. (1953) on locust bark are characteristic of changes found to occur with hardening. In Fig. 22-31 one can see that with the onset of winter, the locust shows a pronounced drop in starch content and increases in the simpler sugars. These changes might be responsible for the increase in sap osmotic values with hardening, but Siminovitch et al. suggest that the disappearance of starch is a critical factor in hardening. In some striking photomicrographs they have shown that the presence of starch grains in the

Fig. 22-30 | Placing newly thawed cabbage leaves in an osmotic medium can reduce the thermal damage. Semihardened leaves were slowly frozen to −7 or −8°C and were thawed by water-dip treatment or 2- to 3-hr standing period; they were then placed in glucose solutions at the concentrations indicated for 1 hr before cell injury was recorded (Levitt, 1957a).

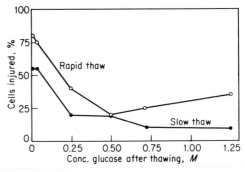

Fig. 22-31 | During the season of frosting in Minnesota, black locust bark accumulates a relatively high sugar content and a low starch content (Siminovitch et al., 1953).

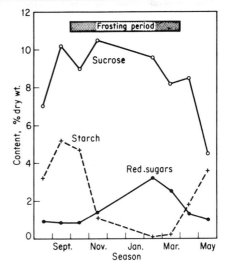

cytoplasm can considerably increase the frost injury through an abrasive action during the physical stresses in the cytoplasm with frost action (Siminovitch and Briggs, 1954).

Using a photographic technique, Modli-bowska and Rogers (1955) observed that ice crystals in one cell can kill that cell and protrude into adjacent cells and there cause the formation of further ice crystals. The structural strength of the cell wall may contribute to hardening by minimizing the seeding effect of ice crystals between cells.

High temperatures can cause many different types of damage to plants, ordinarily most evident as bleaching of chlorophyll from leaves, inhibitions of growth, development of burns or lesions, or death of the plant or plant part. Excessive temperatures are most liable to occur in the field as a consequence of intense illumination. Leaves in strong sunlight often experience temperatures 10 or 15°C above air temperatures,

and bulkier tissues such as fruits, stems, and succulent parts may reach 30°C above air temperatures (Lange, 1959; Geiger, 1957). Leaf temperatures of 60°C are not uncommon in still air.

The temperatures at which injurious reactions set in vary markedly from plant to plant. For example, ordinary strains of *Chlorella* are inhibited in growth by temperatures above about 25°C, whereas a high-temperature strain has been found which is inhibited only at temperatures above 40°C (Sorokin, 1960; Fig. 22-32).

Variations in resistance may be related to morphological structure, and the succulent habit of desert species has been considered for years to favor heat resistance (Sachs, 1864). Lange and Schwemmle (1960) tested the involvement of succulence in heat resistance using *Kalanchoe*, which can be made more or less succulent with photoperiodic treatments, and found a close correlation between heat resistance and succulence under various photoperiodic treatments and with different leaf ages. Mason (1925) observed that the arrangement of the leaves on the stem apex of date palms insulated the apex from much of the diurnal temperature flux, thus avoiding the inhibitory effects of midday temperature maxima.

As in low-temperature hardiness, some species can acquire a hardiness to high temperatures by experiencing them. For example, avocado tissues which had experienced a brief heat treatment at 50°C became markedly hardened against damage from heating to 55°C, as shown in Fig. 22-33 (Schroeder, 1963). Levitt (1956) suggested that the development of hardiness may be a result of increases in the viscosity of the cytoplasm and a resulting higher degree of water binding in the cells.

The physiological nature of heat damage probably involves a denaturation of some protein components of cells (Sachs, 1864). Some data of Belehradek and Melichar (1930) shown in Fig. 22-34 indicate that

Fig. 22-32 | The high-temperature limits may vary widely between species. The growth rates of two strains of *Chlorella* are compared over a temperature range, one strain showing inhibitions above 25°C, and the other showing inhibitions only above 40°C at 1,600 ft-c of light (Sorokin, 1960).

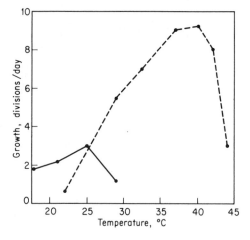

the lethal effects of high temperature on *Elodea* involve at least two separate components, as indicated by the two slopes of the log-temperature-response curve.

Yarwood (1961*b*) demonstrated the translocation of a toxic principle formed as a result of a localized high-temperature treatment to a leaf. This interesting observation suggests not only that damage is due to a deteriorative effect relating to protein denaturation, but also that there may be toxic products formed which contribute to the damaging effects.

In connection with the protein-denaturation involvement in high-temperature damage, Engelbrecht and Mothes (1960) found that the deteriorative yellowing of leaves following heat treatment could be prevented by kinetin applications. They attributed this chemically imposed heat resistance to the kinetin stimulation of protein synthesis, an effect which they had reported earlier (Mothes et al., 1959).

Damage to plants by either high or low temperatures involves the imposition of stresses on the cytoplasm. The development of hardiness appears to be a modification of the cytoplasm which retards the rapidity of water movements, a principal source of cytoplasmic stresses, imposed by temperature. High-temperature hardiness involves a retardation of evaporative loss rates. An additional effect of high temperature is the denaturative action on the plant proteins. The formation of toxic substances may be a consequence of protein-denaturation activities, and the hardening reaction may involve an increase in protein synthesis. In both types of temperature extremes, the structural damage to the cytoplasm is a major component of the forces which impose temperature limits on plant growth.

Fig. 22-33 | Exposure of tissues of avocado fruits to high temperature can cause a hardening of the tissues against subsequent heat damage. Tissue cultures pretreated at 50°C for 2 to 3 min showed markedly higher survival rates when heated to 55°C for 10 min. The hardening persisted for about 5 days (Schroeder, 1963).

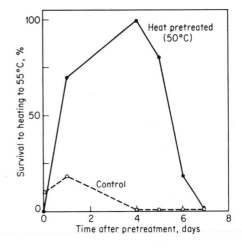

Fig. 22-34 | When *Elodea canadensis* plants are placed in water at high temperatures, the tolerance time (log scale) decreases with increasing extremes of temperature treatment (data of Belehradek and Melichar, 1930; from Levitt, 1956).

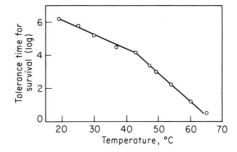

GENERAL REFERENCES

de Vries, D. A. 1963. The physics of plant environments, pp. 5–22. In L. T. Evans (ed.), *Environmental Control of Plant Growth*. Academic Press, Inc., New York.

Gates, D. M. 1962. *Energy Exchange in the Biosphere*. Harper & Row, Publishers, Inc., New York. 151 pp.

Geiger, R. 1957. *The Climate Near the Ground* (tr. by M. N. Stewart). Harvard University Press, Cambridge, Mass. 482 pp.

Levitt, J. 1956. *The Hardiness of Plants*. Academic Press, Inc., New York. 278 pp.

Raschke, K. 1960. Heat transfer between the plant and environment. *Ann. Rev. Plant Physiol.*, 11:111–126.

van Wijk, W. R. (ed.). 1963. *Physics of Plant Environment*. North Holland Publishing Company, Amsterdam. 382 pp.

Went, F. W. 1953. Effect of temperature on plant growth. *Ann. Rev. Plant Physiol.*, 4:347–362.

———. 1957. *The Experimental Control of Plant Growth*. Chronica Botanica Co., Waltham, Mass. 343 pp.

Whyte, R. O. 1946. *Crop Production and Environment*. Faber & Faber, Ltd., London. 372 pp.

REFERENCES CITED

Ansari, A. Q., and W. E. Loomis. 1959. Leaf temperatures. *Am. J. Botany*, 46:713–717.

Arreguin-Lozano, B., and J. Bonner. 1949. Experiments on sucrose formation by potato tubers as influenced by temperature. *Plant Physiol.*, 24:720–738.

Baldwin, E. 1947. *Dynamic Aspects of Biochemistry*. The Macmillan Company, New York. 457 pp.

Barlow, H., and C. Hancock. 1959. Studies on extension growth in coleoptile sections. III. The interaction of temperature and β-indoleacetic acid on section growth. *J. Exptl. Botany*, 29:157–168.

Barney, C. W. 1951. Effects of soil temperature and light intensity on root growth of loblolly pine seedlings. *Plant Physiol.*, 26:146–163.

Belehradek, J., and J. Melichar. 1930. L'action differente des températures élevées et des températures normales sur la survie de la cellule végétale. *Biol. Gen.*, 6:109–124 (cited by Levitt, 1956).

Billings, W. D., and R. J. Morris. 1951. Reflection of visible and infrared radiation from leaves of different ecological groups. *Am. J. Botany*, 38:327–331.

Brown, H. T., and W. E. Wilson. 1905. On the thermal emissivity of a green leaf in still and moving air. *Proc. Roy. Soc. (London)*, B,76:122–137.

Bürstrom, H. 1956. Temperature and root cell elongation. *Physiol. Plantarum*, 9:682–692.

Candolle, A. de. 1855. *Geographic botanique raisonée*. I. Masson et Cie, Paris. 606 pp.

Cook, G. D., J. L. Dixon, and A. C. Leopold. 1964. Transpiration: its effects on plant leaf temperature. *Science*, 144:546–547.

Curtis, O. F. 1936. Leaf temperature and the cooling of leaves by radiation. *Plant Physiol.*, 11:343–364.

——— and D. G. Clark. 1950. *An Introduction to Plant Physiology*. McGraw-Hill Book Company, New York. 752 pp.

Dorland, R. E., and F. W. Went. 1947. Plant growth under controlled conditions. VIII. *Am. J. Botany*, 34:393–401.

Engelbrecht, L., and K. Mothes. 1960. Kinetin als Faktor der Hitzresistenz. *Ber. Deut. Botan. Ges.*, 73:246–257.

Evenari, M. 1952a. The water balance of plants in desert conditions. *Desert Res.* 2:1–9.

———. 1952b. The germination of lettuce seeds. *Palestine J. Botany*, 5:138–160.

Flemion, F. 1959. Effect of temperature, light and gibberellin on stem elongation in dwarfed peach and *Rhodotypos*. *Contrib. Boyce Thompson Inst.*, 20:57–70.

——— and E. Waterbury. 1945. Further studies with dwarf seedlings of non-after-ripened peach seeds. *Contrib. Boyce Thompson Inst.*, 13:415–422.

Geiger, R. 1957. *The Climate Near the Ground* (tr. by M. N. Stewart). Harvard Univ. Press, Cambridge, Mass. 482 pp.

Hartsema, A. M., I. Luyten, and A. H. Blaauw. 1930. The optimal temperatures from flower formation to flowering of Darwin tulips. II. *Proc. Koninkl. Ned. Akad. Wetenschap.*, 27:1–46.

Highkin, H. R. 1958. Temperature-induced variability in peas. *Am. J. Botany*, 45:626–631.

Kaempfert, W. 1951. Ein Phasendiagramm der Besonnung. *Met. Rundsch.*, 4:141–144 (cited by Geiger, 1957).

Kahn, A. J., A. Goss, and D. E. Smith. 1957. Effect of gibberellin on germination of lettuce seed. *Science*, 125:645–646.

Lachman, W. H., and E. F. Upham. 1954. Effect of warm storage on the bolting of onions grown from sets. *Proc. Am. Soc. Hort. Sci.*, 63:342–346.

Lang, A. 1956. Gibberellin and flower formation. *Naturwissenschaften*, 23:544.

——— and E. Reinhard. 1961. Gibberellins and flower formation. *Advan. Chem. Ser.*, 28:71–79.

Lange, O. L. 1959. Untersuchungen über Warmehaushalt und Hitzresistenz maeritanischer Wüsten und Saannen pflanzen. *Flora (Jena)*, 147:595–651.

——— and B. Schwemmle. 1960. Untersuchungen zur Hitzeresistenz vegetativer und bluhender Pflanzen von *Kalanchöe blossfeldiana*. *Planta*, 55:208–225.

Lehenbauer, P. A. 1914. Growth of maize seedlings in relation to temperature. *Physiol. Res.*, 1:247–288.

Leitsch, J. 1916. Some experiments on the influence of temperature on the rate of growth in *Pisum sativum*. *Ann. Botany (London)*, 30:25–46.

Levitt, J. 1956. *The Hardiness of Plants*. Academic Press, Inc., New York. 278 pp.

———. 1957a. The moment of frost injury. *Protoplasma*, 48:289–303.

———. 1957b. The role of cell sap concentration in frost hardiness. *Plant Physiol.*, 32:237–239.

———. 1959a. Effects of artificial increase in sugar content on frost hardiness. *Plant Physiol.*, 34:401–402.

———. 1959b. Bound water and frost hardiness. *Plant Physiol.*, 34:674–677.

Mason, S. C. 1925. Partial thermostasy of the growth center of date palm. *J. Agr. Res.*, 31:415–453.

Medcalf, J. 1949. *Pineapple Res. Inst. Bull.* Honolulu.

Modlibowska, I., and W. S. Rogers. 1955. Freezing of plant tissues under the microscope. *J. Exptl. Botany*, 6:384–391.

Mothes, K., L. Engelbrecht, and O. Kulajewa. 1959. Über die Wirkung des Kinetins auf Stickstoffverteilung und Eiweisssynthese in isoliertre Blättern. *Flora (Jena)*, 147:445–464.

Müller-Thurgau, H. 1882. Über Zuckeranhäufung in Pflanzentheilen in Folge niederer Temperatur. *Landwirtsch. Jahrb. Schweiz*, 11:751–828.

Nuttonson, M. Y. 1948. Some preliminary observations of phenological data, pp. 129–145. In A. E. Murneek and R. O. Whyte (eds.), *Vernalization and Photoperiodism*. Chronica Botanica Co., Waltham, Mass.

Pucher, G. W., C. S. Leavenworth, W. D. Ginter, and H. B. Vickery. 1948. Studies in the metabolism of crassulacean plants: the effect of temperature on the culture of leaves of *Bryophyllum*. *Plant Physiol.*, 23:123–132.

Pollock, B. M. 1962. Temperature control of dwarfing in peach seedlings. *Plant Physiol.*, 37:190–197.

Post, K. 1935. Some effects of temperature and light upon the flower bud formation and leaf character of stock. *Proc. Am. Soc. Hort. Sci.*, 33:649–652.

Rabideau, G. S., C. S. French, and A. S. Holt. 1946. The absorption and reflection spectra of leaves, chloroplast suspensions and chloroplast fragments as measured in Ulbricht sphere. *Am. J. Botany*, 33:769–777.

Richardson, S. D. 1956. Studies of root growth in *Acer saccharinum* L. IV. The effect of differential shoot and root temperature on root growth. *Proc. Koninkl. Ned. Akad. Wetenschap.*, 59:428–438.

Russell, E. W. 1961. *Soil Conditions and Plant Growth*. Longmans Green & Co., Ltd., London. 635 pp.

Sachs, J. 1864. Über die obere Temperatur–Gränze der Vegetations. *Flora (Jena)*, 47:5–12.

Sakai, A. 1956. Survival of plant tissues at super low temperature. *Low Temp. Sci. Ser. B*, 14:17–23 (cited by Levitt, 1956).

Schroeder, C. A. 1963. Induced temperature tolerance in plant tissue *in vitro*. *Nature*, 200:1301–1302.

Shaw, R. H. 1954. Leaf and air temperatures under freezing conditions. *Plant Physiol.*, 29:102–104.

Shull, C. A. 1919. Transpiration as energy dispersal. *School Sci. Math*, 19:1–6.

Siegel, S. M. 1950. Effects of exposures of seeds to various physical agents. I. *Botan. Gaz.*, 112:57–70.

Siminovitch, D., and D. R. Briggs. 1954. Studies on the chemistry of living bark in relation to frost hardiness. VII. *Plant Physiol.*, 29:331–337.

———, C. M. Wilson, and D. R. Briggs. 1953. Studies on the chemistry of living bark in relation to frost hardiness. V. *Plant Physiol.*, 28:383–400.

Sorokin, C. 1960. Kinetic studies of temperature effects on the cellular level. *Biochim. Biophys. Acta*, 38:197–204.

Stout, M. 1946. Relation of temperature to reproduction in sugar beets. *J. Agr. Res.*, 72:49–68.

Toole, V. K., and H. M. Cathey. 1961. Responses to gibberellin of light-requiring seeds of lettuce and *Lepidium virginicum*. *Plant Physiol.*, 36:663–671.

Tukey, H. B., and R. F. Carlson. 1945. Morphological changes in peach seedlings following after-ripening treatments of seeds. *Botan. Gaz.*, 106:431–440.

Turrell, F. M., S. W. Austin, and R. L. Perry. 1962. Nocturnal thermal exchange of citrus leaves. *Am. J. Botany*, 49:97–109.

Ulrich, A. 1952. The influence of temperature and light factors on the growth and development of sugar beets. *Agron. J.* 44:66–73.

Verkerk, K. 1955. Temperature, light, and the tomato. *Mededel. Landbouwhogeschool Wageningen*, 55:175–224.

Wassink, E. A. 1953. Starch conversion in leaves of *Helianthus tuberosus* and *H. annuus:* preliminary observations. *Acta Botan. Neerl.*, 2:327–348.

Went, F. W. 1945. Plant growth under controlled conditions. V. Relation between age, light, variety, and thermoperiodicity of tomatoes. *Am. J. Botany*, 32:469–479.

———. 1948. Thermoperiodicity, pp. 145–157. In A. E. Murneek and R. O. Whyte (eds.), *Vernalization and Photoperiodism*. Chronica Botanica Co., Waltham, Mass.

———. 1957. *The Experimental Control of Plant Growth*. Chronica Botanica Co., Waltham, Mass. 343 pp.

———. 1959. Effects of environment of parent and grandparent generations on tuber production by potatoes. *Am. J. Botany*, 46:277–282.

Wolpert, A. 1962. Heat transfer analysis of factors affecting plant leaf temperatures. Significance of leaf hair. *Plant Physiol.*, 37:113–120.

Yarwood, C. E. 1961a. Acquired tolerance of leaves to heat. *Science*, 134:941–942.

———. 1961b. Translocated heat injury. *Plant Physiol.*, 36:721–726.

23 | Water

Water is the most abundant single component of living matter. It is an integral part of the internal structure of life and a major component of the external system of climates on the earth's surface. Its essentiality for life is biochemical and biophysical, internal and environmental.

The three principal involvements of water with life are (1) as the matrix for cytoplasm, (2) as a major reagent involved in biological transformations, and (3) as a climatic force in the environmental medium.

Cytoplasmic materials are cradled in a water matrix. Living plant cells are constituted of from 80 to over 90 per cent water, but this water does not simply act as a solvent—it is an actual structural component of proteins and nucleic acids. The macromolecules of the cell cannot exist in their complicated secondary foldings or spiraled helices without the support by hydrogen bondings with the water matrix in which they are suspended. If the hydrogen bonding with water is restricted, the macromolecules collapse in a state of denaturation. The water matrix is also critical in that its properties of hydration permit a ready reactivity between molecules in solution and between enzymes and substrates.

Water is a reagent in biological reactions in that it is a substrate for photosynthesis, and is one of the major products of the catabolic reactions of respiration. Numerous respiratory steps such as the hydrolysis or synthesis of polysaccharides or of peptides involve the incorporation or removal of water.

As a climatic force, water constitutes a major form of temperature regulation both at the level of the earth's climates and at the level of controlling temperatures in individual living organisms. Atmospheric water filters the solar radiation as it approaches the earth, and surface water forms an enormous buffer system against temperature extremes. The vast volume of water on the earth (equivalent to a layer 1.5 miles deep over its entire surface) can absorb or give up tremendous amounts of heat. The same qualities of high specific heat and high heat of vaporization which make it a good climatic thermostat also make water an admirable means of controlling temperatures in organisms. Animals and plants both utilize water-evaporating systems for cooling.

Properties of water

Structurally, the water molecule is essentially tetrahedral in electrostatic form. The two hydrogen atoms do not entirely satisfy the electronegative properties of the oxygen, and the hydrogen atoms each retain a small electropositive charge. The two negative positions of the oxygen atom exert an attractive force for the hydrogens of nearby molecules, pulling the liquid into a loose lattice of molecules (Fig. 23-1). These hydrogen bondings, reinforced by dipole forces, give water some properties which would not be expected on the basis of its simple composition. Among these are a high specific gravity and a very high specific heat. Not many earth materials require 1 cal to increase 1 g 1°C. Another relevant property is the high heat of vaporization—it requires over 500 cal to change 1 g of water from a liquid to a gas at 100°C. This enormous requirement can tie up large amounts of heat and is the basis of much of the thermostatic qualities of water both in climates and in organisms. A fourth relevant property of water is its high heat of fusion—it requires the removal of 80 cal from 1 g of water to change it from a liquid to a solid at 0°C. This property contributes to the thermostatic effects of water, releasing rather large amounts of heat as ice is formed and thus tending to stabilize temperatures.

Hydrogen bonding provides weak and transient couplings between the hydrogen atoms of water and atomic groups with slight electronegative charges. In water these bondings are most pronounced with fluorine, oxygen, nitrogen, and chlorine positions. Biologically, in addition to the hydrogen bondings between water molecules, the bondings of water to the nitrogen and oxygen positions of proteins are of paramount importance. Water molecules actually become structurally a part of proteins, and restriction of the bondings between water and proteins destroys the protein structure. This is a principal cause of the temperature limitations for life. The force of hydrogen bonding declines with increasing temperatures, so that as temperatures rise above about 30°C, proteins begin to experience denaturation effects because of diminished hydrogen bondings. As temperatures decrease below 0°C, there is a drastic rearrangement of the water molecules into a relatively static crystalline arrangement, so that even though there are large energies for hydrogen bonding, the static bondings between water molecules limit the availability of hydrogen for bondings with the proteins, and again protein structures are placed under stress of denaturation. Pauling (1944) has stated:

> Because of its small bond energy and the small activation energy involved in its formation and rupture, the hydrogen bond is especially suited to play a part in reactions occurring at normal temperatures. It has been recognized that hydrogen bonds restrain protein molecules to their native configurations, and I believe that as the methods of structural chemistry are further applied to physiological problems it will be found that the significance of the hydrogen bond for physiology is greater than that of any single structural feature.

A further property of water which is highly relevant to its function in plants is its lack of ready means of attraction or movement. The molecule is small, its electric charges are too small to permit easy movement electrically, and its ready resonance characteristics accentuate its slipperiness as an object to be moved. In contrast to the anions and cations taken up by plants, water can be readily moved only by osmotic and tension forces. Suggestions that there may be a metabolic uptake of water have been made at various times, but concrete evidence is available only for osmotic and tension forces moving water through plants.

Tension forces predominate in the movement of water along the transpiration stream, and such forces originate at the surface of the leaf cells at which evaporation occurs. The energy used to create this tension is derived from light and heat, so in the diurnal cycle of transpiration the rates represent something of a compromise between the diurnal-light curve and the air-temperature curve (Briggs and Shantz, 1916; Fig. 23-2). The tension created by transpirational water loss is transmitted down through the plant and is then reflected in a diurnal cycle of water uptake by the roots, as shown in Fig. 23-3 (Kramer, 1937). These data illustrate the conversion of heat energy into tension forces which then may be largely responsible for the flow of water up the plant.

Water uptake

Water will enter the plant in response to a gradient in free energy. If transpiration causes tension in the water column in the plant, an energy gradient for entry can be obtained, or if the osmotic concentration of cells is greater than the osmotic and other holding forces in the soil solution, water will enter the roots. In general it appears that osmotic forces for water entry are more dominant in the growth processes of cells, whereas the gross flow of water through the plant organism may be more dominated by tension forces. Figure 23-3 illustrates the fact that transpiration can create tension forces which will be followed then by the entry of water into roots (Kramer, 1937).

As the water content of the soil decreases, the forces holding the water to the soil increase exponentially, and with these increasing forces there is a decrease in the ability

of the plant to obtain water from the soil. For example, pea seeds placed in soil with various water contents can pull water out of the soil less and less effectively as the soil-withholding forces increase (Maximov, 1929; Fig. 23-4). In this case, the energy for water uptake is osmotic, there being no transpiration involvement.

The presence of salts in the soil solution creates a drag on the ability of the plant to take up water. Eaton (1941) illustrated

Fig. 23-1 | Representations of the structure of water. While spatially water would be tri-lobed in a Hirschfelder model (*a*), its electric charges make it more nearly tetrahedral (*b*) with two slight positive charges and two slight negative charges. Adjoining molecules form hydrogen bondings between these charges (*c*) to form loosely bonded lattices in the case of water (*d*) and firmer symmetrical lattices in the case of ice (*e*) (adapted from Crafts et al., 1949).

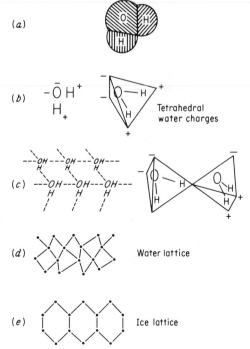

this by placing half of a root system in plain water and the other half in a nutrient solution. He showed that the plant takes up more water from the plain-water side than from the salt solution. In saline soils the relatively high osmotic values for the soil solution must have a considerable drag effect against the entry of water into roots.

There is scattered evidence that there may by an active or metabolically driven uptake of water by roots. It has been shown frequently that water uptake is inhibited by anaerobic conditions or by metabolic inhibitors (Kramer, 1949). The slight positive pressures of water movement up the plant in the form of root pressure and guttation are common evidences of the kind of water movement that has been attributed to metabolic influences. It must be remembered that there are real physical difficulties in the establishment of metabolic pumps for moving water. The disheartening energetic problems to be faced have been vividly described by Levitt (1954).

As water enters the roots of plants, it may sweep in with it large amounts of salts dissolved in the water. Experiments by Hylmo (1953) illustrate that the entry of calcium ions may be proportional to the amount of water transpired by the plant. In Fig. 23-5 some of his data are reproduced, showing the linear uptake of calcium ion with transpiration, the linearity holding for three different concentrations of the solute. If salts in the soil solution entered the plant unhindered, toxic amounts of salts could accumulate in the plant, and yet the amounts of salts accumulating in foliage are often less than would be expected on the basis of their abundance in soil solutions.

Apparently the root may screen the solutes out of the entering water (cf. Fig. 24-7). The existence of ion-specific uptake systems is well known, but the overall action of a salt-screening mechanism in the root has not been adequately explained.

After examining the kinetic properties of water and solute uptake by roots, Philip

Fig. 23-2 | The daily march of transpiration from alfalfa leaves follows the changes in light and air temperature. Each of the three functions is plotted as the per cent of daily maximum rise (Briggs and Shantz, 1916).

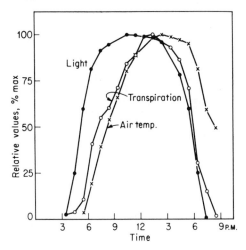

Fig. 23-3 | The daily march in transpiration is reflected in the daily rates of water uptake by the roots. These data are for ash trees and suggest that as water is lost by transpiration, the forces for its uptake are acquired (Kramer, 1937).

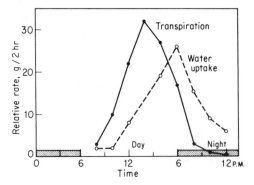

(1958*a*) suggested that under water-stress conditions, a vapor gap may form in the soil around the root surface and that in this manner water uptake would become a movement across a vapor phase, thus leaving behind all solutes during periods of sufficient water stress. The concept has been criticized by Bernstein et al. (1959) on the basis that even when plants are growing in water cultures where there can be no vapor stress on the external water supply, a screening of solutes still occurs. This interesting argument is still not resolved, and the limitations on solute entrance with the transpirational movement of water are obscure.

When a plant is under severe water stress, the cool leaves may encourage water condensation at night leading to the uptake of water by leaves from the atmosphere. Such uptake has been measured by Stone et al. (1950), and it may be extensive under desert conditions, where leaves achieve relatively low night temperatures at high internal osmotic pressures.

Water movement

The movement of water through the plant follows gradients in free energy, and these are generated chiefly by the forces of transpirational pull. Osmotic gradients may assist in water movement, especially through the cortical regions of the root cross section, but the movement from the cortex into the xylem will almost always be from a high to a low osmotic potential. Attempts to find an osmotic gradient up the entire plant have failed to account for water movement.

Considering the flow of water through tissues to be principally a product of tensions created by transpiration, some interesting questions have been raised concerning the kinetics of the flow. Philip (1958*b*) and Bonner (1959*a*) have compared the two possibilities that water may flow through cells with only the outer shell of tissue pro-

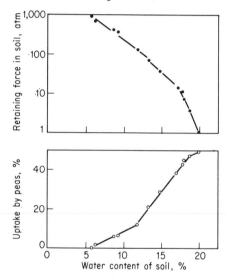

Fig. 23-4 | There is a readier uptake of water from the soil with higher water contents, associated with the decreasing force by which the water is retained by the soil (data of Shull, from Maximov, 1929, for pea seeds).

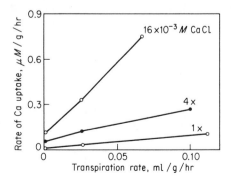

Fig. 23-5 | The uptake of water can be associated with the entry of some solutes. With increasing transpiration rates of pea plants, increasing amounts of calcium ions were taken into the plant. A linear relationship was found for each of three concentrations of $CaCl_2$ (data of Hylmo, 1953).

viding resistance to flow or, alternatively, that it flows as if through a uniformly resistant material (Fick's first and second laws of flow, respectively). Using the movement of deuterium-tagged water in oat coleoptiles to establish the pattern by which an equilibrium is reached between the outside and the inside (Fig. 23-6), Bonner (1959a) produced data which are consistent with the uniform resistance pattern. Thus we can conceive of water movement through nonvascular tissues as a movement through a sheet of resistance.

Once the water has moved into the vascular conducting tissues, however, the movement appears to be a compromise between the relatively free flow through the large xylem vessels and the movement through capillary regions. The dual nature of water movement in xylem has been demonstrated by Scholander et al. (1957) in some experiments with *Tetracera* stems. Stems of this liana were examined for the tension on the xylem sap column using a simple lateral punch manometer. As the stem was severed and the cut was placed in water, the tension in the sap above the cut fell to nearly zero (Fig. 23-7). If the dish of water was withdrawn and air was pulled into the xylem by transpiration, the tension soon rose abruptly; but when the stem was reintroduced into the water supply, tension declined again somewhat, and, surprisingly, the water flow proceeded at the same rate as it had before the introduction of the air bubbles into the xylem. These findings indicate that the water flow up the stem is not a simple flow through open tubes, for the introduction of air bubbles does not break the flow but merely installs a requirement for higher tension on the water column before flow can proceed at full speed.

In earlier theories of water movement, it was believed that transpiration created a negative force on the water column in the xylem and that the natural cohesion of the water column provided the properties necessary for the movement up the stem. This

Fig. 23-6 | The uptake of water by oat coleoptiles follows the kinetics for sheet flow (Fick's second law of water flow) in contrast to a boundary-limited flow. Using water labeled with deuterium, equilibrium between the inside and outside was actually reached in the pattern predicted by sheet flow (solid line) and not by boundary flow (dashed line). Points are experimental data of Ordin and Bonner, from Bonner, 1959a.

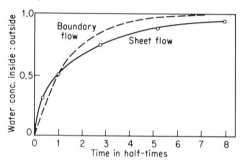

Fig. 23-7 | Changes in water flow and tension forces in the xylem of *Tetracera* stems. When air is introduced into the xylem of a cut stem, the xylem tension increases, but water flow can proceed unchanged if supplied at the stem base (Scholander et al., 1957).

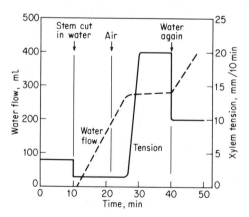

theory of Dixon (1924) was criticized on the basis that the great heights of some trees exceed the cohesion that a column of water can withstand and furthermore that the resistance of the xylem vessels to water flow provides even further strains on the water column (Huber, 1924). A more challenging line of evidence concerning the cohesion theory of water movement is the more recent finding of Scholander et al. (1955) that the water in the xylem of transpiring grape stems is always under a positive hydrostatic pressure. For example, Fig. 23-8 shows that during transpiration the water at the base of a stem 15 m high is under a slight positive pressure and that the pressure increases slightly up the stem. This slight negative gradient is consistent with the concept of transpirational pull providing a drawing force at the top of the plant, but the water pressure indicates that only limited amounts of tensions are achieved. In contrast, when transpiration is not occurring, there is a positive gradient of pressure down the stem, just as there would be in a vertical garden hose filled with water.

The relatively minor effects of air bubbles in disrupting flow in the xylem and the small tension forces on the transpiration stream reaffirm that the forces which move water up the plant are still not understood.

The actual rates of movement of water through the xylem were measured by Huber and Schmidt (1937) using a device which slightly warms the sap locally and then measures its movement by thermocouples placed symmetrically above and below the warmed location. Like transpiration, the rate of water movement up the xylem shows a diurnal periodicity (Fig. 23-9). In spruce trees the rates were about 120 cm/hr at midday, dropping to less than 10 cm/hr at night. While the transpirational pull due to water evaporation from the leaves virtually ceases during the night, there is some water flow up the plant while the increases in osmotic pressures of the stem and foliage

created by the water tension during the day are satisfied.

Transpiration

Measurements of transpiration of broad-leaved plants in sunlight indicate rates of as much as 5 g of water per dm² of leaf per hr. Usual rates range from 0.5 to 2.5 g/dm²/

Fig. 23-8 | The hydrostatic pressure of water in the xylem of grape stems about 15 m tall, showing the increasing gradient of pressure down the stem when transpiration is not occurring and the slight negative gradient under conditions of transpiration (Scholander et al., 1955).

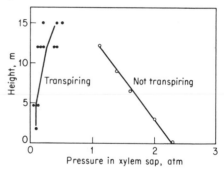

Fig. 23-9 | The rate of water movement up the stem of a spruce tree shows a strong diurnal periodicity, with high rates during the day when transpiration is rapid (Huber and Schmidt, 1937).

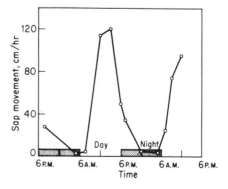

hr, and at night they drop to 0.1 or even less. Meyer and Anderson (1952) state that many herbaceous plants transpire an amount of water equal to several times their own volume in a single day. Calculations of the total amount of water transpired by a cornfield indicate that in a growing season there may be a volume of water transpired equivalent to a layer 15 in. deep (Transeau, 1926).

There are some interesting arguments among plant physiologists concerning the possible value to the plant of transpirational water loss. Its role in heat exchange by the leaf has been championed by some and denied by others (cf. Meyer and Anderson, 1952), but it clearly contributes to the temperature balance in sunlight, as has been shown by the calculations of Wolpert (1962) discussed in Chap. 22 (see Fig. 22-7). It seems doubtful that transpiration provides substantial benefits to the plant in terms of the flow of water per se, other than the uptake and translocation of nutrients. Winneberger (1958) reported that pear-tree seedlings placed in a saturated humidity showed reduced growth rates and concluded that transpiration may be necessary for optimal growth. However, such high humidities as were used in his experiments

may result in limitations of CO_2 entry through the stomata; other experiments have not shown any benefit from graded transpirational conditions (Wadsworth, 1960).

The porous nature of the leaf surface, necessary for the exchange of CO_2 and O_2 to and from the photosynthesizing tissues, makes possible a relatively rapid loss of water. It seems reasonable to consider transpiration a necessary corollary of the photosynthetic function of the green leaf. As the leaf receives light in the morning and rapid gas exchange occurs, there is a resultant lowered water content. Maximov (1929) described diurnal fluctuations in water content of leaves (Fig. 23-10); such fluctuations have also been described for the stems of woody plants, which may contract slightly during the daylight hours when transpirational water loss is occurring relatively rapidly (MacDougal et al., 1929).

Any environmental feature, such as wind, light, temperature, and relative humidity, which facilitates gas exchange by the leaf also facilitates transpiration. The strong effect of wind on transpiration was studied by Martin and Clements (1935) by comparing measurements of water loss by leaves in still air and in various wind velocities. Their data in Fig. 23-11 illustrate the large increases in transpiration obtained by small amounts of air movement. Wind velocities above about 1 or 2 mph yielded only small increases in transpiration under their conditions. The immediate effects of light on water loss by wheat leaves were measured by Virgin (1956) using a sensitive corona hygrometer device. After the leaves were exposed to relatively bright light, detectable increases in transpiration were measured in about 2 min, and after 10 or 15 min transpiration rates had become fairly steady at the new high level (see Fig. 23-17).

Factors which reduce the availability of water to the root system tend to depress transpiration. Some early data of Heinicke and Childers (1935; Fig. 23-12) show that as the soil under apple plants becomes in-

Fig. 23-10 | The water content of *Zygophyllum* leaves drops during the day, when transpiration is rapid, and rises again during the night, reflecting an apparent tension developing in the leaves during periods of transpiration (Maximov, 1929).

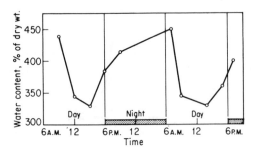

creasingly dry, a decline in transpiration becomes evident as the decline in photosynthesis sets in. The forces by which water is retained in soils increase exponentially with drying, and so under droughty conditions the transpirational pull becomes decreasingly effective in drawing water from the soil into the plant.

The rates of water loss are of course sensitive to structural characteristics of the leaf. Using successive measurements of the weight of severed leaves as they transpire on a balance, Hygen (1951) described three phases of water-loss rates: an initial rapid phase when stomata are open, a shifting phase during stomatal closure, and a steady slow phase after stomata are closed. These three phases are shown in Fig. 23-13, which compares the water-loss curves for blueberry leaves taken from moist and from more xerophytic conditions. The rates are plotted on a log scale, and the xerophytic leaf shows a more rapid stomatal-closure period and a slower water-loss rate in phase 3. Hygen uses these three water-loss rates as indices of xerophytic adaptation.

Williams and Amer (1957) have carried out similar experiments with *Pelargonium* leaves and assert that Hygen's phase 1 of water loss is not linear on a log scale. They believe that the entire curve of water-loss rates is a consequence of the relative water content of the leaf; as the leaf dries out, the accessibility of its water to evaporation surfaces is progressively depressed. Another point of view has been expressed by Milthorpe and Spencer (1957), who assert that the concept of water content as a control of water-loss rate does not adequately emphasize the role of stomatal aperture as a regulator in the leaf. Through measurements of the relative ease by which air can be drawn through the leaf surface, they measured the relative degree of stomatal opening. With wheat leaves they obtained a direct relation of the transpirational rate to the log of the air-flow resistance (degree of stomatal closure).

In some dynamic experiments with water-loss rates, Milthorpe and Spencer (1957) observed that as a leaf is deprived of water, its water content falls first. This is followed by a period of stomatal closure and an associated reduction in transpiration (Fig. 23-14). When water is restored to the leaf, the water content is the first variable to respond, and stomatal-closure and transpira-

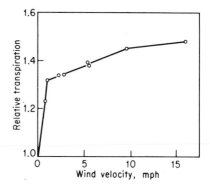

Fig. 23-11 | The increases in transpiration caused by wind are most pronounced at low wind velocities over sunflower leaves (Martin and Clements, 1935).

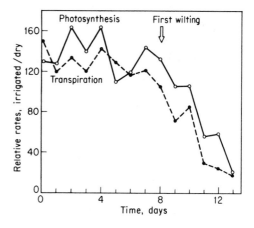

Fig. 23-12 | Permitting the soil under apple seedlings to dry out leads to declining rates of transpiration and declining photosynthetic activity, especially evident as wilting sets in (Heinicke and Childers, 1935).

tion rates remain restricted until some time later, when the transpiration rate again rises toward its initial values. These experiments emphasize the dominant role of the stomata in the control of the rates of water loss from leaves.

Stomatal movements

The efficiency of the minute stomatal apertures on the leaf surface in permitting gas exchange and consequent water loss from the leaf was studied by Brown and Escombe (1905) and by Sayre (1926). They found that the rate of gaseous exchange through pores was more nearly a function of the pore perimeter than of the pore cross-sectional area. Thus many small pores are markedly more efficient as gas exchangers

Fig. 23-13 | The water loss of severed blueberry leaves plotted as changes of leaf weight on a log scale. Three phases of water loss may be distinguished: an initial rapid phase, a changing phase, and a slower phase. The upper curve is for a leaf from a more xerophytic site and illustrates the slower rates obtained especially during phase III (Hygen, 1951).

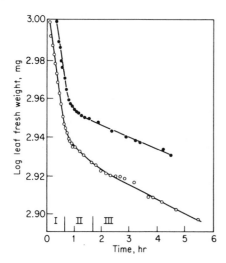

than larger pores of the same total area. Knowing the importance of pore perimeter in the passage of gases, we would expect that the extent of stomatal opening would be most limiting when closure was fairly advanced and that the more open positions of stomata would have relatively fewer effects on gas passage. Stålfelt (1932; Fig. 23-15) measured the sizes of the stomatal apertures in birch leaves and related these values to the transpiration rate under different degrees of relative humidity, finding that transpiration was most limited by the least degree of stomatal, aperture. When evaporative conditions were greater, there was a more pronounced continued increase in transpiration as the stomata opened wider, but under low evaporative conditions only the initial stages of opening were much reflected in increased transpiration rates.

The physiological mechanisms which control the opening and closing of stomata are not clearly understood. It is evident that the movements are hydraulic events operated by the elastic properties of the guard-cell walls and the degree of their turgidity. The entry of water into the guard cells inflates them and bows them in such a way as to open the stoma (Fig. 23-16). If the guard cell loses water, closure will result. The hydraulic changes may be triggered by light or by water relations of the leaf.

Von Mohl (1856) realized that light could cause stomatal opening, and he ascribed the control to photosynthesis-induced changes in the osmotic values of the cell sap. He reasoned that photosynthesis would lead to the formation of osmotically active sugars and thus turgor would be increased and the stoma would open. Modern data demonstrating the effectiveness of light in opening the stomata are shown in Fig. 23-17 (Virgin, 1957), from which it can be seen that, in contrast to normal green leaves, those with little chlorophyll respond only weakly to light and that chlorophyll-free leaves may not respond at all. Von Mohl (1856) was also correct in believing that the sap OP rose as light brought about the opening of the stoma. Such a correlation is shown from more recent experiments by Stålfelt (1955; Fig. 23-18). However, when a leaf is under water stress the stomata generally close during midday even though light is then most intense (Fig. 23-18); this is associated with a drop in the OP of the guard cells. The beneficial effect that such a midday closure of the stomata may have on the water relations of the leaf is also evident from the data of Fig. 23-18, the water deficit markedly improving in the 2 hr following midday stomatal closures.

The light control of stomatal opening yields, then, to some other osmotic regulator under droughty conditions. Water shortage may cause stomatal closure by loss of turgor of the guard cells or of neighboring cells in the epidermis. The osmoregulator system is complex, and many theories have been suggested to account for it, including changes in the pH as they may alter the carbohydrate interconversions, changes in permeability of the guard-cell wall (pH or CO_2 effects?), and changes in colloidal swelling and organic-acid metabolism (cf. Heath, 1959). Even the light effect is complex and may be partly photosynthetic, partly a consequence of changes in CO_2 partial pressures in the cell, and partly quite separate from either function (Heath and Russell, 1954). Williams (1954) has made the remarkable suggestion that the natural position of stomata may be the open one and that the active mechanisms controlling their movements may be mechanisms for closure. He cites the similarities of stomatal behavior to other hydraulic functions which show diurnal periodicity, such as leaf movements, and suggests that an active excretion of water through contractile vacuoles may cause closure of the stomata.

The evidence of Walker and Zelitch (1963) modifies Williams's suggestion, since both opening and closure of stomata were found to be sensitive to metabolic inhibitors. In their plants, stomata inhibited with azide

Fig. 23-14 | A dynamic picture of transpiration rates as a *Pelargonium* leaf is deprived of water (*A*) and then is restored to a water supply again (*B*). As the water content declines, stomatal closure finally retards transpiration, and stomatal opening reinstates transpiration after the water content has recovered (Milthorpe and Spencer, 1957).

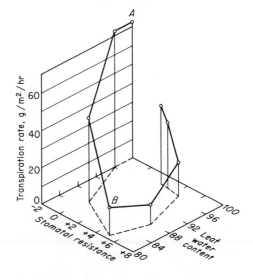

Fig. 23-15 | Transpiration rate as related to visually measured stomatal opening under four different conditions of free water evaporation (as milligrams per hour per 25 cm²). Leaves of *Betula pubescens*. Note the large effect of the initial stages of stomatal opening (Stålfelt, 1932).

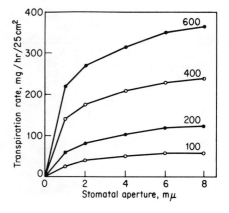

assumed a position about half open. Anaerobic conditions preferentially inhibited opening movements. It appears, then, that both types of stomatal movement are metabolic, but their differences in response to anaerobiosis imply that the two movements may be regulated by somewhat different metabolic functions.

Wilting

As the cells of the leaf lose their turgor and begin to wilt, it may reasonably be expected

Fig. 23-16 | An open stoma of *Cyclamen persica* (above) and the same stoma after the lower guard cell has lost its turgor by puncture with a needle (below) (Heath, 1959).

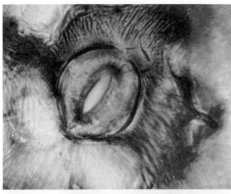

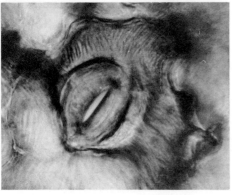

that stomatal closure and physical disruption of the leaf cells will lead to inhibitions of photosynthesis. The data of Heinicke and Childers (1935; Fig. 23-12) indicate that as wilting sets in, photosynthetic activity declines. Some dynamic experiments on this relation have been done with sugarcane leaves by Ashton (1956), who permitted plants to reach the wilting point and then followed the photosynthetic activity during the day. Photosynthesis rose in the morning but then fell off during midday and in late afternoon, each falloff being associated with an evident wilting of the leaves. The slight recovery of photosynthesis at midday is apparently a consequence of the midday closure of the stomata and the associated recovery of the leaf turgor. That wilting can lead to a protracted period of depressed photosynthesis is demonstrated by Ashton's (1956) data in Fig. 23-19, which show that even after water supply is restored, sugarcane leaves require several days for recovery of full photosynthetic activity. Schneider and Childers (1941) observed that photosynthetic recovery from wilting sometimes required a week.

Growth inhibitions are induced by wilting. Data for the growth of tomato leaves in Fig. 23-20 (Gates, 1955a) demonstrate that the degree of inhibition is approximately related to the degree of wilting obtained and that the growth inhibition may persist for several days after the wilting experience. Magness et al. (1933) previously observed that in mature leaves wilting is associated with a depletion of the carbohydrate reserves by translocation out of the leaf, and if wilting is severe enough, leaf senescence follows even though water supply is later restored. Gates and Bonner (1959) later suggested that the inhibition of growth following wilting may be related to an enhancement of RNA destruction in the young leaves by the wilting experience. Surprisingly, wilting preferentially hits the older tissues instead of the young, expanding tissues. Miller (1938) noted that the oldest leaves were the first to wilt with drought. Wilson (1948) observed that tomato plants which develop a water shortage during the day show an actual shrinkage in the size of the older parts of the stem, while the young, expanding parts continue to grow unabated. Kerr and Anderson (1944) observed that growth of cotton fruits continues under water stress, though the older leaves are inhibited. How the growing parts of plants can have first claim on the plant water supply is unknown, but it is clear that drought damage is preferentially felt by the older tissues and leaves. Mothes (1928) analyzed the processes associated with the senescence of the older leaves following wilting and deduced that their deterioration was due not only to the water removal but also to a decline in protein content which we may now consider to be possibly related to the RNA decline observed by Gates and Bonner (1959).

Adaptation to water deficiency

The increasing water shortage inside the plant will first result in a tendency toward closure of the stomata through the altered turgor of the guard and epidermal cells. This will be followed by a depression of photosynthesis, sometimes an altered respiration rate, and finally a wilting of the leaf. If the water deficit becomes sufficiently severe, most plants will be destroyed. Since the experience of water deficiency is so common, it is not surprising that some plants have evolved means of adapting to this limitation. Such adaptations may be classified into three rough categories: (1) adaptation by acquired hardiness, (2) adaptation by morphological xerophytism, and (3) adaptation by tolerance to dehydration. The first two classes minimize the loss of water, and the third simply adapts to the loss.

Hardiness. Hardiness was discovered by Tumanov (1927), who found that exposure of grain seedlings or sunflower seedlings to a water shortage would result in their better

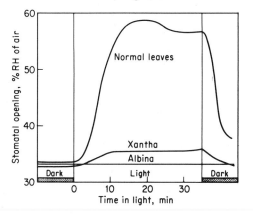

Fig. 23-17 | The effectiveness of light in causing the stomatal opening of barley leaves. Normal green leaves are compared with xantha leaves containing very little chlorophyll and albina leaves with no chlorophyll. Stomatal opening was measured by determining the relative humidity immediately above the leaf surface (Virgin, 1957).

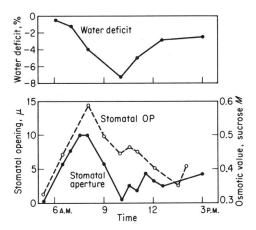

Fig. 23-18 | When *Rumex acetosa* leaves were under water stress, the stomata opened in the morning with the advent of light but then closed again in midmorning as the osmotic pressure of the guard-cell sap declined. Note the recovery of the leaf water content at noon with the stomatal closure (Stålfelt, 1955).

sustaining subsequent drought. He observed that there were varietal differences in the ability of wheat, for example, to adapt to drought resistance. The species which do show this adaptability are mostly mesophytic plants, including some grains and such broad-leaved plants as cabbage and soybean.

Clements (1937) examined the changes induced in the leaves of hardy species and found that there were changes in the hemi-

Fig. 23-19 | Following a single brief wilting experience, leaves of sugarcane only gradually recovered full photosynthetic activity in the subsequent several days with daily irrigation (Ashton, 1956).

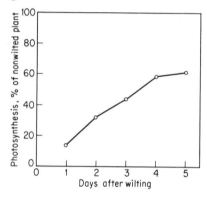

Fig. 23-20 | Following a single brief wilting experience, tomato plants showed an inhibition of growth of the young, expanding leaf for a few days before full growth rate was restored (Gates, 1955a).

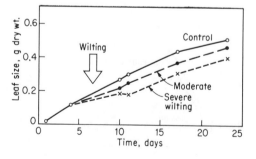

cellulose contents to which he then ascribed the resistance. If the plant developed constituents which served to retain the water, they might thus become drought-resistant.

In contrast to this kind of cytological level of adaptation, Clark and Levitt (1956) produced evidence that drought hardiness may be a feature of the epidermis of the leaf. They hardened soybean leaves and compared their rates of water loss after excision with the water loss of unhardened leaves. Their data (Fig. 23-21) show that the leaves experienced slower water loss after hardening but that if they were sliced up, thus minimizing the influences of the epidermis, there was no longer a slower water loss. They therefore denied the concept of hardening as a cytological change and suggested instead that it is due to the accumulation of waxes in the cuticle associated with the drought experience.

Xerophytism. Xerophytism, or the morphological adaptation of plants to dry conditions, is most commonly evidenced as a reduction in leaf area—or a decrease in surface per unit plant volume. This is in fact a type of succulence and is most readily illustrated by the cactus species. Xerophytic plants are morphologically adapted to avoid dehydration by reducing the water loss per unit of leaf volume, and some may develop water-storage tissues inside the leaf or stem. Maximov (1929) found that the morphological xerophytes transpired at about the same rates per unit surface as mesophytes when water was readily available. Some adaptations may limit water exchange only when water availability is poor. They may also subsidize the plant by an internal photosynthetic utilization of respiratory CO_2, in this way permitting some assimilatory activity when gas exchange is limited.

Dehydration. Dehydration is most commonly observed in seeds. Even in moist, fleshy fruits the seeds have a strikingly low water content. McIlrath et al. (1963) followed the loss of water from tomato seeds during the ripening of fruits and found that the seeds actively lose about 50 per cent of their free water during fruit ripening. This represents a net loss of water and not merely a gain in dry weight. Even seeds placed in distilled water became dehydrated to a similar extent.

Tolerance to dehydration is found in seeds and resting parts of some higher plants. Among the lower plants it is not infrequent even in the vegetative plant parts; for example, lichen, mosses, and some ferns can tolerate extensive dehydration. In seeds and resting parts, the resistance to dehydration appears to involve a binding of the cytoplasm associated with a nearly suspended respiratory activity. In vegetative plant parts, morphological devices permit the folding of the cell walls around the cytoplasm during the drying process, avoiding the tearing of the cell structure or excessive cytoplasmic abrasion while the water shortage develops. Renewed supplies of water permit the germination of seeds (except in cases of dormancy) and the swelling of the vegetative structures into functional forms. The wall-folding apparatus was described many years ago (e.g., Steinbrink, 1903), but the physiological explanation of how the cytoplasmic contents of seeds and dehydrated plants can withstand such extreme desiccation is still lacking.

The flow of water through plants has evolved as a necessary part of their adaptation to terrestrial habitats. As multicellular plants extend their leaves into the air, transpirational flow necessarily occurs, sometimes over long vertical distances and by physiological means which are not understood. Many adaptations have been developed which may help to regulate the transpirational loss or help the plant cope with the resulting deficiency. The xerophytic adaptation to drying of the cytoplasm is one of the common adaptations occurring in nearly all seeds and buds and is a basic component of most states of dormancy.

GENERAL REFERENCES

Crafts, A. S., H. B. Currier, and C. R. Stocking. 1949. *Water in the Physiology of Plants*. Chronica Botanica Co., Waltham, Mass. 240 pp.

Dainty, J. 1963. Water relations of plant cells.. *Advan. Botan. Res.*, 1:279–326.

Kozlowski, T. T. 1964. *Water Metabolism in Plants*. Harper & Row, Publishers, Incorporated, New York. 227 pp.

Kramer, P. J. 1949. *Plant and Soil Water Relationships*. McGraw-Hill Book Company, New York. 347 pp.

Rutter, A. J., and F. H. Whitehead (eds). 1963. *The Water Relations of Plants*. Blackwell Scientific Publications, Ltd., Oxford. 394 pp.

REFERENCES CITED

Ashton, F. M. 1956. Effects of a series of cycles of low and high soil water on the rate of apparent photosynthesis in sugar cane. *Plant Physiol.*, 31:266–274.

Bernstein, L., W. R. Gardner, and L. A.

Fig. 23-21 | Drought hardening of soybean plants resulted in a reduced rate of water loss when whole leaves were measured (above) but did not result in reduced rates when the leaves were sliced into 3 mm strips (Clark and Levitt, 1956).

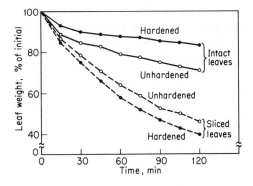

Richards. 1959. Is there a vapor gap around plant roots? *Science,* 129:1750.

Bonner, J. 1959a. Water transport. *Science,* 129:447–450.

———. 1959b. Is there a vapor gap around plant roots? *Science,* 129:1750–1753.

Briggs, L. J., and H. L. Shantz. 1916. Hourly transpiration rate on clear days as determined by cyclic environmental factors. *J. Agr. Res.,* 5:583–649.

Brown, H. T., and F. Escombe. 1905. Researches on some physiological processes of green leaves with special reference to the interchange of energy between the leaf and its surroundings. *Proc. Roy. Soc. (London),* B,76:29–112.

Clark, J. A., and J. Levitt. 1956. The basis of drought resistance in the soybean plant. *Physiol. Plantarum,* 9:598–606.

Clements, F. E. 1937. Studies in drought resistance of the soybean. *Res. Studies State Univ. Wash.,* 5:1–16 (cited by Kramer, 1949).

Dixon, H. H. 1924. *The Transpiration Stream.* University of London Press, Ltd., London.

Eaton, F. M. 1941. Water uptake and root growth as influenced by inequalities in the concentration of the substrate. *Plant Physiol.,* 14:545–564.

Gates, C. T. 1955a. The response of the young tomato plant to a brief period of water shortage. I. The whole plant and its principal parts. *Australian J. Biol. Sci.,* 8:196–214.

———. 1955b. The response of the young tomato plant to a brief period of water shortage. II. The individual leaves. *Australian J. Biol. Sci.,* 8:215–230.

——— and J. Bonner. 1959. The response of the young tomato plant to a brief period of water shortage. IV. Effects of water stress on the ribonucleic acid metabolism of tomato leaves. *Plant Physiol.,* 34:49–55.

Heath, O. V. S. 1959. Light and carbon dioxide in stomatal movements. *Handbuch Pflanzenphys.,* 17:415–464.

——— and J. Russell. 1954. Studies of sto-

matal behaviour. VI. An investigation of the light responses of wheat stomata with the attempted elimination of control by the mesophyll. I. *J. Exptl. Botany,* 5:1–15.

Heinicke, A. J., and N. F. Childers. 1935. The influence of water deficiency in photosynthesis and transpiration of apple leaves. *Proc. Am. Soc. Hort. Sci.,* 33:155–159.

Huber, B. 1924. Die Stromungsgeschwindigkeit und die Grosse der Widerstande in den Leitbahnen. *Ber. Deut. Botan. Ges.,* 42:27–32.

——— and E. Schmidt. 1937. Eine Kompensationsmethode zur Themoelektrischen Messung langsames Saftströme. *Ber. Deut. Botan. Ges.,* 55:514–529.

Hygen, G. 1951. Studies in plant transpiration. I. *Physiol. Plantarum,* 4:57–183.

Hylmo, B. 1953. Transpiration and ion absorption. *Physiol. Plantarum,* 6:333–405.

Kerr, T., and D. B. Anderson. 1944. Osmotic quantities in growing cotton balls. *Plant Physiol.,* 19:338–348.

Kramer, P. J. 1937. The relation between rate of transpiration and rate of absorption of water in plants. *Am. J. Botany,* 24:10–15.

———. 1949. *Plant and Soil Water Relationships.* McGraw-Hill Book Company, New York. 347 pp.

Levitt, J. 1954. Steady state versus equilibrium thermodynamics in the concept of "active" water absorption. *Physiol. Plantarum,* 7:592–594.

MacDougal, D. T., J. B. Overton, and G. M. Smith. 1929. The hydrostatic-pneumatic system of certain trees: movements of liquids and gases. *Carnegie Inst. Wash. Publ.,* 397.

McIlrath, W. J., Y. P. Abrol, and F. Heiligman. 1963. Dehydration of seeds in intact tomato fruits. *Science,* 142:1681–1682.

Magness, J. R., L. O. Regeimbal, and E. S. Degman. 1933. Accumulation of carbohydrates in apple foliage as influenced by moisture supply. *Proc. Am. Soc. Hort. Sci.,* 29:246–252.

Martin, E. V., and F. E. Clements. 1935. Studies of the effect of artificial wind on growth and transpiration in *Helianthus annuus*. *Plant Physiol.*, 10:613–636.

Maximov, N. A. 1929. *The Plant in Relation to Water* (tr. by R. H. Yapp). The Macmillan Company, New York. 451 pp.

Meyer, B. S., and D. B. Anderson. 1952. *Plant Physiology.* D. Van Nostrand Company, Inc., Princeton, N.J. 784 pp.

Miller, E. C. 1938. *Plant Physiology.* McGraw-Hill Book Co., New York, 1201 pp.

Milthorpe, F. L., and E. J. Spencer. 1957. Experimental studies of the factors controlling transpiration. III. The interrelations between transpiration rate, stomatal movement, and leaf-water content. *J. Exptl. Botany*, 8:413–437.

Mohl, H. von. 1856. Welche Ursachen bewirken die Erweiterung und Verengung der Spaltöffnung? *Botan. Z.*, 14:697–704 (cited by Heath, 1959).

Pauling, L. 1944. *The Nature of the Chemical Bond.* Cornell University Press, Ithaca, N.Y.

Philip, J. R. 1958*a*. The osmotic cell, solute diffusibility and the plant water economy. *Plant Physiol.*, 33:264–271.

———. 1958*b*. Propagation of turgor and other properties through cell aggregations. *Plant Physiol.*, 33:271–274.

Sayre, J. D. 1926. Physiology of stomata of *Rumex patienta*. *Ohio J. Sci.*, 26:233–266.

Schneider, G. W., and N. F. Childers. 1941. Influence of soil moisture of photosynthesis, respiration and transpiration of apple leaves. *Plant Physiol.*, 16:565–583.

Scholander, P. F., B. Ruud, and H. Leivestad. 1957. The rise of sap in a tropical liana. *Plant Physiol.*, 32:1–6.

———, W. E. Love, and J. W. Kanwisher. 1955. The rise of sap in tall grapevines. *Plant Physiol.*, 30:93–104.

Stålfelt, M. G. 1932. Der stomataic Regulator in der pflanzlichen Transpiration. *Planta*, 17:22–85.

———. 1955. The stomata as hydrophobic regulators of the water deficit of the plant. *Physiol. Plantarum*, 8:572–593.

Steinbrink, C. 1903. Versuche über die Luftdurchlassigkeit der Zellwande von Farn— und *Selaginella*—Sporangien sowie von Moosblättern. *Flora (Jena)*, 92:102–131.

Stone, E. C., F. W. Went, and C. L. Young. 1950. Water absorption from the atmosphere by plants growing in dry soil. *Science*, 111:546.

Transeau, E. N. 1926. The accumulation of energy by plants. *Ohio J. Sci.*, 26:1–10 (cited by Meyer and Anderson, 1952).

Tumanov, J. J. 1927. Ungenugende Wasserversorgung und das Welken der Pflanzen als Mittel zur Erhohung ihrer Durresistanz. *Planta*, 3:391–480 (cited by Maximov, 1929).

Virgin, H. I. 1956. Light induced stomatal movements in wheat leaves recorded as transpiration. *Physiol. Plantarum*, 7:280–303.

———. 1957. Stomatal transpiration of some variegated plants and of chlorophyll deficient mutants of barley. *Physiol. Plantarum*, 10:170–186.

Wadsworth, R. 1960. The effect of artificial wind on the growth-rate of plants in water culture. *Ann. Botany (London)*, 24:200–211.

Walker, D. A., and I. Zelitch. 1963. Some effects of metabolic inhibitors, temperature, and anaerobic conditions on stomatal movement. *Plant Physiol.*, 38:390–396.

Williams, W. T. 1954. A new theory of the mechanism of stomatal movement. *J. Exptl. Botany*, 5:343–352.

——— and F. A. Amer. 1957. Transpiration from wilting leaves. *J. Exptl. Botany*, 8:1–19.

Wilson, C. C. 1948. Diurnal fluctuations of growth in length of tomato stem. *Plant Physiol*, 23:156–157.

Winneberger, J. H. 1958. Transpiration as a requirement for growth of land plants. *Physiol. Plantarum*, 11:56–61.

Part V | CHEMICAL MODIFICATIONS OF PLANTS

24 | Applications of chemicals to plants

The facility with which chemicals can modify plant growth and development indicates a relatively easy entry of applied materials into the cells of the organism.

The ability of applied chemicals to enter the leaves of plants depends on their penetration of the cuticle which encloses the leaf and the membrane which encloses each cell. Many chemical materials can pass through these layers, particularly inorganic materials, sugars, organic acids, and various smaller aromatic organic substances. The permeability of plant cells offers a generous range of possibilities for the chemical modification of plant growth. All the endogenous regulators of growth and development are within the range of substances which can readily pass through cell membranes.

Applications of chemicals to plants are of great use not only agriculturally, as modifiers of nutrition or as regulators of growth, but in the experimental sense of offering a wide range of possibilities for exploring physiological phenomena inside the plant.

Entry of chemicals

The ready entry of water and chemicals into plants may be a carryover from primitive conditions; plant cells may have never entirely lost their abilities for heterotrophic existence. The maintenance of a ready access of materials through cell walls may be related to the fact that the nutrient-translocation systems and the regulatory systems which direct differential functions both depend upon the movement of solutes from cell to cell.

Absorption by roots is less selective than that by leaves, associated with the gross entry of water and solutes through the roots to nourish the plant. To enter the leaf, substances must pass through either a stoma or epidermal cuticle; to enter a root, they need pass through only a mucilaginous cell wall without a cuticle.

Leaf absorption. A pioneer work on the

entry of chemicals into leaves was done by Aslander (1927) in connection with the development of sulfuric acid as an herbicide. Using surprisingly modern types of analysis, he found that the herbicide enters chiefly through the stomata, since the first cellular damage was localized in the mesophyll cells adjoining the stomata. He noted that entry was rapid and was not averted by an artificial rain even 1 hr after application. Elevated temperatures increased the herbicide effectiveness, and dry conditions lowered the effectiveness. The species selectivity of the herbicide could be accounted for on the basis of selective entry.

The time patterns of entry of chemicals into leaves may be diverse, as illustrated in Fig. 24-1 (Rice, 1948), ranging from rapid

Fig. 24-1 | The time course of absorption of 2,4-D into bean leaves. Elution of unabsorbed 2,4-D was measured after applications of 67 μg to a primary leaf. Carbowax (0.5 per cent) extended the absorption time from below 10 to over 72 hr, and elevated temperatures increased the absorption rates (Rice, 1948).

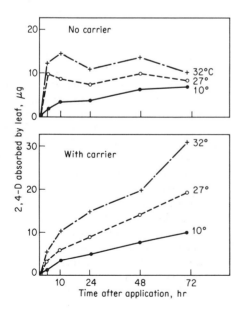

but brief uptake for 2,4-D at 32°C to prolonged but slow uptake at lower temperatures. The abilities of a carrier or wetting agent to extend the uptake period and of temperature to modify the rate will be discussed below.

A concentration curve for entry is illustrated in Fig. 24-2 (Pramer, 1956). In this case there is a concentration range over which entry is approximately linear, and at higher concentrations this linearity is lost, presumably because the sites at which entry can readily occur become limiting.

The first and major barrier to uptake is the cuticle (Fig. 24-3). This varnishlike skin of polymerized fatty acids, esters, and soaps is apparently formed by an oxidative drying process on the exposed cell-wall surfaces. Its acidic nature and associated ionic capacity to take up water give it a spongelike quality which allows expansion or contraction as water becomes more or less available. Cuticles tend to increase in thickness with leaf age (Fig. 24-4) and with higher light intensities, and they form more extensively on the upper leaf surface than on the lower. Cuticles form not only on the surfaces of epidermal cells but to a lesser extent on the surfaces of mesophyll and palisade cells inside the leaf where exposed to air spaces (Scott, 1950).

Permeating the cuticle and some parts of the cell wall are cuticular waxes which are composed principally of fatty alcohols and esters. These exist as solids at ordinary temperatures and show decreasing solubilities with increasing chain length in the range of 24 to 36 carbons. They are formed in the cytoplasm (Chibnall and Piper, 1934) and accumulate as plates in the outer layers of the epidermal wall, from which they are often extruded in large amounts. The "blooms" on cabbage leaves, grapes, and apple fruits are common examples of extruded waxes, and in some leaves they are prolific enough to yield commercial sources of waxes, for example, carnauba and candelilla waxes. The penetrability of aqueous sprays through the cuticle is determined principally by the waxes, where they exist. Using a clever retting technique, Skoss (1955) isolated the cuticles from leaves of numerous species and found them almost impermeable to water because of the impregnated waxes; with increasing leaf age there was an increasing content of waxes (Fig. 24-4). The extruded wax on the surface of the cuticle may have various novel forms (Fig. 24-5), including granules, rods, and nets (Mueller et al., 1954; Schieferstein and Loomis, 1956, 1959), and these irregular particles lower the wettability of the leaf by a water droplet, sometimes holding the droplet out of contact with the cuticle.

Inside the cuticle is the cell wall, usually composed of an outer pectin layer and an inner secondary wall layer of cellulose fibers imbedded in pectin and other noncellulosic polysaccharides. The wall is quite permeable to water unless the frequency of wax plates in it is too high. The greater frequency of waxes in the outer layer may result in a gradient of increasing polarity from the cuticle to the inside of the cell wall (van Overbeek, 1956a).

The last barrier which an applied chemical must pass is the protoplasmic membrane. Like the other principal membranes of the plant cell, this is composed of a fatty layer (which principally determines the permeability) between two layers of protein. Passage can occur as diffusion through pores in the fatty layer, by solubilization into the fatty layer, or by attachment to carrier sites within the membrane. Therefore entry through the membrane can be influenced by the size, shape, or charge of a molecule; its solubility in the fatty membrane layer; and by any molecular features which would alter its ability to become attached to carrier sites in the membrane.

Electron micrographs of cell walls have indicated that like the plasmodesmata, which provide connecting channels between adjoining cells, tiny channels of protoplasm, or ectodesmata, may permeate the walls of epi-

dermal cells (Lambertz, 1954; Franke, 1961). These tiny pores may serve as convenient channels for permeation of epidermal cell walls by aqueous materials, though the possibility remains that they may be artifacts in the photographic preparations.

In view of the structures of the cell wall, penetration through the wall by chemicals

Fig. 24-2 | The absorption of streptomycin by *Nitella* cells increased linearly with concentration for a limited range and less rapidly at higher concentrations. Solutions buffered at pH 6, uptake for 30 min (Pramer, 1956).

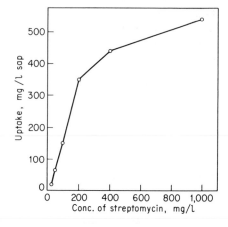

Fig. 24-3 | Components of an epidermal cell wall, showing extruded wax overlying a cuticle, then cell-wall layers of pectin and of pectin plus cellulose with some wax plates included. Inside the cell wall is the protoplasmic membrane enclosing the protoplasm (modified from Schieferstein and Loomis, 1959).

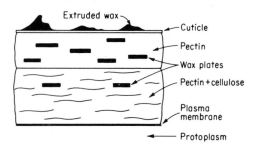

and solvents can apparently be via three pathways: hydrophilic materials can enter through the aqueous phases from the acidic components of the cutin to the pectins and the water-permeable protoplasmic membrane; lipophilic substances can enter through the fatty components (waxes, cutins, and the lipoidal layer of the membrane); and chemicals with both hydrophilic and lipophilic end groups can enter along the interphases between the two types of wall components. This latter feature may be illustrated by the auxins, with their lipophilic ring and hydrophilic-acid chain. Drying of the epidermis can greatly retard entry of the materials with hydrophilic tendencies because of the shrinking of the aqueous phases of the wall and the decreasing wettability of the cuticle surface. There is actually a diurnal cycle of wettability; it is greater at night and lesser with the drying actions of the day (Fogg, 1947).

Stomata can provide a means of entry to some sprays and not to others. In the early days of auxin herbicides, it was found that 2,4-D salts were equally effective when applied to leaf surfaces with or without open stomata. These pores in the cuticle were

not considered important pathways of entry (Weaver and DeRose, 1946; Thimann, 1948). Aslander (1927) established that sulfuric acid entered preferentially through stomata, and calculations of the relations between stomatal-aperture sizes and movement of volatiles led to the deduction that volatile materials should be able to enter stomata from a spray solution (Turrell, 1947). The accuracy of these deductions was slow to be confirmed, but it is now clear that the stomata are major pathways of entry of lipophilic dyes, auxin esters, and volatile oil herbicides (Minshall and Helson, 1949; Currier and Dybing, 1959; van Overbeek and Blondeau, 1954). Figure 24-6 shows a comparison of the extent of rapid entry of a fluorescent dye when stomata are open and closed (Dybing and Currier, 1961).

Root absorption. There are much less effective barriers against the entry of water-soluble chemicals into roots than into leaves. The roots do show some selectivity for the absorption of chemicals, but the selectivity is sufficiently weak that it is usually of no concern to people involved with soil applications of herbicides (Woodford, 1958). A clear-cut restraint of the entry of chemicals by the roots was established by Pramer (1954), who recorded great increases in the uptake of antibiotics by bean and tomato plants when the roots were removed and the stems placed directly in the antibiotic solutions. One of the most dramatic illustrations of restraints on root entry is the herbicide EPTC (ethyl N,N-di-*n*-propylthiolcarbamate), which can enter the leaf of *Echinochloa* but can not apparently enter through the root (Dawson, 1963).

The entry of chemicals through roots is frequently tied to the transpiration rate (cf. Fig. 5–8). This correlation is illustrated for the uptake of three antibiotics in Fig. 24-7 (Crowdy and Rudd-Jones, 1956). The fact that some of the chemicals enter more readily than others per unit of water transpired suggests a selectivity of uptake by the root. Some large molecules may enter in this

Fig. 24-4 | The weight of cuticle and its two components, cutin and waxes, increases with leaf age. Weights of samples retted from leaves of *Hedera helix* at various nodes from the tip down (Skoss, 1955).

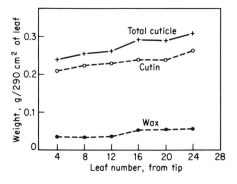

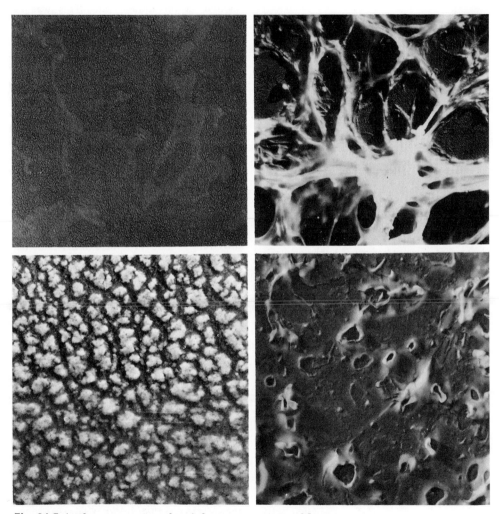

Fig. 24-5 | Electron micrographs of the wax extrusions of leaves
(× 12,000). *Asplenium* almost lacking wax, *Picea* showing nets of wax,
Peperomia showing rods, and *Nicotiana* with heavy plates of wax (Mueller
et al., 1954).

Fig. 24-6 | The entry of the dye fluorochrome
into leaves of *Pyrus communis* as related to
the concentration of a surfactant (Vatsol OT)
and the state of opening of the stomata. Entry
of 0.17 per cent fluorochrome for 6 min
before washing and measuring entry by
fluorescence in ultraviolet light (Dybing and
Currier, 1961).

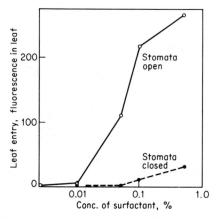

Fig. 24-7 | The uptake of three sulfa drugs
through the roots of bean plants, showing
the relation between the amount taken up and
the amount of water transpired by the plants.
Although all three chemicals were supplied at
equal concentrations (100 mg/liter) and for
the same period (13 days), the amounts
extractable from the plants per unit transpiration were quite dissimilar for the three
(Crowdy and Rudd-Jones, 1956).

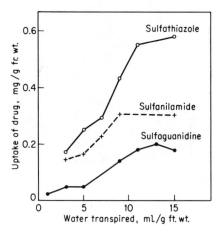

manner; the antibiotic griseofulvin, with a
molecular weight of over 350, has been followed through the plant after root entry
without any apparent structural change
(Crowdy and Pramer, 1955b).

Entry rates. When plant cells are immersed in solutions containing inorganic or
organic materials, one can perceive two
stages in the kinetics of entry: an initial rapid
entry for about 20 min, followed by a steady
though slower uptake rate. This was described for the entry of inorganic ions into
roots by Epstein and Leggett (1954), as
illustrated in Fig. 24-8. They interpreted the
first rapid uptake as an adsorption event, for
they found that removing the roots from
solutions of a radioactive ion to similar
molarities of a nonradioactive ion would result in the elution of most of the label that
had entered in the initial phase; they measured the amounts of ion that had been physiologically fixed as the amount that was not
eluted in this manner.

The two phases of uptake are also found
with the entry of materials into leaves. For
example, Johnson and Bonner (1956) followed the kinetics of uptake of 2,4-D by oat-
coleoptile sections and found precisely the
same sequence: a rapid initial uptake followed by a slower, steady uptake and an
ability to elute the bulk of the ions taken up
initially with transferral to nonradioactive
solutions of the same composition (Fig.
24-9). Comparing concentrations in the solutions with the total amounts of 2,4-D taken
up and the amounts taken up in just the first
rapid phase of uptake, one finds the interesting relationships shown in Fig. 24-10, where
in both cases the log of the uptake is proportional to the log of the concentration
applied. This is the kinetic relationship
which would be expected if the phenomena
were limited by an adsorption event, in the
manner of the Freundlich adsorption iso-
therms (Freundlich, 1926; Adamson, 1960).

The characteristics of the uptake time
curves, then, imply that there may be an
adsorption of the applied material as it enters

the leaf or root. Consistent with the idea that the initial rapid uptake is an adsorptive process are the facts that (1) the amounts initially taken up are freely exchangeable, (2) there does not appear to be a respiratory involvement, since inhibitors do not interfere markedly with the initial uptake, and (3) the quantitative characteristics are those of adsorption events. While it is not at all certain that the presumed adsorption step is the first step of accumulation, this would certainly seem to be a reasonable possibility, as was specifically suggested by van Overbeek (1956*b*). The two phases of uptake seem to be general for both organic and inorganic materials entering leaves or roots from aqueous solutions (e.g., Fisher and Walker, 1955).

Various lines of evidence indicate that metabolism is critical to some aspect of the uptake of solutes. The uptake of ions by excised roots is markedly reduced when carried out under nitrogen gas instead of air (Epstein and Hagen, 1952; Fig. 24-11). The uptake of auxins is inhibited by metabolic poisons (Reinhold, 1954; Johnson and Bonner, 1956), and the temperature responses of uptake of antibiotics and of auxins show Q_{10} values up to 1.8 and 2.8, respectively, indicative of enzymatic catalyzed processes (Litwack and Pramer, 1957; Sargent and Blackman, 1962). The metabolic component has been specifically identified with the second, slower phase of the uptake.

Rates of entry can be markedly influenced by the pH of the solution. For weak acids, such as the auxins and other organic acids, entry is much better at low pH levels, implying that it may be restricted to the undissociated acid (Albaum et al., 1937). Simon and Beevers (1952) compared the pH curves for many organic acids and concluded that at the pK value or lower, the undissociated acid would completely account for the activity but that at higher pH values, the anions must contribute to the biological activity. These relations are illustrated in Fig. 24-12 (Blackman and Robertson-Cunning-

Fig. 24-8 | The uptake of strontium by barley roots shows a rapid initial phase for about 20 min, followed by a slower, steady uptake rate. When the roots were transferred from the 1-mg/liter Sr[89]Cl₂ to unlabeled SrCl₂, considerable elution of the label out of the roots was obtained, indicating a freely exchangeable form (Epstein and Leggett, 1954).

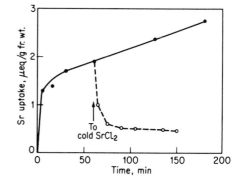

Fig. 24-9 | The uptake of 2,4-D by oat-coleoptile sections again shows the two rates of uptake—a rapid initial rate, followed by a steady, slower rate. Extrapolation of the slower rate to the ordinate permits an estimate of the total amount taken up initially. Note the elution of 2,4-D when sections were moved from the 0.5-mg/liter labeled solution to an unlabeled solution (Johnson and Bonner, 1956).

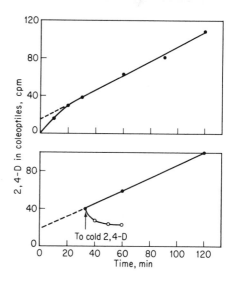

Fig. 24-10 | Using the type of experiment shown in Fig. 24-9, it is found that both the total amount of 2,4-D uptake and the initial amount of uptake are increased logarithmically with log increases in concentration of solutions (Data of Johnson and Bonner, 1956).

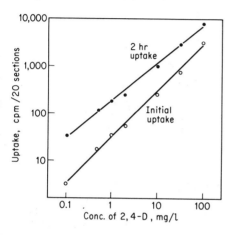

Fig. 24-11 | The uptake of sodium by barley roots is strongly suppressed by a nitrogen atmosphere, indicating a respiratory involvement in uptake. After 3 hr in $Na^{24}Cl$, roots were rinsed three times before counting (Epstein and Hagen, 1952).

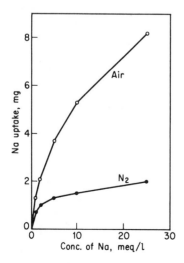

hame, 1953). At pH levels above the pK value (3.2 in the case of 2,4-D), the biological activities are no longer proportional to the amounts of undissociated acid molecules present; this led Blackman (1957) to suggest that the ions enter the tissues, though less rapidly than the undissociated acids.

Van Overbeek (1956) pointed out that solutions buffered to pH levels near neutrality would cause a dissociation of the acid moieties in the cuticle of the leaf, hence increasing its permeability to hydrophilic solutes. This may help to account for the frequent cases in which the first response of a plant to an auxin application seems to parallel the dissociation curve (Fig. 24-13), whereas slower responses extend the responsive ranges up to near neutrality.

It appears, then, that weak acids can enter plant cells most readily as the undissociated molecule (perhaps because they partition more readily into the lipoidal barriers) but that at pHs that would cause dissociation, there may be some entry of the ion associated with the dissociation of the cuticle materials and the resultant increase in cuticle permeability.

The entry of nonionizable compounds is almost unaffected by the pH of the solution in which it is applied (e.g., indoleacetonitrile, Anker, 1958; coumarin, Audus, 1949), but some nonionizable solutes have an improved entry at pHs near neutrality (e.g., maleic hydrazide, Crafts, 1959b), which would logically be attributable to the greater permeability of the cuticle with dissociation. The pH factor can sometimes alter the effectiveness of an applied chemical through an activation of the chemical. For example, the phenolics are weakly acidic, and hence their effectiveness is improved with lowering of the pH from about 5 to 3; but they also show a high effectiveness at a pH near 8 (Smith et al., 1946), probably partly because of the increased chemical reactivity of the quinone form in the alkaline range.

There can be a radical foreshortening of

the entry from a sprayed solution due to drying of the spray droplets. Thus, instead of entry continuing over a period of days, it may be terminated in a few hours (Fig. 24-1). For this reason, the addition of solubilizing or carrier materials to the solution can be especially important.

Carriers in aqueous spray solutions were first utilized by Mitchell and Hamner (1944). They may be of three general types: surfactants, humectants, and oil emulsions. All three may function as wetting agents to increase the solvent continuum between spray droplet and leaf surface. Surfactants include the propylene glycols, detergents, and a variety of other carriers which may increase the wettability of the leaf surface. Humectants include glycerine, calcium salts, and other additives which attract water to the drying spray droplet. Oil emulsions solubilize the more lipophilic materials, which then are suspended in water by the formation of emulsions. All these carriers increase the spreading properties of the droplet and the ability of the droplet to wet the leaf surface, and they can improve entry through the spreading action and/or the prolonging of the drying period for the droplet. Effects of carriers in prolonging the period of chemical entry into leaves are well illustrated in the data of Rice (1948; Fig. 24-1); effects in facilitating the spreading action through the stomata are illustrated in Fig. 24-6.

Buffering a spray to an acidic pH can as markedly influence the entry of chemicals from sprays as from solutions, though the effect is most pronounced for acidic or dissociable materials such as phosphate (e.g., Swanson and Whitney, 1953) or auxins (e.g., Crafts, 1948). It is much less evident with neutral materials such as maleic hydrazide (Crafts, 1959*b*), where the buffer effect may be only on the dissociation of the cuticle. Darlington and Cirulis (1963) were unable to find a change in permeability of isolated leaf cuticle of apricot with changes in pH.

Environmental factors, especially temperature and relative humidity, can have strong influences on the entry of applied sprays. The increases in uptake with increases in temperature have been mentioned, and in fact the Q_{10} of entry indicates that there is an enzymatic involvement. This appears to hold for both organic and inorganic materials (Sargent and Blackman, 1962; Barrier and Loomis, 1957). The most dramatic case of humidity affecting entry is that of maleic hydrazide (Crafts et al., 1958; Smith et al., 1959). As illustrated in Fig. 24-14, entry of the potassium salt is almost obliterated at humidities below 75 per cent. The more humectant diethanolamine salt enters more readily at each of the humidities. Chlor et al. (1963) reported that low humidities also suppressed the entry of 2,4-D, amino triazole and some other leaf sprays.

Other factors affecting entry include light, water deficit, and leaf age, all of which may be explained on the basis of their effects on

Fig. 24-12 | For a standard response to weak organic acids with increasing pH above the pK value, one must supply increasing doses of the acid. While the necessary dosage increases, the amount of undissociated acid per unit activity goes down. The general curves are taken from Simon and Beevers (1952), and the specific data are given here for 50 per cent kill of *Lemna minor* by the weak acid 2,4-D (Blackman and Robertson-Cunninghame, 1953).

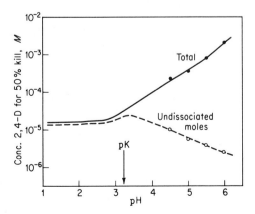

Fig. 24-13 | The dissociation curve for 2,4-D at various pH values (above) is strikingly similar to short-term growth responses of bean stems (3 hr) but less similar for responses after longer periods of time (6 hr). In each case, single bean leaves were treated with the 2,4-D, and stem curvature was taken as the response (Crafts, 1961).

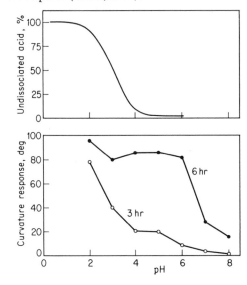

Fig. 24-14 | The absorption of maleic hydrazide by tomato leaves is strongly influenced by the relative humidity. After application of 1 ml of 1600-mg/liter solution of the K salt or diethanolamine salt, the time required for absorption of half the chemical was found to be markedly shorter at higher humidities. Absorption measured as the amount not eluted with a 200-ml wash of detergent solution (Smith et al., 1959).

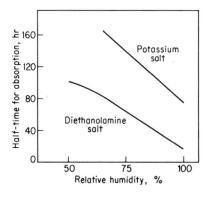

the thickness and degree of hydration of the cuticle.

Apparent free space

As chemicals enter the root from the soil solution, a considerable proportion may be eluted out again by washing (Figs. 24-6 and 24-7). Quantitative measurements of the amounts of ions that could be eluted from roots led Hope and Stevens (1952) to the concept of an apparent free space as a region of the root which was freely accessible to soil solution and solutes and from which an active accumulation of nutrients could proceed. Calculations of the extent of this accessible space on the basis of the amounts of ions which can be eluted after exposure of roots to known molarities of the ion indicate that apparent free space may constitute as much as 13 or up to 23 per cent of the root volume (Butler, 1953). Subsequent investigations indicated similar extents of apparent free space for numerous plant and animal cells (Kramer, 1957). To accommodate such an extensive space, Hope and Robertson (1953) suggested that the cytoplasm was all freely accessible to the soil solution and that the vacuole was the site of final accumulation of ions into a state from which they were not readily eluted. Kramer (1957) suggested the organelles of the cytoplasm, such as the mitochondria, as additional accumulation sites.

If it is true that most of the cell cytoplasm is free space, then close proportionality of salt uptake with transpiration rates (Fig. 24-7) is to be expected. Furthermore, the entry of large molecules such as organic materials and chelating chemicals into roots may be conveniently explained in this way, as well as the ready leaching of some organic and inorganic materials out of leaves and roots. Apparent free space also provides a logical manner of flow of soil solution from the soil to the transpiring leaves.

The morphological extent of free space is

not experimentally established, however. Calculations of the root volume which may be freely accessible to chemicals may well be deceptively high, for adsorptive phenomena may be expected to concentrate the chemicals (as, for example, the exchangeable materials adsorbed onto cell walls), and so the calculations of the volume of apparent free space on the basis of the solute concentration would be in error. Scott and Priestley (1928) proposed that the soil solution could freely move in the cell walls, which would provide the equivalent of a free space from the epidermis to the endodermis of the root. Strugger (1949) assumed that the cell walls could account for much of the water and solute movement in roots. The occasional clear cases of selectivity of entry of chemicals into roots raise some interesting questions concerning the concept of an apparent free space in the cytoplasm. The existence of a free space in cell walls seems certain, and Butler (1953) deduced that the cell walls could account for all the free space in the roots of wheat, a deduction further championed by Levitt (1957).

Translocation

There appear to be four principal pathways for the translocation of materials after uptake by the roots or leaves. Movement may occur (1) in the xylem along with the transpirational stream, (2) through the phloem or other cells such as ray parenchyma, (3) through the cell walls, or (4) through the intercellular spaces.

The upward movement through the xylem was described by Hitchcock and Zimmerman (1935) for some organic compounds which were applied to the soil solution; the movement of inorganic nutrients through such a pathway was already well known. Wiebe and Kramer (1954) established that a wide variety of radioisotopes were translocated most effectively from the subterminal region of the root, where the xylem begins, and

Weaver and DeRose (1946) found that steam-killing a sector of stem would still permit the upward movement of organic materials in the xylem from the soil solution into the foliage.

The downward movement in the phloem was clearly established for applied dyes by Schumacher (1933). This is the principal pathway of movement of materials applied to the leaves (Hay, 1956b). In the case of herbicidal substances, the translocation may be of relatively short duration (Hay and Thimann, 1956b) either because of the metabolism of the substance or sometimes because of the disruption of the phloem itself (Eames, 1950). The word *downward* is sometimes misleading, and here it means any movement which is initially downward out of the leaf. Once out of the leaf, phloem flow may take solutes up to the stem apex as easily as down to the lower parts of the plants—a dualism that caused some heated misunderstandings in the earlier days of interest in translocation (Curtis and Clark, 1950).

The movement of inorganic materials through the cell walls has been known for many years. Münch (1930) described the aqueous network through the cell walls as the *apoplast,* meaning outside the protoplast. The movement of dyes through the apoplast was clearly described by Bauer (1949), and then using exquisitely fine autoradiographs Lüttge and Weigl (1962) established that sulfur taken up as sulfate was specifically localized in the cell-wall areas. In contrast, calcium was not localized in the apoplast, indicating differences in distribution immediately after uptake of different ions. The apoplast seems to be generally accepted as the region of the apparent free space, as had been indicated by Butler (1953), for reasons that have been emphasized by Levitt (1957).

There appear to be two forces limiting the freedom of movement of materials through the apoplast: the region of the endodermis seems to act as a screen which may limit the passage of solutes from the cortex into the stele, and the accumulation of solutes by the cells may limit the freedom of movement in the apoplast. The action of the endodermal region was clearly visualized by Priestley (1920) as a discontinuity in the aqueous continuum between the cell walls of the cortex and the stele. It is presumed that solutes must pass through the cell protoplasts of this region before they can progress into the xylem. Experiments with radioactive ions indicate a clear pileup of solutes in the region just external to the endodermis, consistent with the idea that the endodermis is a barrier to solute passage (Fig. 24-15, Lüttge and Weigl, 1962). Arnold (1952) believes that the passage through the endodermal cells is effected by an active transport system.

The accumulation of solutes by cells has been described many times (Rouschal, 1941; Bauer, 1949; Arnold, 1952), and may clearly

Fig. 24-15 | Microautoradiography of a pea root exposed to $S^*O_4^-$ for 5 min shows accumulation of the radioactivity just outside the region of the endodermis and markedly less isotope inside the stele (plerome), indicating a screening action by the endodermal region of the root (Lüttge and Weigl, 1962).

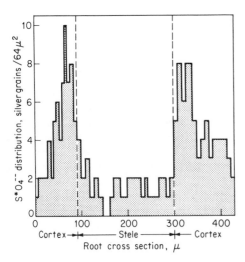

serve to limit the translocation of solutes through the plant. The inability of some herbicides such as 2,4-D to move out of the roots of treated plants (Crafts and Yamaguchi, 1960) is apparently a consequence of such accumulative action.

The movement of herbicides in oils is apparently a capillary flow of the oil through the cell walls (Minshall and Helson, 1949) and results in patterns of distribution not unlike those of solutes which move through the aqueous medium of the apoplast.

The rapid systemic permeation of gases and volatiles through plants indicates a ready movement through intercellular spaces, which must be very extensive in some species, especially rice (Barber et al., 1962).

The movement of materials through these various pathways will provide some distinctive patterns of translocation. For example, materials moving in the xylem or phloem will be first concentrated in the vascular bundles of the leaves and stems (Fig. 24-16). Materials which move in the apoplast tend to permeate continuous blocks of tissue rather than follow the vascular patterns, especially when applied to leaves as illustrated in Fig. 24-17 (Crafts, 1959a).

Translocation rates. The rates or velocities of movement of applied chemicals will strongly resemble the rates of translocation in phloem and xylem, as discussed in Chaps. 3 and 4. Xylem translocation of exogenous chemicals may be as fast as 9 m/hr, and phloem translocation between 10 and 100 cm/hr (Day, 1952; Little and Blackman, 1963). Oils moving in cell walls may go from 4 cm/hr (Rice and Rohrbaugh, 1953) to 24 m/hr for very short periods (Hay, 1956), and gases may permeate through the plant at as much as 36 m/hr (Barber et al., 1962).

Chemical specificity. One of the most remarkable characteristics of the translocation of exogenous chemicals is the striking specificity of movement for different chemical materials. This subject is best known to the herbicide workers, who have recognized that some herbicides move only in the xylem, e.g., most triazines, substituted ureas, IPC (isopropylphenylcarbamate) and related compounds, and trichloroacetic acid. With foliar applications, some herbicides tend to remain in the phloem (e.g., 2,4-D and related auxins), and still others can move readily from one pathway to the other (e.g., maleic hydrazide). Materials which move principally in the phloem without readily crossing into the xylem may accumulate in the root tips and be released out into the soil solution (e.g., amino triazole). Some phenols and antibiotics are essentially nontranslocatable (Dye, 1956).

There are curious changes in translocation characteristics with altered molecular structures. For example, the movement of 2,4-D ethyl sulfate is essentially restricted to xylem, but oxidation to the acid permits preferential movement in the phloem. The mobility of amino triazole in phloem is greatly reduced when a hydroxyl group is substituted into its ring (Massini, 1959*a*). Most striking of the chemical specificities described so far has been the dramatic increase in translocation of various aromatic acids, such as the auxins, and the N-phenylcarbamates, such as IPC, by a lactic acid grouping in the side chain (Mitchell and Preston, 1953; Mitchell et al., 1954; Mitchell and Linder, 1962).

One structural feature which can logically account for differences in translocation abilities is the electric charge. This has been used to account for the slower movement of dyes and antibiotics with basic charges, on the assumption that the acidic residual charge on plant cell walls would retard the movement of such substances (Charles, 1953; Crowdy and Pramer, 1955*a*). But the charges cannot explain the differences in translocation of most chemicals.

Another feature affecting translocation is adsorption. The abilities of plants to hold chemicals by adsorptive means have been emphasized by Brian and Rideal (1952), and the strong adsorption of 2,6-dichlorobenzonitrile has been used to account for its slow

Fig. 24-16 | The movement of radioactivity of 2,4-D applied at the base of a bean leaf, showing concentration in the vascular strands and movement both up and down. Fifty micrograms 2,4-D applied 3 hr before freezing the plant for autoradiography. (*Courtesy of A. S. Crafts.*)

translocation, even in the xylem (Massini, 1961). Differences in phloem translocation of inorganic ions have likewise been attributed to adsorptive differences in the manner of selective partitioning in chromatography (Swanson and Whitney, 1953).

Physiological factors. For any chemical to flow in the phloem translocation system, there must be flow of the phloem sap, and this in turn requires an osmotic gradient according to the mass flow concept (see Chap. 3). Thus it is not surprising that applied chemicals cannot move readily out of leaves without an accumulation of photosynthates. This requirement was first reported for auxins (Mitchell and Brown, 1946; Weaver and DeRose 1946; Penfound and Minyard, 1947) but also applies to the movement of other organic materials such as insecticides (Thomas and Bennett, 1954) and inorganic compounds (Barrier and Loomis, 1957). Usually the movement of applied materials out of leaves can be obtained in the dark by the simple means of applying sugar to the leaves (Rohrbaugh and Rice, 1949; Weintraub and Brown, 1950). Applied sugars can be readily translocated out of the leaf via the phloem, and it is assumed that other applied substances can be swept along in the current created by the sugar. The similar kinetics of translocation of organic and inorganic materials out of leaves (Chaps. 3 and 4) are consistent with the assumption.

The movements of applied chemicals in the xylem, the cell walls, or the intercellular spaces are relatively rapid and insensitive to various physiological functions. If the chemicals get into these media, movement will occur *ipso facto*.

Translocation differences between species have received considerable attention from herbicide physiologists, as these differences might contribute to the selectivity of some herbicides. Extensive comparisons of herbicide selectivity and translocation in various species led Weintraub et al. (1956) to suggest that differences in movement were the best possibility to account for the selective action of 2,4-D. The suggestion has been extended to other species and other herbicides as well (Petersen, 1958; Ashton, 1958).

A further factor in translocation is the assimilation or accumulation of the chemical by the plant cells. The fact that some inorganic ions such as phosphate are strongly assimilated by rapidly growing tissues has been described as a mobilization effect (Chap. 5), and there is a striking contrast between the accumulation of such materials in the apex and the accumulation of a nonassimilated ion such as cobalt in the tips of leaves. Among the organics, translocation is likewise strongly suppressed or altered by abilities of cells to assimilate the chemical,

withdrawing it from the translocation system. Crafts and Yamaguchi (1958) suggested this as an explanation for the much readier translocation of maleic hydrazide than of 2,4-D, the latter being more readily assimilated. Foy (1961) attributed the movement of the herbicide dalapon to the growing points as a mobilization effect, by which the chemical would presumably be assimilated preferentially by the growing points. Such preferential assimilation may account for variations in herbicide translocation between tissues of different ages and for translocation differences between plant species (Petersen, 1958; Koontz and Biddulph, 1957).

One of the most surprising features of the translocation of exogenous chemicals is the great diversity of chemicals which can enter the phloem and be transported therein. The mass flow concept of phloem function requires that there be strong limitations of permeability for the maintenance of osmotic gradients, and it is perplexing to consider how the presumed metabolic loading system that introduces sugars into the phloem might also introduce such diverse chemicals as fluorescein, the auxins, amino triazole, and maleic hydrazide. Much less surprising is the poor entry into the phloem of such materials as the triazines, the substituted ureas, and the phenols, which probably accounts for their relative inability to be translocated out of leaves (Woodford, 1957).

Movement out of plants

It has been known for some time that natural plant products such as organic nutrients or toxic substances can move out of plants (Virtanen et al., 1936, 1937; Slankis, 1958; Bonner and Galston, 1944). Only recently has it become recognized that applied chemicals can be lost from the plant in this manner. This was first noticed by herbicide physiologists, who found that 2,3,5-triiodobenzoic acid could move out of *Lemna* roots

(Blackman, 1957; Blackman and Sargent, 1959) and that 2,4-D could move out into the culture solution from cotton roots (Crafts and Yamaguchi, 1958). In the former case it was established that this exit was a metabolic function, for it increased with elevated temperatures and was prevented by steam-killing the roots.

Studying the highly mobile α-methoxyphenylacetic acid, Mitchell et al. (1961) found that the translocation out through the roots of treated plants occurred in large amounts (Fig. 24-18), and chromatographic analyses showed that the discharged chemical was still intact.

Fate of chemicals in plants

Despite the lack of an organ such as a liver which can specifically remove and dispose of foreign chemicals, the plant organism is amazingly effective in getting rid of applied chemicals. Unless applied at lethal doses, most exogenous chemicals are disposed of by the plant within a few days.

The persistence of applied chemicals varies enormously between compounds and between plants. The auxin herbicide 2,4-D persists for relatively short periods after application; Dhillon and Lucas (1951) were able to recover 2,4-D from treated plants for periods of only 1 to 5 days, depending upon the species. Hay and Thimann (1956a) found that half of the applied 2,4-D had been destroyed 2 days after application. Morphological evidence of persistence may continue over longer periods; the phenoxyacetic acids may cause morphological irregularities over a period of 25 days in corn (McIlrath and Ergle, 1953) or may alter fruit abscission for 50 days in apples and for 7 months in citrus. Periods of dormancy may extend the period of morphological response to a year (Tullis and Davis, 1950) probably because of suspended metabolic degrada-

Fig. 24-17 | A bean plant (left) treated with radioactive calcium at the base of one leaf, showing a creeping movement up the leaf tissues (right) without movement down the petiole to the stem. One microgram Ca⁴⁵ applied 4 days before fixing for autoradiography (Crafts and Yamaguchi, 1960).

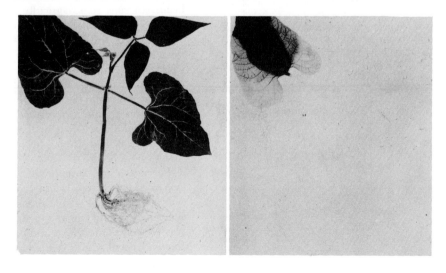

tion. Some herbicides may cause apparent alterations of the genetic mechanisms in plants, for morphological aberrations may continue for as long as three generations after application (Pridham, 1947; Foy, 1961).

Loss curves. There seem to be three general types of disappearance curves for exogenously applied chemicals. If the plant has the chemical or enzymatic means for ready disposal of the material, disappearance will proceed in a roughly log-type curve, as indicated in curve *A* of Fig. 24-19. If the plant has only limited means of disposal of the chemical, disappearance may proceed only for a short time until adsorption or binding forces can hold the material in a steady state as in curve *B*. If the plant must develop new enzymatic means to dispose of the chemical, there may be a lag period before disappearance proceeds, as in curve *C*. (Note that curve *C* is for losses from soil.) Where adaptive enzymes are formed, the subsequent disappearance may be precipitous, as in curve *C*, rather than logarithmic, as in curve *A*, and subsequent repeat

Fig. 24-18 | The movement of methoxyphenylacetic acid down to the roots and out of the plant into the nutrient solution. Labeled acid was applied at 50 μg to each primary leaf of pinto beans, and radioactivity was measured in the roots and in the solution at intervals after treatment (Mitchell et al., 1961).

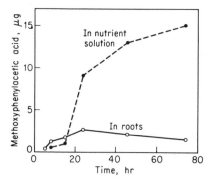

applications of the chemical may be disposed of without additional lag periods and at a faster rate than before (Audus, 1949; Pramer and Starkey, 1951; Thiegs, 1955, for soil applications). As representative examples of each of these loss curves, 2,4-D disappearance in beans or other susceptible dicotyledonous plants would proceed logarithmically (e.g., Hay and Thimann, 1956a), the urea herbicides such as CMU disappear in beans with a short-term decline followed by a steady state (Fang et al., 1955), and the trazines such as simazine disappear in corn and other susceptible species with a lag period followed by rapid disposal (Montgomery and Freed, 1961).

The persistence of any given chemical depends on many factors, such as the plant involved, its growth condition, and environmental factors such as light and temperature. But the half-life of most agricultural chemicals is fairly short. As can be seen in Fig. 24-19, the half-life of 2,4-D in beans will be about 1 day, though in other species it may be about 1 month (Leonard and Weaver, 1961). The half-life of triazines such as simazine may be estimated at about 1 week in a resistant species but at over 1 month in susceptible corn (Montgomery and Freed, 1961). The half-life of amino triazole may be about 2 days in grapes but much longer in beans. In soils some agricultural chemicals may persist essentially undiminished for 9 years (Marth and Mitchell, 1960).

Determinations of persistence are complicated by the formation of derivatives in the plant which may be hydrolyzed during extraction; thus from data on extractions there may be an apparent persistence of the applied materials, whereas in the intact plant the material had been effectively detoxified.

Formation of derivatives. The conversion of added chemicals into derivatives from which the original chemical can be restored is usually found in the growth-regulator classes such as the auxins and natural inhibitors and possibly also in the kinins and gibberellins. The formation of derivatives of auxins was first described by Andreae and Good (1955), with their identification of indoleacetyl aspartic acid, and since that time there has appeared evidence of peptide derivatives of several auxins (Zenk, 1962) and also probably of amino triazole (Massini, 1959*b*; Carter and Naylor, 1961). Glycosides are commonly formed with auxins (Zenk, 1961, 1962). The formation of growth substances by gentle hydrolysis of plant extracts suggests that similar derivatives may be formed with kinins (Zwar et al., 1963) and gibberellins (Most and Vlitos, 1963). Glycosides are formed with many of the phenolic and lactone types of inhibitors in plants. Amino triazole may form complexes with metal cations in the plant, from which the original chemical may be restored (Ashton, 1963).

Some applied chemicals may be adsorbed onto various materials in the plant and held in this way for extended periods. The adsorption of chemicals within the plant was first specifically suggested by Brian and Rideal (1952), who showed the adsorption of the auxin herbicide 2-methyl-4-chlorophenoxyacetic acid onto fatty materials taken from tomato, cress, and oat plants. An example of their evidence for adsorption, where changes in the surface tension of the plant diffusate are obtained with the addition of increasing amounts of the auxin, is shown in Fig. 24-20. It is well known that auxins and many other common herbicides may be readily adsorbed (Leopold et al., 1960; Geissbahler et al., 1963), but it is difficult to assess the importance of adsorption of chemicals in plants because of the difficulties of distinguishing between free and adsorbed materials upon extraction of the tissues.

Degradation. In many instances, applied chemicals will be susceptible to enzymatic degradation by the plant.

The enzymatic loss of indoleacetic acid was described by Tang and Bonner (1947). The products formed from this action are quite complicated; the formation of some

Fig. 24-19 | Some representative disappearance curves for herbicides, illustrating (*A*) a logarithmic disappearance of 2,4-D in bean plants (Hay and Thimann, 1956*a*); (*B*) a short-term disappearance of CMU from bean plants (Fang et al., 1955); and (*C*) a delayed disappearance of 2,4-D from soil (Audus, 1949). The time intervals for (*A*) were multiplied by 5 for clarity.

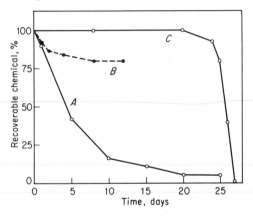

Fig. 24-20 | The surface potential of a monolayer of diffusate from cress seedlings is markedly altered by the introduction of increasing amounts of auxin, 2-methyl-4-chlorophenoxyacetic acid, indicating an adsorption of the auxin onto cress components (Brian and Rideal, 1952).

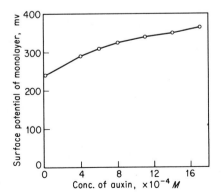

apparent derivatives has been illustrated in Fig. 6-11. Enzymatic destruction of 2,4-D can also occur, and the production of subsequent derivatives has been followed in time by Jaworswki and Butts (1951; Fig. 24–21). The derivatives obtained seem to be degradation products, for there is no evidence that they retain biological activity or can be converted to materials with biological activity.

If some species are capable of degrading an herbicide better than others, this could well be the basis of selectivity, and in some extensive comparisons, Luckwill and Lloyd-Jones (1960*a*,*b*) found that 2,4-D was degraded markedly better by resistant than by sensitive varieties of currant and apple. This is probably not a general difference, however, for Weintraub et al. (1956) were unable to correlate destruction of 2,4-D with susceptibility of corn and bean, and Ragab and McCullum (1960) were unable to correlate destruction of simazine with susceptibility of corn and cucumber.

In some instances, the degradation of applied chemicals may be by nonenzymatic means. It has been found that a natural component of corn sap can directly detoxify simazine to the 2-hydroxy triazine (Hamilton and Moreland, 1961). The component appears to be a natural hydroxamate in corn. Photochemical degradations have been described for several herbicides, including 2,4-D (Bell, 1956), the benzoic acids (Sheets, 1963), and the substituted ureas (Weldon and Timmons, 1961).

For some herbicides the product of degradation may be the toxic material. The use of phenoxy acid auxins with side chains of four or even six carbon lengths takes advantage of the tendencies of plants for beta oxidation of straight chain acids, resulting in the degradative formation of the herbicidal phenoxyacetic acid in the plant (Wain, 1960; Fawcett et al., 1958). In this case additional selectivity can be achieved on the basis of the ability of some species to carry out the beta oxidation. Other examples of activation within the plant may be the cases of the light-activated herbicides such as the triazines, phenylureas, acylanilides, and quaternary dipyridyl compounds (cf. Hilton et al., 1963). Applied to plants in darkness, most of them are essentially without effect, but when treated parts of the plant are exposed to light, a toxic principle is formed which then may have lethal effects on the plant. Most of these herbicides are inhibitors of photosynthesis, but their actual toxicity seems to reside in the light-activated formation of some toxic substance. That the herbicide itself is converted to the toxic principle seems likely in the case of the quaternary dipyridyl herbicides (Mees, 1960) but is uncertain in the other cases.

These examples illustrate that plants have diverse means of degrading applied chemicals, and at least in some instances such degradations may regulate the effectiveness of the application in modifying plant performance.

Fig. 24-21 | The degradation of 2,4-D by bean plants is associated with the appearance of radioactive label from the 2,4-D in two derivatives. Fifty micrograms 2,4-D° followed by alcoholic extraction and chromatographic separation at subsequent time intervals (Jaworski and Butts, 1951).

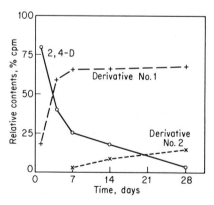

Chemical modification of plants

Since 1950, there has been a spectacular development in technology of chemical applications to regulate plant growth and development. Just as the exploitation of metabolic inhibitors permitted the development of knowledge concerning metabolism, so also are regulators of growth and development permitting dramatic new advances in understanding this area of physiology.

As new chemicals for modifications of plants have become available, each of the major areas of developmental physiology has become subject to chemical manipulation. Chemicals can be applied to modify assimilative activities, growth functions, and developmental functions and to intensify or ameliorate the effects of environmental variables.

With respect to assimilation, the chemical modifications of photosynthesis have become basic tools in the science of herbicides as well as in the analysis of photosynthetic mechanisms. Chemical interference with the Hill reaction (Cooke, 1956) is among the best known of these, but disruption of chloroplast structure by streptomycin (Siegesmund et al., 1962) or by amino triazole (Ashton et al., 1963) represents another range of effects. Intensification of mobilization activities with kinins (Mothes and Englebrecht, 1959) is another assimilatory modification.

Among the growth reactions, the chemical actions are legion. The effects of gibberellin in modifying germination and growth of stems (Brian et al., 1955) are among the most dramatic. Gibberellin applications can have such surprising effects as the conversion of dwarf plants into standard-sized plants (Fig. 7-11) and of bush types into climbing vines (Fig. 7-2). Its enhancement of stem length may be useful in the production of stem fibers (Lona and Bocchi, 1956). Many new growth inhibitors have been developed which can cause dwarfing without interfering with the normal reproductive de-

velopment of the plant (Wirwillie and Mitchell, 1950; Preston and Link, 1958; Marth et al., 1954; Wittwer and Tolbert, 1960; Riddell et al., 1962; Hamaker et al., 1963). Kinins can alter differentiation processes in tissue cultures (Skoog and Miller, 1957) and also in greenhouse practice (Plummer and Leopold, 1957). All the correlation effects can be altered with chemicals related to the auxin materials. For example, apical dominance can be accentuated (Jankiewicz, 1956) or alleviated (Beach and Leopold, 1953; Wickson and Thimann, 1958), tropistic developments can be prevented in florists' materials (Teas and Sheehan, 1957), and rooting and abscission can be induced or inhibited with auxins, gibberellins, kinins, and a diverse array of defoliating chemicals.

Among the developmental processes, again no general class of plant function seems beyond the reach of chemical modification. Kinins can defer senescence in leaves (Richmond and Lang, 1957) or in stored green vegetables (Kaufman and Ringel, 1961). Flowering can be induced or prevented (Clark and Kerns, 1942; Zeevaart and Lang, 1963); developing flowers can be made sterile (Eaton, 1957) or the sex expression altered (Laibach and Kribben, 1950). The effects of auxins and gibberellins on fruit set, fruit growth, ripening, and coloration are widely used agriculturally (cf. Leopold, 1958). The stimulation of tuber formation by auxins (van Schreven, 1956) suggests a parallel to the possible involvement of auxins in bulb formation (Clark and Heath, 1959). The dramatic effects of gibberellin in removing dormancy are among the most startling of the growth-regulator effects.

Chemical alterations of environmental factors include the alleviation of light inhibitions of growth with gibberellins (Lockhart, 1961), the protective effects of sulfhydryl compounds against radiation damage (Barron and Flood, 1950), the avoidance of heat damage by kinins (Englebrecht and

Mothes, 1960) or of frost damage by auxins (Crane, 1954), and the protection of seedlings against water loss by chemical treatments which will close the stomata (Zelitch, 1961) or cover the leaves with a film that resists transpiration (Gale, 1961).

Two other chemical responses of plants should be mentioned, including the chemical modification of disease resistance and the chemical selective herbicidal uses. Together these represent the most widely used chemical treatments of plants.

The basic underlying feature of plants which makes their chemical modifications feasible seems to be the sometimes astonishing ease with which chemicals can enter the plant leaf, root, or individual cell. Knowing of the existence of chemical control systems which naturally regulate growth and development functions in the multicellular organism, it is not surprising that applied chemicals of similar sorts should be able to alter these activities strikingly in plants.

This brief statement of the representative types of plant functions which can be chemically manipulated illustrates the enormity of the chemical influences on growth and developmental functions. It is consistent with the diverse evidence that chemical systems are principal regulators of growth and development of plants and that the growth and function of individual cells in the multicellular organism are to a considerable extent products of a special molecular ecology—a dynamic exchange of chemical signals between cells of the plant which makes possible the regulation of activities in the multicellular organism.

GENERAL REFERENCES

Crafts, A. S. 1961. *The Chemistry and Mode of Action of Herbicides.* Interscience Publishers, Inc., New York. 269 pp.

Epstein, E. 1956. Mineral nutrition of plants: mechanics of uptake and transport. *Ann. Rev. Plant Physiol.,* 7:1–24.

Kramer, P. J. 1957. Outer space in plants: some possible implications of the concept. *Science,* 125:633–635.

Overbeek, J. van. 1956. Absorption and translocation of plant regulators. *Ann. Rev. Plant Physiol.,* 7:355–372.

———. 1956. Studies on the relation between molecular structure and penetration of growth regulators into plants, pp. 205–210. In R. L. Wain and F. Wightman (eds.), *Chemistry and Mode of Action of Plant Growth Substances.* Butterworth Scientific Publications, London.

———. 1962. Physiological responses of plants to herbicides. *Weeds,* 10:170–174.

REFERENCES CITED

Adamson, A. W., 1960. *Physical Chemistry of Surfaces.* Interscience Publishers, Inc., New York, 629 pp.

Albaum, H. G., S. Kaiser, and H. A. Nestler. 1937. The relation of hydrogen ion concentration to the penetration of indoleacetic acid into *Nitella* cells. *Am. J. Botany,* 24:513–518.

Andreae, W. A., and N. E. Good. 1955. The formation of indoleaspartic acid in pea seedlings. *Plant Physiol.,* 30:380–382.

Anker, L. 1958. The influence of the pH on the growth and the geotropism of decapitated *Avena* coleoptiles supplied either with indoleacetic acid or with indoleacetonitrile. *Acta. Botan. Neerl.,* 7:69–76.

Arnold, A. 1952. Über den Funktionsmechanismus der Endodermiszellen der Wurzeln. *Protoplasma,* 41:189–211.

Ashton, F. M. 1958. Absorption and translocation of radioactive 2,4-D in sugarcane and bean plants. *Weeds,* 6:257–262.

———. 1963. Fate of amitrole in soil. *Weeds,* 11:167–170.

———, E. M. Gifford, and T. Bisalpatra. 1963. Structural change in *Phaseolus vulgaris* induced by atrazine. I. Histological changes. *Botan. Gaz.,* 124:329–335.

Aslander, A. 1927. Sulphuric acid as a weed spray. *J. Agr. Res.*, 34:1065–1091.

Audus, L. J. 1949. The biological detoxication of 2,4-D in soil. *Plant Soil*, 2:31–35.

Barber, D. A., M. Ebert, and N. T. S. Evans. 1962. The movement of O^{15} through barley and rice plants. *J. Exptl. Botany*, 13:397–403.

Barrier, G. E., and W. E. Loomis. 1957. Absorption and translocation of 2,4-dichlorophenoxyacetic acid. *Plant Physiol.*, 32:225–231.

Barron, E. S. G., and V. Flood. 1950. Studies on the mechanism of action of ionizing radiation. VI. *J. Gen. Physiol.*, 33:229–241.

Bauer, L. 1949. Über den Wanderungsweg fluorezierenden Farbstoffe in den Siebrohren. *Planta*, 37:221–243.

Beach, R. G., and A. C. Leopold. 1953. The use of maleic hydrazide to break apical dominance of chrysanthemum. *Proc. Am. Soc. Hort. Sci.*, 61:543–547.

Bell, G. R. 1956. On the photochemical degradation of 2,4-D and related compounds in the presence and absence of riboflavin. *Botan. Gaz.*, 118:133–136.

Blackman, G. E. 1957. Selective toxicity in relation to specific differences in retention, penetration and uptake. *Proc. Intern. Congr. Crop Protection 4th*, 1:481–487.

——— and R. C. Robertson-Cunninghame. 1953. The influence of pH on the phytotoxicity of 2,4-dichlorophenoxyacetic acid to *Lemna minor. New Phytologist*, 52:71–75.

——— and J. A. Sargent. 1959. The uptake of growth substances. II. *J. Exptl. Botany*, 10:480–503.

Bonner, J., and A. W. Galston. 1944. Toxic substances from the culture media of guayule which may inhibit growth. *Botan. Gaz.*, 106:185–198.

Brian, P. W., H. G. Hemming, and M. Radley. 1955. A physiological comparison of gibberellic acid with some auxins. *Physiol. Plantarum*, 8:899–912.

Brian, R. C., and E. K. Rideal. 1952. On the action of plant growth regulators. *Biochim. Biophys. Acta*, 9:1-18.

Butler, G. W. 1953. Ion uptake by young wheat plants. II. The apparent free space of wheat roots. *Physiol. Plantarum*, 6:617–635.

Carter, M. C., and A. W. Naylor. 1961. Studies on an unknown metabolic product of 3-amino-1,2,4 triazole. *Physiol. Plantarum*, 14:20–27.

Charles, A. 1953. Uptake of dyes into cut leaves. *Nature*, 171:435.

Chibnall, A. C., and S. H. Piper. 1934. The metabolism of plant and insect waxes. *Biochem. J.*, 28:2209–2219.

Chlor, M. A., A. S. Crafts, and S. Yamaguchi. 1963. Effects of high humidity on translocation of foliar applied compounds. *Plant Physiol.*, 38:501–508.

Clark, H. E., and K. R. Kerns. 1942. Control of flowering with phytohormones. *Science*, 95:536–537.

Clark, J. E., and O. V. S. Heath. 1959. Auxin and bulbing of onions. *Nature*, 184:345–347.

Cooke, A. R. 1956. A possible mechanism of action of the urea type herbicides. *Weeds*, 4:397–398.

Crafts, A. S. 1948. A theory of herbicidal action. *Science*, 108:85–86.

———. 1956. The mechanism of translocation: methods of study with C^{14} labeled 2,4-D. *Hilgardia*, 26:287–334.

———. 1959*a*. Further studies on comparative mobility of labeled herbicides. *Plant Physiol.*, 34:613–620.

———. 1959*b*. Improvement of growth regulator formulation, pp. 789–801. In R. M. Klein (ed.), *Plant Growth Regulation*. Iowa State University Press, Ames, Iowa.

———. 1961. *The Chemistry and Mode of Action of Herbicides*. Interscience Publishers, Inc., New York. 269 pp.

———, H. B. Currier, and H. R. Drever. 1958. Some studies on the herbicidal properties of maleic hydrazide. *Hilgardia*, 27:723–757.

——— and S. Yamaguchi. 1958. Comparative tests on the uptake and distribution of labeled herbicides by *Zebrina pendula* and *Tradescantia fluminensis. Hilgardia,* 27:421–454.

—— and ——. 1960. Absorption of herbicides by roots. *Am. J. Botany,* 47: 248–255.

Crane, J. C. 1954. Frost resistance, and reduction in drop of injured apricot fruits effected by 2,4,5-trichlorophenoxyacetic acid. *Proc. Am. Soc. Hort. Sci.,* 64:225–231.

Crowdy, S. H., and D. Pramer. 1955a. Movement of antibiotics in higher plants. *Chem. Ind. (London),* 160–162.

—— and ——. 1955b. The occurrence of translocated antibiotics in expressed plant sap. *Ann. Botany (London),* 19: 80–86.

—— and D. Rudd-Jones. 1956. The translocation of sulphonamides in higher plants. ᵗ. *J. Exptl. Botany,* 7:335–346.

Currier, H. B., and C. D. Dybing. 1959. Foliar penetration of herbicides: review and present status. *Weeds,* 7:195–213.

Curtis, O. F., and D. G. Clark. 1950. *An Introduction to Plant Physiology.* McGraw-Hill Book Company, New York. 752 pp.

Darlington, W. A., and N. Cirulis. 1963. Permeability of apricot leaf cuticle. *Plant Physiol.,* 38:462–467.

Dawson, J. H. 1963. Development of barnyardgrass seedlings and their response to EPTC. *Weeds,* 11:60–67.

Day, B. E. 1952. The absorption and translocation of 2,4-D by bean plants. *Plant Physiol.,* 27:143–152.

Dhillon, A. S., and E. H. Lucas. 1951. Absorption, translocation, and persistence of 2,4-D in plants. *Botan. Gaz.,* 112:198–207.

Dybing, C. D., and H. B. Currier. 1961. Foliar penetration by chemicals. *Plant Physiol.,* 36:169–174.

Dye, M. H. 1956. Intake of streptomycin by peach leaves. *Nature,* 178:551–552.

Eames, A. J. 1950. Destruction of phloem in

young bean plants after treatment with 2,4-D. *Am. J. Botany,* 37:840–847.

Eaton, F. M. 1957. Selective gametocide opens way to hybrid cotton. *Science,* 126: 1174–1175.

Englebrecht, L., and K. Mothes. 1960. Kinetin als Faktor der Hitzresistenz. *Ber. Deut. Botan. Ges.,* 73:246–257.

Epstein, E., and C. E. Hagen. 1952. Kinetic study of absorption of alkali cations by barley roots. *Plant Physiol.,* 27:457–474.

—— and J. E. Leggett. 1954. The absorption of alkaline earth cations by barley roots: kinetics and mechanism. *Am. J. Botany,* 41:785–791.

Fang, S. C., V. H. Freed, R. H. Johnson, and D. R. Coffee. 1955. Absorption, translocation and metabolism of radioactive CMU by bean plants. *Agr. Food Chem.,* 3:400–402.

Fawcett, C., R. L. Wain, and F. Wightman. 1958. Beta-oxidation of omega (3-indolyl) alkanecarboxylic acids in plant tissues. *Nature,* 181:1387–1389.

Fisher, E. G., and D. R. Walker. 1955. The apparent absorption of phosphorus and magnesium from sprays applied to apple leaves. *Proc. Am. Soc. Hort. Sci.,* 65: 17–24.

Fogg, G. E. 1947. Quantitative studies on the wetting of leaves by water. *Proc. Roy. Soc. (London),* B,134:503–522.

Foy, C. L. 1961. Absorption, distribution and metabolism of 2,2-dichloropropionic acid in relation to phytotoxicity. II. Distribution and metabolic fate of dalapon in plants. *Plant Physiol.,* 36: 698–709.

Franke, W. 1961. Ectodesmata and foliar absorption. *Am. J. Botany,* 48:683–690.

Freundlich, H. 1926. *Colloid and Capillary Chemistry.* Metheun & Co. Ltd., London.

Gale, J. 1961. Studies on plant antitranspirants. *Physiol. Plantarum,* 14:777–786.

Geissbahler, H., C. Haselbach, and H. Aebi. 1963. The fate of N(4-chlorophenoxy) phenyl NN dimethyl urea in soils and plants. *Weed Res.,* 3:140–153.

Hamaker, J. W., H. Johnston, R. T. Martin,

and C. T. Redmann. 1963. A picolinic acid derivative: a plant growth regulator. *Science*, 141:363.

Hamilton, R. H., and D. E. Moreland. 1961. Simazine degradation by corn seedlings. *Science*, 135:373–374.

Hay, J. R. 1956a. Translocation of herbicides in Marabu. I. *Weeds*, 4:218–226.

———. 1956b. Translocation of herbicides in Marabu. II. *Weeds*, 4:349–356.

——— and K. V. Thimann. 1956a. The fate of 2,4-dichlorophenoxyacetic acid in bean seedlings. I. Recovery of 2,4-dichlorophenoxyacetic acid and its breakdown in the plant. *Plant Physiol.*, 31:382–387.

——— and ———. 1956b. The fate of 2,4-dichlorophenoxyacetic acid in bean seedlings. II. Translocation. *Plant Physiol.*, 31:446–451.

Hilton, J. L., L. L. Jansen, and H. M. Hull. 1963. Mechanisms of herbicide action. *Ann. Rev. Plant Physiol.*, 14:353–377.

Hitchcock, A. E., and P. W. Zimmerman. 1935. Absorption and movement of synthetic growth substances from soil as indicated by responses of aerial parts. *Contrib. Boyce Thompson Inst.*, 7:447–476.

Hope, A. B., and R. N. Robertson. 1953. Bioelectric experiments and the properties of plant protoplasm. *Australian J. Sci.*, 15:197–203.

——— and P. G. Stevens. 1952. Electrical potential differences in bean roots and their relations to salt uptake. *Australian J. Sci. Res.*, B5:335.

Jankiewicz, L. 1956. The effect of auxins on crotch angles in apple trees. *Acad. Polon. Sci.*, 4:173–178.

Jaworski, E. G., and J. S. Butts. 1951. Studies in plant metabolism. II. The metabolism of C^{14}-labeled 2,4-dichlorophenoxyacetic acid in bean plants. *Arch. Biochem. Biophys.*, 38:207–218.

Johnson, M. P., and J. Bonner. 1956. The uptake of auxin by plant tissue. *Physiol. Plantarum*, 9:102–118.

Kaufman, J., and S. M. Ringel. 1961. Tests of growth regulators to retard yellowing and abscission of cauliflower. *Proc. Am. Soc. Hort. Sci.*, 78:349–352.

Koontz, H., and O. Biddulph. 1957. Factors affecting absorption and translocation of foliar applied phosphorus. *Plant Physiol.*, 32:463–470.

Kramer, P. J. 1957. Outer space in plants: some possible implications of the concept. *Science*, 125:633–635.

Laibach, F., and F. J. Kribben. 1950. Über die β-Indolylessigsaure für die Blutenbildung. *Ber. Deut. Botan. Ges.*, 63:119–120.

Lambertz, P. 1954. Untersuchungen über das Vorkommen von Plasmodesmen in den Epidermisaussenwanden. *Planta*, 44:147–190.

Leonard, O. A., and R. J. Weaver. 1961. Absorption and translocation of 2,4-D and amitrole in shoots of the tokay grape. *Hilgardia*, 31:327–368.

Leopold, A. C. 1958. Auxin uses in the control of flowering and fruiting. *Ann. Rev. Plant Physiol.*, 9:281–310.

———, P. van Schaik, and M. Neal. 1960. Molecular structure and herbicide adsorption. *Weeds*, 8:48–54.

Levitt, J. 1957. The significance of apparent free space in ion absorption. *Physiol. Plant.*, 10:882–888.

Little, E. C. S., and G. E. Blackman. 1963. The movement of growth regulators in plants. III. Comparative studies of transport in *Phaseolus vulgaris*. *New Phytologist*, 62:173–197.

Litwack, G., and D. Pramer. 1957. Absorption of antibiotics of plant cells. III. Kinetics of streptomycin uptake. *Arch. Biochem. Biophys.*, 68:396–403.

Lockhart, J. A. 1961. Photoinhibition of stem elongation by full solar radiation. *Am. J. Botany*, 48:387–392.

Lona, F., and A. Bocchi. 1956. La distensione culinare nella canapa incrementata dall' acido gibberellico. *Riv. Intern. Agr.*, 7:58–60.

Luckwill, L., and C. Lloyd-Jones. 1960a. Metabolism of plant growth regulators. I.

2,4-dichlorophenoxyacetic acid in leaves of red and of black currant. *Ann. Appl. Biol.*, 48:613–625.

―――― and ――――. 1960*b*. Metabolism of plant growth regulators. II. Decarboxylation of 2,4-dichlorophenoxyacetic acid in leaves of apple and strawberry. *Ann. Appl. Biol.*, 48:626–636.

Lüttge, J. and J. Weigl. 1962. Mikroautoradiographische Untersuchungen der Aufnahme und des Transports von $S^{35}O_4$ und Ca^{45} in Keimwurzeln von *Zea mays* und *Pisum sativum. Planta*, 58:113–126.

McIlrath, W. J., and D. R. Ergle. 1953. Further evidence of the persistence of the 2,4-D stimulus in cotton. *Plant Physiol.*, 28:693–702.

Marth, P. C., and J. W. Mitchell. 1960. Plant growth suppressants with special reference to persistence of amo-1618 in soil. *Proc. Am. Soc. Hort. Sci.*, 76:673–678.

――――, W. H. Preston, and J. W. Mitchell. 1954. Growth controlling effects of some quaternary ammonium components on various species of plants. *Botan. Gaz.*, 115:200–204.

Massini, P. 1959*a*. Uptake and translocation of 3-amino- and 3-hydroxy-1,2,4,-triazole in plants. *Proc. Intern. Conf. Atomic Energy 2nd*, 58–62.

――――. 1959*b*. Synthesis of 3,3-amino-1,2,4-triazolyl alanine from 3-amino-1,2,4-triazole in plants. *Biochim. Biophys. Acta*, 36:548–549.

――――. 1961. Translocation of amino triazole in plants. II. *Acta Botan. Neerl.*, 10:99–104.

Mees, G. C. 1960. Experiments on the herbicidal action of 1,1'ethylene-2,2' dipyridylium dibromide. *Ann. Appl. Biol.*, 48:601–612.

Minshall, W., and V. A. Helson. 1949. The herbicidal action of oils. *Proc. Am. Soc. Hort. Sci.*, 53:294–298.

Mitchell, J. W., and J. W. Brown. 1946. Movement of 2,4-D stimulus and its relation to the translocation of organic food materials in plants. *Botan. Gaz.*, 107:393–407.

―――― and C. L. Hamner. 1944. Polyethylene glycols as carriers for growth regulating substances. *Botan. Gaz.*, 105:474–483.

―――― and P. Linder. 1962. Effect of alpha-methoxylation and nitrogen acetylation on absorption and translocation of a plant regulator, methyl indoleacetate. *Agr. Food Chem.*, 10:82–83.

――――, P. J. Linder, and M. B. Robinson. 1961. Mechanism of root exudation of α-methoxyphenylacetic acid in the bean plant. *Botan. Gaz.*, 123:134–137.

――――, P. C. Marth, and W. H. Preston. 1954. Structural modification that increases translocatability of some growth-regulatory carbamates. *Science*, 120:263–265.

―――― and W. A. Preston. 1953. Secondary galls and other plant growth modifying effects induced by translocated α-methoxyphenylacetic acid. *Science*, 118:518–519.

Montgomery, M., and V. H. Freed. 1961. The uptake, translocation and metabolism of simazine and atrazine by corn plants. *Weeds*, 9:231–237.

Most, B. H., and A. J. Vlitos. 1963. Preliminary studies on the gibberellin-like substances in sugar cane, pp. 287–302. In J. P. Nitsch (ed.), *Régulateurs Naturels de la Croissance Végétale*, CNRS, Paris.

Mothes, K., and L. Englebrecht. 1959. Kinetin und das Problem der Akkumulation löslicher Stickstoff-Verbindung. *Monatsber. Deut. Akad. Wiss. Berlin*, 1:367–375.

Mueller, L. E., P. H. Carr, and W. E. Loomis. 1954. The submicroscopic structure of plant surfaces. *Am. J. Botany*, 41:593–600.

Münch, E. 1930. *Die Stoffbewegung in der Pflanze*. Fischer Verlag, Jena. 234 pp.

Overbeek, J. van. 1956*a*. Absorption and translocation of plant regulators. *Ann. Rev. Plant Physiol.*, 7:355–372.

――――. 1956*b*. Studies on the relation between molecular structure and penetration of growth regulators into plants, pp. 205–

210. In R. L. Wain and F. Wightman (eds.), *Chemistry and Mode of Action of Plant Growth Substances.* Butterworth Scientific Publications, London.

—— and R. Blondeau. 1954. Mode of action of phytotoxic oils. *Weeds,* 3:55–65.

Penfound, W. T., and V. Minyard. 1947. Relation of light intensity to effect of 2,4-dichlorophenoxyacetic acid on water hyacinth and kidney bean plants. *Botan. Gaz.,* 109:231–234.

Petersen, H. I. 1958. Translocation of C^{14}-labelled 2,4-dichlorophenoxyacetic acid in barley and oats. *Nature,* 192:1685–1686.

Plummer, T. H., and A. C. Leopold. 1957. Chemical treatment for bud formation in *Saintpaulia. Proc. Am. Soc. Hort. Sci.,* 70: 442–444.

Pramer, D. 1954. The movement of chloramphenicol and streptomycin in broad bean and tomato plants. *Ann. Botany.* (*London*), 18:463–470.

——. 1956. Absorption of antibiotics of plant cells. II. Streptomycin. *Arch. Biochem. Biophys.,* 62:265–273.

—— and R. L. Starkey. 1951. Decomposition of streptomycin. *Science,* 113:127.

Preston, W. H., and C. B. Link. 1958. Use of 2,4-dichlorobenzylphosphonium chloride to dwarf plants. *Plant Physiol.,* 33:49.

Priestley, J. H. 1920. The mechanism of root pressure. *New Phytol.,* 19:189–200.

Pridham, A. M. S. 1947. Effect of 2,4-D on bean progeny seedlings. *Science,* 105:412.

Ragab, M. T. H., and J. P.McCollum. 1960. Degradation of C^{14}-labeled simazine by plants and soil microorganisms. *Weeds,* 9:72–84.

Reinhold, L. 1954. The uptake of indoleacetic acid by pea epicotyl segments and carrot disks. *New Phytologist,* 53:217–239.

Rice, E. L. 1948. Absorption and translocation of ammonium 2,4-dichlorophenoxyacetate by bean plants. *Botan. Gaz.,* 109: 301–314.

—— and L. M. Rohrbaugh. 1953. Effect of kerosene on movement of 2,4-D and some derivatives through destarched bean leaves in darkness. *Botan. Gaz.,* 115:76–81.

Richmond, A. E., and A. Lang. 1957. Effect of kinetin on protein content and survival of detached *Xanthium* leaves. *Science,* 125:650–651.

Riddell, J. A., H. A. Hageman, C. M. J. Anthony, and W. L. Hubbard. 1962. Retardation of plant growth by a new group of chemicals. *Science,* 136:391.

Rohrbaugh, L. M., and E. L. Rice. 1949. Effect of application of sugar on the translocation of sodium 2,4-D by bean plants in the dark. *Botan. Gaz.,* 111:85–89.

Rouschal, E. 1941. Die protoplasmiche Mechanismus und Funktion des Siebröhren. *Flora* (*Jena*), 35:135–220.

Sargent, J. A., and G. E. Blackman. 1962. Studies of foliar penetration. I. *J. Exptl. Botany,* 13:348–368.

Schieferstein, R. H., and W. E. Loomis. 1956. Wax deposits on leaf surfaces. *Plant Physiol.,* 31:240–247.

—— and ——. 1959. Development of the cuticular layers in angiosperm leaves. *Am. J. Botany,* 46:625–635.

Schumacher, W. 1933. Untersuchungen über die Wanderung des Fluoreszenz in den Siebröhren. *Jahrb. Wiss. Bot.,* 77:685–732.

Scott, F. M. 1950. Internal suberization of tissues. *Botan. Gaz.,* 111:378–394.

Scott, L., and J. H. Priestley. 1928. The root as an absorbing organ. *New Phytologist,* 27:125–140.

Sheets, T. J. 1963. Photochemical alteration and inactivation of amiben. *Weeds,* 11: 186–190.

Siegesmund, K. A., W. G. Rosen, and S. R. Gawlik. 1962. Effects of darkness and streptomycin on the fine structure of *Euglena gracilis. Am. J. Botany,* 49:137–145.

Simon, E. W., and H. Beevers. 1952. The effect of pH on the biological activities of weak acids and bases. I. The most usual relationship between pH and activity. *New Phytologist,* 51:163–190.

Skoog, F., and C. O. Miller. 1957. Chemical regulation of growth and organ formation in plant tissues cultured *in vitro*. *Symp. Soc. Exptl. Biol.*, 11:118–131.

Skoss, J. D. 1955. Structure and composition of plant cuticle in relation to environmental factors and permeability. *Botan. Gaz.*, 117:55–72.

Slankis, V. 1958. The role of auxin and other exudates in mycorrhizal symbiosis of forest trees, pp. 427–443. In K. V. Thimann (ed.), *The Physiology of Forest Trees*. The Ronald Press Company, New York.

Smith, A. E., J. W. Zukel, G. M. Stone, and J. A. Riddell. 1959. Factors affecting the performance of maleic hydrazide. *Agr. Food Chem.*, 7:341–344.

Smith, F. G., J. C. Walker, and W. J. Hooker. 1946. Effect of hydrogen ion concentration on the toxicity to *Colletotrichium circinans* of some carboxylic acids, phenols and crucifer extracts. *Am. J. Botany*, 33:351–356.

Strugger, S. 1949. *Praktikum der Zell und Gewebephysiologie der Pflanzen*. Springer-Verlag OHG, Berlin (cited by Kramer, 1957).

Swanson, C. A., and J. B. Whitney. 1953. Studies on the translocation of foliar applied P^{32} and other radioisotopes in bean plants. *Am. J. Botany*, 40:816–832.

Tang, Y. W., and J. Bonner. 1947. The enzymatic inactivation of indoleacetic acid. I. *Arch. Biochem. Biophys.*, 13:11–25.

Teas, H. J., and T. V. Sheehan. 1957. Chemical modification of geotropic bending in the snapdragon. *Proc. Fla. Sta. Hort. Soc.*, 70:391–398.

Thiegs, B. J. 1955. The stability of dalapon in soils. *Down to Earth*, 11:2–4.

Thimann, K. V. 1948. Use of 2,4-D herbicides on some woody tropical plants. *Botan. Gaz.*, 109:334–340.

Thomas, W. D. E., and S. H. Bennett. 1954. The absorption, translocation and breakdown of schrodan applied to leaves, using P^{32}-labelled material. III. Translocation and breakdown. *Ann. Appl. Biol.*, 41:501–519.

Tullis, E. C. and W. C. Davis. 1950. Persistence of 2,4-D in plant tissue. *Science*, 111:90.

Turrell, F. M. 1947. Citrus leaf stomata: structure, composition and pore size in relation to penetration of liquids. *Botan. Gaz.*, 108:476–483.

van Schreven, D. A. 1956. On the physiology of tuber formation in potatoes. I and II. *Plant Soil*, 8:49–86.

Virtanen, A. L., S. von Hausen, and T. Laine. 1937. Investigations of the root nodule bacteria of leguminous plants. 19. Influence of various factors on the excretion of nitrogenous compounds from nodules. *J. Agr. Sci.*, 27:332.

Virtanen, A. L., T. Laine, and S. von Hausen. 1936. Excretion of amino acids from the root nodules and their chemical nature. *Suomen Kemistilehti*, B,9:1.

Wain, R. L. 1960. Some developments in research on plant diseases and weed control. *J. Roy. Agr. Soc. England*, 121:117–124.

Weaver, R. J., and H. R. DeRose. 1946. Absorption and translocation of 2,4-D. *Botan. Gaz.*, 107:509–521.

Weintraub, R. L., and J. W. Brown. 1950. Translocation of exogenous growth-regulators in the bean seedling. *Plant Physiol.*, 25:140–149.

———, J. H. Reinhart, and R. A. Scherff. 1956. Role of entry, translocation, and metabolism in specificity of 2,4-D and related compounds *AEC Rept.* TID-7512: 203–208.

Weldon, L. W., and F. L. Timmons. 1961. Photochemical degradation of diuron and monuron. *Weeds*, 9:111–116.

Wickson, M., and K. V. Thimann. 1958. The antagonism of auxin and kinetin in apical dominance. *Physiol. Plantarum*, 11:62–74.

Wiebe, H. H., and P. J. Kramer. 1954. Translocation of radioactive isotopes from various regions of roots of barley seedlings. *Plant Physiol.*, 29:342–348.

Wirwillie, J. W., and J. W. Mitchell. 1950. Six new plant growth inhibiting compounds. *Botan. Gaz.*, 111:491–494.

Wittwer, S. H., and N. E. Tolbert. 1960. (2-chloroethyl) trimethylammonium chloride and related compounds as plant growth substances. III. *Am. J. Botany*, 47: 560–565.

Woodford, E. K. 1957. The toxic action of herbicides. *Outlook Agr.*, 1:145–154.

————. 1958. How a selective herbicide works. *World Crops*, 1958:1–4.

Zeevaart, J. A. D., and A. Lang. 1963. Suppression of floral induction in *Byrophyllum* by a growth retardant. *Planta*, 59: 509–517.

Zelitch, I. 1961. Biochemical control of stomatal opening in leaves. *Proc. Natl. Acad. Sci. U.S.*, 47:1423–1433.

Zenk, M. H. 1961. Indoleacetylglucose: a new compound in the metabolism of indoleacetic acid in plants. *Nature*, 191: 493–494.

————. 1962. Aufnahme und Stoffwechsel von Naphthylessigsaure durch Erbsenepicotyle. *Planta*, 58:75–94.

Zwar, J. A., M. J. Bruce, W. Bottomley, and N.P. Kefford. 1963. On the nature of the native kinin of apple and coconut and modifications produced by purification procedures, pp. 123–130. In J. P. Nitsch (ed.), *Régulateurs Naturels de la Croissance Végétale*, CNRS, Paris.

Author index

Page numbers in *italic* type refer to bibliographic citations.

Subject index

455